IF LOST PLEASE RETURN TO

KELOWNA SECONDARY SCHOOL
575 HARVEY AVENUE, KELOWNA, B.C.

YEAR	NAME	DIV

9

REVISED EDITION

Robert Alexander
Formerly with the
Toronto Board of Education
Toronto, Ontario

Katie Pallos-Haden
Memorial Composite High School
Stony Plain, Alberta

Ron Lancaster
St. Mildred's Lightbourn School
Oakville, Ontario

Fred Crouse
Kings County District School Board
Kentville, Nova Scotia

David DeCoste
Dr. J.H. Gillis Regional High School
Antigonish, Nova Scotia

Brendan Kelly
University of Toronto
Toronto, Ontario

Florence Glanfield
Consultant
Edmonton, Alberta

Paul Atkinson
Waterloo County Board of Education
Kitchener, Ontario

Jane Forbes
E.C. Drury High School
Milton, Ontario

Addison-Wesley Publishers Limited
Don Mills, Ontario • Reading, Massachusetts • Menlo Park, California
New York • Wokingham, England • Amsterdam • Bonn
Sydney • Singapore • Tokyo • Madrid • San Juan • Paris •Seoul • Milan
Mexico City • Taipei

SENIOR EDITORS
Claire Burnett
Lesley Haynes
Sarah Mawson

EDITORS
Mei Lin Cheung
Lynne Gulliver
Anna-Maria Garnham
Rajshree Shankar
Anita Smale

RESEARCHER
Louise MacKenzie

DESIGN/ART DIRECTION
Pronk&Associates/Joe Lepiano, David Montle

ELECTRONIC ASSEMBLY/TECHNICAL ART
Pronk&Associates/Steve Doinidis, Lisa Finlayson,
Aleksandar Janicijevic, Linda Stephenson, Craig Swistun,
Stanley Tran.

COVER DESIGN
Pronk&Associates

Acknowledgments appear on pages 530 and 531.

For their help in the development of the model for this book, the
authors and publisher wish to express special thanks to
Kim Garner, Michael Grosman, Keith Hall, Wendy Solheim, and
their students at Thornhill Secondary School in Thornhill, Ontario,
and to Dave Boag, Joyce Finley, Dave Petker, and their students at
E.C. Drury High School in Milton, Ontario.

Canadian Cataloguing in Publication Data

Main entry under title:
    Minds on math 9
Rev. student ed.
Includes index.
ISBN 0-201-42682-X

1. Mathematics — Juvenile literature.
I. Alexander, Bob, 1941—

QA107.M56 1996   510   C95-932833-5

REVIEWERS/CONSULTANTS
Andrew Adler, Ph.D.
University of British Columbia
Vancouver, British Columbia

Lynda E. C. Colgan, Ph.D.
Scarborough Board of Education
Scarborough, Ontario

Liliane Gauthier
Saskatoon Public School Board
Saskatoon, Saskatchewan

E. Haines
Beamsville District Secondary School
Beamsville, Ontario

Ivan Johnson
Burnaby South School
Burnaby, British Columbia

Bob Michie
Calgary Board of Education
Calgary, Alberta

Linda Rajotte
Georges P. Vanier Senior Secondary School
Courtenay, British Columbia

Connie A. Shaver
Silver Heights Collegiate
Winnipeg, Manitoba

Elaine Simmt
University of Alberta
Edmonton, Alberta

Elizabeth Wood
National Sport School
Calgary, Alberta

CONTENTS

CHAPTER 1: DATA ANALYSIS

CHAPTER 2: ALGEBRAIC OPERATIONS AND EQUATIONS

4 m

6 m

5 m

CHAPTER 3: CONGRUENCE AND SIMILARITY

CHAPTER 4: RIGHT TRIANGLE CALCULATIONS

CHAPTER 5: POWERS AND ROOTS

CHAPTER 8: GEOMETRY

WELCOME TO *MINDS ON MATH 9*

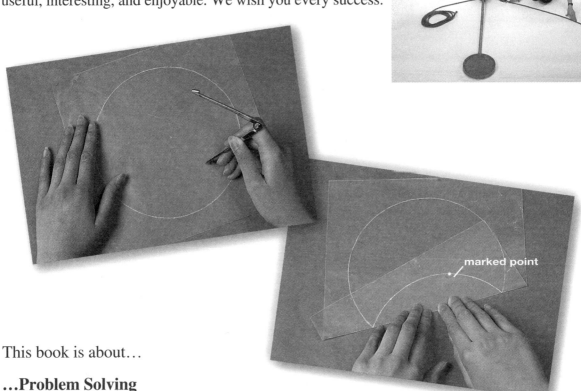

We hope that this book helps you see that mathematics can be useful, interesting, and enjoyable. We wish you every success.

marked point

This book is about…

…Problem Solving

Learning to solve problems is the main reason for studying mathematics. You will find that all the parts of this book are designed to help you improve your problem-solving skills.

…Math in the Real World

This book describes many new ways you can use mathematics to understand your everyday world. You'll also learn about how people use mathematics in their careers.

…Calculators and Computers

Technology is a tool you will be using often in your life, and in your study of mathematics. You'll need a scientific calculator to complete some of the activities and exercises in this book. You'll also want to use a computer and some popular software to work with spreadsheets and databases. This book will help you add these tools to the paper and pencil you already use every day.

Take a few moments to read the following pages. They explain how this book is organized and how you will be using it.

CHAPTER CONTENTS

Each chapter begins with a magazine-style Contents. This gives you an idea of what you will be studying and what problems the mathematics can help you solve.

WHAT'S COMING UP?

This is a list of the mathematics topics that are covered in the chapter.

DEPARTMENTS

Most chapters contain five departments. You'll get to know the departments as you use the book. For example, a Quest always offers you an interesting opportunity to build your problem-solving skills — and to discover something new.

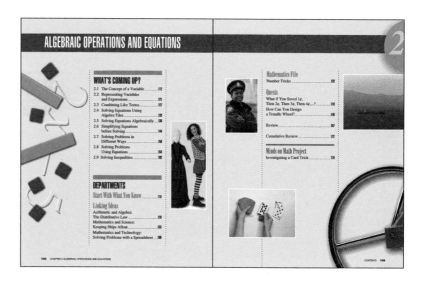

START WITH WHAT YOU KNOW

Each chapter begins with Start With What You Know. These questions and activities give you a chance to review so that you can be successful with the new material.

For example, this Start With What You Know describes how human heights have changed over the past 200 years. The questions help you recall how to work with variables in formulas.

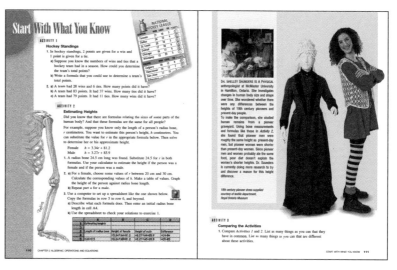

DEVELOPING THE IDEAS

The mathematics in this book is developed in a variety of ways.
Two or more of these ways are often used in the same lesson.

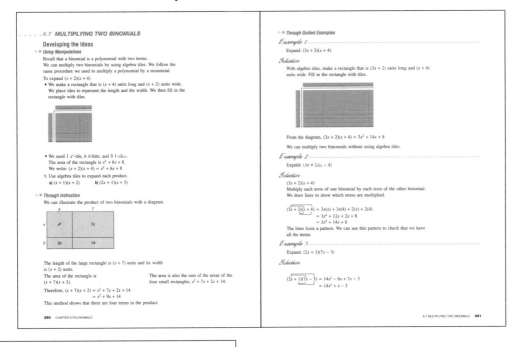

Through Activities

I hear and I forget
I see and I remember
I do and I understand

One of the best ways to learn anything new is to become actively involved with it. This is true whether you are learning to play a musical instrument, learning a new sport, or learning to use a computer.

The same is also true of mathematics. When you use this book you will be actively doing mathematics. Many ideas are developed through activities you can do with a partner or in a small group.

Using Manipulatives

Some ideas are best understood using concrete materials, called manipulatives. This is an excellent way to develop new ideas in algebra and to help you see the connections between arithmetic and algebra.

Through Discussion

New ideas are often introduced through discussion with a partner, in a small group, or as a class.

Through Instruction

Some Through Instruction sections help you consolidate the ideas you learned through activities or discussion. In other cases, ideas are easiest to understand when you can read a straightforward explanation of the concepts involved.

Through Guided Examples

After you have learned some new ideas through activity or discussion, it helps to see examples showing how to use the ideas. The examples in this book are called guided examples because they usually contain explanations of the steps in the solution.

Using a Computer

Some ideas in probability are developed using computer simulations.

WORKING WITH MATHEMATICS

There are five different kinds of exercises in the lessons in this book.

Something to talk about

These exercises get you talking. They give you and your classmates a chance to check your understanding together before you solve problems on your own.

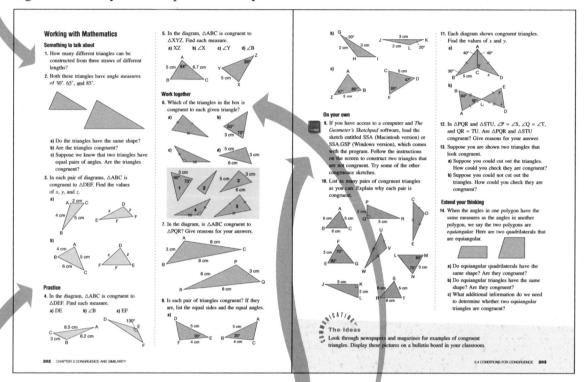

Practice

Learning anything new requires practice. These exercises let you practise the new skills you have learned.

On your own

After you have gained confidence working with a partner, complete these exercises on your own.

Work together

Complete these exercises with a partner or in a group. Talking with other students helps you learn because you see how they make connections and what they already know. There are two more advantages:

• Other students can sometimes explain new ideas to you in ways that make sense.

• Explaining something you understand to someone else can help you to understand it better.

Technology

The computer is a tool for learning and doing mathematics in ways that weren't possible just a few years ago. Some of the computer exercises give you a chance to work with popular computer applications, such as spreadsheets and Draw programs. The *Minds on Math 9 Template Disk* lets you get started right away.

TEMPLATE DISK   DATA DISK

For other computer activities, you'll need to use a computer database. The *Minds on Math 9 Data Disk* provides a vast amount of data that you can use to answer questions and to understand and present information.

Using ClarisWorks® or Microsoft Works™ for your applications software will make it easiest for you to do the spreadsheet and Draw computer exercises in this book. You will need one of these programs to use the *Minds on Math 9 Template Disk* and the *Minds on Math 9 Data Disk*.

Extend your thinking

These exercises are extensions of the ideas in the lesson. Some of these exercises may require you to think about what you have been doing and to apply your thinking to related ideas. Others may be more challenging than the previous exercises.

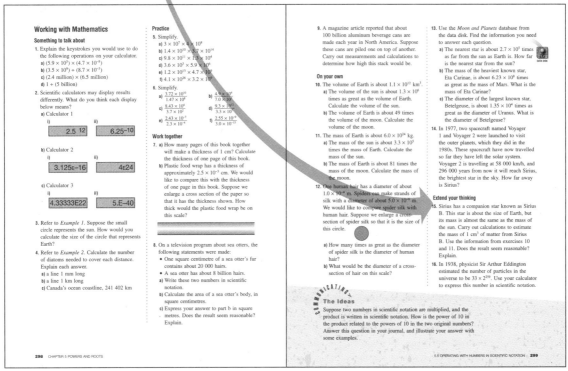

COMMUNICATING THE IDEAS

Communicating your knowledge about a concept or skill can help you learn mathematics. Also, when you learn something interesting or puzzling or exciting, it makes sense to talk about it! In this book you will be asked to communicate your ideas in a variety of ways, such as:

- writing in your journal
- explaining to a friend
- talking on the telephone
- writing a report

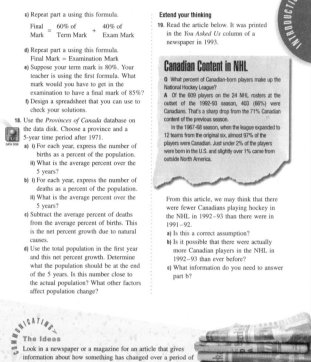

c) Repeat part a using this formula.

$$\frac{\text{Final}}{\text{Mark}} = \frac{60\% \text{ of}}{\text{Term Mark}} + \frac{40\% \text{ of}}{\text{Exam Mark}}$$

d) Repeat part a using this formula.
Final Mark = Examination Mark

e) Suppose your term mark is 80%. Your teacher is using the first formula. What mark would you have to get in the examination to have a final mark of 85%?

f) Design a spreadsheet that you can use to check your solutions.

18. Use the *Provinces of Canada* database on the data disk. Choose a province and a 5-year time period after 1971.
a) i) For each year, express the number of births as a percent of the population.
ii) What is the average percent over the 5 years?
b) i) For each year, express the number of deaths as a percent of the population.
ii) What is the average percent over the 5 years?
c) Subtract the average percent of deaths from the average percent of births. This is the net percent growth due to natural causes.
d) Use the total population in the first year and this net percent growth. Determine what the population should be at the end of the 5 years. Is this number close to the actual population? What other factors affect population change?

Extend your thinking

19. Read the article below. It was printed in the *You Asked Us* column of a newspaper in 1993.

Canadian Content in NHL

Q What percent of Canadian-born players make up the National Hockey League?
A Of the 609 players on the 24 NHL rosters at the outset of the 1992-93 season, 403 (66%) were Canadians. That's a sharp drop from the 71% Canadian content of the previous season.

In the 1967-68 season, when the league expanded to 12 teams from the original six, almost 97% of the players were Canadian. Just under 2% of the players were born in the U.S. and slightly over 1% came from outside North America.

From this article, we may think that there were fewer Canadians playing hockey in the NHL in 1992–93 than there were in 1991–92.
a) Is this a correct assumption?
b) Is it possible that there were actually more Canadian players in the NHL in 1992–93 than ever before?
c) What information do you need to answer part b?

COMMUNICATING
The Ideas
Look in a newspaper or a magazine for an article that gives information about how something has changed over a period of time. Use the information to explain to a friend the two ways of expressing how something changes. Be sure that your friend clearly understands the difference between the amount by which something has changed and the percent by which it has changed.

PERCENTS **43**

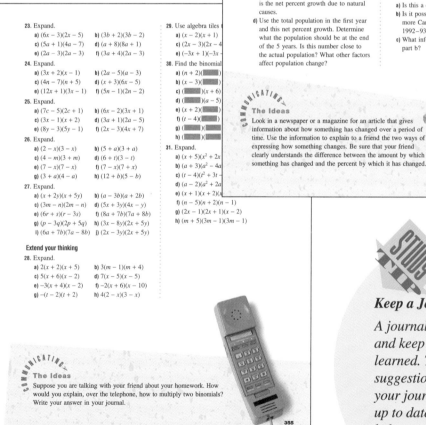

23. Expand.
a) $(6x - 3)(2x - 5)$ **b)** $(3b + 2)(3b - 2)$
c) $(5a + 1)(4a - 7)$ **d)** $(a + 8)(8a + 1)$
e) $(2a - 3)(2a - 3)$ **f)** $(3a + 4)(2a - 3)$

24. Expand.
a) $(3x + 2)(x - 1)$ **b)** $(2a - 5)(a - 3)$
c) $(4n - 7)(n + 5)$ **d)** $(x + 3)(6x - 5)$
e) $(12x + 1)(3x - 1)$ **f)** $(5n - 1)(2n - 2)$

25. Expand.
a) $(7c - 5)(2c + 1)$ **b)** $(6x - 2)(3x + 1)$
c) $(3x - 1)(x + 2)$ **d)** $(3a + 1)(2a - 5)$
e) $(8y - 3)(5y - 1)$ **f)** $(2x - 3)(4x + 7)$

26. Expand.
a) $(2 - x)(3 - x)$ **b)** $(5 + a)(3 + a)$
c) $(4 - m)(3 + m)$ **d)** $(6 + t)(3 - t)$
e) $(7 - x)(7 - x)$ **f)** $(7 - x)(7 + x)$
g) $(3 + a)(4 - a)$ **h)** $(12 + b)(5 - b)$

27. Expand.
a) $(x + 2y)(x + 5y)$ **b)** $(a - 3b)(a + 2b)$
c) $(3m - n)(2m - n)$ **d)** $(5x + 3y)(4x - y)$
e) $(6r + s)(r - 3s)$ **f)** $(8a + 7b)(7a + 8b)$
g) $(p - 3q)(2p + 5q)$ **h)** $(3x - 8y)(2x + 5y)$
i) $(6a + 7b)(7a - 8b)$ **j)** $(2x - 3y)(2x + 5y)$

Extend your thinking

28. Expand.
a) $2(x + 2)(x + 5)$ **b)** $3(m - 1)(m + 4)$
c) $5(x + 6)(x - 2)$ **d)** $7(x - 5)(x - 5)$
e) $-3(x + 4)(x - 2)$ **f)** $-2(x + 6)(x - 10)$
g) $-(t - 2)(t + 2)$ **h)** $4(2 - x)(3 - x)$

29. Use algebra tiles
a) $(x - 2)(x + 1)$
c) $(2x - 3)(2x - 4)$
e) $(-3x + 1)(-3x$

30. Find the binomial
a) $(n + 2)($ ▇ $)$
b) $(x - 3)($ ▇ $)$
c) $($ ▇ $)(x + 6)$
d) $($ ▇ $)(a - 5)$
e) $(x + 2)($ ▇ $)$
f) $(t - 4)($ ▇ $)$
g) $($ ▇ $)($ ▇ $)$
h) $($ ▇ $)($ ▇ $)$

31. Expand.
a) $(x + 5)(x^2 + 2x$
b) $(a + 3)(a^2 - 4a$
c) $(t - 4)(t^2 + 3t$
d) $(a - 2)(a^2 + 2a$
e) $(x + 1)(x + 2)(x$
f) $(n - 5)(n + 2)(n - 1)$
g) $(2x - 1)(2x + 1)(x - 2)$
h) $(m + 5)(3m - 1)(3m - 1)$

COMMUNICATING
The Ideas
Suppose you are talking with your friend about your homework. How would you explain, over the telephone, how to multiply two binomials? Write your answer in your journal.

355

STUDY TIP

Keep a Journal.

A journal helps you explore ideas and keep a record of what you have learned. This book gives you many suggestions for what to write about in your journal. If you keep your journal up to date, you'll discover that it can help you review your thinking when you're studying for tests or exams.

QUESTS

Most chapters contain one or two Quests. Each Quest is a significant problem for you to solve.

You'll want to approach Quest problems in a thoughtful way. You can use the four-step problem solving plan built into each Quest to help you. As you work, you'll be finding interesting answers to meaningful questions and learning how to be a successful problem solver.

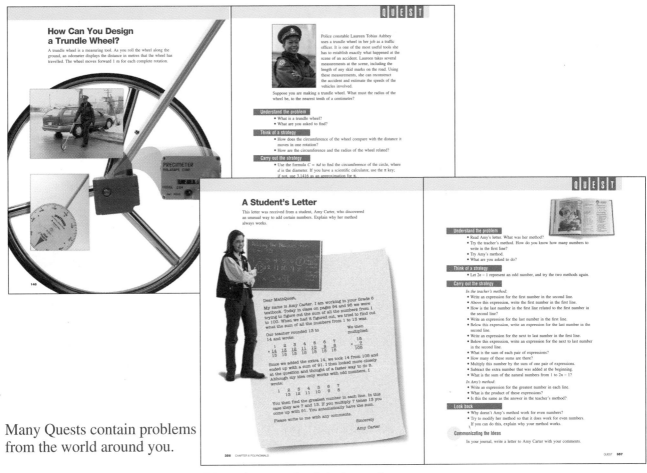

Many Quests contain problems from the world around you.

• How can you predict when an Olympic record might be set?
• How can you design a trundle wheel?
• Why might a laser gun be better for catching speeeders than a radar gun?

Other Quests involve patterns in arithmetic or geometry.

• Why does a shortcut for adding numbers give correct results?
• What if you saved 1¢, then 2¢, then 3¢, then 4¢,…?

LINKING IDEAS

In the Linking Ideas department, you'll find activities that help you explore connections between mathematics and other subject areas, or between strands in mathematics.

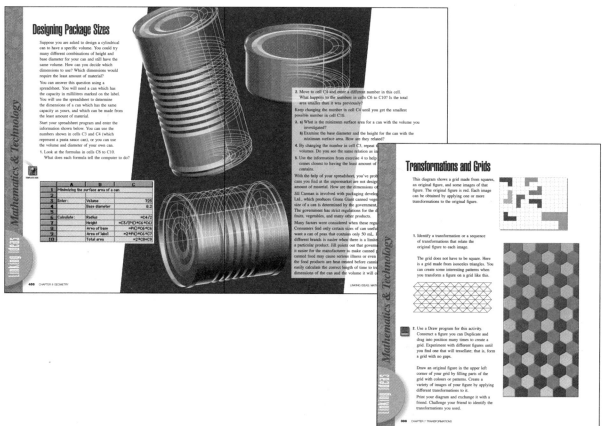

Links with Technology

The computer lets you investigate problems that would be too difficult or involve too much computation to solve with paper and pencil, or even with a calculator. You can also use a computer to explore geometry in a dynamic way that is impossible without a computer.

Other examples of links with technology

- Using Regular Polygons to Estimate π
- Solving Problems with a Spreadsheet
- Investigating the Medians of a Triangle

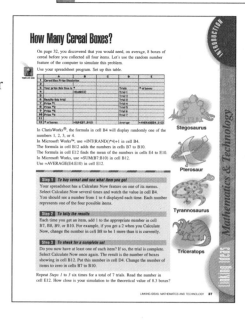

Links with Science

Several linking features show mathematics at work in different fields of science.

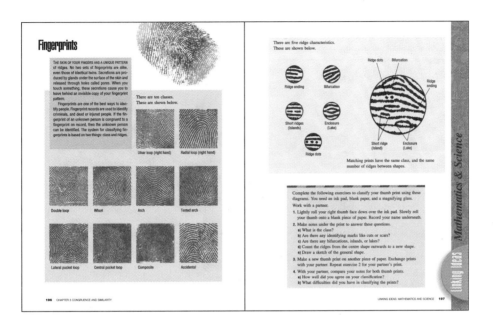

Other Links

- Mathematics and the Media
- Mathematics and Art
- Mathematics and History
- Linking strands within mathematics

MATHEMATICS FILES

Mathematics Files provide opportunities for you to develop your mathematical understanding. These pages may help you see why many people believe mathematics is a fascinating and even beautiful field of study all on its own, with no need for "uses" or "connections" to make it important.

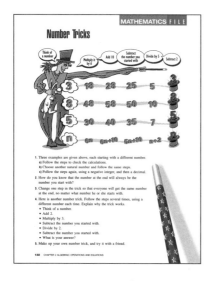

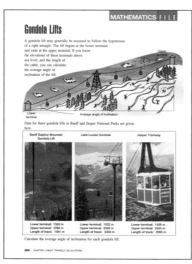

Other examples of Mathematics Files

- Games of Chance
- Powers of 2
- Distortions

BOGGLE YOUR MIND

Many problems involving interesting facts and questions occur throughout the text. These give you more opportunities to practise your problem-solving skills. Often the answers you reach will boggle your mind.

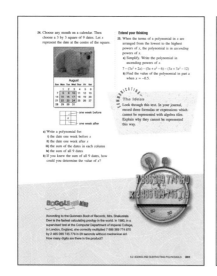

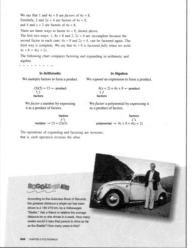

Other Boggle Your Mind topics
- The origins of the Celsius scale
- The thickness of gold leaf
- Canada's crayon production
- The world's fastest calculating prodigy, Shakuntala Devi

MINDS ON MATH PROJECT

Each chapter ends with a project that gives you freedom to use and develop mathematics in your own way. You'll need to plan, research, experiment, and make choices and decisions. Probably your project will take a few weeks to complete.

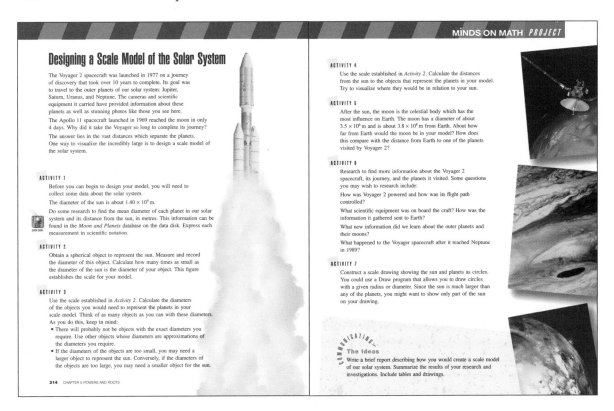

- Each project contains several related activities for you to do over a period of time.
- You can work alone or with a partner.
- The projects are open-ended. This means there may be more than one answer, or other students doing the same project may get different results.
- You will be asked to write a report or to make a presentation so that you can share your thinking and results with others.

Other topics to explore in Minds on Math Projects

- The effect of rounding prices to eliminate the use of pennies
- Determining how a card trick works
- Measuring inaccessible heights using knowledge of trigonometry
- Investigating transformations using *The Geometer's Sketchpad*

CHANGE

Mathematics is a useful tool for measuring changes in the world around us. In this introductory section, you will find activities involving change. These activities will help you review concepts and skills you learned in previous grades. You will need to use these skills as you work through the chapters in this book.

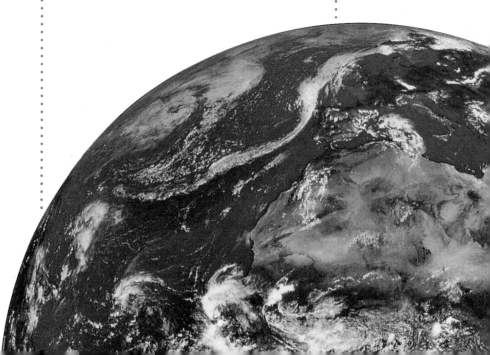

WHAT'S COMING UP?

DEPARTMENTS

Start With What You Know

1. **a)** How has your taste in music changed over the past 5 years?
   b) How has the number of hours per day that you listen to music on the radio changed during those 5 years?

2. **a)** Describe how the price of a case of your favourite soft drink changes from week to week.
   b) How does the price of a litre of gasoline change over the course of a year?

3. Describe how your heart rate changes when you walk up a long flight of stairs or before you write an exam. Why does this happen?

4. Describe how your height has changed since you were born. Were there times when your height changed dramatically? Is your height still changing?

5. **a)** How does the cost of a long-distance phone call change during a week?
   b) When is the best time to make a long-distance phone call?
   c) How might competing long-distance companies change the way we pay for long-distance calls? Explain.

Mathematics is a useful tool for measuring changes in the world around us. We can look for patterns in the changes and make predictions. We can decide if we should be concerned about the changes. In this chapter you will study many examples of change. You will use the mathematical skills you learned in earlier grades.

Developing the Ideas

▶ ▶ *Through Discussion*

Are you familiar with the wind-chill factor?
On a cold day the wind can make it feel
colder than the temperature indicated on the
thermometer.

A table like the one below is often used by
the media for weather reports. The wind-chill
equivalent temperature is the temperature you
would feel under typical wind conditions. For
example, when the temperature is −5°C and
the wind speed is 30 km/h, the wind-chill
equivalent temperature is −18°C. This means
that it would feel like −18°C.

Wind-Chill Equivalent Temperature						
Temperature (°C)	Wind speed (km/h)					
	10	20	30	40	50	60
5	4	−2	−5	−7	−8	−9
0	−2	−8	−11	−14	−16	−17
−5	−7	−14	−18	−21	−23	−24
−10	−12	−20	−25	−28	−30	−32
−15	−18	−26	−32	−35	−38	−39
−20	−23	−32	−38	−42	−45	−47
−25	−28	−39	−45	−49	−52	−54
−30	−33	−45	−52	−56	−60	−62
−35	−39	−51	−59	−64	−67	−69
−40	−44	−57	−65	−71	−74	−77

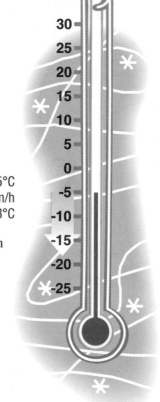

Temperature, −5°C
Wind speed, 30 km/h
Feels like −18°C

Several years ago, in an area of northern Canada, there was a day when
the temperature was 5°C in the morning. The temperature changed
dramatically throughout the day. It dropped at a rate of about 5°C
every hour. Eventually, the temperature was −40°C! The wind speed
was about 10 km/h throughout the day.

1. Use the table.
   a) How did the wind-chill equivalent temperature
      change throughout the day?
   b) Did it drop at the rate of about 5°C per hour?
      If not, how did it change?

▶ ▶ ▶ *Through Guided Examples*

You have probably worked with integers in earlier grades. Here are some examples to help you recall the four operations with integers.

Example 1 ···

a) The morning temperature was −4°C. During the day, the temperature rose 13°C. Write an addition statement to determine the highest temperature for the day.

b) The evening temperature was −3°C. During the night, the temperature changed by −8°C. Write an addition statement to determine the lowest temperature for the night.

c) On another night, the temperature reached a low of −14°C. By mid-morning the next day, the temperature had risen by 6°C. Determine the mid-morning temperature.

Solution

Show the change on a number line. The number line is like a thermometer placed on its side.

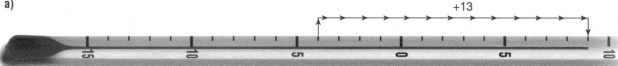

$(-4) + (+13) = +9$

The highest temperature was 9°C.

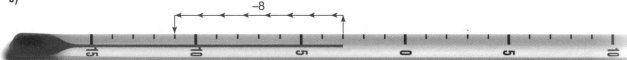

$(-3) + (-8) = -11$

The lowest temperature was −11°C.

c)

$(-14) + (+6) = -8$

The mid-morning temperature was −8°C.

You will use addition skills when subtracting integers. Recall that, to subtract an integer, you add its opposite.

Example 2..

Subtract.

a) $(+3) - (+12)$ **b)** $(-4) - (-7)$

Solution

To subtract in each case, add the opposite.

a) $(+3) - (+12) = (+3) + (-12)$ **b)** $(-4) - (-7) = (-4) + (+7)$
$= -9$ $= +3$

Multiplying and dividing integers involve rules based on the signs of the starting numbers. You will examine the patterns behind these rules in exercises 1 and 2.

- Multiplying or dividing two integers with the same sign gives a positive product or quotient.

  $(+2) \times (+4) = +8$ $(+8) \div (+2) = +4$
  $(-2) \times (-4) = +8$ $(-8) \div (-2) = +4$

- Multiplying or dividing two integers with opposite signs gives a negative product or quotient.

  $(-2) \times (+4) = -8$ $(+8) \div (-2) = -4$
  $(+2) \times (-4) = -8$ $(-8) \div (+2) = -4$

Example 3..

Multiply or divide.

a) $(+4) \times (-8)$ **b)** $(-45) \div (-5)$
c) $(-33) \div (+3)$ **d)** $(-3) \times (+6) \times (-2)$

Solution

Apply the rules for multiplying and dividing integers.

a) $(+4) \times (-8) = -32$ **b)** $(-45) \div (-5) = +9$
c) $(-33) \div (+3) = -11$ **d)** $(-3) \times (+6) \times (-2) = (-18) \times (-2)$
$= +36$

You can also use the $\boxed{+\text{-}}$ key on a calculator to perform calculations with integers. Here is a possible keying sequence for *Example 3d*. Being able to predict the sign of the result can help you check calculator results.

Press: 3 $\boxed{+\text{-}}$ $\boxed{\times}$ 6 $\boxed{\times}$ 2 $\boxed{+\text{-}}$ $\boxed{=}$
To display: **36**

Working with Mathematics

Something to talk about

1. a) Here is a way to develop the rules for multiplying integers. Start with a product you know, such as $3 \times 3 = 9$. Change the second integer by subtracting 1, then calculate the new product.

$3 \times 3 = 9$
$3 \times 2 = 6$
$3 \times 1 = 3$
$3 \times 0 = 0$
$3 \times (-1) = ?$

Continue the pattern. What is the product in the last line? What is the rule for multiplying a positive integer by a negative integer?

b) Continue the pattern, but now subtract 1 from the first integer at each step. You will eventually have two negative integers multiplied together.

$3 \times (-1) = -3$
$2 \times (-1) =$
$1 \times (-1) =$
$0 \times (-1) =$
$(-1) \times (-1) =$

c) What is the rule for multiplying two negative integers?

2. Explain how you can extend the multiplication rules for integers to describe rules for dividing integers. Use this starting point: Since $(-4) \times 2 = -8$, we know that $(-8) \div (-4) = 2$.

3. The temperature in Vancouver was $-3°C$. A radio broadcaster in Winnipeg said it was five times as cold in her city that morning. What was the temperature in Winnipeg? Explain how your answer helps to show that a negative integer multiplied by a positive integer results in a negative integer.

Practice

4. Add.
a) $14 + 5$ b) $(-7) + 9$
c) $16 + (-8)$ d) $(-3) + (-8)$
e) $(-15) + (-3)$ f) $(-9) + 5$
g) $23 + 10$ h) $23 + (-10)$
i) $(-8) + (-17)$ j) $27 + (-6)$

5. Subtract.
a) $-8 - 3$ b) $-9 - 5$
c) $-7 - 2$ d) $3 - (-8)$
e) $5 - (-9)$ f) $2 - (-7)$
g) $-8 - (-3)$ h) $-9 - (-5)$
i) $-7 - (-2)$ j) $-3 - (-8)$

6. Multiply.
a) $5 \times (-4)$ b) $4 \times (-4)$
c) $3 \times (-4)$ d) $2 \times (-4)$
e) $1 \times (-4)$ f) $0 \times (-4)$
g) $(-1) \times (-4)$ h) $(-2) \times (-4)$
i) $(-3) \times (-4)$ j) $(-4) \times (-4)$
k) $(-5) \times (-4)$ l) $(-6) \times (-4)$
m) $(-4) \times (-1) \times (-2)$ n) $(-3) \times 2 \times (-2)$

7. Divide.
a) $12 \div 4$ b) $12 \div (-4)$
c) $(-12) \div 4$ d) $(-12) \div (-4)$
e) $(-40) \div 8$ f) $24 \div (-8)$
g) $(-18) \div (-3)$ h) $(-54) \div 9$
i) $72 \div (-9)$ j) $\frac{72}{9}$
k) $\frac{-72}{9}$ l) $\frac{-72}{-9}$

8. Calculate.
a) $12 \times (-3)$ b) $(-4) - (-4)$
c) $7 \times (-2)$ d) $3 - (-11)$
e) $(-42) \div 6$ f) $\frac{-48}{-12}$
g) $3 - 5 - (-8)$ h) $8 \times (-3) \times (-2)$

9. Multiply.
a) $(-1) \times (-1)$
b) $(-1) \times (-1) \times (+1)$
c) $(-1) \times (+1) \times (+1)$
d) $(-1) \times (-1) \times (-1)$
e) $(-1) \times (-1) \times (-1) \times (-1)$

10. Use the results of exercise 9 to predict the sign of each product. You do not need to calculate the products.
    a) $(-2) \times (-6) \times (-2)$
    b) $(-3) \times (+5) \times (-1)$
    c) $(+8) \times (-2) \times (+1)$
    d) $(+3) \times (-6) \times (-2)$
    e) $(-5) \times (-3) \times (-10) \times (+3)$
    f) $(-4) \times (+12) \times (-8) \times (+4) \times (-2) \times (-1)$

Work together

11. Illustrate each addition on a number line. Record each answer.
    a) $(+2) + (-3)$ b) $8 + (+3)$
    c) $(-4) + (+5)$ d) $(-8) + (+7)$
    e) $(-3) + (-2)$ f) $(-7) + (-5)$

12. Copy and complete the chart. Add 4 when you move to the right. Subtract 3 when you move up. Describe how the numbers change along the diagonals. Explain why these patterns occur.

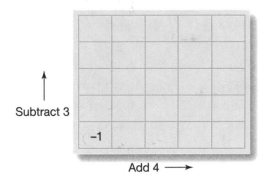

13. Create exercises similar to exercises 6 and 7. Each product or quotient must be an integer. Your partner calculates the answer and explains why it is correct. Take turns creating exercises, calculating, and explaining.

14. Create four word problems that involve integers. Write your problems on one side of a sheet of paper, and your answers on the other side. Exchange your paper with a partner and check each other's work.

On your own

15. Write each expression as a sum of integers. Simplify the expression.
    a) $-4 + 3 - 8$
    b) $-15 - 5 + 30 - 10$
    c) $14 + 5 - 9 + 2$
    d) $15 - 12 + 3 - 6 - 8 + 2$
    e) $4 - 4 - 4 + 8 - 2$

16. A company started the year with a staff of 215. The table shows the monthly changes in staff.

Month	Staff change	Month	Staff change
January	+5	July	−1
February	+2	August	−3
March	−3	September	−2
April	−3	October	−4
May	+1	November	+1
June	0	December	+1

   a) In which month was there no change in the number of staff?
   b) What was the net change in staff over the year?
   c) How many staff members did the company have at the end of December?

17. Copy and complete the chart below. Multiply by 3 when you move to the right. Multiply by −2 when you move up. Describe how the numbers change along the diagonals. Explain why these patterns occur.

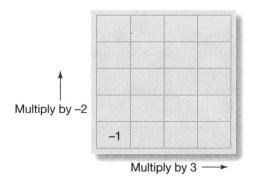

18. Recall the cold day in northern Canada discussed at the beginning of this section.

a) Suppose the wind speed had been 60 km/h. How would the wind-chill equivalent temperature have changed throughout the day?

b) Suppose the wind speed had increased by 10 km/h every hour and at the start of the day the wind speed was 10 km/h. How would the wind-chill equivalent temperature have changed throughout the day?

Extend your thinking

19. The values of wind-chill equivalent temperature in the table were calculated by using a formula. In the formula, W represents the wind-chill equivalent temperature, S represents the wind speed in kilometres per hour, and T represents the temperature in degrees Celsius.

$$W = 33 - \frac{(10 - 0.28 \times S + \sqrt{28 \times S}) \times (33 - T)}{22.727}$$

Use this formula to check three of the values for wind-chill equivalent temperature in the table on page 26.

20. Exposed flesh freezes when the wind-chill equivalent temperature is approximately $-30°C$.

a) Use the table on page 26 to estimate some combinations of wind speed and temperature that result in a wind-chill equivalent temperature of $-30°C$.

b) Draw a graph that shows the combinations of temperature and wind speed that cause exposed flesh to freeze.

The Ideas

In your journal, write a few sentences about what the world would be like without integers. Respond to these questions.

Without integers:

- What changes would have to be made to thermometers?
- How could we describe a situation where something decreases in size?
- What changes would occur in how we score in golf?

The Celsius temperature scale is based on the freezing and boiling points of water. When Anders Celsius first proposed this scale in 1742, he chose 100° to represent the freezing point and 0° to represent the boiling point. What if this scale had not been reversed? What do you think it would be like to use this scale?

Developing the Ideas

▶ ▶ *Through Instruction*

Many cereal companies package their products to appeal to young children. In each box, there is an item that is part of a collection of similar items.

How many boxes must be purchased to obtain the entire collection? If there are quite a few items in the set, then it seems reasonable that a consumer will have to buy many boxes to complete the set.

There is a method to calculate the average number of boxes needed to complete a set.

Suppose there are 4 items in the collection. All the items are distributed randomly and in equal numbers. Each box has only one item. Then the average number of boxes needed is equal to:

$$4 \times \left(1 + \frac{1}{2} + \frac{1}{3} + \frac{1}{4}\right)$$

The steps involved in calculating the answer are given below.

$$4 \times \left(\frac{12}{12} + \frac{6}{12} + \frac{4}{12} + \frac{3}{12}\right)$$
$$= 4 \times \left(\frac{25}{12}\right)$$
$$= \frac{100}{12}$$
$$\doteq 8.3$$

This means that if there are 4 items in the set, then, on average, a consumer will have to buy about 8 boxes to collect the entire set.

Another way to add the fractions is to use a common denominator of 24, because $2 \times 3 \times 4 = 24$. Take a few minutes to try this. The answer is $\frac{200}{24}$, or approximately 8.3. Use this method when you do exercise 15.

It is interesting to see how the average number of boxes needed to complete the set changes when the number of items in the set changes. You will look at this in exercise 15.

The cereal box problem involves the use of fractions. Positive and negative numbers that can be written in fraction form are *rational numbers*. Here are examples of rational numbers.

$$\frac{1}{4} \qquad -3.5 \qquad -\frac{5}{8} \qquad 5\frac{3}{8} \qquad 0 \qquad -7$$

Calculations with rational numbers can be done mentally, using paper and pencil, or a calculator. Changing fractions to decimals often simplifies calculations.

Example 1 ···

Calculate. Explain the solution method used.

a) $\frac{3}{4} - 0.5$ b) $40.5 - 3.9$ c) $\frac{-42.5}{9.3 + 2.5}$

Solution

a) We know that $\frac{3}{4} = 0.75$, so we can write $0.75 - 0.5 = 0.25$

b) $40.5 - 3.9$ is about $40.5 - 4$, or 36.5. Since 4 is $3.9 + 0.1$, add 0.1 to obtain 36.6.

c) Use a calculator. Here is a typical keying sequence.
Press: **42.5 +⊝ ÷ (9.3 + 2.5) =**
To display: **−3.601694915**
Round the quotient to one decimal place: −3.6.

Example 2 ···

A vat is filled by 2 taps. One tap can fill the vat in 20 min. The other tap can fill the vat in 10 min. How long will it take the two taps to fill the vat?

Solution

The first tap fills the vat in 20 min. In 1 min, it fills $\frac{1}{20}$ of the vat.

The other tap fills $\frac{1}{10}$ of the vat in 1 min.

Both taps fill $\frac{1}{20} + \frac{1}{10}$ of the vat in 1 min.

$$\frac{1}{20} + \frac{1}{10} = \frac{1}{20} + \frac{2}{20} \quad \text{◂ To add, use a common denominator.}$$
$$= \frac{3}{20}$$

The two taps fill $\frac{3}{20}$ of the vat in 1 min.

We want to fill $\frac{20}{20}$ of the vat.

$$\frac{20}{20} \div \frac{3}{20} = 1 \times \frac{20}{3} \quad \text{◂ To divide, multiply by the reciprocal.}$$
$$= 6\frac{2}{3}$$

It will take $6\frac{2}{3}$ min.

$$\frac{2}{3} \text{ min} = \frac{2}{3} \times 60 \text{ s}$$
$$= 40 \text{ s}$$

The two taps will fill the vat in about 6 min 40 s.

Working with Mathematics

Something to talk about

1. State the rational number indicated at each lettered point.

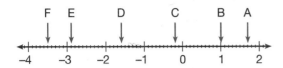

2. a) Refer to the cereal box problem on page 32. Is it possible to get a complete set of items by purchasing only 4 boxes? Do you think this is likely to happen? Why?
   b) Is it possible to purchase many boxes and still not get a complete set? Do you think this is likely to happen? Why?

3. Refer to the cereal box problem. If there are 3 items in the set, then the average number of boxes you must purchase is $3 \times \left(1 + \frac{1}{2} + \frac{1}{3}\right)$. If there are 7 items in the set, then the average number of boxes is $7 \times \left(1 + \frac{1}{2} + \frac{1}{3} + \frac{1}{4} + \frac{1}{5} + \frac{1}{6} + \frac{1}{7}\right)$.

   What is the pattern relating the number in the set, and the number of boxes you need to buy?

Practice

4. Reduce to lowest terms
   a) $\frac{5}{-10}$
   b) $\frac{10}{-15}$
   c) $\frac{-12}{-30}$
   d) $-\frac{6}{15}$
   e) $-\frac{-6}{11}$
   f) $-\frac{-6}{18}$
   g) $-\frac{4}{-14}$
   h) $-\frac{-14}{-25}$
   i) $-\frac{-15}{-35}$
   j) $-\frac{-24}{-72}$
   k) $-\frac{-42}{-28}$
   l) $-\frac{54}{-81}$

5. Round each rational number to the nearest integer.
   a) -3.7
   b) -5.2
   c) -6.7
   d) -0.4
   e) 0.2
   f) -0.6
   g) -0.97
   h) -0.35
   i) -7.52
   j) $-\frac{22}{5}$
   k) $-\frac{67}{4}$
   l) $-\frac{37}{5}$

6. Write in decimal form.
   a) $\frac{3}{5}$
   b) $\frac{2}{-3}$
   c) $\frac{4}{9}$
   d) $-\frac{3}{8}$
   e) $\frac{7}{21}$
   f) $\frac{-3}{22}$
   g) $\frac{15}{7}$
   h) $-\frac{1}{6}$
   i) $\frac{5}{16}$
   j) $\frac{-17}{27}$
   k) $\frac{11}{12}$
   l) $\frac{13}{11}$

7. Compare each pair of rational numbers. Replace the comma with < or >.
   a) $6.4, -\frac{25}{4}$
   b) $-\frac{23}{7}, -3.5$
   c) $\frac{3}{8}, -\frac{5}{11}$
   d) $\frac{-57}{100}, -0.5$
   e) $-8.6, -\frac{75}{9}$
   f) $-15.8, -\frac{76}{5}$
   g) $\frac{51}{16}, 3.175$
   h) $\frac{7}{11}, \frac{16}{25}$

8. Simplify.
   a) $-2.387 + 4.923$
   b) $33.78 - (-64.35)$
   c) $204.9 - 256.1$
   d) $-0.405 - 18.924$
   e) $-12.37 + 8.88$
   f) $-45.8 - (-327.6)$
   g) $4.29 + 563.08$
   h) $84.91 - 37.08$

9. Simplify.
   a) $(-14.6) \times (-23.7) \times 10.4$
   b) $(-12.958) \div (-2.2) \div 1.9$
   c) $(145.0) \times (-14.6) \div (-12.5)$
   d) $(966.52) \div (-29.2) \times 0.9$
   e) $(0.017\,67) \div (-0.95) \div (-0.31)$
   f) $0.08 \times (-1.03) \times 0.5$

Work together

10. Discuss with a partner whether each statement is true or false, and why.
    a) -8 is both a rational number and an integer.
    b) -4 is both an integer and a whole number.
    c) -9 is a rational number, but not a whole number.
    d) 3.5 is a rational number and an integer.
    e) -18 is a rational number but not an integer.
    f) $-5\frac{2}{3}$ is a rational number and an integer.

11. Nahal coaches a baseball team. She calculates the batting average of the team players. Nahal divides the number of hits by the number of times at-bat, and rounds the quotient to 3 decimal places.

a) Calculate the batting averages of Nahal's 5 top batters.

Batter	Times at bat	Number of hits
Maral	106	23
Ari	119	24
Kim	104	20
Ange	116	21
Nicki	91	18

b) List the players in order of their batting averages from greatest to least.

c) Who do you think is Nahal's most reliable batter? Discuss your reasons with a partner.

12. a) Add $\frac{2}{3} + \frac{5}{6}$, and write the sum in decimal form.

b) Write $\frac{2}{3}$ and $\frac{5}{6}$ in decimal form and find their sum. How does this sum compare with the sum for part a?

c) Repeat the procedure of parts a and b for these expressions.

i) $\frac{3}{4} + \frac{2}{5}$ ii) $\frac{5}{8} - \frac{1}{4}$

iii) $\frac{1}{6} - \frac{5}{9}$ iv) $\frac{2}{9} - \frac{5}{11}$

v) $\frac{7}{16} + \frac{5}{12}$ vi) $\frac{29}{37} - \frac{11}{37}$

13. Without calculating the answers, state which expressions are positive.

a) $\frac{5}{-3}$ b) $\frac{(5)(-3)}{-7}$

c) $\frac{5}{(-5)(-7)}$ d) $\frac{-3}{(5)(-7)}$

e) $\frac{5}{(-3)+(-7)}$ f) $\frac{5-(-3)}{-7}$

g) $\frac{5-(-3)}{5-(-7)}$ h) $\frac{5}{-3} + \frac{5}{-7}$

i) $\frac{-3}{-7} - \frac{5}{-3}$ j) $\frac{(-7)(-3)(-7)}{(-5)(5)(-3)}$

14. Use a calculator. Do each calculation using as few key strokes as possible. Record the keying sequences as well as the answers. Discuss your method with a partner. Is there a more efficient calculator key sequence?

a) $37.4 \times (64.1 - 37.8)$

b) $(56.2 + 12.7) \times (42.7 - 29.4)$

c) $(13.7 - 8.9) \times (41.3 - 59.7)$

d) $(27.8 - 45.2) \times (36.4 - 97.8)$

e) $\frac{26.3 \times 14.7}{19.5}$

f) $\frac{109.4}{9.2 \times 4.1}$

g) $\frac{32.5 - 16.9}{12.8 \times 3.5}$

h) $\frac{(9.3 - 16.2) \times (42.7 - 65.3)}{23.8 \times (47.2 - 73.6)}$

i) $(-36.5 - 13) \div (14.7 - 22.3)$

j) $\frac{259.3}{7.5 \times 25.4} - 100$

k) $\frac{0.015 \times 20\,000}{12} + 20\,000$

l) $\frac{0.095 \times 2550 + 0.125 \times 4229}{5}$

15. Use the formulas in exercise 3. Write the formula for the average number of boxes you must purchase, for each number of items up to 10.

a) Copy and complete the table. Use your calculator to change each fraction to a decimal if you wish. Round your answers to the nearest whole number.

Number of items in the set	Average number of boxes needed
1	
2	
3	
4	8

b) Graph the average number of boxes against the number of items in the set.

c) Discuss how the average number of boxes needed to complete the set changes when the number of items in the set increases.

On your own

16. For each of the following:
   a) record the keystrokes used to get the answer
   b) complete the calculation in a different way and record the keystrokes used
   c) explain why one method uses fewer keystrokes than the other
      i) $(18.3 - 4.7) \times (32.5 + 12.6)$
      ii) $(76.1 - 47.1) \times (5.9 - 17.6)$
      iii) $\dfrac{28.4}{42.5 + 12.3}$
      iv) $\dfrac{16.3 - 29.7}{9.3 \times (14.3 - 32.7)}$

17. El-ran fences off a section of his yard using these lengths of fencing material: 5.9 m, 1.5 m, and 6.3 m. The fencing material costs $12.79/m. How much will the fencing cost?

18. A swimming pool is filled by three different pipes. The first fills the pool in 12 h. The second fills the pool in 18 h. The third fills the pool in 24 h. All three pipes are turned on. About how long will it take to fill the pool?

19. a) Add 1 to the numerator of the fraction $\dfrac{1}{3}$. How does the size of the fraction change?

   b) Add 1 to the denominator of $\dfrac{1}{3}$. How does the size of the fraction change?

   c) How does the size of the fraction $\dfrac{1}{3}$ change when both the numerator and the denominator are increased by 1?

20. Repeat exercise 19 for the fraction $\dfrac{7}{3}$.

21. Compare your answers to exercises 19 and 20. What do you notice?

Extend your thinking

If a spreadsheet program is available, use it to complete exercise 22.

22. a) Look at the sequence of fractions given below. Determine the pattern that was used to generate the sequence.
   $$\frac{1}{2}, \frac{5}{3}, \frac{11}{8}, \frac{27}{19}, \frac{65}{46}, \cdots$$

   b) Make a sequence of your own that is similar to the one in part a. Use the same pattern, but start with a fraction of your choice. Write the first 10 terms of your sequence.

   c) Convert each fraction in part b to a decimal. As you go from one term to the next, how do the terms change? Compare your findings with other students. Write a brief report on your findings.

   d) Graph the term expressed as a decimal against the number of the term in the sequence.

23. Repeat exercise 22, using the sequence of fractions given below.
   $$\frac{7}{10}, \frac{37}{17}, \frac{88}{54}, \frac{250}{142}, \frac{676}{392}, \cdots$$

24. If $x > 0$, $y < 0$, and $z < 0$, which expressions are always positive?

   a) $\dfrac{x}{y}$ **b)** $\dfrac{xy}{z}$

   c) $\dfrac{x}{yz}$ **d)** $\dfrac{y}{xz}$

   e) $\dfrac{x}{y+z}$ **f)** $\dfrac{x-y}{z}$

   g) $\dfrac{x}{x-y}$ **h)** $\dfrac{x-y}{x-z}$

   i) $\dfrac{x}{y} + \dfrac{x}{z}$ **j)** $\dfrac{y}{z} - \dfrac{x}{y}$

COMMUNICATING

The Ideas

Look up the word "fraction" in a dictionary. In your journal, describe the various ways this word is used. Ask several people to say a sentence that contains the word "fraction." Compare these uses to those you found in the dictionary. Which use is the most common?

How Many Cereal Boxes?

On page 32, you discovered that you would need, on average, 8 boxes of cereal before you collected all four items. Let's use the random number feature of the computer to simulate this problem.

TEMPLATE DISK

Use your spreadsheet program. Set up this table.

	A	B	C	D	E
1	Cereal Box Prize Simulation				
2					
3	Your prize this time is #			Trials	# of boxes
4		=RAND(4)		Trial 1	
5				Trial 2	
6	Results this trial			Trial 3	
7	Prize #1			Trial 4	
8	Prize #2			Trial 5	
9	Prize #3			Trial 6	
10	Prize #4			Trial 7	
11					
12	# of boxes	=SUM(B7..B10)		Average	=AVERAGE(E4..E10)

In ClarisWorks®, the formula in cell B4 will display randomly one of the numbers 1, 2, 3, or 4.
In Microsoft Works™, use =INT(RAND()*4)+1 in cell B4.
The formula in cell B12 adds the numbers in cells B7 to B10.
The formula in cell E12 finds the mean of the numbers in cells E4 to E10.
In Microsoft Works, use =SUM(B7:B10) in cell B12.
Use =AVERAGE(E4:E10) in cell E12.

Stegosaurus

Pterosaur

Tyrannosaurus

Triceratops

Step 1 To buy cereal and see what item you get

Your spreadsheet has a Calculate Now feature on one of its menus. Select Calculate Now several times and watch the value in cell B4. You should see a number from 1 to 4 displayed each time. Each number represents one of the four possible items.

Step 2 To tally the results

Each time you get an item, add 1 to the appropriate number in cell B7, B8, B9, or B10. For example, if you get a 2 when you Calculate Now, change the number in cell B8 to be 1 more than it is currently.

Step 3 To check for a complete set

Do you now have at least one of each item? If so, the trial is complete. Select Calculate Now once again. The result is the number of boxes showing in cell B12. Put this number in cell D4. Change the number of items to zero in cells B7 to B10.

Repeat *Steps 1* to *3* six times for a total of 7 trials. Read the number in cell E12. How close is your simulation to the theoretical value of 8.3 boxes?

Mathematics & Technology

Linking Ideas

A Ring around Earth

Imagine wrapping a steel band around the Equator. How long would the band be? Suppose you change the position of the band so that it still wraps around the Equator, but it is 1 m above Earth's surface. How much extra steel would you need?

Understand the problem

- What is the Equator?
- Do you think that a much longer steel band will be required when the band is raised 1 m?

Think of a strategy

- Consider a similar problem with a circle that is much smaller than the Equator. For example, use a dinner plate and a piece of rope in place of the steel band.

Carry out the strategy

- You will need several lengths of rope, a metre stick, and a measuring tape.
- Wrap a piece of rope or string around a circular object; for example, a garbage pail, a glass or cup, a pan, a tire, or a big flower pot. Measure the length of this rope. Take another piece of rope. Lay it around the same object so that the rope is always 1 m away from the rim. Measure this piece of rope. Compare this length to the length of the first piece of rope.
- Repeat the process with four different circular objects. What do you notice about your results?
- How does the extra amount of rope that is required for the new position vary as the size of the circle changes?
- Use your observations to predict the difference in lengths of steel bands wrapped around Earth.

DATA DISK

- Find the diameter of Earth by using an encyclopedia or the *Moon and Planets* database on the data disk. Use this information and the formula: Circumference = $\pi \times$ Diameter. Calculate the circumference of Earth and the circumference 1 m above Earth. Find the extra length needed for the steel band to be 1 m above Earth's surface.

Look back

- Carry out similar investigations for other figures such as a square and a triangle.

Communicating the Ideas

In your journal, write a description of this problem and your solution. Include an explanation of why you think this problem is important.

Developing the Ideas

▶ ▶ *Through Discussion*

Like many other provinces in Canada, British Columbia has changed a great deal over the past few years. In fact, in 1993, its population boomed, with record increases in new arrivals from overseas and other provinces. The table gives specific details about the changes that occurred in Vancouver between 1986 and 1991.

First language	1986	1991
English	1 043 015	1 151 975
Chinese	76 115	130 680
Punjabi	20 830	38 255
German	35 175	34 765
French	17 715	20 585
Italian	17 170	17 775
Tagalog (Filipino)	6755	14 025
Dutch	10 685	10 740
Japanese	9470	10 340

What can we learn from the table?
We shall look at how the populations of some groups changed in 5 years.

1. Consider the group whose first language is Punjabi.
   a) Did the population increase or decrease?
   b) By how much did the population change?
   c) Write the change as a fraction of the 1986 population.
   d) Write this fraction as a percent to the nearest whole number.

2. Repeat exercise 1 for the group whose first language is English.

3. Which group, English or Punjabi, had the greater increase in number?

4. Which group, English or Punjabi, had the greater percent increase?

The exercises above illustrate two ways to measure change. One way is to calculate the increase (or decrease) by using subtraction. The second way is to divide the increase (or decrease) by the original number, then express the result as a percent.

Working with Mathematics

Something to talk about

1. Two people each deposit $1000 in an account. One person is a student. Prior to making the deposit, the balance in her account was $1200. The other person is near retirement. She deposited the money into a registered retirement fund for which the balance prior to the deposit was $456 000. For each account, describe the change in the balance in two ways.

Practice

2. Express each fraction or decimal as a percent.

   a) 0.8
   b) 0.25
   c) $\frac{1}{8}$

   d) $\frac{1}{3}$
   e) $\frac{5}{6}$
   f) $\frac{5}{9}$

   g) 2.5
   h) $\frac{8}{3}$
   i) 1.6

   j) 2.4
   k) $\frac{17}{25}$
   l) $\frac{23}{40}$

3. Express each percent as a decimal.

   a) 24%
   b) 39%
   c) 57.4%

   d) 3%
   e) 5.8%
   f) 11.5%

   g) 1.6%
   h) 0.9%
   i) 137%

   j) 264%
   k) 375%
   l) 375.8%

   m) 0.1%
   n) 2.03%
   o) 0.25%

4. Express each percent as a fraction in lowest terms.

   a) 27%
   b) 36%
   c) 60%

   d) 28%
   e) 75%
   f) 45%

   g) 48%
   h) 16%
   i) 85%

   j) 19%
   k) 125%
   l) 215%

5. Find.

   a) 25% of 40
   b) 20% of 40

   c) 0.6% of 150
   d) 5% of 35

   e) 109% of 75
   f) 4% of 150

   g) 0.7% of 95
   h) 65% of 18

   i) 112% of 92
   j) 0.25% of 500

   k) 115% of 752
   l) 0.5% of 25 000

6. Determine the number in each statement.

   a) 50% of a number is 10.
   b) 20% of a number is 3.
   c) 40% of a number is 10.
   d) 75% of a number is 30.
   e) 60% of a number is 42.
   f) 15% of a number is 15.
   g) $66\frac{2}{3}$% of a number is 18.
   h) 10% of a number is 8.
   i) 104% of a number is 26.
   j) 130% of a number is 91.

7. a) What percent of 80 is 16?
   b) What percent of 135 is 15?
   c) What percent of 75 is 125?
   d) What percent of 50 is 45?
   e) What percent of 144 is 18?
   f) What percent of 81 is 270?
   g) What percent of 1900 is 1.9?
   h) What percent of 6000 is 3?

Work together

8. The regular price of a bicycle is $227.50. It is on sale for 15% off. What is the price change? What is the sale price?

9. Skis are on sale for 45% off. Jamil is buying a pair of skis that regularly sell for $180. What is the price after the discount?

10. Economists predict that food costs will change over the coming year. They estimate an increase of 11.7%. Last year, Chloe's family spent $8400 on food. How much might they expect to spend in the coming year?

11. A calculator is on sale for $9.98. This price reflects a 25% discount. What is its regular price?

12. Express each reduction as a percent, to 1 decimal place, of the original price.
   a) A TV set regularly priced at $540 is selling for $499.
   b) A trench coat regularly priced at $195 is selling for $156.

13. The table shows the percent of households that had certain products in 1988, and the estimated percents for the year 2000.

Estimated Percents of Households Using Selected Products

	% in Canada		% in USA	
	1988	2000	1988	2000
Colour televisions	92	96	93	96
Projection televisions	1	7	3	12
Stereo televisions	10	40	20	50
Video cassette recorders	52	75	56	80
Laptop and personal computers	15	35	17	40
Microwave ovens	54	85	70	90
Compact disc/ digital tape equipment	8	75	4	85
Electronic home security systems	5	12	8	15
Three or more telephones	22	45	25	50

a) Which product is expected to have the largest percent change in use from 1988 to 2000:

i) in Canada? ii) in the United States?

b) Which product is expected to have the smallest percent change in use from 1988 to 2000:

i) in Canada? ii) in the United States?

c) i) Can you think of any item on the list that may not live up to its expectations?

ii) Do you think that there will be any item for which the use decreases?

d) i) Can you think of any product that was invented after the table was produced?

ii) How well is this product doing in the Canadian market place?

On your own

14. The managers of a recording company expect sales income to change this year. They hope for a 60% increase over last year's sales of $2 500 000. What is the company's projected income for this year?

15. In April, 800 000 people were unemployed. In May this figure decreased by 0.16%. How many fewer people were unemployed in May?

16. Create two problems involving a change that can be described using percent. Write your problems on a sheet of paper, and record solutions on the back. Exchange with a classmate and check each other's work.

17. At some point in your high school career, you will have to write examinations. In a course where there is an examination, a teacher may use an equation like this to calculate the students' final marks.

$$\text{Final Mark} = \text{80\% of Term Mark} + \text{20\% of Exam Mark}$$

The term mark is usually based on tests, assignments, projects, and portfolios.

a) Suppose your term mark is 84%. How will your mark change when the examination mark has been taken into account? Copy and complete the table.

Term mark	Examination mark	Final mark
84%	100%	
84%	90%	
84%	80%	
84%	70%	
84%	60%	
84%	50%	
84%	40%	
84%	30%	
84%	20%	
84%	10%	
84%	0%	

b) Write a brief report on how your final mark changes as your examination mark goes from great to not so good.

c) Repeat part a using this formula.

$$\frac{\text{Final}}{\text{Mark}} = \frac{60\% \text{ of}}{\text{Term Mark}} + \frac{40\% \text{ of}}{\text{Exam Mark}}$$

d) Repeat part a using this formula.
Final Mark = Examination Mark

e) Suppose your term mark is 80%. Your teacher is using the first formula. What mark would you have to get in the examination to have a final mark of 85%?

f) Design a spreadsheet that you can use to check your solutions.

DATA DISK

18. Use the *Provinces of Canada* database on the data disk. Choose a province and a 5-year time period after 1971.

a) i) For each year, express the number of births as a percent of the population.
ii) What is the average percent over the 5 years?

b) i) For each year, express the number of deaths as a percent of the population.
ii) What is the average percent over the 5 years?

c) Subtract the average percent of deaths from the average percent of births. This is the net percent growth due to natural causes.

d) Use the total population in the first year and this net percent growth. Determine what the population should be at the end of the 5 years. Is this number close to the actual population? What other factors affect population change?

Extend your thinking

19. Read the article below. It was printed in the *You Asked Us* column of a newspaper in 1993.

Canadian Content in NHL

Q What percent of Canadian-born players make up the National Hockey League?

A Of the 609 players on the 24 NHL rosters at the outset of the 1992-93 season, 403 (66%) were Canadians. That's a sharp drop from the 71% Canadian content of the previous season.

In the 1967-68 season, when the league expanded to 12 teams from the original six, almost 97% of the players were Canadian. Just under 2% of the players were born in the U.S. and slightly over 1% came from outside North America.

From this article, we may think that there were fewer Canadians playing hockey in the NHL in 1992–93 than there were in 1991–92.

a) Is this a correct assumption?

b) Is it possible that there were actually more Canadian players in the NHL in 1992–93 than ever before?

c) What information do you need to answer part b?

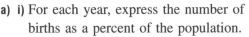

The Ideas

Look in a newspaper or a magazine for an article that gives information about how something has changed over a period of time. Use the information to explain to a friend the two ways of expressing how something changes. Be sure that your friend clearly understands the difference between the amount by which something has changed and the percent by which it has changed.

The Cost of Natural Gas

DID YOU KNOW THAT ONE CUBIC METRE OF NATURAL GAS HAS LESS ENERGY VALUE AT higher elevations (when it is expanded) than it does at lower elevations (when it is compressed)?

Before 1991 this fact was not taken into account. This meant that some consumers were overpaying while others were not paying enough. To create a fairer system, Union Gas changed the way it charged its customers for the natural gas that they had used. This change occurred in December 1991 and other natural gas companies in Canada made similar changes at about the same time.

At sea level, a sealed balloon with a diameter of 20 cm contains about 4200 cm^3 of gas.

If this balloon were taken to the top of Mount Everest, it would expand to a diameter of 29 cm. Its volume would be about 3 times as great, 12 600 cm^3.

Union Gas split the area that it serves into 11 zones. It assigned each zone a number. The average altitude above sea level of an area was used to designate its zone.

Zone	Zone number	Zone	Zone number
1	1.009 73	7	0.986 28
2	1.005 66	8	0.982 03
3	0.999 20	9	0.980 33
4	0.997 49	10	0.975 23
5	0.993 08	11	0.971 83
6	0.990 02		

The money that a consumer owes is calculated as shown below. By reading a meter, a person from the gas company determines the total amount of natural gas that was used.

Cost for consumer = amount of gas used (m^3) × zone number × rate ($\$/m^3$)

The rate is the cost in dollars for 1 m^3 of gas.

1. Calculate the cost for each gas consumption.
   a) 1000 m^3 was used in zone 2 and the rate is $\$0.18/m^3$.
   b) 1000 m^3 was used in zone 9 and the rate is $\$0.18/m^3$.
   c) Which zone has the lowest average altitude above sea level? Which zone has the highest?

The rate card below is typical of the kind used by natural gas companies all across Canada.

It's rather nice to hear some good news for a change

SSSHHH...

Don't tell anybody, but YOUR GAS BILL JUST WENT DOWN

GENERAL SERVICE RATE

Monthly fixed charge.		$7.50
	and	
First	1 400 m^3 consumed per month	19.3999¢ per m^3
Next	4 600 m^3 consumed per month	16.1416¢ per m^3
Next	124 000 m^3 consumed per month	14.9178¢ per m^3
Next	270 000 m^3 consumed per month	14.0333¢ per m^3
All over	400 000 m^3 consumed per month	13.9128¢ per m^3

2. Calculate the bill a consumer would get for each gas consumption.
   a) 1000 m^3 of gas was used in zone 3.
   b) 120 000 m^3 of gas was used in zone 9.

Developing the Ideas

▶ ▶ *Through Discussion*

As noted in the article below, in January 1992, The Toronto Star and The Financial Post newspapers became smaller.

Papers Shrink Pages

Post, Star to use smaller formats

You could forgive the publishers of The Financial Post and The Toronto Star if scenes from the 1989 comedy movie *Honey, I Shrunk The Kids* have lately been flashing through their minds.

The Post is set to shrink its traditional broadsheet weekly edition into the 50% smaller tabloid format—measuring about 30 cm wide by 38 cm deep—it uses for its weekday papers.

By contrast, The Star is expecting to make "huge" savings on its newsprint bill by trimming its pages to about 32 cm by 56 cm from their present 34 cm by 59 cm.

"There may be a small increase in the number of pages, but we're looking at probably over $10 million a year in savings."

Discuss the following questions.

1. How did the dimensions of each paper change?

2. How did the area of one page of each newspaper change? Find the percent decrease in the area.

3. During the week, The Toronto Star is often about 90 pages long. About 500 000 papers are sold per day. What is the area of newsprint that was saved daily by making the change?

4. Is there a newspaper in your area of the country that has made some changes that are similar to those made by The Financial Post and The Toronto Star?

▶▶ *Through an Activity*

Arrange for some of your classmates to bring the following items into your mathematics class: kitchen scales, several different newspapers, and a large pair of scissors.

- Weigh each newspaper.
- Record the mass of each newspaper.
- Cut each newspaper in half length-wise and then width-wise.

1. By what percent have the length and width been reduced?

2. By what percent has the area been reduced?

- Weigh each "reduced" newspaper. Compare each new mass with the original mass.

3. By what percent has the mass of each newspaper been reduced?

Working with Mathematics

Something to talk about

1. Have you ever bought chocolate milk in a 500-mL container? Would you notice a difference if the container held 501 mL? If you live in Quebec you might not notice the change in volume, but you would notice a change in price. As indicated in the article below, which was printed in October 1991, there is a tax difference between the two sizes. The dairies made a change to save consumers paying a tax on their purchases.

   a) Do you think the dairies had to change their containers to accommodate the extra 1 mL?

   b) Can you think of any other products that may have been changed (or could be changed) to save consumers from paying tax on them?

TAX/ *Quebec dairies have made a major minor change that shields their product from the tax man*

Milking the Rules to the Smallest Drop

Call it the one-millilitre solution.

With a little help from the Quebec government, the province's dairies have found a way to avoid provincial and federal sales taxes on some single-serving containers of chocolate milk.

That is because in designing the GST, Ottawa determined that single-serving containers of flavoured milk—including chocolate milk—would be taxed, while larger sizes would be exempt as basic groceries. And Revenue Canada decided 500 mL was a reasonable cutoff.

The dairies have started to sell chocolate milk in containers holding 501 mL of milk, instead of the standard 500 mL. By doing so, they avoid the 7% GST and the 8.56% Quebec provincial sales tax.

Practice

2. For each rectangle below, determine the perimeter and the area.

   a) 75 cm by 45 cm

   b) 32.5 cm by 47.5 cm

   c) 9.8 m by 1.2 m

   d) 4.5 m by 7.6 m

3. Julia plans to rope off a rectangular area for a garden in a corner of her yard. Her yard has dimensions 10 m by 5 m. She has 8 m of rope to form two sides of the garden; her backyard fence forms the other two sides. What are possible areas of the garden?

4. Determine the volume of each rectangular prism.

   a) 4 cm by 5 cm by 8 cm

   b) 9.5 cm by 12.5 cm by 18.0 cm

   c) 9.2 m by 3.4 m by 12.4 m

   d) 15.8 cm by 24.5 cm by 27.0 cm

5. Skylights in the entrance to a new medical centre measure 1.2 m by 0.8 m.

   a) Find the perimeter and area of each skylight.

   b) Suppose the length of the skylight increases by 20%. How much more light, expressed as a percent, will be admitted?

   c) Suppose the width of the skylight increases by 20%. How much more light, expressed as a percent, will be admitted?

   d) Suppose both dimensions increase by 20%. What is the percent increase in the amount of light admitted?

6. A box of cereal measures 28 cm by 18 cm by 6 cm.

   a) If the box is full, how much cereal will it contain?

   b) Suppose the indicated dimension increases by 2 cm. What volume of cereal will the box contain?

      i) height   ii) width   iii) depth

   c) Is a box of cereal full when you first open it? Explain.

Work together

7. Measure the length and width of a page from your local newspaper. Suppose the publishers reduce each dimension by 10%. There are 48 pages in the newspaper. The daily circulation is about 135 000.
   a) What are the new dimensions of the page?
   b) Compare the area of the reduced page to that of the original, expressed as a percent.
   c) How much newsprint will the publishers save in one day?
   d) How much newsprint will they save in one week?

8. Use the dimensions of your local newspaper. Suppose the publishers reduce the length *or* the width of the page by 15%.
   a) Which change would save the most newsprint?
   b) Use the information in exercise 7. How much newsprint would be saved in one week?

9. a) What is the area of your classroom floor?
   b) Suppose your classroom were to be carpeted. How many square metres of carpet would you need?
   c) Suppose you cover the floor with 30-cm square tiles. How many will you need?
   d) Suppose you use tiles with dimensions 50% greater than the tiles in part c. How many tiles will you need?

Extend your thinking

10. a) What are the dimensions of a chalkboard in your classroom?
   b) Suppose the length and width of the chalkboard increase by 10%. As a percent, how much more writing space is available?
   c) Suppose the length and width of the chalkboard decrease by 10%. As a percent, how much less writing space is available?
   d) Are your answers to parts b and c the same? Explain.

COMMUNICATING

The Ideas

Look through a magazine. Estimate the percent of space devoted to advertising. How do you think this percent may change throughout the year? Would this percent be different in a magazine that appealed to a different age group? In your journal, write a report to summarize your comments.

 BOGGLE YOUR MIND

In January 1994, Canada's national debt was $500 billion. With this amount of money, one media report said, the TransCanada highway from Vancouver to Ottawa could be "paved" in both directions with $100 bills. Find the dimensions of a $100 bill and the width of the highway. Use these values to calculate the distance from Vancouver to Ottawa. Was the media report correct?

Review

1. The greatest temperature variation in a single day in Alberta's Chinook belt was from 17°C to −28°C. What was the change in temperature?

2. Determine each sum or difference.
   a) $5 + (−5)$
   b) $(−13) + 13$
   c) $7 + (−8)$
   d) $3 + (−5)$
   e) $4 + (−3)$
   f) $14 + (−5)$
   g) $(−4) − (−6)$
   h) $(−4) − 5$
   i) $2 − 4$
   j) $(−5) − 3$
   k) $(−5) − (−2)$
   l) $1 − 9$

3. Simplify.
   a) $(−7)(+8)$
   b) $(−6)(−9)$
   c) $(−16) ÷ 4$
   d) $(+5)(−7)$
   e) $(−18) ÷ (−9)$
   f) $(−48) ÷ 16$
   g) $(+12)(+12)$
   h) $81 ÷ (−3)$
   i) $(−4)(+15)$
   j) $(−64) ÷ (−8)$

4. Determine each quotient.
   a) $\dfrac{−96}{12}$
   b) $\dfrac{39}{−13}$
   c) $\dfrac{−121}{−11}$
   d) $\dfrac{−42}{7}$
   e) $\dfrac{60}{−12}$
   f) $\dfrac{144}{12}$
   g) $\dfrac{(−15)(5)}{−25}$
   h) $\dfrac{(32)(−4)}{8}$
   i) $\dfrac{(−24)(−3)}{−6}$
   j) $\dfrac{(−8)(42)}{(−21)(−4)}$

5. Reduce to lowest terms.
   a) $\dfrac{−45}{60}$
   b) $\dfrac{−24}{−30}$
   c) $\dfrac{15}{−18}$
   d) $\dfrac{49}{56}$
   e) $\dfrac{81}{−27}$
   f) $\dfrac{−25}{−40}$

6. Write in decimal form.
   a) $\dfrac{5}{−6}$
   b) $−\dfrac{1}{3}$
   c) $5\dfrac{3}{8}$
   d) $−7\dfrac{1}{9}$
   e) $3\dfrac{2}{5}$
   f) $\dfrac{−4}{−9}$
   g) $\dfrac{7}{−2}$
   h) $\dfrac{98}{−16}$
   i) $\dfrac{−56}{100}$

7. A pool is filled from 3 pipes. The first pipe can fill the pool in 12 h. The other 2 pipes can each fill the pool in 18 h. How long will it take all 3 pipes to fill the pool?

8. Use the minimum number of key strokes to calculate each of the following:
   a) $(−56.28) × 0.09$
   b) $14.46 ÷ (−24.1)$
   c) $143.7 × (−206.8)$
   d) $(−1433.36) ÷ 43.7$
   e) $(−7.9808) ÷ (−92.8)$
   f) $(−0.029) × (−33.370)$

9. Express each percent as a decimal and as a fraction in lowest terms.
   a) 20%
   b) 4%
   c) 15%
   d) 75%
   e) 110%
   f) 150%
   g) $1\dfrac{1}{2}\%$
   h) $3\dfrac{1}{2}\%$
   i) 0.5%

10. Sacha purchased some ski equipment. Here is the list of prices.

Skis	$275
Boots	$180
Bindings	$145
Clothing	$165

   a) Suppose the boots and bindings are on sale at a 20% discount. What was the total cost for all the items?
   b) Suppose the clothing was on sale at a 35% discount. What was the total cost for all the items?
   c) Suppose Sacha bought the items at the listed prices. She paid 8% provincial sales tax and 7% GST. What was the total cost?
   d) Suppose the skis were on sale for $195. What percent reduction is this?

11. A used car has a "For sale" sign, and a price of $8999 on the windshield. The dealer wants to sell it quickly so she adds a "15% off this price" to the sign.
   a) What will the car cost at the lower price?
   b) The purchaser will have to pay provincial sales tax of 8%. What is the total cost of the car?

12. Some integers can be written as the sum of two or more consecutive integers; for example, +7 = (+3) + (+4). Write each integer as the sum of consecutive integers.
   a) −11   b) 18   c) −14
   d) −17   e) 21   f) 20

13. This chart shows the weekday discounts for long-distance telephone rates.

08:00 to 18:00	no discount
18:00 to 23:00	35% discount
23:00 to 08:00	60% discount

   a) A 5-min call from Nanaimo to Saskatoon at 10:00 costs $4.30. Calculate the cost of the same call at 20:00; At 07:00.
   b) A 5-min call from Vancouver to Thunder Bay at 21:00 costs $3.06. Calculate the cost of the same call at noon; At 02:00.

14. Carlos wants to enclose an area using 36 lengths of railroad ties. He cannot cut the ties. How many different rectangles could he form? Record the dimensions and area of each possible rectangle.

15. An interior designer plans to turn a schoolhouse into a private home. He will knock out the connecting wall between the cloakroom and the main classroom to enlarge the living space. Use the dimensions provided in the diagram at the bottom of this page. What is the percent increase in the area of living space?

16. A carton measures 60 cm by 45 cm by 40 cm.
   a) The manufacturer needs another carton that will hold twice as much as the first. What are possible dimensions of the larger carton?
   b) Do you think it is possible to design a carton with square sides that will hold twice as much as the smaller carton? If it is possible, what are its dimensions? If it is not possible, explain why not.

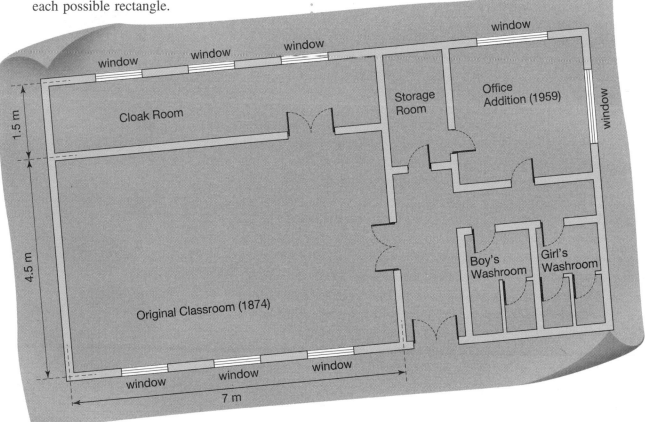

Rounding Prices

The CD Café opened for business in 1993 in Ontario. It was one of the first music stores in Canada to allow a customer to listen to a CD before deciding whether or not to buy it.

Trevor Poczynek is the owner and manager. He created a casual and relaxed atmosphere in which customers can sip on coffee, pop, or tea while they listen to CDs of their choice.

When Trevor was planning his store, he decided that he did not want to be bothered with making change. He chose his retail prices carefully so that the after-tax price was always a multiple of 25¢. The multiples that he decided to use are: $18.25, $19.50, $20.50, $22.75, $24.00, and $25.25.

ACTIVITY 1

In Ontario there are two taxes that consumers pay on most things they buy. There is an 8% provincial sales tax (PST) and a 7% federal goods and services tax (GST). These taxes are applied separately. In effect, there is a 15% sales tax on purchases that are taxable.
How should Trevor price each CD so that its after-tax price is one of the multiples of 25¢?

ACTIVITY 2

Suppose Trevor decides to open a store in Alberta. Here, there is no provincial sales tax and the GST is 7%. Trevor wants to use the same after-tax prices that he uses in Ontario.
What changes should he make in his retail prices?

ACTIVITY 3

Trevor has set his prices on single purchases so that the only change he needs is quarters.
What happens if someone buys two or more CDs?
What happens if these CDs have different retail prices?
In these cases, is it possible for the after-tax price *not* to be a multiple of 25¢?

The article below was printed in July, 1993. There is a trend throughout the United States not to give change when the amount is small.

Pennies From Hell: Businesses Starting to Keep the Change

In trendy Georgetown, Rocklands Barbecue Restaurant programs its cash register to round off to $5.70 a check that would normally total $5.66.

More than 1,000 Winn-Dixie, Kroger and other supermarkets offer customers the option of raising their tabs to the next dollar, with the extra pennies and other small change designated for charity.

And uncounted bars, restaurants and other retail establishments across the land are ignoring register exactitude, preferring to allow 1 to 4 cents a transaction—occasionally more—simply to go uncollected.

Opposition to Small Change

Americans have become impatient with transactions involving small change, especially pennies. Increasingly, they eliminate the one-cent coin, so prominent in popular imagination and idiom—penny pincher, penny arcade, "a penny saved is a penny earned"—from daily life.

ACTIVITY 4

Keep track of purchases made by you, your family, and your friends over a period of time. Investigate how many times the total amount is rounded up or down or not at all. Assume that the rounding is done to the nearest multiple of 10¢. What do you think of this idea?
Do you think this idea would be accepted by most people?

ACTIVITY 5

How many stores do you know where there is a container of pennies that is used when a customer does not have the exact money?
Do you think this is costly for stores that do this?

COMMUNICATING
The Ideas

Write a brief report that summarizes the results of your investigations.

DATA ANALYSIS

WHAT'S COMING UP?

DEPARTMENTS

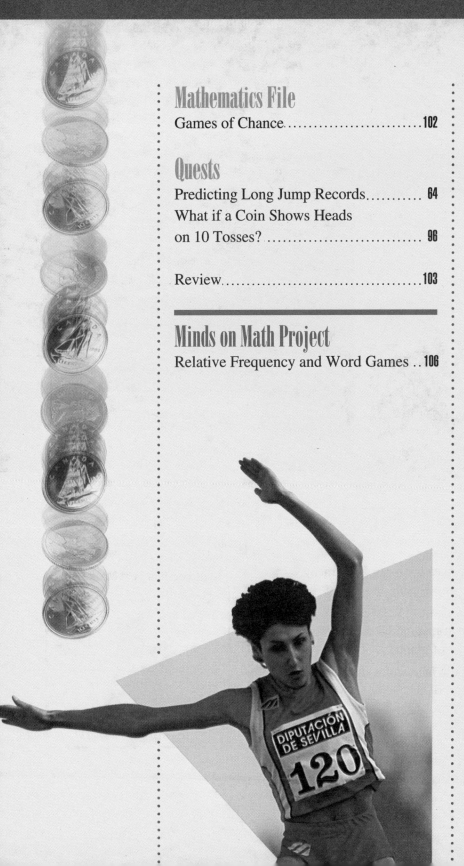

Start With What You Know

Miscellaneous
15%

Industrial
4%

Railway
7%

Resident
12%

Recreation
19%

Lightning
43%

Causes of Ontario Forest Fires

ONTARIO WILDFIRES BURN HUNDREDS OF thousands of hectares of forest each year. The Ministry of Natural Resources keeps records of the causes of the fires. In this way it can target the right groups for fire-prevention education.

Interval	Number of Students	Frequency
40–49	II	2
50–59	III	3
60–69	HHT HHT	10
70–79	HHT HHT IIII	14
80–89	HHT	5
90–99	I	1

1. What percent of Ontario's forest fires are caused by lightning?

2. There were 2560 fires last year. How many were caused by people using the forests for recreation?

3. How could this information be displayed using another type of graph?

Two ways to show the marks of a mathematics test are shown on the right.

4. What percent of students scored above 79?

5. In which interval is the median mark?

6. What percent of students had marks below 60?

7. The pass mark is 50. How many students failed the test?

Mathematics Test Marks

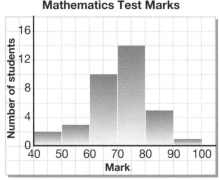

St. John's, Newfoundland, is renowned for its fog. However, as this graph shows, it has its share of rain and snow, too.

8. What appears to be the rainy season in St. John's?

9. In which month did the rainfall equal the snowfall?

10. Explain the difference between:
   a) a pictograph and a bar graph
   b) a broken-line graph and a continuous-line graph

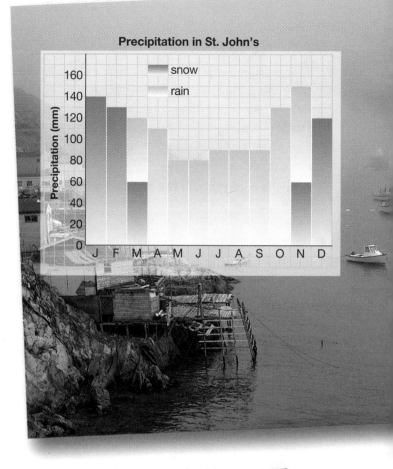

Precipitation in St. John's

Suppose you and your friend are deciding who should pay for a movie you want to rent.

You shuffle a deck of cards. You say you will pay if you pick a card which is 6 or less (ace counts as 1). You pick a card.

11. Who is more likely to pay for the movie? Explain your thinking.

In front of you are 3 paper bags. They contain red and purple "jaw-breakers." Without looking at the candies, you pick one from a bag.

12. From which bag are you most likely to pick a red candy? Explain.

13. Suppose you picked a red candy from that bag. Another candy is picked from the same bag. What are the chances that it is also red?

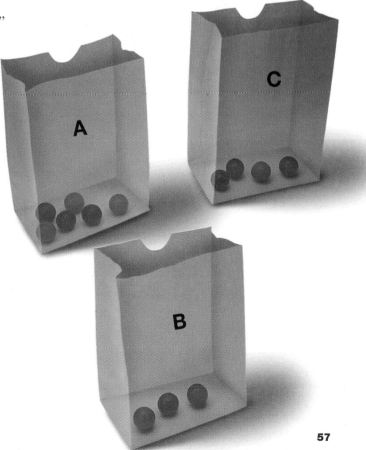

1.1 INVESTIGATING RELATIONSHIPS IN DATA

By conducting experiments and making measurements, we may discover many interesting relationships. Sometimes the relationships are simple and obvious. For example, the more hours you work, the more you are paid. Sometimes the relationships are difficult to prove. For example, it took many years for scientists to prove the connection between smoking and lung cancer.

In this lesson, you will use graphing to investigate possible relationships in data.

▶▶ *Through an Activity*

Work with a partner or in a group to investigate how far an elastic band will stretch when it holds objects of different masses.

You will need a spring balance, a long elastic band, a tack, a plastic bag with handles, a metre stick, and several objects of different masses.

Loop the elastic band through the handles of the plastic bag. Tack the elastic band to a bulletin board so the bag hangs freely. Measure the length of the elastic band.

1. Follow this procedure for each object you are using.
   a) Measure and record the mass of the object.
   b) One group member holds the tack firmly as you place the object in the plastic bag.
   c) Measure and record the length of the elastic band.

2. Enter your results in a table similar to that shown.

Object	Mass	Length of band
Empty bag	0 g	13.7 cm

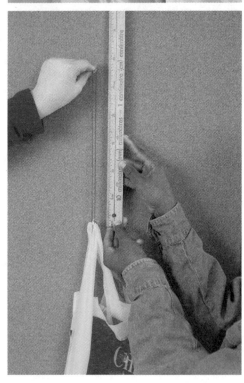

3. Graph your results. Join the points.

4. Describe the graph. What does it tell you about your experiment?

5. Compare your graph with those of other students. Explain any differences you see.

6. Use your graph. Predict how far the elastic band might stretch when it holds each mass.
   a) 250 g **b)** 750 g **c)** 2 kg

When we make measurements, then draw a graph, we can use the graph to estimate values not measured in the experiment.

Example ···

Alfredo was in the hospital with pneumonia. Nurses took his temperature every 2 h from 08:00 to 24:00, then at 04:00. This continued for the first 48 h of Alfredo's stay.

The graph shows the temperatures. Pairs of adjacent points are joined with a straight line.

a) What was Alfredo's temperature at 10:00 on the first day?

b) Estimate Alfredo's temperature at 05:30 on the second day.

c) Normal body temperature is 36.9°C. A patient's temperature may be dangerously high if it is more than 2°C above normal. During which times was Alfredo's temperature dangerously high?

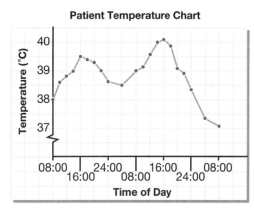

Solution

a) To find Alfredo's temperature at 10:00 on the first day, draw a vertical line from 10:00 on the horizontal axis to meet the graph. Draw a horizontal line from the graph to meet the vertical axis. The temperature is about 38.6°C.

b) Repeat the method of part a. Draw a vertical line from 05:30. Draw a horizontal line from the point where the vertical line meets the graph. The horizontal line meets the vertical axis at about 38.7°C. This is Alfredo's approximate temperature at 05:30.

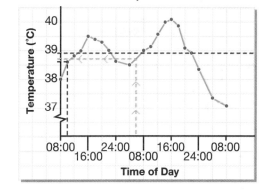

c) Normal body temperature is 36.9°C. 2°C above this is 36.9°C + 2°C = 38.9°C

Draw a horizontal line through 38.9°C on the vertical axis. This line meets the graph at about 13:00 and 22:00 on the first day, and about 07:00 and 22:00 on the second day.

Alfredo's temperature was dangerously high between 1 p.m. and 10:00 p.m. on the first day, and between 7 a.m. and 10 p.m. on the second day.

When we use a graph to determine a value we did not measure, we are *interpolating*.

Working with Mathematics

Something to talk about

1. Describe the relationship indicated by each graph.

a)

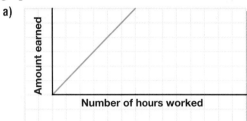

b)

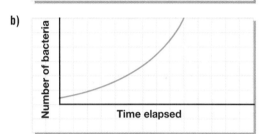

c)

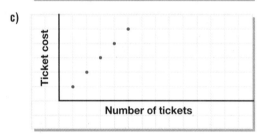

d)

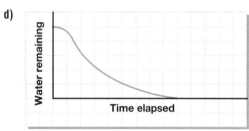

2. Give examples of two quantities that might be described by each statement.

a) When one quantity increases, the other increases.

b) When one quantity decreases, the other decreases.

c) When one quantity decreases, the other increases.

d) When one quantity increases, the other decreases.

e) Both quantities change independently of each other.

3. Describe the relationship between the quantities in each table. Explain how one quantity changes as the other quantity increases or decreases.

a)

Mass suspended from a spring, m grams	1	2	3	4	5
Extension of the spring, e centimetres	2.4	4.8	7.2	9.6	13.1

b)

Distance from the basket, d metres	2	3	4	5	6
Percent of baskets sunk, p	82	68	50	30	25

c)

Time of day, t hours	10:00	11:00	12:00	13:00	14:00
Temperature, T degrees Celsius	22	25	28	27	25

Practice

4. a) Construct a graph of the following data.

Number of coins	4	8	12	16	20
Mass (g)	100	200	300	400	500

b) How did you join the points? Explain.

c) What is the mass of one coin?

d) What is the mass of 18 coins?

5. a) Construct a graph of the following data.

Length of side (cm)	1	2	3	4	5
Area of square (cm²)	1	4	9	16	25

b) How did you join the points? Explain.

c) What is the area of a square that has a side measuring 3.5 cm?

d) What is the side length of a square with area 20 cm²?

6. a) Construct a graph of the following data.

Number of stairs climbed	5	10	15	20	25
Heart rate (beats/min)	70	80	98	119	147

b) How did you join the points? Explain.

c) What is the heart rate after climbing 18 stairs? 13 stairs?

d) About how many stairs were climbed when the heart rate was 85 beats/min? 130 beats/min?

Work together

7. You will need a set of scales that measures up to 20 kg. Digital bathroom scales are ideal.

a) Measure and record the mass of 1 copy of *Minds on Math 9* text.

b) Repeat with 2 and more copies of *Minds on Math 9*. Record your results in a table.

Number of textbooks	Mass
1	
2	
3	
4	
5	
6	
7	
8	
9	
10	

c) Draw a graph to show the mass of each number of text books.

d) Should the points on the graph be joined? Explain.

e) How does the mass change as the number of books increases?

f) Describe your graph to your partner or small group. Explain what it represents.

8. You will need a thermometer, a clock or watch with a second hand, an electric kettle, a mug, water, and some hot chocolate powder.

a) Make a mug of hot chocolate. Measure and record its temperature every minute for 20 min. Record your results in a table.

b) Draw a graph showing the temperature of the hot chocolate against time.

c) Describe how the temperature changes as time increases.

d) Did the temperature of the hot chocolate change as much during the tenth minute as it did during the first minute?

e) Do you think you would get different results if you repeated the experiment with plain hot water? Explain your thinking.

9. Plan and conduct an experiment to investigate the change in temperature as the ice cubes in a glass melt.

a) Draw a graph to show how the temperature changes with time.

b) Compare this graph with the graph in exercise 8. Describe similarities and differences to your partner or a small group.

10. Refer to your results for the *Activity* on page 58. Subtract each stretched length from the length of the elastic band with the empty bag attached. This is the *extension* of the elastic band. Record your results in a table.

Object	Mass (g)	Extension (cm)

a) Draw a graph of extension against mass. Join the points.

b) Does your graph represent a proportional situation? How do you know?

11. Use the graph from exercise 5. When the length of the side of a square is doubled, does the area double? Explain.

12. Use the graph from exercise 6. Suppose you climbed a very long flight of stairs. Would your heart rate change more rapidly near the beginning of your climb or near the end of your climb? Explain.

13. You will need a thermometer for measuring outdoor temperatures.
   a) Measure and record the outdoor temperature every 4 h from 08:00 to 20:00. Continue taking temperature readings for two days.
   b) Graph your data.
   c) Estimate the outdoor temperature at 15:00 the first day, and at 18:00 the second day.
   d) Explain whether you think you can use the graph to estimate the lowest overnight temperature. Give reasons.

On your own

14. a) Graph each relationship in exercise 3.
   b) In each case, describe how one quantity changes as the other changes.

15. The table shows the population of Canada every twenty years since Confederation.

Year	1871	1891	1911	1931	1951	1971	1991
Population (millions)	3.7	4.8	7.2	10.4	14.0	21.6	27.3

   a) Graph these data.
   b) Interpolate to estimate the year when the population was 15 000 000.
   c) Interpolate to estimate the population in 1916.

16. Psychologists have experimented to measure how much a person remembers of material that was learned. The results of one experiment are shown in the table.

Time in days	1	5	15	30	60
Percent remembered	84%	71%	61%	56%	54%

   a) Draw a graph to show the data.
   b) Suppose you graphed the percent forgotten instead of the percent remembered. How would this graph differ from the graph you drew in part a?

17. The chart shows the stopping distances for speeds from 20 km/h to 130 km/h on dry, clean, level pavement. This information is used in drivers' education courses. Stopping distance is the sum of the driver reaction distance and the braking distance. Many factors affect stopping distance: road conditions, the incline of the road, tire conditions, and so on.

Speed (km/h)	Average stopping distance (nearest metre)
20	8
30	12
40	17
50	23
60	31
70	41
80	52
90	66
100	81
110	99
120	120
130	143

   a) What is meant by "driver reaction distance"?
   b) What is meant by "braking distance"?
   c) Graph these data. How did you join the points? Explain.
   d) What is the stopping distance for a speed of: **i)** 65 km/h?   **ii)** 95 km/h?
   e) How does a wet road affect stopping distance?

Extend your thinking

18. In a science experiment, a mass is suspended from a beam by a spring. When it is pulled down and released, the mass moves up and down. The graph was drawn from measurements of the heights of the mass above the floor during the first few seconds of motion.

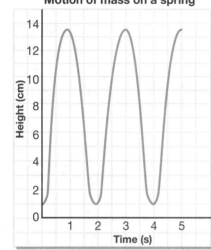

Motion of mass on a spring

a) Find the height of the mass after each time.

   i) 1 s   ii) 2 s   iii) 3 s

b) Find when the mass was at each height.
   i) 6 cm above the floor
   ii) 10 cm above the floor

c) Find how long it takes the mass to move up and down once.

d) How does the height change:
   i) during the 1st second?
   ii) during the 2nd second?
   iii) during the 3rd second?

e) For each answer in part d, describe how the mass is moving in relation to the floor.

f) Suppose measurements were taken for 5 min, then plotted on the graph. Describe how you think the graph would look.

COMMUNICATING

The Ideas

In your journal, give a few examples of related quantities in everyday life. Explain how they are related. Try to be original.

BOGGLE YOUR MIND

Some species of bamboo, one of the fastest growing plants in the world, can grow 91 cm in a single day. What if a bamboo plant could grow at this rate indefinitely? How long would it take for the plant to grow as high as the CN Tower? Why do you think bamboo plants do not reach such heights?

Predicting Long Jump Records

The world record for the women's long jump has increased steadily for many years. If it continues to increase at the same rate, when might the record be 7.75 m?

Selected Women's Long Jump World Records, 1964–1988		
Name	Year	Distance (m)
Mary Rand (Great Britain)	1964	6.76
Viorica Viscopoleanu (Romania)	1968	6.82
Heidemarie Rosendahl (West Germany)	1970	6.84
Siegrun Siegl (East Germany)	1976	6.99
Vilma Bardauskiene (Soviet Union)	1978	7.09
Valeria Ionescu (Romania)	1982	7.20
Aniscara Stanoiu-Cusmir (Romania)	1983	7.43
Heike Drechsler (East Germany)	1985	7.44
Heike Drechsler (East Germany)	1986	7.45
Galina Chistyakova (Soviet Union)	1988	7.52

Understand the problem

- What does "increased steadily for many years" mean?

Think of a strategy

- You could try graphing the data.
- If the data appear to lie on a straight line, you could use the line to estimate when the world record might be 7.75 m.

Carry out the strategy

- Graph the data.
- Use a ruler to draw a straight line that passes through or as close as possible to the plotted points.
- Extend the line until it passes the point where the length is 7.75 m.
- Approximately what year corresponds to this point?

Look back

DATA DISK

- What major assumption are you making when you solve this problem by sketching a line? Do you think this assumption is justified? Explain.
- Use the *Olympic Summer Games* database from the data disk. Choose a track-and-field event. Investigate how the winning distances or times have changed over time. Do the data you chose appear to lie along a straight line? Could you use the data to predict winning distances or times for future Olympic games?

Communicating the Ideas

In your journal, explain how you decided when the women's long jump record might be 7.75 m. Include diagrams to illustrate your explanation.

Developing the Ideas

▶▶ *Through an Activity*

Work with a partner or a group to investigate the relationship between time spent studying and test marks.

The 20 students in Ms. Jensen's class each recorded the number of minutes, to the nearest 5 min, they spent studying for a mathematics test. They also recorded their marks on this test. The results are shown below.

Graph the data in the table as a set of ordered pairs.

Minutes of study	Test mark	Minutes of study	Test mark	Minutes of study	Test mark	Minutes of study	Test mark	Minutes of study	Test mark
20	55	40	58	15	35	30	75	70	85
30	50	85	82	90	80	60	74	110	86
5	64	75	74	125	93	120	65	45	65
100	75	125	80	140	95	60	78	70	76

The points you have graphed form a *scatterplot*. Use the scatterplot.

1. Describe the graph.

2. a) Did students who studied for a short time tend to get low marks?
   b) Did students who studied for a long time tend to get high marks?
   c) Do the answers to parts a and b surprise you?

▶▶ *Through Discussion*

In the *Activity*, you drew a scatterplot of test marks against time spent studying. You should have discovered that when the study time is short, the test mark is usually low. Similarly, when the study time is long, the test mark is usually high.

In the exercises that follow, you will study examples of 3 types of scatterplots.

- a scatterplot, similar to the one in the *Activity*, where both variables tend to increase together
- a scatterplot where one variable decreases as the other increases
- a scatterplot where there appears to be no relationship between the variables

1. Describe each scatterplot below. Explain what each scatterplot tells you about the two quantities being graphed.

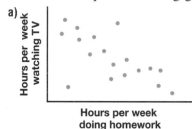

Working with Mathematics

Something to talk about

1. Suppose you were to draw a scatterplot of how much a person spends against how much she or he earns. Which of the three scatterplots below do you think it would look like? Explain your reasoning.

a)

Amount spent ($)

Earnings ($)

b)

Amount spent ($)

Earnings ($)

c)

Amount spent ($)

Earnings ($)

2. Suppose you were to draw a scatterplot of how many cavities a teenager gets in a year against how often she or he brushes her or his teeth in a week. Which of the three scatterplots below do you think it would look like? Explain your reasoning.

a)

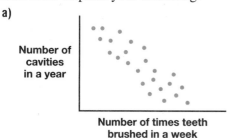

Number of cavities in a year

Number of times teeth brushed in a week

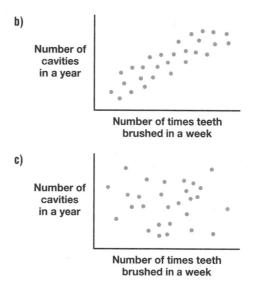

b)

Number of cavities in a year

Number of times teeth brushed in a week

c)

Number of cavities in a year

Number of times teeth brushed in a week

3. a) Do you think there is a relationship between the height of a person and the height of her or his mother? What do you think this scatterplot would look like?

b) Would the scatterplot be different if the heights of the fathers were used instead?

c) Does your answer to part a depend on the age of the person? Explain.

Practice

In exercises 4 and 5, predict what each relationship will be, then construct a scatterplot of the data. Describe the relationship, if any, in each case.

4. The table below shows the lengths and widths of several rectangular building lots, each having a perimeter of 60 m.

Length (m)	5	10	15	20	25
Width (m)	25	20	15	10	5

5. The tables below show the number of floors of several downtown buildings along with their ages.

Age (decades)	1	2	3	2	2	3	1	4	2	2
Number of floors	2	2	3	1	2	4	15	3	3	5
Age (decades)	4	1	3	3	4	3	1	2	1	3
Number of floors	1	8	2	12	3	5	10	5	14	1

6. The tables below show the heights of several seedlings after various growing times.

Time (days)	1	1	4	2	4	2	3	3
Height (mm)	5	7	19	9	21	11	14	14

Time (days)	1	3	2	3	3	2	1	2
Height (mm)	6	13	11	14	15	10	4	7

a) What relationship do you expect to find between growing time and height?

b) Use the data in the tables to construct a scatterplot.

c) Examine the scatterplot. Does it support the prediction you made in part a?

Work together

7. Work with a partner. Take and record these measurements in centimetres.
- height
- hand span (the distance from thumb to last finger on an outstretched hand)
- arm span (the distance from fingertip to fingertip with arms outstretched)
- foot length
- head circumference

Enter your data in a class chart to create a complete set of data for your class.

a) Draw a scatterplot to determine whether height and arm span are related. If you think there is a relationship, describe it.

b) Draw a scatterplot to show height against foot length. Describe any relationships displayed by your graph.

c) Draw a scatterplot to show hand span against arm span. Describe any relationships displayed by your graph.

d) Draw a scatterplot showing height against head circumference. Describe any relationships displayed by your graph.

e) Select two other quantities not yet graphed. Draw a scatterplot and describe what you think it demonstrates.

8. Create a class chart to show the distance each student lives from school, and the average length of time it takes to travel to school in the morning.

a) Draw a scatterplot to show your class results.

b) Describe your scatterplot to a partner or a small group. Explain whether you can make any general observations, and why.

c) What different factors affect the length of travel time for students?

9. Suppose a scatterplot were drawn to describe each pair of quantities. What do you think this scatterplot would look like? Explain your thinking.

a) a person's height and her or his mass

b) the maximum number of chin-ups a person can do and the maximum number of push-ups

10. The tables below show data for 20 people chosen at random. Construct a scatterplot to determine whether height and mass are related. If so, describe the relationship.

Height (cm)	150	170	162	180	161
Mass (kg)	45	65	58	92	62

Height (cm)	198	155	173	158	166
Mass (kg)	99	48	74	64	65

Height (cm)	173	166	174	186	177
Mass (kg)	64	75	65	88	82

Height (cm)	196	154	157	182	165
Mass (kg)	93	53	50	94	76

11. Some spreadsheet programs allow you to draw scatterplots. Check whether the program you use does. If so, follow these steps to create a scatterplot of height against mass.

a) Start a new spreadsheet file. Set up the columns as shown. Enter the data from the table in exercise 10 in the appropriate columns of your spreadsheet.

TEMPLATE DISK

	A	B
1	Height (cm)	Mass (kg)
2	150	45
3	170	65
4	162	58

b) Select the cells from A2 to B21.

- In ClarisWorks, choose Make Chart from the Options menu. You are given a choice of several types of charts to draw. Select the X-Y Scatterplot. Click OK.
- In Microsoft Works for Windows, choose New Chart from the Chart menu. Double click on the chart that is displayed and change the type to X-Y Scatterplot. Click OK.
- If you are using a different program, check your user's manual for the steps to follow.

c) Save the spreadsheet file with the scatterplot displayed. Print the scatterplot. How does it compare to the scatterplot you drew in exercise 10?

DATA DISK

12. Do you think the population of a country is related to its land area? Investigate this question using the *Land Use* database from the data disk.

a) Set up a new spreadsheet file as shown below. Open the *Land Use* database. Sort the database so that all the European countries are together. For the 28 European countries, transfer the information from the fields giving country name, land area, and population, into the appropriate columns of the spreadsheet. In the spreadsheet, delete the row containing data for the former USSR. Removing this row of data will make your scatterplot more readable.

	A	B	C
1	Country	Land area	Population
2			
3			

b) Use the method in exercise 11. Create a scatterplot of population against land area for the European countries.

c) Describe the scatterplot. Explain whether you think there is a relationship between the area of a European country and its population, and why.

13. The tables below show data for 20 women chosen at random.

Height (cm)	156	163	166	170	157
Shoe size	6	$7\frac{1}{2}$	8	10	7

Height (cm)	168	160	169	178	161
Shoe size	7	$8\frac{1}{2}$	9	10	$7\frac{1}{2}$

Height (cm)	168	163	160	163	157
Shoe size	8	$9\frac{1}{2}$	6	8	5

Height (cm)	170	160	154	174	170
Shoe size	8	8	$5\frac{1}{2}$	9	$8\frac{1}{2}$

a) Would you expect to find a relationship between the heights of the women and their shoe sizes? Why?

b) Make a scatterplot of these data. Describe any relationship you find.

c) Think about how men's and women's shoes are sized. Why do you think it is important that all the data in this example were collected from women?

On your own

14. The table below shows data for 17 cities. The food costs are the prices paid for a basket of similar food items in each city. All costs are given in $U.S.

City	Net hourly wage ($ U.S.)	Food basket cost ($ U.S.)
Abu Dhabi	6.5	336
Athens	4.9	275
Bangkok	2.0	325
Bogotá	2.8	258
Chicago	13.0	351
Copenhagen	11.7	379
Geneva	15.5	558
Jakarta	1.8	235
Johannesburg	3.8	217
Mexico City	2.6	253
Montreal	10.1	291
Nairobi	0.4	112
Nicosia	4.8	239
Paris	8.5	471
Singapore	5.0	443
Sydney	7.2	262
Zürich	17.3	570

a) Create a scatterplot of food cost against hourly wage. Describe the scatterplot. How are the two quantities related?

b) In 1994, the average hourly wage in Lagos was $0.50 U.S. The cost of a basket of food was $736 U.S. Where does this point lie on the scatterplot? What does its position tell you about the relative cost of food in Lagos?

15. In a study of 30 North American cities, the population of the city and the number of pets were compared in a scatterplot. Describe the shape of the scatterplot you would expect. Explain your thinking.

16. Red pine is a coniferous tree found throughout Eastern Canada. The table below shows data for 16 red pines. All the diameters were measured 1.3 m above the ground.

Age (years)	Diameter (cm)	Age (years)	Diameter (cm)
9	8	27	30
20	12	5	5
11	6	16	9
4	1	22	12
16	20	3	4
18	9	29	19
12	9	23	19
23	14	21	13

a) Make a scatterplot of diameter against age.

b) Is there a relationship between the age of a red pine and its diameter? Explain your answer.

Extend your thinking

17. Would you expect to find a relationship between a person's height at age 16 and her or his adult height? If so, describe what a scatterplot describing these data would look like. Explain your thinking.

18. The shoe sizes and the reading levels of 150 students from various grades in an elementary school were plotted in a scatterplot. The scatterplot showed that as shoe size increased so did reading level. Does this mean that people with larger than average feet have higher than average reading abilities? Explain.

COMMUNICATING The Ideas

In your journal, sketch each of the three shapes of scatterplots that you have seen. For each graph, label each axis with a quantity that it could represent.

Developing the Ideas

▶ ▶ *Through an Activity*

The table shows the winning distances for the discus throw at the Olympic Summer Games.

Year	Men's distance (m)	Women's distance (m)
1928	47.32	39.62
1932	49.49	40.58
1936	50.48	47.63
1948	52.78	41.92
1952	55.03	51.42
1956	56.36	53.69
1960	59.18	55.10
1964	61.00	57.27
1968	64.78	58.28
1972	64.40	66.62
1976	67.50	69.00
1980	66.64	69.96
1984	66.60	65.36
1988	68.82	72.30

We shall look for a trend in the data. If there is a trend, we can use it to predict what the winning distances might be in future Olympic Games, such as the 2008 Games.

1. On grid paper, draw a set of axes. Label the horizontal axis "Year." Label the vertical axis "Winning distance in metres."
   On the vertical axis, let each square represent 5 m. Label the distances from 0 m to 100 m. On the horizontal axis, choose a scale to include the years from 1928 to 2008.

2. Plot a point for each pair of data for the men's distances.

3. Place a ruler so that it passes as close as possible to all the plotted points. Draw a straight line along the ruler. This is called a *line of best fit.*

4. Compare your graph to those of your classmates.

5. What is your estimate of the winning distance for the men's discus throw in 2008? Compare your answer with those of your classmates.

You probably found that you and your classmates drew different straight lines and obtained different estimated distances. This is a natural part of this estimation method.

In the *Activity*, you created a line of best fit for given data. Drawing a line of best fit is a useful method for predicting and estimating.
- Plot the ordered pairs corresponding to the given data.
- Place a ruler so that it passes as close as possible to all the plotted points. Use visual estimation.
- Draw a line along the ruler. This is a line of best fit.

Here is a line of best fit for the women's data on page 71.

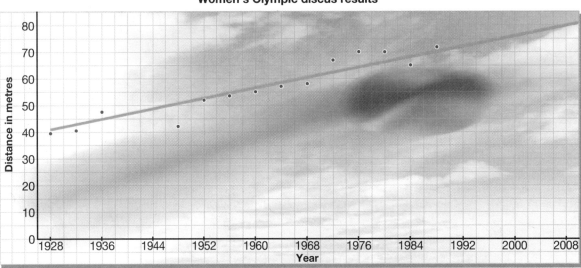

Women's Olympic discus results

When data points lie close to a line of best fit, we can use the line to predict data at points for which measurements were not taken. However, the more loosely scattered the data points are around a line of best fit, the less reliable the predictions are. We must also use common sense when we make predictions. For example, if we extend a line of best fit for record discus throws far enough into the future, it will eventually represent a throw of 1000 m. But no person will ever be able to throw a discus this far.

1. Examine the line of best fit above. What is the expected winning distance for the women's discus in 2008?

2. Do you think the women's gold medalist will achieve that distance? Explain your thinking.

3. Is it possible for the women's gold medalist in 2008 to throw under 60 m? Is it likely? Explain your thinking.

4. Discuss whether you would be surprised by a winning throw of 90 m in 2008, and why.

5. Describe how a line of best fit gives an estimated range for any predicted event.

Working with Mathematics

Something to talk about

1. Examine the graph below.

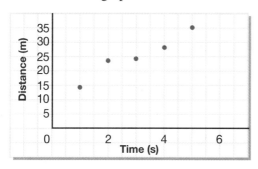

a) Would it be appropriate to draw a line of best fit on the graph?

b) Should a line of best fit pass through the origin? Explain.

c) Should we always construct a line of best fit by connecting the first and last points?

2. Would it be appropriate to construct a line of best fit for the data in the graph below? Explain.

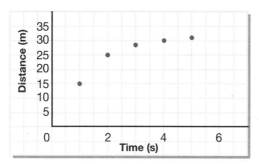

3. For these diagrams, which line of best fit do you think would provide the most reliable predictions? Explain your choice.

a)

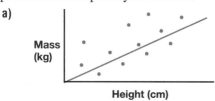

b)

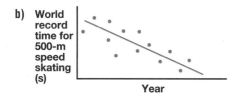

c)

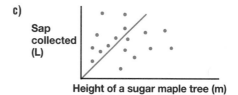

Practice

4. For each table of data below, graph the points in a scatterplot and construct a line of best fit.

a)

Amount spent on advertising ($1000)	100	200	400	700	800	900
Number of new customers	10	16	28	40	52	58
Amount spent on advertising ($1000)	140	300	400	600	850	700
Number of new customers	15	25	32	29	49	35

b)

Distance to school (km)	0.8	1.5	1.2	0.9	1.4	1.5
Time to travel (min)	15	25	22	20	25	30
Distance to school (km)	0.9	1.2	0.5	1.3	1.5	0.9
Time to travel (min)	10	24	12	23	12	21

5. During a fishing contest, an official kept track of the total catch for all participants. At regular time intervals, she collected all the fish caught and recorded the total mass before releasing them. The chart shows her records.

Time elapsed (min)	10	20	30	40
Total fish caught (kg)	25	60	75	105
Time elapsed (min)	50	60	70	80
Total fish caught (kg)	120	150	175	190

a) Plot the data. Construct a line of best fit.

b) Use the line of best fit to predict the total catch after 2 h.

6. A hockey coach mounted a radar gun behind the goal to measure the speed of each player's best shot. He tabulated the results against the number of years of experience each player had playing hockey.

a) What relationship might you expect to find between experience and shot speed?

b) Plot the data in the chart below. Construct a line of best fit.

Years of experience	Shot speed (km/h)
1	100
2	120
4	145
4	155
1	110
3	130
4	145
2	115
3	130
3	115
1	90
4	135
2	125
5	150
5	120
2	120

c) Describe the relationship suggested by the line of best fit.

Work together

7. Refer to the graph you drew for the men's discus events, and the graph on page 72 for the women's discus events.

a) Estimate the winning distances for men and women in the 1996 Olympic Games. Find the results for that year in an almanac or database. How do they compare to your estimates?

b) According to the graphs, in which Olympic Games did the women first surpass the men? Look at the results. When did the women first surpass the men in the discus throw?

8. The table shows the winning times for the 800-m race at the Olympic Summer Games.

Year	Men's time (seconds)	Women's time (seconds)
1960	106.30	124.30
1964	105.10	121.10
1968	104.30	120.90
1972	105.90	118.55
1976	103.50	114.94
1980	105.40	113.42
1984	103.00	117.60
1988	103.45	116.10
1992	103.66	115.54

a) Construct a line of best fit for each set of data. Predict the winning times in the year 2024.

b) In approximately what year would the men's and women's winning times be about the same?

9. Use the *Olympic Summer Games* database to find the winning times for the men's 100-m freestyle event from 1956 to 1988.

DATA DISK

a) Graph the winning times and years.

b) Construct a line of best fit.

c) How many of the winning times are within 1 s of the line of best fit? Do you think the line is a good representation of the winning times?

d) Use the line of best fit to estimate the result for the 1992 Olympics. Find the result in an almanac. How close was your estimate?

10. Graphing calculators can be used to graph data sets involving two quantities, and to draw a line of best fit. Keying sequences may vary between different models of calculator. If you have a graphing calculator, use the owner's manual to explore how you can use it to create a scatterplot and construct a line of best fit.

On your own

11. The standard measure for tree size is the diameter at breast height (DBH). The table shows the DBH of two trees of different species at various ages. The measures are typical for trees of these species.

Age (years)	White Pine DBH (cm)	Black Spruce DBH (cm)
13	6.0	3.8
20	12.5	7.1
28	17.8	9.7
42	22.3	14.3
54	29.6	17.5
63	39.5	18.6
83	44.3	24.1
88	46.8	26.4
99	50.0	27.8
104	53.6	29.4
120	57.1	33.5
130	60.9	36.5

a) Construct a line of best fit for each set of data.

b) What diameter would a tree of each species have when its age is 50 years?

c) Estimate the age of a tree of each species when it has a DBH of 30 cm.

d) What was each tree's average growth rate per year over the years included in the table? About how many times as fast as the black spruce did the white pine grow?

12. The table shows the dimensions used in the construction of birdhouses and their platforms.

Species	Entrance diameter (cm)	Inside length, width (cm)	Wall height (cm)
House wren	2.5	6	15
Chickadee Downy woodpecker	3.1	8	20
Bluebird Tree swallow English sparrow	3.8	10	26
Hairy woodpecker Crested flycatcher Starling	5	12	31
Common flicker	6.3	15	38
Kestrel	7.5	18	43

a) Why do you think different birds require different sizes of entrances?

b) Plot a graph of inside length and width against entrance diameter for the bird houses.

c) Construct a line of best fit.

d) A red-headed woodpecker needs an entrance hole with a diameter of 4.4 cm. Estimate the inside length and width for a red-headed woodpecker's house.

13. a) Use one of the scatterplots you constructed for exercise 7 on page 68. Construct a line of best fit for the data in the scatterplot.

b) Use the line of best fit to predict the value of one quantity for any given value of the other quantity. For example, how long is the armspan of a person with a height of 1.5 m?

Extend your thinking

14. Points that lie close to a line of best fit show a relationship between two variables. Points that are farthest from a line of best fit don't show the same relationship. These points are called *outliers*. For one exercise in this section, list the coordinates of an outlier. Write a sentence or two to describe what the outlier shows. For example, in a plot showing mass and height for various people, an outlier could be a point representing a short person with a large mass or a tall person with a small mass.

The Ideas

In your journal, describe how to construct a line of best fit and how to use it to make predictions. Explain also how you can decide how reasonable the predictions you obtain from a line of best fit are.

1.4 RELIABLE SAMPLING METHODS

Developing the Ideas

▶▶ *Through Discussion*

Sampling is useful to gain information about a very large body by observing or testing only a portion of it.

- When you sip a spoonful of soup to test how hot a bowl of soup is, you are sampling. Based on the temperature of the soup in your spoon, you decide if it is too hot to eat. In this case, the bowl of soup is the population.

- When you listen to one song on a CD before buying it, you are sampling the music on the CD. All the songs on the CD make up the population.

Various companies use sampling to survey the Canadian population. These companies usually obtain reliable results because they use statistically sound sampling methods. Constructing the sample carefully increases the likelihood of obtaining valid predictions.

- Gallup is a company that publishes monthly opinion surveys to identify trends in Canada. For a national survey, Gallup interviews 1000 people in Canada. This sample represents the population of 18 000 000 people in Canada who are 18 years and older.

- A. C. Nielsen is a company that monitors the TV viewing habits of Canadians. The company installs monitoring devices on TV sets in 1500 Canadian households. This sample represents the population of nearly 10 500 000 TV viewing households in Canada.

- The Society of Composers, Authors, and Music Publishers of Canada (SOCAN) is an organization that samples, in one year, about two weeks of air time on every Canadian radio station. SOCAN uses these data to decide how much royalty should be paid to each recording artist whose songs are played on the radio.

For each company named above, discuss these questions:

1. What method of collecting data is used?

2. What fraction of the population is chosen as the sample?

3. Why is the entire population not surveyed?

347

If a sample is to represent a population, we must be sure that:

- the sample accurately reflects the population.
- all members of the population have an equal chance of being selected; that is, it is a *random sample.*

Suppose a survey is conducted to determine the favourite TV program of students in your school. Only students in your class are surveyed. Since students in other classes have not been asked, the sample is not a random sample. It is not representative of your school population.

If the sample is selected at random then it accurately reflects the population, and conclusions about the population are likely to be valid.

▶ ▶ *Through a Guided Example*

Example ···

A Vancouver company is hired by a sports magazine to find out which teams Canadians think will meet in the World Series later in the year. To collect the data, the company considers sampling Canadians in one of the following ways.

a) Poll a random sample of 1000 people in British Columbia.

b) Put an advertisement in all major newspapers asking people to tell their preferences.

c) Send 100 questionnaires to all major businesses to be completed by anyone selected at random.

Describe the main weakness of each method.

Solution

a) Preferences in sports are often regional. A sample of people in British Columbia is not likely to be representative of the opinions of all Canadians.

b) Generally, only ardent baseball fans would take the trouble to respond to this advertisement. The sample will not be random.

c) This sample tends to exclude groups such as students, farmers, homemakers, and senior citizens. Therefore, it is not a random sample.

Working with Mathematics

Something to talk about

1. Explain why each sample may not provide accurate information about its population.
   a) A survey of your classmates is used to estimate the average age of students in your school.
   b) A survey of senior citizens is used to determine the music that is best liked by Canadians.
   c) To determine the proportion of domestic cars to foreign cars purchased by Canadians, a person records the numbers of domestic cars and foreign cars in the parking lot of the General Motors Assembly Plant in Oshawa, Ontario.
   d) To determine which movie is best liked by teenagers, 12 of your closest friends are interviewed.
   e) To estimate how many Canadians want the legal drinking age raised, a radio station runs an open-line talk show titled "Should we lower the drinking age?" and tallies the number of callers who are in favour and against.

2. For each case in exercise 1, describe how data might be collected to obtain valid information about each issue.

3. When a sample is used to find out about a population, some people think that the predictions are not valid. They do not believe that a well-constructed sample can provide data that are accurate. These people say that the information would be more accurate if the entire population was surveyed. Do you support this argument?

4. Gallup poll results are often published in the weeks leading up to an election. Discuss whether publicizing these results can influence voters on election day.

On your own

5. For each situation, identify what you think the population is. Explain why data are collected from a sample and not the population.
   a) The quality of flash bulbs
   b) The number of Canadian families who eat at least one meal together as a family per week
   c) The purity of processed food
   d) The strength of aluminum extension ladders
   e) The cost of ski equipment
   f) The percent of the population with each blood type

6. For each study described, answer these questions.
   i) What is the population about which the information is sought?
   ii) How is the sample chosen?
   iii) Is it a random sample?
   a) You decide to purchase a new CD because you like the title song.
   b) Researchers are investigating the percent of farms that have started growing canola instead of wheat. They purchase mailing lists from farm equipment supply companies, and mail a survey form to every 50th name on each list.
   c) Researchers are trying to determine the percent of popular support in Alberta for extending the school year to 12 months. They telephone people selected randomly from the Edmonton telephone directory.
   d) To determine the spending habits of Canada's teenagers, researchers interviewed young shoppers at a downtown mall.
   e) To determine whether Canadian voters support Canada's peacekeeping role abroad, researchers telephoned five residences in each political riding.

Work together

7. How would you collect data to find the following information? Give reasons for your answers.
   a) The popularity of a TV program
   b) The most popular breakfast cereal
   c) The average number of compact discs owned by high-school students
   d) The average number of people in one car in rush hour
   e) The most popular recording artist or group
   f) The average weekly fast-food budget for a teenager

8. For *one* of the following statements, decide what kind of sample you need. Work in a group of three or four to collect the data.
   a) The average age and height of the students in your class
   b) The average amount spent on lunch in the school's cafeteria
   c) The most popular musical group
   d) The average time spent waiting in line in the cafeteria
   e) The average weekly earnings of students with part-time jobs
   f) The average number of letters in English words

9. In each situation, why would data be collected from a sample and not from the population?
   a) To find the average age of drivers when they get their drivers' licences
   b) To find the number of hours a high-efficiency light bulb will burn
   c) To find the average volume of milk in a 4-L bag

10. For each study described, answer these questions.
    i) What is the population about which the information is sought?
    ii) How is the sample chosen?
    iii) Is it a random sample?
       a) To assess the opinions of Canadians regarding the team who will win the Stanley Cup, researchers conducted telephone surveys of 10 000 people selected randomly from the Calgary telephone book.
       b) To assess the support of the Canadian people for a tax on the wealthy, a researcher tallied the number of callers for and against this tax on the Money Matters TV phone-in show.
       c) To estimate the annual income of the typical Canadian, researchers interviewed 5000 pedestrians randomly encountered on the streets of several Canadian cities.
       d) To determine what legal drinking age is preferred by Canadian teenagers, researchers interviewed 8000 randomly-selected high-school students from across Canada.

Extend your thinking

11. The written material that accompanied the first CD players available in stores included a reference to "sampling" or "over-sampling." The quality of the machine was determined by how much over-sampling it did: 4 times, 8 times, 16 times. Contact a manufacturer of CD players to find out what this means.

The Ideas

In your journal, briefly describe the advantages of using a sample to collect data from a population. What must you remember when you work with samples?

Sampling and TV Ratings

How do television stations know which programs are the most popular?
Why is this information important?

For the week of April 5–11, 1993, the top 5 programs in North America
are shown.

RANK	PROGRAM	RATING POINT	SHARE	VIEWERS
1	NCAA Championship	22.2	34	32.9
2	Home Improvement	19.3	30	31.3
3	Roseanne	18.7	30	28.6
4	20/20	16.9	30	24.4
5	Seinfeld	16.2	27	23.1

One *Rating point* represents 931 000 households.
The *Share* is the percent of sets in use.
The *Viewers* is the number of viewers in millions.

Suppose 20% of households in Saint John watched a particular show. We
can be sure, 15 times out of 20, that between 18.6% and 21.4% of the
population with TV sets has watched the program.

There are more than 10 000 000 TV sets in Canada. The favourite
programs are determined by using a random sample of viewers. Every
home containing one or more TV sets has an equally-likely chance of
being selected.

The A. C. Nielsen company monitors the TV viewing habits of
Canadians. Since 1990, "people meters" have been used in 1500
households. Each meter records the television programs that are watched.
A television set is connected to a small computer device, which in turn
is connected to a special telephone line. Information about which station
is watched, and by how many people, is stored at one-minute intervals
throughout the day and night. A central computer retrieves these data
daily, by using the special telephone line.

Mathematics & the Media

Linking Ideas

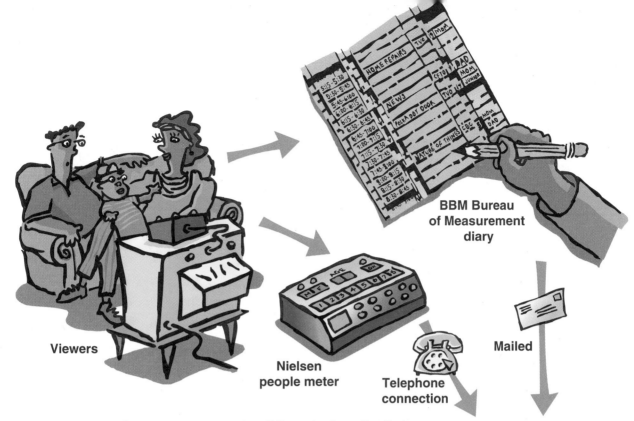

Viewers

Nielsen people meter

Telephone connection

Mailed

BBM Bureau of Measurement diary

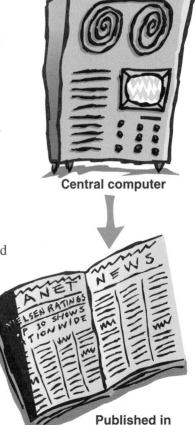

Central computer

Published in newspaper

The BBM Bureau of Measurement samples differently. It mails diaries to 60 000 homes each week. About 33 000 diaries are returned. There is one diary for each TV set in the home. When a person in the home watches TV, he or she records the name of the program every 15 min. Also recorded is the number of people watching the program.

The Nielsen ratings are frequently reported in the newspaper, as shown on the preceding page. These ratings rank the popularities of the shows by listing the numbers of people who watch them. Television ratings do not pass judgment on the quality of the program.

1. In the paragraph following the chart on the previous page, why do you think the phrase "15 times out of 20" is included?

2. What percent of TV sets in Canada have a "people meter"?

3. How many households in North America watched each program listed on the preceding page?

4. How many more viewers watched the NCAA championship than Seinfeld?

5. How many TV sets in Canada were tuned to Roseanne?

6. Why do the numbers in the Share column not add to 100%?

7. Check a newspaper to find the ratings for last week. How do they compare with the ratings above?

8. Why do you think the research companies have developed such sophisticated methods to determine viewer preferences?

Developing the Ideas

▶ ▶ *Through Discussion*

The cartoon illustrates that when we read or hear a statement involving statistics (especially a sensational one), we should think carefully about it. In this case, we must consider which groups of people are included in the 25 million.

From time to time, people may misinterpret statistics. In some cases, these misuses are by accident or lack of knowledge. In other cases, the misuse is deliberate and intentionally misleading.

A news commentator introduces a story with the statement: "32% of high-school students drop out."

Upon hearing this, you should ask questions like these:

• What is meant by "drop out"?
• Is the statement true for students in your school?
• If a student moves to another school, is he or she a "dropout"?
• If a student leaves school to take a job, is he or she a "dropout"?

What other questions could we ask?

Why would the commentator make such a statement?

Read the excerpt from a real-estate newspaper. How is it misleading?

The heading states that the sales had "soared." The first sentence says that the real-estate slump may be over. This September's sales were 18% more than August's sales. However, last year's September sales were 35% higher than this September's. Also, since August is said to be a slow month for sales, we would expect September sales to be higher. A more accurate heading might be "Real-Estate Sales Improve in September."

REAL-ESTATE SALES SOAR THIS SEPTEMBER

The slump in the real-estate market may be over. Sales of houses in September jumped by 18% over August, which is a traditionally slow month for real estate. Sales in September last year were 35% higher than the same month this year.

In the previous section, we discussed the uses of sampling to survey a population. The sample must be random and must accurately reflect the population.

Sometimes data are collected in a way that may appear to be valid, but which in fact introduces a bias. In such a case, the biased sample has characteristics which are not typical of the population. Here is an example.

Ann Landers, an advice columnist, once asked readers, "If you had to do it over again, would you have children?"

Almost 10 000 letters from parents poured in and about 70% of these answered no. These letters typically expressed parents' anger at their children's behaviour and often reflected resentment.

Later, a scientific survey was conducted, using random sampling. It revealed that about 90% of the respondents answered yes to the same question.

Discuss these questions.
- In what ways might the people who wrote the letters to Ann Landers differ from the typical reader of her column?
- Do you think that a parent who would respond yes would be as likely to send a letter?
- Would you consider those who responded to be a random sample of parents?
- Is it reasonable to conclude that 70% of parents wish they didn't have children?

Here is another example.
Do you feel that the information presented in the newspaper report reflects an accurate use of statistics?
Discuss these questions.
- Are Dr. Cole's patients representative of the general population?
- Is the headline accurate?

A graph can be used to persuade people to believe claims that are untrue. You will see exercises relating to this on the next page.

A2   THE GAZETTE

Two out of Three Have Heart Trouble

In an interview with a Gazette reporter, Dr. Cole of Eastern Hospital stated that she was consulted by 30 patients last week. Of those 30, she found that 20 had had heart trouble. This is alarmingly high.

Working with Mathematics

Something to talk about

1. Explain why each graph is misleading.

a)

Winter Resort Industry Takes Off

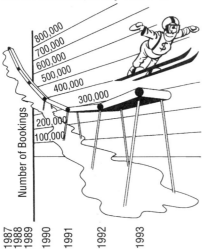

b)

Unemployment (Annual Average)

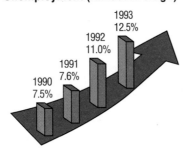

2. Some of these statements are misleading. Which ones do you think they are? Explain why they are misleading.

a) Last year approximately 55% of skiing injuries were suffered by people who had taken skiing lessons. This suggests that it may be better not to take lessons.

b) Saskatchewan, one of three Prairie provinces which grows wheat for export, produced almost half of all the wheat shipped to other countries.

c) In 1991, 1775 drivers and 102 cyclists were killed in traffic accidents. This shows that it is safer to ride a bike than to drive a car.

On your own

3. A company sells ice skates, in-line skates, and hockey equipment. The table shows the annual sales for several years.

a) Draw an honest graph of the data.

b) Draw a graph on which the annual sales do not appear to change very much.

c) Draw a graph that exaggerates the increase in sales.

YEAR	SALES ($)
1988	105 923
1989	98 263
1990	143 829
1991	149 066
1992	177 062

4. Use a favourite magazine. Find an article that uses numerical information to reach a conclusion.

a) What does the author want you to believe?

b) How do you think the data were collected?

c) Do you think the data are accurate? Why?

d) Do you agree with the author's conclusion?

e) Suppose you were collecting this information. How might you do it differently?

f) How could the author use the same data to reach a different conclusion?

5. Watch a television commercial and answer these questions.

a) What product is being sold?

b) What information or image does the commercial present to persuade you to buy the product?

c) What claims are made?

d) Suppose you wanted to investigate the product on behalf of consumers. What data would you collect? How would you collect the data?

e) What precautions would you take to ensure the data were not biased?

Work together

6. a) Interview 10 people. Record their yes/no responses to the question: "Do you believe that the number of days in a school year should be increased?"

b) Interview 10 people (not included in your first survey). Record their yes/no responses to the question: "Statistics indicate that students in countries where the school year is longer receive a better education and obtain better paying jobs. Would you support increasing the length of the school year?"

c) Compare the results of the two surveys. Explain the difference (if any) in the results.

d) How can the wording of a question in a survey affect the results?

7. Choose an issue on which you would like to survey the opinions of other students. Write the question in two significantly different ways. Interview 10 students using one wording of the question and 10 students using the other wording. Compare the results of the two surveys.

8. Comment on the reasoning in this sentence. As few accidents happen in the early morning, very few of these as a result of fog, and fewer still as a result of travelling faster than 150 km/h, it would be best to travel at high speeds on a foggy morning.

9. For each population in exercise 10, on page 79, describe how you would select a sample and collect data to obtain valid, unbiased information.

10. Use the *Billboard Number One Hits* database on the data disk. Consider this statement. "The oldies were better. Elvis and the Beatles are much better performers than any of the number one artists of the 90s."

DATA DISK

a) Use the database to support this statement.

b) Use the database to argue against this statement.

In each case, use a graph to illustrate your arguments.

Extend your thinking

11. At the beginning of the school year, the dance committee of the Students' Council set a goal to increase the attendance of grade 9 students at the six dances held during the year. At the end of the school year, the number of grade 9 students who attended each dance is as follows:

Dance #	1	2	3	4	5	6
Attendance	125	110	140	135	160	150

a) Do you think the committee met its goal?

b) What statistics would you use to support your answer?

c) The chairperson of the dance committee plans to run for Student Council president for the next year. She wants to use her "success" on the committee to enhance her chances of being elected. Draw a graph that uses these data, but is misleading to the students.

1.6 MAKING PREDICTIONS

Developing the Ideas

▶▶ *Through Instruction*

One of the principal uses of statistics is in making predictions.

- By determining the blood types of a sample of Canadians, the Red Cross attempts to predict the number of people with type AB blood who will attend the next clinic.
- By testing a sample of flashlight batteries, a technician can estimate the life of the batteries.
- By sampling the garbage at a landfill site, an engineer can determine how much of the garbage could have been recycled.
- By comparing the frequency of letters in a secret code with the frequency of letters in the English language, we can "crack" secret codes.
- By studying samples of voter opinions, analysts attempt to predict who will be elected in a general election.

There is no guarantee that any prediction will come true. However, based on what has been learned from the sample, a good guess can be made. The accuracy of the prediction depends on the sample being truly representative of the population, that is, it must be a random sample.

When a question is asked on a survey, or an experiment is performed, the answer or result is known as an *outcome*.

Recall that the *relative frequency* of an outcome is a measure of how often that outcome occurs, relative to the total number of outcomes.

$$\text{Relative frequency of an outcome} = \frac{\text{Number of times the outcome occurs}}{\text{Total number of outcomes}}$$

▶▶ *Through an Activity*

When a paper cup is tossed it can land in one of three ways: on its top, on its side, or on its bottom.

a) With a partner, toss a paper cup 40 times. Record the frequency of each outcome — top, side, or bottom.

b) Calculate the relative frequency of each outcome.

c) Combine your results with those of 9 other students. Determine the relative frequency of each outcome for these combined results.

d) Use these results to predict how many times the cup would land on its bottom if it were tossed 400 times.

Example ···

A die has these faces.

The die was rolled 100 times.
The frequency of each outcome is shown on the graph.

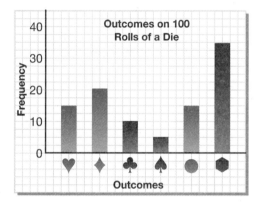

a) Find the relative frequency of each outcome.

i)   ii)   iii)

b) Do you think it is a fair die? Give reasons for your answer.

c) Suppose the die were rolled 250 times. The faces showed in the same proportions as indicated by the graph. About how many times would each of these outcomes occur?

   i) a heart   **ii)** a diamond   **iii)** a spade or a circle

Solution

a) From the graph, we read the number of times each outcome occurred. The total number of outcomes is 100.

  i) The heart showed 15 times.
     The relative frequency of a heart is $\frac{15}{100}$, or 0.15.

  ii) The circle showed 15 times.
     The relative frequency of a circle is $\frac{15}{100}$, or 0.15.

  iii) The club showed 10 times.
     The relative frequency of a club is $\frac{10}{100}$, or 0.10.

b) It does not appear to be a fair die. A hexagon is more likely to occur than any of the other outcomes. A spade is least likely to occur. If the die were fair, each of the faces would turn up approximately the same number of times.

c) We write each relative frequency as a percent. We assume that each outcome occurs the same percent of the time for 250 rolls as it did for 100 rolls.

i) For 250 rolls of the die, a heart would occur approximately

$$15\% \text{ of } 250 \text{ times } = 0.15 \times 250$$
$$= 37.5$$

An outcome cannot appear 0.5 times. So we approximate the answer to 37 or 38 times.

ii) The relative frequency of a diamond is $\frac{21}{100}$, or 0.21.
For 250 rolls of the die, a diamond would occur approximately

$$21\% \text{ of } 250 \text{ times } = 0.21 \times 250$$
$$= 52.5$$

We approximate this to 52 or 53 times.

iii) On 100 rolls, a spade occurred 5 times and a circle occurred 15 times. We add these numbers to get the number of times the outcome "a spade or a circle" occurs.
The relative frequency of the outcome "a spade or a circle" is $\frac{20}{100}$, or 0.20.
For 250 rolls of the die, a spade or a circle would occur approximately

$$20\% \text{ of } 250 \text{ times } = 0.20 \times 250$$
$$= 50$$

▶▶ *Using a Computer*

TEMPLATE DISK

Most computers have functions or commands which generate random numbers. These can be used to represent the toss of a coin or the roll of a die. You can access the random-number generator through the spreadsheet program. The computer can "toss" a coin and "roll" a die instead of you!

Start a new spreadsheet. In cell A1,
in ClarisWorks, type =RAND(2)
in Microsoft Works, type =INT(RAND()*2)+1

Choose the Calculate Now option many times. The numbers 1 and 2 are displayed randomly in cell A1. Assume that each time a 1 shows that represents a coin landing heads. Each time a 2 shows that represents a coin landing tails.

To do many tosses at once, copy the formula in cell A1 into many cells below or to the right. Recalculate, and count the heads (1) and the tails (2).

To get the computer to "roll" a die, replace the 2 in the formula with a 6.

You can also generate random numbers using other programs such as Maple®, Basic, and LOGO.

Working with Mathematics

Something to talk about

1. a) By the end of the second week of the 1993 baseball season, John Olerud had 20 hits out of 50 times at bat. Calculate his batting average.

   b) In his next game, John had 1 hit out of 4 times at bat. Calculate his batting average after this game.

   c) By the final month of the season, John had 175 hits out of 458 times at bat. Calculate his batting average.

   d) John had 1 hit out of his next 3 times at bat. What did this make his average?

   e) To predict John's chances of getting a hit, is it better to use his batting average at the start of the season, or near the end of it? Why?

Practice

2. Multiply.

   a) $\frac{2}{5} \times 60$ b) $\frac{3}{7} \times 77$

   c) $\frac{4}{13} \times 390$ d) $\frac{5}{17} \times 1020$

3. Convert to a decimal.

   a) $\frac{12}{32}$ b) $\frac{15}{40}$ c) $\frac{85}{136}$ d) $\frac{17}{18}$

4. Convert to a decimal.

   a) 13%   b) 12.75%   c) 136%   d) 0.35%

5. A regular die was rolled 130 times. The results are shown below. Determine the relative frequency of each outcome, to three decimal places.

Outcome	1	2	3	4	5	6
Frequency	18	22	23	24	22	21

6. A student rolled a pair of dice 100 times. She rolled a pair of ones three times. What was the relative frequency of a pair of ones?

7. In the first period of a hockey game, there were 42 shots on goal. Three goals were scored. What was the relative frequency of shots that scored goals?

8. A student tossed two coins 50 times. The results are shown below.

Outcome	Two heads	Two tails	One head, one tail
Frequency	12	14	24

   a) Determine the relative frequency of each outcome.

   b) Determine the relative frequency of at least one coin showing heads.

9. A bag contains 50 red marbles and 50 green marbles. A student picked 2 marbles without looking, recorded the colours, and put the marbles back in the bag. The process was conducted 75 times. The results are shown below.

Outcome	Two red	Two green	Red and green
Frequency	19	20	36

   a) Determine the relative frequency of each outcome.

   b) Determine the relative frequency of two marbles of the same colour being drawn.

10. Ari works part-time in a shoe store. He surveyed the types of footwear worn at his school.

Type of footwear	Frequency
High top sneakers	106
Regular sneakers	214
Hiking boots	17
Leather oxfords	5
Canvas sneakers	78
Sandals	31

    a) Determine the relative frequency of students who wore regular sneakers.

    b) Determine the relative frequency of students who did not wear any type of sneakers.

11. Patti works part-time at a garage. She records the types of work requested by customers.

Type of work	Frequency
Front brakes	18
Rear brakes	29
Chassis lubrication	21
Windshield replacement	2

a) Determine the relative frequency of people who requested a chassis lubrication.

b) Determine the relative frequency of people who requested brake work.

On your own

12. The owner of a craft shop decided to make and sell wooden letters used for signs and crafts. She intends to make a total of 500 letters. She needs to know how many of each letter to make. In a sample paragraph of 301 letters, Jane found there were these numbers of letters — a: 29; e: 39 ; n: 20; and s: 15. How many of each of these letters should she make?

13. A computer simulated the roll of a die 7200 times. The frequency of each outcome is shown in the table.

Outcome	1	2	3	4	5	6
Frequency	1175	1225	1142	1168	1273	1217

a) What is the relative frequency of each outcome?

b) Do you think the computer gives a reliable representation of a fair die? Explain your answer.

14. A computer simulated the roll of a pair of dice 5350 times. A pair of 6s occurred 140 times. What was the relative frequency of a pair of 6s?

15. A dental survey of 360 students at a local high school revealed that 135 of them had two or more cavities. The total school enrolment is 1656. About how many students would you expect to have two or more cavities?

16. The table shows the blood types of a random sample of residents in an isolated northern community. Estimate the number of residents with each blood type in a population of 1850.

Blood type	O	A	B	AB
Number of residents	75	59	14	8

Work together

17. a) Toss two coins 30 times. Record the number of times they show each outcome.
    i) two heads
    ii) two tails
    iii) one head, one tail

b) Calculate the relative frequency of each outcome.

c) Combine your results with those of other students. Find the relative frequency of each outcome again.

d) Suppose two coins were tossed 5000 times. About how many times would they show each outcome?

18. When a thumbtack is tossed, there are two outcomes: point up and point down.
   a) Work with a partner. Decide how many times you should toss a thumbtack before you can calculate the relative frequency of each outcome. Toss the thumbtack and do the calculations.
   b) Suppose 10 000 thumbtacks were tossed. How many do you predict would land point up?
   c) Combine your data with several other groups. Determine the relative frequency of each outcome.
   d) Do the combined results cause you to change your answer to part b?

19. When a cylinder is tossed, there are two outcomes: it can land on an end or on its side. From a broom handle, cut cylinders 1 cm, 2 cm, 3 cm, and 4 cm long.

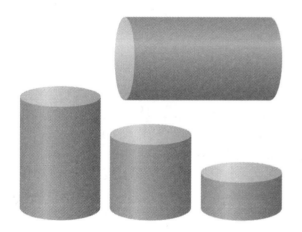

   a) Toss each cylinder 50 times. Record the outcomes.
   b) For each cylinder, calculate the relative frequency of its landing on an end.
   c) How does the length of the cylinder affect how it lands?

20. a) Roll two dice 25 times. Record the total showing on the dice.
   b) Combine your results with those of three other groups.
   c) Suppose two dice were rolled 750 times. Based on your results, how many times would you expect the dice to show each outcome?
      i) a sum of 7
      ii) a sum of 11
      iii) a product of 12

Extend your thinking

21. Decode each secret message.
   a) Npafsdxgb jrnjsrno ao igr dgcgrrgh, lad sc X rnspy igr dgpsy?
   b) Hxde odsdxodxfo yga fsb iggv cgod gi den jngjvn cgod gi den dxcn, lad bgd svv gi den jngjvn svv gi den dxcn.

22. Type a message in your word processor. Use the Replace (or Change) command to replace each a with 1, e with 2, i with 3, o with 4, u with 5, and y with 6. Then replace 6 consonants with vowels. Don't forget what you changed. Then replace 6 more consonants with the ones you have just deleted, and so on. When you have changed all the letters, print your message. Give it to a friend to decode.

Suppose you are the vice-president of an entertainment company that specializes in promoting music concerts. It is your responsibility to conduct surveys to determine which musical groups to book for future concerts. Suppose a decision you made concerning a particular band turned out to be a bad one; that is, very few people came to the concert. How would you explain the "mistake"?

1.7 PROBABILITY

Developing the Ideas

▶ ▶ *Through Instruction*

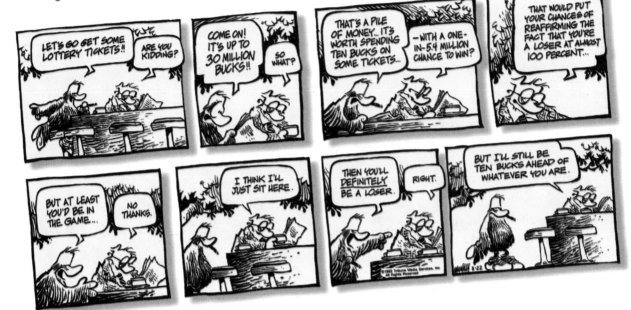

Every ticket sold in a raffle is assumed to have an equal chance of winning.

A large number of tickets are sold and the person with the winning ticket wins the prize.

If 10 000 tickets are sold, there are 10 000 possible outcomes on the drawing of a single ticket.

Since one outcome is just as likely to occur as any other outcome, we say the outcomes are *equally likely*.

If you buy a ticket, there is one chance in 10 000 that you will win.

If you buy 5 tickets, and 10 000 in total are sold, there are 5 chances in 10 000 that you will win.

We say that there are 5 winning outcomes, or 5 outcomes that are favourable to your winning.

When we talk about the chances of winning, recall that we use the word *probability*. We can express probability as a fraction.

We say: the probability of winning with 5 tickets out of 10 000 is $\frac{5}{10\ 000}$.

We write: $\text{P(Winning)} = \frac{5}{10\ 000}$

For a situation where the outcomes are equally likely, the probability of an event A is given by $\text{P(A)} = \dfrac{\text{Number of outcomes favourable to A}}{\text{Total number of outcomes}}$

For the raffle, the outcomes are the different tickets that can be drawn. The event is the result that the ticket drawn will be yours.

Probability and relative frequency are closely linked. To see how, consider the spinner shown. There are three equally-likely outcomes: landing on blue; landing on red; and landing on yellow. The probability that the spinner lands on blue is $P(\text{blue}) = \frac{1}{3}$

This does not mean that if you spin the spinner 3 times it will land on blue once. Nor does it mean that if you spin the spinner 30 times it will land on blue 10 times. It means that if you spin the spinner many times, the fraction of times it lands on blue will get closer and closer to $\frac{1}{3}$.

▶ ▶ *Through a Guided Example*

Example ··

Use the graph to calculate the probability of each event. For each event, the name of a student is picked at random.

a) A is the event that the student picked has a birthday in January.

b) B is the event that the student picked has a birthday in October, November, or December.

c) C is the event that the student was not born in February.

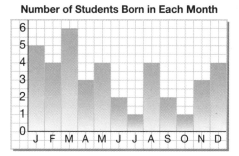

Number of Students Born in Each Month

Solution

From the graph, the total number of students in the class is 39.
When picking a student name at random, the outcomes are equally likely.

a) Five students were born in January.
$$P(A) = \frac{5}{39}$$

b) A total of $1 + 3 + 4 = 8$ students were born in the last three months of the year.
$$P(B) = \frac{8}{39}$$

c) Four students were born in February.
So, $39 - 4 = 35$ were not born in February.
$$P(C) = \frac{35}{39}$$

Working with Mathematics

Something to talk about

1. In the SCRABBLE game, 100 tiles have the letters of the alphabet, as shown below.

DISTRIBUTION OF TILES					
A – 9	F – 2	K – 1	P – 2	U – 4	Z – 1
B – 2	G – 3	L – 4	Q – 1	V – 2	Blank–2
C – 2	H – 2	M – 2	R – 6	W – 2	
D – 4	I – 9	N – 6	S – 4	X – 1	
E – 12	J – 1	O – 8	T – 6	Y – 2	

Suppose you put your hand into a full bag of tiles. What is the probability of selecting each tile?

   a) B   b) E   c) S

2. The diagram shows a jar of pistachio nuts the same size and shape. You put your hand in the jar and do not look at the nuts. What is the probability of each nut being selected?
   a) natural
   b) green
   c) pink
   d) not natural
   e) either natural or pink
   f) neither natural nor pink

3. For each experiment:
   i) List the outcomes.
   ii) State whether the outcomes are equally likely.
      a) Without looking, a golf ball is drawn from a bag containing one pink ball, one yellow ball, and one orange ball.
      b) A quarter and a nickel are tossed.
      c) Without looking, a marble is taken from a bag containing 2 purple marbles, 3 green marbles, and 5 red marbles.
      d) A circle is divided into 8 equal sectors. Each letter A to H is printed in a sector. A spinner connected to the centre of the circle is spun.

Practice

4. Determine the probability in each case.
   a) rolling a 1 with a fair die
   b) choosing a heart when selecting 1 card from a shuffled deck of playing cards
   c) choosing an ace when selecting 1 card from a shuffled deck of playing cards
   d) choosing a face card (king, queen, or jack) from a shuffled deck of cards
   e) choosing the 2 of diamonds when selecting 1 card from a shuffled deck
   f) choosing a card between 2 and 9, inclusive, when selecting 1 card from a shuffled deck

5. A paper bag contains a certain number of coloured marbles. You select one marble without looking. In each case described below, what is the probability of removing a red marble?
   a) The paper bag contains 1 green marble, 1 red marble, and 1 white marble.
   b) The paper bag contains 2 green, 1 red, and 2 white marbles.
   c) The paper bag contains 3 green, 3 red, and 3 white marbles.
   d) The bag contains 5 green, 3 red, and 7 white marbles.

6. Tony shuffles the four aces from a deck of playing cards, and lays them face down on a table. Angela picks two cards.
   a) What are the possible outcomes?
   b) What is the probability of each outcome?

Work together

7. Some board games use a tetrahedral die. It has 4 numbered faces. A die has each set of numbers below on its faces. Calculate the probability of rolling each die so that it lands with the 4-face down.
   a) 2, 4, 6, 8
   b) 1, 4, 4, 7
   c) 1, 3, 5, 7

8. The table lists the numbers of loaves of bread on a store shelf by their "use-by" dates.

Date	Oct 24	Oct 25	Oct 26	Oct 27	Oct 28
Number	3	12	17	24	21

Suppose that today is October 26. Calculate the probability that a loaf selected at random:
a) will be out of date
b) will be 2 days beyond its "use-by" date
c) will be 2 days ahead of its "use-by" date
d) should be eaten today

On your own

9. The words ENVIRONMENTAL AWARENESS are spelled out with Scrabble tiles. These tiles are put in a bag. What is the probability of each outcome for a tile drawn at random from the bag?
a) a vowel
b) a consonant
c) one of the first ten letters of the alphabet

10. To win the card game "In-Between," the third card dealt must lie between the first two cards dealt. What is the probability of winning for each pair of first cards listed?
a) a 2 and a 6   b) a 5 and a queen
c) a 7 and an 8   d) a jack and a king

11. Our calendar repeats itself every 400 years. There are 4800 months during this period. The table shows how often the 13th day of the month occurred on each day of the week.

Day of the week	S	M	T	W	T	F	S
How often the 13th day occurs	687	685	685	687	684	688	684

a) Triskaidekaphobia is the fear of the number 13. Find the probability that the 13th day of the month will fall on a Friday.
b) Is this probability greater than, less than, or equal to the probability of its falling on any other day of the week?
c) What is the probability that the first day of the month falls on a Sunday?

Extend your thinking

12. Life insurance companies use statistics to calculate the premiums for their policies. The table shows how many of 100 000 people at age 10 are still living at ages 30, 50, 70, and 90.

Age (years)	10	30	50	70	90
Number of people living	100 000	95 144	83 443	46 774	2220

a) What is the probability that a 10-year-old child will live to each age?
   i) 50   ii) 70   iii) 50 but not 70
b) What is the probability that a 30-year-old person will live to age 90?
c) Why do you think life-insurance premiums are greater for older people?

COMMUNICATING

The Ideas

A student says that the probability of his passing the next mathematics test is 0.5 because there are only two possible outcomes, pass or fail. Do you agree? In your journal, explain your answer.

What if a Coin Shows Heads on 10 Tosses?

Suppose you toss a dime 10 times, and it shows heads every time. What do you think will happen the next time you toss the dime?

Three students were discussing this question.

Mei-Lin: "Since it came up heads 10 times, it will probably come up heads again. I think it is more likely to come up heads the eleventh time."

Fred: "Since it came up heads 10 times, it will probably come up tails because heads and tails should even out in the long run. I think it is more likely to come up tails the eleventh time."

Indira: "I don't agree with either of you. The dime doesn't have a memory. It doesn't know that it came up heads 10 times. I think heads and tails are equally likely the eleventh time."

With which student do you agree? Design and conduct an experiment to test your prediction.

Understand the problem

- When a dime is tossed, are heads and tails equally likely?
- What are you asked to do?

Think of a strategy

- You would have to toss a dime until you get 10 heads in a row. Then record the result on the next toss.
- You would have to repeat this many times.
- It would take too long to toss a dime until you get 10 heads in a row. Try for 3 heads in a row instead.

Carry out the strategy

- Toss a dime until you get 3 heads in a row. Toss the dime one more time and record the result.
- Repeat this experiment as many times as you can.
- With which student do you agree now?

Look back

- How would your experiment differ if you kept tossing the dime until you get 10 heads in a row?
- On the average, how many times do you have to toss a dime until you get 3 heads in a row?

Communicating the Ideas

In your journal, explain how you decided which student was correct.

Suppose you toss 3 coins simultaneously. How likely do you think it is for the 3 coins to show heads? The following activities provide different approaches to this problem.

ACTIVITY 1

Conduct an experiment to determine the relative frequency of 3 coins showing heads when tossed simultaneously. Use the relative frequency to estimate the probability.

1. Make a prediction. What is the probability of tossing 3 heads?

Work with a partner. Select 3 different coins, such as a penny, a dime, and a quarter.

2. Toss the coins 50 times. Tally the outcomes in a table.

Outcome	Tally	Frequency
Three heads		
Two heads, 1 tail		
Two tails, 1 head		
Three tails		

3. a) Calculate the relative frequency of 3 heads showing.
   b) What do you think is the probability of 3 heads?

4. Combine your data with those of other students. Repeat exercise 3 to refine your estimate.

5. Compare your results with your prediction from exercise 1. Discuss whether your results support your prediction.

ACTIVITY 2

Have a computer "toss" 3 coins for you.

1. Start a new spreadsheet. In cell A1, in ClarisWorks, type =RAND(2); in Microsoft Works, type =INT(RAND()*2)+1. Copy the formula to cells B1 and C1.

TEMPLATE DISK

2. Suppose a 1 represents a coin landing heads. What should you see in row 1 to represent 3 heads?

3. Copy row 1 down to fill the screen. Each row represents the toss of 3 coins. Tally the results in the spreadsheet. Use a table similar to the one in *Activity 1*.

4. Create further trials. Choose the Calculate Now option. Continue to tally results. Repeat for as many trials as you wish.

5. a) Calculate the relative frequency of 3 heads showing.
   b) Estimate the probability of 3 heads showing.

ACTIVITY 3

Make a tree diagram to represent the outcomes of tossing 3 coins. Each final branch of the tree should show one combined outcome of tossing 3 coins.

1. Copy, then continue the tree diagram started on the right.

2. Use the tree diagram to calculate the probability of each outcome.
   a) three heads
   b) three tails
   c) two tails and one head
   d) two heads and one tail

▶ ▶ *Through Instruction*

From your tree diagram in *Activity 3*, you should have found

P(3 heads) = $\frac{1}{8}$

From previous work with probability, you know that the probability of tossing a single coin and obtaining heads is $\frac{1}{2}$.

P(Heads on penny) = $\frac{1}{2}$

P(Heads on dime) = $\frac{1}{2}$

P(Heads on quarter) = $\frac{1}{2}$

Notice how the fractions $\frac{1}{2}$, $\frac{1}{2}$, and $\frac{1}{2}$ are related to the fraction $\frac{1}{8}$.

$$P(3 \text{ heads}) = P(H) \times P(H) \times P(H)$$
$$= \frac{1}{2} \times \frac{1}{2} \times \frac{1}{2}$$
$$= \frac{1}{8}$$

Tossing heads on the penny has no influence on tossing heads on the dime or the quarter. For this reason, we say that the events "heads on penny," "heads on dime," and "heads on quarter" are *independent events*.

This observation relates to a rule for independent events, which you learned in grade 8:

If P(A) is the probability of event A, and P(B) is the probability of event B, then the probability that A and B both occur is P(A and B). If A and B are independent events, then P(A and B) = P(A) × P(B).

Extending the multiplication rule for independent events leads to this result:

• • • • • • • •

> The probability of two or more independent events is the product of the probability of each independent event.

▶▶ *Through a Guided Example*

Example ···

Backgammon players roll a pair of dice to determine each move. They hope to roll doubles because this doubles the number of moves they can make. What is the probability that a backgammon player will roll two 6s followed by two 2s?

Solution

Each roll of the dice combines two events; the two rolls represent four independent events.

$$P(\text{two 6s followed by two 2s}) = P(6) \times P(6) \times P(2) \times P(2)$$
$$= \frac{1}{6} \times \frac{1}{6} \times \frac{1}{6} \times \frac{1}{6}$$
$$= \frac{1}{1296}$$

Do you know anyone who plays backgammon, or another game where dice are used? Find out whether these players think it is possible, or whether it is likely, to roll doubles twice in a row.

BOGGLE YOUR MIND

It is estimated that by the time the average child reaches the age of 13, he or she will have heard the word "no" 13 000 times. Do you think this is a reasonable estimate? How do you think a person would make such an estimate?

Working with Mathematics

Something to talk about

1. Explain what is meant by the statement that two events are independent. Give an example.

Practice

2. List all the possible outcomes in each case.
   a) One coin is tossed twice.
   b) One coin is tossed three times.
   c) One coin is tossed and one die is rolled.

3. Two dice are rolled.
   a) List all the possible outcomes.
   b) Are the outcomes equally likely? Explain.

4. A bag contains 1 green marble, 1 red marble, and 1 white marble. A student removes 1 marble without looking, records the colour, then returns the marble to the bag. The process is repeated.
   a) List all the possible outcomes for the two consecutive draws.
   b) Determine the probability of each outcome.

5. A six-sided die has two faces marked A, two marked B, and two marked C. The die is rolled. What is the probability of each outcome?
   a) rolling A
   b) rolling B
   c) rolling an A followed by a B
   d) rolling a B followed by an A
   e) rolling two As
   f) not rolling an A

6. Copy and complete this chart to confirm your results for exercise 5.

	A	A	B	B	C	C
A	A, A	A, A	A, B	A, B	A, C	A, C
A	A, A	A, A	A, B			
B	B, A	B, A				
B	B, A					
C						
C						

Work together

7. You could use a chart like the one below to solve the *Example* on page 99.
   a) Copy and complete the chart.

	1	2	3	4	5	6
1	1, 1	1, 2	1, 3	1, 4	1, 5	1, 6
2	2, 1	2, 2	2, 3			
3	3, 1	3, 2				
4	4, 1					
5						
6						

   b) Use the chart to find the probability of rolling a pair of 6s.
   c) Use the chart to find the probability of rolling any double pair.
   d) Use the chart and the multiplication rule for independent events to explain why
   P(two 6s followed by two 2s) = $\frac{1}{36} \times \frac{1}{36}$

8. A backgammon player hopes to roll one of these pairs in his opening move: 6 and 5, 6 and 6, 3 and 4, or 2 and 2. Use the chart you completed in exercise 7 to find the probability the player will roll any one of these four combinations.

9. A backgammon player hopes to roll a pair of 6s twice in a row.
   a) Determine the probability of rolling one pair of 6s twice in a row.
   b) Compare your result to the probability found in the *Example* on page 99. Explain any similarities you see.

10. Joshua tracked winning lottery numbers, hoping to improve his chances of winning. He obtained data on how often winning numbers had been drawn in a particular lottery over a 6-month period. He then bought a ticket using numbers that had come up the least often. Explain whether these numbers have a greater, equal, or lesser chance of being drawn in the next lottery.

On your own

11. Use a computer. Estimate the answer to exercise 8. For information on computer simulations, see pages 88 and 97.

12. Nadine's lock has a dial with digits from 0 to 9. She chooses 3 numbers for her secret combination. Repeated numbers are allowed. What is the probability that someone could guess her combination by randomly selecting a number from 0 to 9 three times?

13. Lise creates a six-digit password for her voice mail. What is the probability that someone else can get into her voice mail by randomly selecting 6 digits?

14. Ching Yin has a combination lock with numbers that go up to 60. The instructions that come with the lock direct her to select three different numbers for her combination. She decides to select only one-digit numbers for her combination.

    a) What is the probability that someone can guess her combination by selecting numbers randomly?

    b) Suppose a person knows Ching Yin has used single-digit numbers only. What is the probability the person can guess her combination by randomly selecting digits?

15. King Yip takes four queens from a deck of playing cards, and places them face down without letting Fatimeh see. Fatimeh selects the queen of spades in the first draw. What is the probability she will select the queen of hearts in the second draw?

Extend your thinking

16. In *Activity 3*, you found the probability of obtaining 3 heads when tossing 3 coins simultaneously was $\frac{1}{8}$. This result corresponds to the multiplication rule for independent events:
    $P(3\ \text{Heads}) = P(H) \times P(H) \times P(H)$

    a) Use your tree diagram to determine the probability of obtaining two tails and a head when you toss 3 coins simultaneously.

    b) Explain how you can relate your result from part a to the multiplication rule for independent events. Pay attention to the order in which the outcomes occur.

17. Four bridge players each cut a deck of cards to select the dealer at the start of a game.

    a) What is the probability that each player's cut will turn up a 10?

    b) What is the probability that each player's cut will turn up the same face value as the first player's selection?

18. Use a computer. Estimate the probability of obtaining a 7-digit telephone number where the last two digits are even.

Games of Chance

Games of chance have been played for thousands of years. Dice have been found in the tombs of ancient Greeks and Egyptians. However, it was not until the 16th and 17th centuries that mathematicians studied games of chance.

Chevalier de Méré was a professional gambler and amateur mathematician. He had many questions about dice probabilities. He turned to the mathematician, Blaise Pascal, for answers. Pascal, with his associate, Pierre de Fermat, began a study of games of chance.

One of de Méré's questions was,

"What is the probability of rolling two dice and *not* getting a 1 or a 6?"

Pascal answered,

"For each die, the probability is $\frac{4}{6}$, or $\frac{2}{3}$.

For both dice, the probability is $\frac{2}{3} \times \frac{2}{3}$, or $\frac{4}{9}$."

With this information, de Méré offered the equivalent of this gamble.

Bet $1. Roll two dice. If 1 or 6 do NOT show, you win $2.

De Méré knew that for every 9 people who played the game, about 4 would win. That meant that he would take in $9 and pay out $8. He could expect to win about $1 every time 9 people played. Now that you know this, would you spend $1 to play this game?

For each game of chance:

a) Determine whether you can expect to win or lose if you play the game many times.

b) Decide whether you are willing to play the game.

c) Explain your decision.

1. Bet $1. Toss a coin. If it shows a head, you win $2.

2. Bet $1. Draw a card from a well-shuffled deck. If it shows a spade, you win $5.

3. Bet $1. Draw a card from a well-shuffled deck. If it shows an ace, you win $10.

4. Bet $1. Toss two coins. If they show heads, you win $3.

Blaise Pascal

Review

714987

1. Lee works as a server at a restaurant. The table shows his tips for a week, rounded to the nearest dollar.

Day	Monday	Tuesday	Wednesday
Tips ($)	15	23	19

Day	Thursday	Friday	Saturday
Tips ($)	47	63	69

a) Graph the data from the table.

b) Describe what the graph represents and whether it is appropriate to join the points.

2. The table gives data on world population.

Year	World population (billions)
1900	1.6
1910	1.8
1920	1.9
1930	2.0
1940	2.4
1950	2.5
1960	3.0
1970	3.1
1980	4.5
1990	5.3

a) Use the data to construct a graph.

b) Describe whether it is appropriate to join the points. Explain.

c) Describe the trend of the graph.

3. a) Use the data below to construct a graph.

Size of turkey (kg)	2	4	6	8	10
Cooking time required (min)	250	300	350	400	450

b) How much time would be required to cook a turkey with a mass of 5 kg?

c) How much time would be required to cook a turkey with a mass of 12 kg?

d) Suppose the mass of a turkey is doubled. Will the cooking time be doubled? Explain.

e) How much additional time is required for each kilogram?

4. Survey the students in your class to obtain data on each pair of quantities.

a) height and stride length

b) number of siblings and number of pets

c) time taken to travel to school and time spent in class

d) number of subjects and number of extracurricular activities

5. Construct a scatterplot for each set of data you collected in exercise 4. Describe any relationships you think are represented by each scatterplot.

6. Use the scatterplots you constructed for exercise 5. In each case, decide whether a line of best fit could reliably be used to make predictions. If so, construct a line of best fit and describe what it represents.

7. As part of a science project, Kirsty studied the effect that conditioning would have on her ability to ride a bicycle up a hill. She began a training program and recorded her average speed climbing the same hill at regular times during her training program. The results are shown below.

Time spent in training (weeks)	1	2	3	4	5
Speed (km/h)	11	10	12	13	17
Time spent in training (weeks)	6	7	8	9	10
Speed (km/h)	18	22	21	23	22

a) What do you predict will be the effect of conditioning on Kirsty's speed?

b) Use the data to construct a scatterplot.

c) Examine the scatterplot. Does it support your prediction?

d) Will the trend continue at the same pace for future weeks into the training program? Explain your thinking.

8. Miguel is saving up for a school ski trip. The table shows the amount he has saved after each week since he first learned about the trip.

Time (weeks)	1	2	3	4	5
Amount saved ($)	40	80	160	205	315
Time (weeks)	6	7	8	9	10
Amount saved ($)	400	445	505	535	560

a) Plot the points on a graph. Construct a line of best fit.

b) Your line of best fit probably does not pass through the origin. Suggest possible reasons for this.

9. Some students placed a beaker outdoors on a rainy day as part of a weather experiment. At half-hour intervals, they measured the height of water in the beaker. Their results are shown below.

Elapsed time (h)	0.5	1.0	1.5	2.0
Height of water (mm)	3	4	9	12
Elapsed time (h)	2.5	3.0	3.5	4.0
Height of water (mm)	17	18	21	24

a) Plot a graph of the results. Construct a line of best fit.

b) Use the line of best fit to estimate the height of the water after 75 min.

c) Explain whether the line of best fit can be extended to predict the water height after 4.0 h.

10. How would you collect data to find the following information? Give reasons for your answers.

a) the most popular sports car sold in Canada

b) the average distance students walk to school

c) the average cost of a compact disc

d) the most popular brand of athletic shoe

e) the average number of words in an English sentence

11. Bell Canada used this graph in its financial report in 1989 to show how money paid to shareholders had grown from 1985. How is this graph misleading?

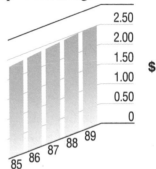

12. Are the following statements correct interpretations of the data in the table?

Age of skier (in years)	Percent of skiing accidents
under 10	10
10 – 19	61
20 – 29	19
30 – 39	5
40 – 49	3
over 50	2

Teenagers are more likely to have skiing accidents than persons in other age groups. People over 50 years of age are the best skiers.

13. At the annual meeting of a large company, the president used a graph to display the company's profit over the past 5 years.

Year	Profit ($)
1990	540 000
1991	590 000
1992	670 000
1993	720 000
1994	770 000

Draw a graph the president could use to show:

a) the profit in an honest way

b) a very small increase in profit each year

c) a large increase in profit each year

14. A computer simulates the roll of a dodecahedral die. This die is a regular polyhedron with 12 faces labelled 1 to 12. It was rolled 1000 times. The outcomes are shown below.

Outcome	1	2	3	4	5	6
Frequency	80	83	85	84	83	79
Outcome	7	8	9	10	11	12
Frequency	84	85	82	81	86	88

a) Determine the relative frequency of obtaining 1.

b) Determine the relative frequency of obtaining either 1 or 2.

c) Determine the relative frequency of obtaining an even number.

15. A computer simulates the tossing of 3 coins 6000 times. The frequency of each outcome is shown in the table.

Outcome	3 heads	2 heads, 1 tail	1 head, 2 tails	3 tails
Frequency	725	2175	2325	775

a) What is the relative frequency of each outcome? Give the answers to three decimal places.

b) Suppose 3 coins were tossed 100 times.
   i) About how many times would you expect 2 heads and 1 tail to occur?
   ii) Suppose 2 heads and 1 tail occurred 52 times. Are the coins fair? Explain your answer.

16. A regular die is rolled. What is the probability of its showing each number?

a) 5

b) an odd number

c) a prime number

d) a number less than 1

e) a one-digit number

f) a two-digit number

17. A drawer contains 2 black socks, 2 white socks, and 2 striped socks.

a) Suppose you remove 2 socks at random from the drawer. What is the probability of getting 1 pair of black socks?

b) How many socks must you remove to ensure you pull out 2 black socks?

c) How many socks must you remove to ensure you pull out any pair?

18. Two paper bags each contain a muffin, a donut, and a cookie. An item is randomly removed from each bag.

a) Make a tree diagram to show all the possible outcomes.

b) What is the probability of removing a donut from both bags?

c) What is the probability of removing a donut and a cookie?

19. A tetrahedral die has four congruent faces, labelled A, B, C, and D. The die is rolled 3 times. What is the probability of obtaining A all 3 times?

20. In a mixed doubles tennis game, Boris and Martina play against Andre and Teresa. After the game one member of one team shakes hands with one member of the opposing team.

a) List all the possible outcomes.

b) What is the probability that Boris will shake hands with Teresa?

21. Erica creates a four-digit password for her electronic organizer. Suppose someone tries to get into her secret files by randomly selecting four digits. What is the probability of this person finding the password?

22. Suppose a hospital nursery receives 5 newborns one day. What is the probability that all the babies are girls?

23. A true/false test has 5 questions. Suppose all the questions are answered by guessing.

a) Draw a tree diagram to show the possible combinations of answers.

b) What is the probability of guessing all answers correctly?

Relative Frequency and Word Games

We have learned that some letters in the English language are used more frequently than others. The table shows the relative frequency of each letter in a huge sample of written material.

Letter	Relative frequency	Letter	Relative frequency	Letter	Relative frequency
A	0.082	J	0.001	S	0.060
B	0.014	K	0.004	T	0.105
C	0.028	L	0.034	U	0.025
D	0.038	M	0.025	V	0.009
E	0.130	N	0.070	W	0.015
F	0.030	O	0.080	X	0.002
G	0.020	P	0.020	Y	0.020
H	0.053	Q	0.001	Z	0.0007
I	0.065	R	0.068		

ACTIVITY 1

- According to the table, which five letters occur most frequently?
- Select two pages from a school anthology. Find the relative frequency of each letter in these two pages. How do your results compare to those above?
- Suppose you selected a letter at random from a newspaper. What is the probability that the letter you select is the most frequently used letter?
- About how many times would you expect the letter B to occur in a random passage of text containing 1000 letters?

ACTIVITY 2

The game, *Hangman*, has two players. One player, the word-maker, thinks of a word and draws a line to stand for each letter in the word. It might look like this:

____   ____   ____   ____   ____

The other player, the word-guesser, names a letter such as L. If the letter L is in the mystery word, the word-maker writes it wherever it occurs. For example, if the mystery word is "hello," the word-maker fills in the blanks like this:

____   ____   L   L   ____

The word-maker draws a diagram of a person on a scaffold. Each time the word-guesser chooses a letter that does not appear in the word, the word-maker adds another part to the diagram. When the diagram is completed or the word has been guessed, the round is over and the roles are reversed.

Play several games of *Hangman* with a partner. Use the letter frequency table to help you guess the other player's secret word. Explain how the frequency table helped you to guess letters. One strategy for the word-maker is to think of a word with letters with low relative frequencies. Explain why this is a good strategy.

ACTIVITY 3

Wheel of Fortune has been a popular television game show for many years. As in *Hangman*, contestants attempt to guess a mystery message in as few turns as possible by guessing one letter at a time. Contestants can choose only consonants. If they want to choose a vowel, they must pay money for it.

• Watch *Wheel of Fortune* for five nights as part of your homework.
• For each round, record the letters and the mystery message the contestants guessed. When you have the data for all five programs, calculate the relative frequencies of all the letters in the messages. Compare the relative frequencies of these letters with the relative frequencies in the table. Calculate the relative frequencies of the letters the contestants guessed. Compare them with the relative frequencies in the table.
• Do contestants choose the most frequently used letters?
• Are the messages deliberately written so they contain letters with low relative frequencies?
• Why do you think contestants must pay to choose vowels?

COMMUNICATING

The Ideas

Write a report explaining what you did in each activity you completed. For *Activity 2*, describe the strategy you used to guess letters. What strategy did you use when you were the word-maker in the game? Did your strategy change as you played more games?

For *Activity 3*, describe whether you think the contestants on *Wheel of Fortune* know which letters are most and least commonly used. Do you think that the people who create the messages for *Wheel of Fortune* try to include letters with low relative frequencies?

ALGEBRAIC OPERATIONS AND EQUATIONS

WHAT'S COMING UP?

DEPARTMENTS

Start With What You Know

Mathematics File

Quests

Minds on Math Project

Start With What You Know

NATIONAL HOCKEY LEAGUE				
CENTRAL	WIN	LOSS	TIE	POINTS
Toronto	27	10	3	57
Dallas	24	12	4	52
St. Louis	20	18	3	43
Detroit	17	18	4	38
Chicago	16	17	6	38
Winnipeg	13	23	5	31
PACIFIC	WIN	LOSS	TIE	POINTS
Calgary	20	12	8	48
Vancouver	19	12	7	45
San Jose	17	15	7	
Edmonton				

ACTIVITY 1

Hockey Standings

1. In hockey standings, 2 points are given for a win and 1 point is given for a tie.

   a) Suppose you know the numbers of wins and ties that a hockey team had in a season. How could you determine the team's total points?

   b) Write a formula that you could use to determine a team's total points.

2. a) A team had 28 wins and 6 ties. How many points did it have?

   b) A team had 83 points. It had 37 wins. How many ties did it have?

   c) A team had 79 points. It had 11 ties. How many wins did it have?

ACTIVITY 2

Estimating Heights

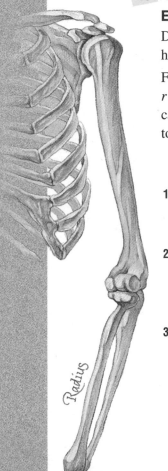

Did you know that there are formulas relating the sizes of some parts of the human body? And that these formulas are the same for all people?

For example, suppose you know only the length of a person's radius bone, r centimetres. You want to estimate this person's height, h centimetres. You can substitute the value for r in the appropriate formula below. Then solve to determine her or his approximate height.

Female $h = 3.34r + 81.2$
Male $h = 3.27r + 85.9$

1. A radius bone 24.5 cm long was found. Substitute 24.5 for r in both formulas. Use your calculator to estimate the height if the person was a female and if the person was a male.

2. a) For a female, choose some values of r between 20 cm and 30 cm. Calculate the corresponding values of h. Make a table of values. Graph the height of the person against radius bone length.

   b) Repeat part a for a male.

3. Use a computer to set up a spreadsheet like the one shown below. Copy the formulas in row 5 to row 6, and beyond.

   TEMPLATE DISK

   a) Describe what each formula does. Then enter an initial radius bone length in cell A4.

   b) Use the spreadsheet to check your solutions to exercise 1.

	A	B	C	D
1	Estimating heights			
2				
3	Length of radius bone	Height of female	Height of male	Difference
4		=3.34*A4+81.2	=3.27*A4+85.9	=C4-B4
5	=A4+0.5	=3.34*A5+81.2	=3.27*A5+85.9	=C5-B5

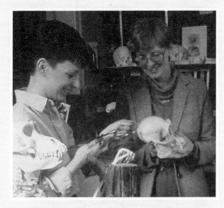

DR. SHELLEY SAUNDERS IS A PHYSICAL anthropologist at McMaster University in Hamilton, Ontario. She investigates changes in human body size and shape over time. She wondered whether there were any differences between the heights of 19th century pioneers and present-day people.

To make the comparison, she studied human remains from a pioneer graveyard. Using bone measurements and formulas like those in *Activity 2*, she found that pioneer men were roughly the same height as present-day men, but pioneer women were shorter than present-day women. Since pioneer men and women probably ate the same food, poor diet doesn't explain the women's shorter heights. Dr. Saunders is currently doing more research to try and discover a reason for this height difference.

19th century pioneer dress supplied courtesy of textile department, Royal Ontario Museum

ACTIVITY 3

Comparing the Activities

1. Compare *Activities 1* and *2*. List as many things as you can that they have in common. List as many things as you can that are different about these activities.

2.1 THE CONCEPT OF A VARIABLE

Developing the Ideas

▶ ▶ *Through Activities*

Work in a group to complete the two activities below.

ACTIVITY 1

Extending Patterns

Here is a pattern of figures made from squares.

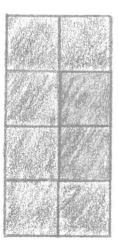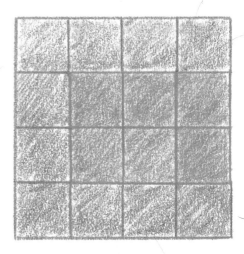

Draw two more figures in this pattern. Count the number of green squares and the number of blue squares in each figure. Record the results in a table.

Number of green squares	Number of blue squares

1. Suppose the pattern is continued.
   a) One of the figures will have 20 green squares. How many blue squares will it have?
   b) How many blue squares are there on the figure which has 100 green squares?

2. Suppose you know the number of green squares in one figure. How would you find the number of blue squares?

3. Let s represent the number of green squares in one figure. Write an expression for the number of blue squares. What kind of number is s?

4. In one figure there are 74 green squares. Use your expression to determine the number of blue squares.

5. In one figure there are 100 blue squares. Use your expression to determine the number of green squares.

6. Use your table to draw a graph. Should you connect the points in the graph? Explain. How does the graph show the way the number of blue squares is related to the number of green squares?

Using Measurement Formulas

A rectangular flower bed has a length of 5 m.

5 m

1. Calculate the perimeter of the flower bed for a width of 2 m, and for a width of 3.5 m.

2. Calculate the perimeters for four other widths. Record the results in a table.

Width (m)	Perimeter (m)

3. **a)** Suppose you know the width of a flower bed with length 5 m. How would you find its perimeter?

   b) Let w metres represent the width of the flower bed. Write an expression for its perimeter.

   c) Write this expression in another way.

   d) What kind of number is w?

4. Suppose the width is 2.4 m. Use your expression to determine the perimeter.

5. Suppose the perimeter is 13 m. Use your expression to determine the width.

6. **a)** Use your table to draw a graph of perimeter against width. Should you connect the points in the graph? Explain.

   b) How could you use the graph to determine the perimeter if you know the width?

   c) How could you use it to determine the width if you know the perimeter?

In *Activity 1*, you can determine the number of blue squares by adding 4 to the number of green squares. So, if you let s represent the number of green squares, then $s + 4$ represents the number of blue squares.

In *Activity 2*, there are two ways to determine the perimeter:
- You can double the width and add 10. So, if you let w metres represent the width, then $2w + 10$ represents the perimeter.
- You can add 5 to the width and double the result. Therefore, $2(w + 5)$ represents the perimeter.

In these activities, $s + 4$, $2w + 10$, and $2(w + 5)$ are called *algebraic expressions*. The parts of an expression that are added or subtracted are called *terms*. Each expression contains a letter representing a number that can vary. For this reason, these letters are called *variables*. When you use a variable, you should know the possible numbers it can represent.

In the expression $s + 4$ in *Activity 1*, s must be an even number. You do not join the points on the graph because s cannot represent numbers between those in the table.

In the expressions $2w + 10$ and $2(w + 5)$ in *Activity 2*, w is a rational number. You join the points on the graph because w can represent numbers between those in the table. Also, w must be between 0 and 5.

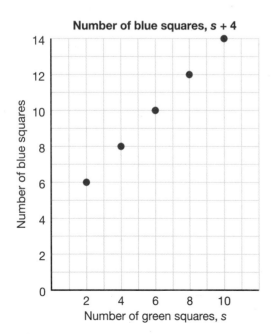

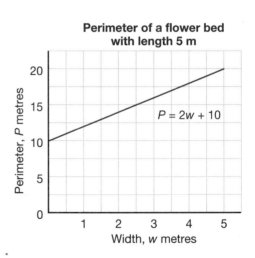

Working with Mathematics

Something to talk about

1. a) What is a variable?

b) Do you think it is correct to say that a variable is "an unknown number"? Explain.

c) Do you think you could use symbols other than letters as variables? Explain.

2. a) In the expression $s + 4$ in *Activity 1*, why must s be an even number?

b) In the expressions $2w + 10$ and $2(w + 5)$ in *Activity 2*, why must w be a rational number between 0 and 5?

3. Some common formulas are given below.

a) Identify the variables in each formula. For each variable you identify, explain what it represents, and why it is a variable.

b) Is π a variable? Explain your answer.

i)

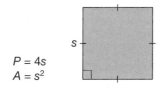

$P = 4s$
$A = s^2$

ii)

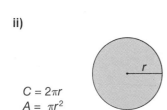

$C = 2\pi r$
$A = \pi r^2$

iii)

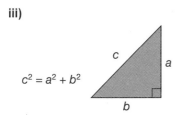

$c^2 = a^2 + b^2$

4. a) Can an expression contain more than one variable?

b) Can a variable occur more than once in an expression?

Give examples to illustrate your answers.

Work together

5. A series of cubes are grouped on a table, as shown. You can look at each group from all sides. The total number of faces that can be seen are counted. Suppose this pattern is continued.

5 faces

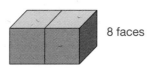
8 faces

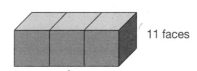
11 faces

a) In each group, check that the number of faces shown is correct.

b) Make a table showing how the number of faces that can be seen is related to the number of cubes.

c) How many faces could be seen if there are 4 cubes? 5 cubes? Include these results in your table.

d) How many faces could be seen if there are 10 cubes? 30 cubes?

e) If you know the number of cubes, how would you determine the number of faces that can be seen?

f) Let n represent the number of cubes. Write an expression for the number of faces that can be seen.

g) If there are 16 cubes, how many faces can be seen?

h) Use your table to draw a graph. Should you connect the points? Explain.

i) How does the graph illustrate the way the number of faces that can be seen is related to the number of cubes?

6. A rectangular flower bed has a length of 5 m.
   a) Calculate the area of the flower bed if its width is 2 m and if it is 3.5 m.
   b) Calculate the areas for four other widths. Record the results in a table.
   c) Suppose you know the width of a flower bed with length 5 m. How would you find its area?
   d) Let w metres represent the width of a flower bed with length 5 m. Write an expression for its area. What kind of number is w? What are the possible values of w?
   e) Suppose the width is 1.2 m. Use your expression to determine the area.
   f) Suppose the area is 15 m². Use your expression to determine the width.
   g) Use your table to graph area against width.
      i) Should you connect the points in the graph? Explain.
      ii) How could you use the graph to find the area if you know the width?
      iii) How could you use the graph to find the width if you know the area?
   h) Compare your results with the results of *Activity 2* on page 113. What similarities and differences can you find?
   i) Suppose you were to graph area against length for the rectangles in this exercise. What do you think the graph would look like?

7. Take a calendar for any month.

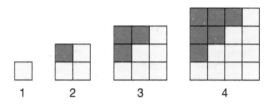

a) Choose any 2 by 2 square of four dates. Write the number in the upper left corner (UL). Add the numbers in the upper right corner (UR) and the lower left corner (LL).

b) Repeat part a for other 2 by 2 squares. Repeat for 2 by 2 squares on the calendars for other months. Record the results in a table.

Number in the UL corner	Sum of the numbers in the UR and LL corners

c) Suppose you know the number in the UL corner. How would you find the sum of the numbers in the UR and LL corners?
d) Let n represent the number in the UL corner.
   i) Write an expression for the sum of the numbers in the UR and LL corners.
   ii) What are the possible values of n?

On your own

8. A pattern of squares is shown below. Each small square has sides 1 cm long.

a) Determine the following information for each large square shown above. Account for any patterns you see in the results.
   i) its perimeter
   ii) the perimeter of the figure formed by the yellow squares
   iii) the perimeter of the figure formed by the red squares
b) Draw one more large square in this pattern. Repeat part a for this large square.
c) Without drawing the large squares, repeat part a for the 10th large square and the 100th large square in the pattern.

d) Suppose you know only the side length of one of the large squares. How could you use this to answer part a?

e) Let *n* represent the side length of one of the large squares in the pattern. Write formulas you could use to calculate the things in part a.

f) One of the large squares in the pattern has a perimeter of 60 cm. How long is the side of this square?

g) On one of the large squares, the perimeter of the figure formed by the red squares is 44 cm. How long is the side of this square?

h) Is it possible for one of the large squares to have a perimeter of 29 cm? Explain your answer.

9. In *Activity 1* on page 112, *s* represented the number of green squares in one diagram. Write an expression for:

a) the total number of squares in the diagram

b) the perimeter of the diagram

10. For the flower bed in *Activity 2* on page 113, decorative fencing for the flower bed sells for $1.50/m. Suppose *w* metres represents the width of the flower bed. Write an expression for the cost of decorative fencing to go around it.

Extend your thinking

11. Canada started using the Celsius scale for temperatures in the 1970s. Suppose a tourist from the United States wants to convert a Celsius temperature to Fahrenheit. Let *C* represent a temperature reading in degrees Celsius. Let *F* represent the equivalent reading in degrees Fahrenheit.

a) A rule of thumb for converting Celsius to Fahrenheit is "to double and add 30". Write a corresponding formula for *F*.

b) The exact formula for converting Celsius temperatures to Fahrenheit is $F = 1.8C + 32$. Choose some values of *C*. Determine how closely the rule of thumb gives the correct Fahrenheit temperatures.

12. Use a computer to set up a spreadsheet like the one below to compare the approximate and exact conversions used in exercise 11. Adjust the Celsius values by entering new numbers in cell A4. Include some negative values among those you try. When are the results of the approximate formula closest to those of the exact formula?

TEMPLATE DISK

	A	B	C	D
1	Celsius to Fahrenheit Converter			
2				
3	Celsius	Approximate	Exact	Difference
4	0	=A4*2+30	=A4*1.8+32	=C4-B4

The Ideas

Look up the word "variable" in a dictionary. In your journal, write some examples that illustrate the use and meaning of this word in everyday speech. How does its mathematical meaning compare with these examples?

ver'ē ə bəl

What if You Saved 1¢, Then 2¢, Then 3¢, Then 4¢,...?

Suppose you save 1¢ today, 2¢ tomorrow, 3¢ the next day, 4¢ the day after that, and so on. Assume that you continue to save according to this pattern.

1. How much money would you save after 30 days? After 100 days? After one year?

2. Determine a formula you could use to calculate the amount you would have if you know the number of days that you saved.

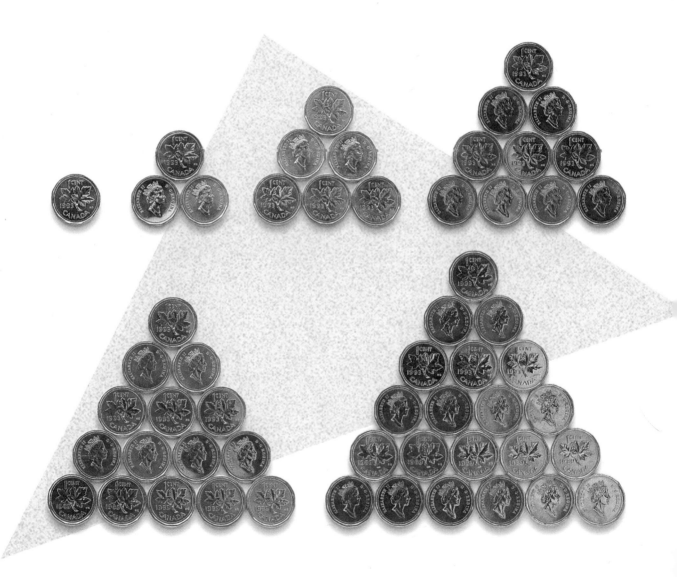

Understand the problem

- Describe the pattern.
- What are you asked to do?
- You could use cents throughout and convert to dollars at the end. How do you convert cents to dollars?

Think of a strategy

- Look at the pattern of yellow squares in the last diagram in exercise 8 on page 116. Describe a relation between the number of yellow squares in each column and the amount of money you save each day. How many days' savings are represented by these yellow squares?
- Notice how the yellow squares and the red squares fit together to form a rectangle. You might be able to answer the questions using patterns like these.

Carry out the strategy

- Using graph paper, create two identical figures like the one on the right, and cut them out. Think of each small square as representing 1¢. Each figure represents the amount you would save after 7 days.
- Fit the two figures together to form a rectangle.
- What are the dimensions of the rectangle? What is the area of the rectangle? How is the area related to the number of squares in each figure?
- Answer these questions for figures with other numbers of squares.
- What is the sum $1 + 2 + 3 + \cdots + 30$? How much would you save after 30 days?
- What is the sum $1 + 2 + 3 + \cdots + 100$? How much would you save after 100 days?
- What is the sum $1 + 2 + 3 + \cdots + 365$? How much would you save after 365 days?
- What is a formula for the sum $1 + 2 + 3 + \cdots + n$? How much would you save after n days?

Look back

- How long would it take you to save $100?
- The numbers 1, 3, 6, 10, 15, … are called the *triangular numbers*. Why is this name appropriate? What is a formula for the nth triangular number?

Communicating the Ideas

In your journal, write a description of this problem and your solution. Illustrate with diagrams showing how the figures fit together. Explain how you can use these diagrams to answer the questions.

The Distributive Law

You are planting both flowers and vegetables in a rectangular garden. To buy fertilizer for the garden, you need to know its area. You can calculate the area in two ways.

Method 1

Total area = width × length

Method 2

Total area = area with flowers + area with vegetables

1. **a)** Calculate the area of the garden using both methods. Are the two results the same?
   b) Repeat part a using a rectangular garden with different measurements. Use positive rational numbers. Are the two results the same for this garden?

Since you can calculate the area of the garden above using either *Method 1* or *Method 2*, you write:

$$5(4 + 6) = 5 \times 4 + 5 \times 6$$

You get similar results with other numbers:

$$3(7 + 2) = 3 \times 7 + 3 \times 2$$
$$4.5(2.4 + 6.3) = 4.5 \times 2.4 + 4.5 \times 6.3$$

In arithmetic, you write equations such as those above. In algebra, you use variables and write only one equation $a(b + c) = ab + ac$. This equation is called the *Distributive Law* for multiplication over addition.

In exercise 1 above, you verified that the variables a, b, and c can be positive rational numbers. Do you think the variables could be negative?

2. Substitute some negative numbers for a, b, and c in the left side of $a(b + c) = ab + ac$. Substitute the same numbers in the right side. Do you get the same result on both sides? Repeat with other negative numbers. What kinds of numbers can a, b, and c represent in this equation?

3. There is also a Distributive Law for multiplication over subtraction. Make up some examples to illustrate this law.

Distributive Law

$a(b + c) = ab + ac$

$a(b - c) = ab - ac$ a, b, and c can be any real numbers

Linking Ideas • ARITHMETIC & ALGEBRA

... 2.2 REPRESENTING VARIABLES AND EXPRESSIONS

Developing the Ideas

▶ ▶ *Using Manipulatives*

In the preceding section, you worked with expressions such as $s + 4$, $2w + 10$, and $2(w + 5)$. You can use algebra tiles to represent expressions like these.

This tile, called a 1-tile, represents one unit, or 1.

To represent –1, flip the tile.

This tile, called a variable-tile, represents a variable. For example, if you are using s, you can call this tile an s-tile. If you are using w, you call it a w-tile.

To represent the opposite of s, or $-s$, flip the tile.

To represent the expression $s + 4$ with algebra tiles, use one s-tile and four 1-tiles.

To represent $2w + 10$, use two w-tiles and ten 1-tiles.

To represent $2(w + 5)$, form two equal groups of tiles. Each group contains one w-tile and five 1-tiles.

In *Activity 2* on page 113, you knew that the expressions $2(w + 5)$ and $2w + 10$ are equal because they represent the perimeter of a rectangle. The algebra tiles demonstrate again that $2(w + 5) = 2w + 10$.

1. What expression does each group of algebra tiles represent?

a)

b)

2. Use algebra tiles to represent each expression.

a) $2x + 1$ b) $3y - 5$ c) $2 - n$ d) $-4x + 3$

3. Use algebra tiles to represent each expression. Then use the tiles to write the expression without brackets.

a) $2(x + 4)$ b) $3(2x - 1)$ c) $6(2 - a)$ d) $-2(2m - 3)$

4. In each part of exercise 3, compare the algebraic expression with the algebra-tiles expression.

   a) What patterns can you find?

   b) Without using the algebra tiles, how can you write an expression without brackets?

   c) Make up some examples to illustrate your method. Check with the algebra tiles.

▷ ▶ *Through Guided Examples*

Example 1 ···

   a) Use algebra tiles to represent the expression $5 - 2x$.

   b) What is the value of this expression when $x = 6$? When $x = -3$?

   c) Use algebra tiles to represent the expression $-(5 - 2x)$.

Solution

   a) Use five 1-tiles and two flipped x-tiles.

   b) Think:

      If each x-tile represents 6, each flipped x-tile represents -6. Replace each flipped x-tile with six flipped 1-tiles.

      Since a 1-tile represents $+1$ and a flipped 1-tile represents -1, a pair of opposite tiles add to 0. You can remove five 0-pairs, leaving seven flipped 1-tiles, or -7.

      In symbols, you substitute 6 for x and write:
$$5 - 2x = 5 - 2 \times 6$$
$$= 5 - 12$$
$$= -7$$

      Think:

      If each x-tile represents -3, each flipped x-tile represents 3.

      Replace each flipped x-tile with three 1-tiles. This gives eleven 1-tiles, or 11.

      In symbols, you substitute -3 for x, and write:
$$5 - 2x = 5 - 2(-3)$$
$$= 5 + 6$$
$$= 11$$

   c) Just as $-x$ represents the opposite of x, so $-(5 - 2x)$ represents the opposite of $5 - 2x$. Start with the expression in the brackets (which is the same as in part a), and flip the tiles. You obtain $-(5 - 2x) = -5 + 2x$, or $2x - 5$.

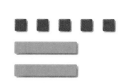

Example 2

Use algebra tiles to represent each expression. Use the result to write the expression without brackets.

a) $2(3x - 4)$ **b)** $-3(p - 3)$

Solution

a) Think:

2 equal groups of tiles

Each group has three x-tiles and four flipped 1-tiles.

In all, there are six x-tiles and eight flipped 1-tiles.
This means that $2(3x - 4) = 6x - 8$

b) Think:

3 equal groups of tiles

$-3(p - 3)$

Each group has one p-tile and three flipped 1-tiles.   The negative sign means flip all the tiles.

There are three flipped p-tiles and nine 1-tiles.
This means that $-3(p - 3) = -3p + 9$

Instead of using algebra tiles, you can use the Distributive Law to write expressions without brackets. This process is called *expanding*.

Example 3

Expand using the Distributive Law.

a) $6(3n + 4)$ **b)** $-3(4b - 7)$

Solution

a) $6(3n + 4) = 6 \times 3n + 6 \times 4$
$\qquad\qquad\quad = 18n + 24$

b) $-3(4b - 7) = (-3)(4b) + (-3)(-7)$
$\qquad\qquad\quad\quad = -12b + 21$

Working with Mathematics

Something to talk about

1. Decide if each statement is always true, sometimes true, or never true. Explain your answers.

   a) A 1-tile is positive and a flipped 1-tile is negative.

   b) A variable-tile is positive and a flipped variable-tile is negative.

   c) x is positive and $-x$ is negative.

2. Could a variable tile have a value of 0? Could it represent a rational number? Explain your answers.

3. How could you represent the number 0 using algebra tiles?

4. Which statement is equivalent to $3(2y - 5)$? Explain your choice.

   a) $2y - 15$ b) $6y - 15$

   c) $2y + 15$ d) $6y - 5$

5. Can the Distributive Law be extended to the sum or difference of more than two terms? Explain.

Practice

6. What expression does each group of algebra tiles represent?

   a)

   b)

   c)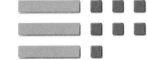

   d)

7. Suppose you flipped all the tiles in exercise 6. What expression would each group of algebra tiles then represent?

8. Determine the value of each expression in exercise 6 when the variable represents 4, and when it represents -3.

9. a) Determine the value of each expression in exercise 7 when the variable represents 4, and when it represents -3.

   b) Compare your answers with those for exercise 8. What do you notice?

10. What expression does each group of algebra tiles represent?

    a)

    b)

    c)

    d)

11. Suppose you flip all the tiles in exercise 10. What expression would each group of algebra tiles represent?

12. Expand using the Distributive Law.

    a) $3(5 + 8)$ b) $5(6 - 4)$

    c) $11(5 - 7)$ d) $-6(8 - 4)$

    e) $12(5 - 6)$ f) $-4(7 - 9)$

    g) $13(1 + h)$ h) $8(11 - d)$

    i) $4(k + 5)$ j) $-9(8 - x)$

    k) $3(6 + m)$ l) $-5(f + 9)$

13. Expand using the Distributive Law.

    a) $5(4 + 10 + 2)$ b) $4(11 - 5 - 2)$

    c) $9(4 + 5 - 8)$ d) $-8(9 - 2 + 8)$

Work together

14. Use algebra tiles to represent each expression. Determine the value of the expression when the variable represents 4 and when it represents −5.
    a) $5 + 3n$　　　　 b) $2x − 4$
    c) $−3y − 6$　　　 d) $−4 + k$
    e) $4d + 2$　　　　 f) $−8 − 2p$
    g) $−5a + 6$　　　 h) $−3 + 4h$

15. Use algebra tiles to represent each expression. Determine the value of the expression when the variable represents 5, and when it represents −6.
    a) $5y − 1$　　　　 b) $2 − 4t$
    c) $3n + 5$　　　　 d) $−1 + 3b$
    e) $−6 − 2t$　　　 f) $−3s − 7$

16. Use algebra tiles to represent each expression. Use the tiles to write the expression without brackets.
    a) $5(k + 1)$　　　 b) $2(3 − 2w)$
    c) $4(2m + 1)$　　 d) $−1(4 + 5y)$
    e) $−3(2 − p)$　　 f) $3(1 − 3b)$
    g) $−2(4t − 5)$　 h) $−4(2s + 2)$

17. Determine the value of each expression in exercise 16 when the variable represents −8.

18. Only two of the expressions in each set below are equal. Which ones are they? Use algebra tiles to justify your answer.
    a) $3x + 2$　　$3x − 2$　　$2 + 3x$　　$2 − 3x$
    b) $−4g + 5$　$−5g + 4$　$−5g − 4$　$4 − 5g$
    c) $2j − 7$　　$7 − 2j$　　$−7 − 2j$　$−2j + 7$
    d) $−5b + 3$　$−3 − 5b$　$−5 + 3b$　$−5b − 3$

19. Use algebra tiles to expand each expression.
    a) $2(3 − 2x)$　　 b) $−(3z + 4)$
    c) $5(2 − a)$　　　 d) $−3(−2s + 1)$
    e) $2(4y + 3)$　　 f) $−8(1 − p)$
    g) $−5(1 + b)$　　 h) $−3(−2t − 3)$

20. Only two expressions in each set below are equal. Which ones are they? Use algebra tiles to justify your answer.
    a) $−3(2 + y)$　$3(2 − y)$　　$−6 − y$　　$−6 − 3y$
    b) $8x − 4$　　$8x − 1$　　$4(2x − 1)$　$2x − 4$

21. Expand using the Distributive Law.
    a) $3(5x + 7)$　　　 b) $−8(5 − 3y)$
    c) $11(3y − 7)$　　 d) $6(5a + 1)$
    e) $2v(3y + 9)$　　 f) $4a(1 − c)$
    g) $5m(7n − 2)$　　 h) $−p(s − 7)$

22. Expand using the Distributive Law.
    a) $7(11 + 3 − 8)$　　 b) $−4(8 − 2 + 3)$
    c) $5(4a + b − 3)$　　 d) $−8(9 − 2f − 8s)$
    e) $4(11b − 5a + 2a)$　 f) $9(4c + 5d − 3)$

23. Expand using the Distributive Law.
    a) $6(2.5y − 9.3)$　　 b) $1.4(2x + 7.5)$
    c) $\frac{1}{2}(6 + 8z)$　　　　 d) $9(6.8x − 3.1)$
    e) $−3.5(2 + 3m)$　　 f) $\frac{1}{3}(4 − 6z)$

24. Which of the following expressions is equal to $\frac{x + 4}{5}$? Explain your choice.
    a) $5(x + 4)$
    b) $\frac{1}{5}(x + 4)$
    c) $x + 4 \div 5$

25. Simplify using the Distributive Law.
    a) $5(m + 3) + 13$
    b) $26 + 7(3a − 9)$
    c) $−2(5x − 7) − 3x − x$
    d) $−12k + 3(5 − 2k) − 7$
    e) $7c − 3(2c − 9 − d)$
    f) $−3(p + 4) + 2(2p − 3)$

On your own

26. Use algebra tiles to represent each expression. Determine the value of the expression when the variable represents 3.
    a) $3a + 5$　　　　 b) $−4c − 6$
    c) $−2e + 4$　　　 d) $−1 − 6g$
    e) $4q + 7$　　　　 f) $−6 − 3k$
    g) $7 − 2t$　　　　 h) $−3 + 5s$

27. Use algebra tiles to represent each expression. Determine the value of the expression when the variable represents −1.
    a) $4z − 6$　　　　 b) $−3 + 2a$
    c) $−3x + 5$　　　 d) $−7 − k$
    e) $8 + 6c$　　　　 f) $−p − 4$
    g) $6x + 1$　　　　 h) $−7 − 4t$

28. Use algebra tiles to represent each expression. Determine the value of the expression when the variable represents 3 and when it represents −4.
    a) $-2 + 3x$ b) $4x + 3$
    c) $-5y + 2$ d) $-1 - 3h$
    e) $7c - 6$ f) $-2p - 3$
    g) $-4s - 5$ h) $6 - 3e$

29. Use algebra tiles to expand each expression.
    a) $3(2a + 1)$ b) $2(3 - x)$
    c) $4(1 - 2t)$ d) $-2(4 + 3x)$
    e) $-3(2v + 1)$ f) $2(2u - 3)$
    g) $6(1 - 2t)$ h) $-3(-2 - 4s)$

30. Expand using the Distributive Law.
    a) $6(4x + 9)$ b) $-3(5c + 3)$
    c) $11(3 - 8z)$ d) $-10(-2 + 7y)$
    e) $5(6z + 2)$ f) $-(3y - 6)$
    g) $-2(11x - 3)$ h) $-12(4w + 1)$

31. Which of the following expressions is equal to $8(5 - n)$? Explain.
    a) $40 - 8n$ b) $85 - 8n$ c) $40 - n$

32. Which of the following expressions is equal to $5(m + 3) - 16$? Explain.
    a) $5(m + 3 - 16)$
    b) $5m + 15 - 16$
    c) $5m + 15 - 80$

33. Which of the following expressions is equal to $\frac{2x - 3}{7}$? Explain.
    a) $2(x - \frac{3}{7})$ b) $\frac{2}{7}(x - 3)$ c) $\frac{1}{7}(2x - 3)$

34. Expand using the Distributive Law.
    a) $3(x + 2y - 7)$ b) $-2(a - 5b + 2)$
    c) $-(6m - 7n)$ d) $4(9p + q - 9r)$
    e) $5(x + 6y - 4)$ f) $3(7c - 9 + d)$

35. Expand each expression.
    a) $2.5(n + 2)$ b) $3.2(2 - 1.5r)$
    c) $2(x - 2)$ d) $2\pi(R - r)$
    e) $-1.1(2c - 9)$ f) $3(3 + b)$
    g) $13(\pi - 2y)$ h) $0.1(100d - 25)$

Extend your thinking

36. Do you think it is possible to illustrate expansions like those in exercise 22, parts d and e with the algebra tiles you have been using? If so, describe how you would do this. If not, describe a set of tiles for which it would be possible.

37. Use the Distributive Law to simplify.
    a) $2x(y - x) + (y - 2x^2)$
    b) $3x - 5y(x - y) + y^2$
    c) $4p(q - p) - (p^2 - q^2)$
    d) $8c(b - 3a) - 2c(b - a)$
    e) $6a(a + b) + 3b(b - a)$
    f) $4x(x^2 - 2x + 3) - 5x^2(x^2 - x)$

COMMUNICATING The Ideas

What do you think the word "distribute" means? Look up this word in a dictionary. Why do you think the law $a(b + c) = ab + ac$ is called the Distributive Law? Write your ideas in your journal.

BOGGLE YOUR MIND

Gold leaf is an extremely thin sheet of gold used in ornamental gilding. A single ounce of gold can be beaten into a sheet measuring 25 m². Gold leaf is sold in booklets of 25 leaves, each 8.25 cm square. About how many of these booklets could be made from a single ounce of gold?

2.3 COMBINING LIKE TERMS

Developing the Ideas

In arithmetic, you learned how to add, subtract, multiply, and divide numbers.

In algebra, you will learn how to add, subtract, multiply, and divide algebraic expressions.

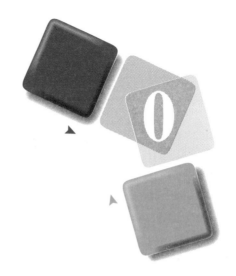

▶ Using Manipulatives

When you add or subtract expressions using algebra tiles, you use the Zero Principle.

The Zero Principle

You have already seen that a 1-tile and a flipped 1-tile add to 0. In fact, any two opposite tiles add to 0. This means that you can add or remove pairs of opposite tiles without changing an expression.

You see: or

You think:
The sum of each pair is 0.

You use the Zero Principle when you combine groups of tiles. For example, here are three groups of tiles, which represent $4x$, $-2x$, and 5.

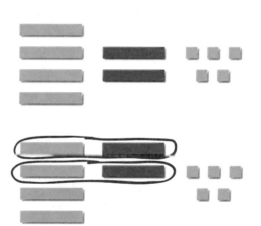

You think:
To combine them, you can use the Zero Principle to remove two pairs of opposite tiles. Then two variable tiles and five 1-tiles remain. You cannot combine the variable tiles and 1-tiles since they are not the same type.

You write: $4x - 2x + 5 = 2x + 5$

The terms $4x$ and $-2x$ are examples of *like terms*. They contain the same variable. Similarly, 7 and -3 are like terms. They contain no variables. They are called *constant* terms. The terms $2x$ and 5 are not like terms and cannot be combined.

You can combine like terms with algebra tiles, or by thinking about algebra tiles.

1. Use algebra tiles to combine like terms.

   a) $3x + 2x$ **b)** $4n - n - 5n$ **c)** $-4a - 2a + 3a$

2. Use algebra tiles to combine like terms.

   a) $2x + 1 + 4x + 3$ **b)** $5y - 4 - 3y + 3$ **c)** $6 - 3a - a - 1$

3. Use algebra tiles to combine like terms.

   a) $2(x - 2) + 3x + 1$ **b)** $4m - 1 - 3(m - 2)$ **c)** $3(k - 2) - (k - 3)$

▶▶ *Through Guided Examples*

When you use algebra tiles, the terms which are represented by the same type of tile are called like terms. The terms represented by variable tiles are all like terms. The terms represented by the 1-tiles are also like terms.

These are like terms: $2x$ $-5x$ x

These are also like terms: 4 -7

These are not like terms: $3a$ $2b$ 8

When you combine like terms you make the expression simpler than it was originally.

Example 1 ··

Use algebra tiles to simplify the expression $4a + 3 + 2a - 4$.
What is the value of this expression when $a = 8$? When $a = -2$?

Solution

Think:

four *a*-tiles   three 1-tiles

   and two *a*-tiles   and four flipped 1-tiles

$$4a + 3 + 2a - 4$$

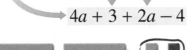

From the tiles, $4a + 3 + 2a - 4 = 6a - 1$

When $a = 8$, the value of the expression is $6 \times 8 - 1 = 48 - 1$, or 47.

When $a = -2$, the value of the expression is $6 \times (-2) - 1 = -12 - 1$, or -13.

You could have simplified this expression without using algebra tiles.

Example 2

Simplify the expression $4a + 3 + 2a - 4$ by combining like terms.

Solution

$$4a + 3 + 2a - 4 = 4a + 2a + 3 - 4$$
$$= 6a - 1$$

Example 3

Use algebra tiles to combine like terms: $2(x + 2) - 3(2 - x)$

Solution

Think:

Combine two groups of these tiles ...   ... and flip three groups of these tiles.

$$2(x + 2) - 3(2 - x)$$

two x-tiles and four 1-tiles

Flip six 1-tiles and three flipped x-tiles

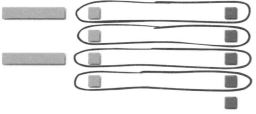

From the tiles, $2(x + 2) - 3(2 - x) = 5x - 2$

When you do not use algebra tiles, you use the Distributive Law.

Example 4

Simplify the expression $2(x + 2) - 3(2 - x)$.

Solution

$$2(x + 2) - 3(2 - x) = 2x + 4 - 6 + 3x$$
$$= 2x + 3x + 4 - 6$$
$$= 5x - 2$$

BOGGLE YOUR MIND

The two main cables which support the Golden Gate Bridge in San Francisco are made of many strands of thick steel wire – thousands more than in the cable pictured at the right. They contain enough wire to encircle the Equator three times. Each cable is about 4 km long. The Equator is about 40 000 km long. How many wires are in each cable?

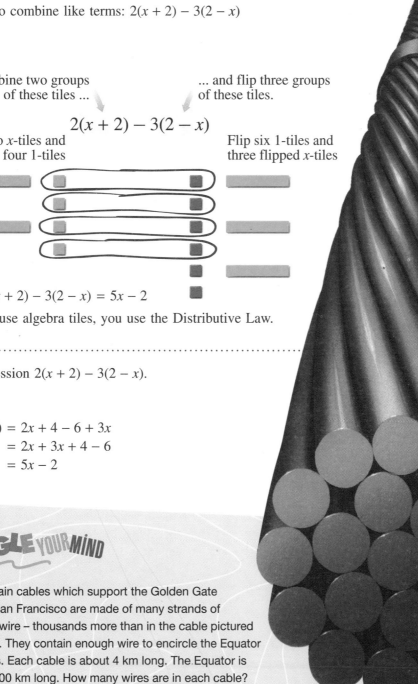

Working with Mathematics

Something to talk about

1. In *Example 1* on page 128, you could have found the value of the expression when $a = 8$ and when $a = -2$ without combining like terms. What advantage is there to combining like terms before substituting?

2. Which are like terms?
   a) $5x, -2x$ b) $3a, 7$ c) $2x, -1$
   d) $4, 8$ e) $2x, 3y$ f) $-5c, c$
   g) $-x, 4x$ h) $3, 3s$ i) $8k, -4k, 3$

3. There are ten pairs of like terms below. Try to find all ten pairs.
   $$2x \quad -3y \quad 5x \quad -y \quad 3 \quad -x \quad 5 \quad 4x \quad -1$$

Practice

4. Which are like terms?
   a) $3, -8$ b) $5j, 6g$ c) $11b, -7$
   d) $-6, -6v$ e) $12, 5, -9$ f) $-4x, 7x, -8x$
   g) $9p, -4, 7p$ h) $2s, 2t, 2u$ i) $-82, 6w, -8v$

5. Combine like terms.
   a)

   b)

   c)

6. Use algebra tiles to combine like terms.
   a) $6s + 3s$ b) $4v - 2v$
   c) $-5b + 2b + 4b$ d) $7p - p + 3p$
   e) $-6c - 2c - c$ f) $6t + 5 + 2t$
   g) $5 - 2a - 3a$ h) $11n - 12n + 6$
   i) $9 - 4d + 3d$ j) $4u - 6 + u + 3$
   k) $-k + 2k - 3k + 4k$ l) $-6q - 2q + q - 7$

7. Use algebra tiles to combine like terms. Determine the value of each simplified expression when $x = -2$, and when $x = 0$.
   a) $3(x - 2) + 4$
   b) $-x - 5 + 2(1 + 3x)$
   c) $-3 + 4(1 - x) + 5x$
   d) $-8(-x - 1) - 3x - 5$
   e) $2(x + 3) - (5 - x)$
   f) $-3(2 + 3x) + 8x - 3$
   g) $-(x - 5) - (4x + 2)$
   h) $2(3x + 2) + 4(2 + x)$

Work together

8. Combine like terms. Use algebra tiles if you like.
   a) $3x + 4x - 3x$ b) $-3a + 2a - a$
   c) $-8 + 5c - 3c$ d) $3k - 2 - k + 6$
   e) $5(2b + 1) + 3b$ f) $-4u + 8 - (2 + 3u)$

9. Simplify each expression. Determine its value when $x = 1$, and when $x = -1$.
   a) $-7x + 12 - 2x$
   b) $8x + 3 - 11x - 7$
   c) $10(x - 5) + 7x - 2$
   d) $9 + 3x - (8x - 12)$
   e) $5x + 3(4x - 2) - 12$

10. Simplify each expression. Determine its value when $x = 4$, and when $x = -3$.
    a) $4x + 2x - 2$
    b) $5x - 6x - 2$
    c) $11x - 5 - 7x - 4$
    d) $9 + 3x - (8x - 12)$
    e) $2x + 3(4x - 2)$
    f) $-8(3 - 2x) - 7 - 6x$

11. Simplify each expression.
    a) $7a + 3a + 2b - 5b$
    b) $-3m + 2n - 7n + 4m$
    c) $45s + 15t - 7 - 5t - 5s$
    d) $4x - 3y - (x - y)$
    e) $48p - 16q - 3r - 18p - 3r$
    f) $-32g + 10 - 15g + 4h - 3$
    g) $-2(11 - 3c) + 2d - 9c$
    h) $7(1 - x) - 3(1 - 2x)$

On your own

12. Combine like terms. Use algebra tiles if you like.
  a) $2x + 4x - 3 + 5$
  b) $9x - 5 + 7 - 6x$
  c) $-x + 2 - 3x - 4$
  d) $5a - 2(a - 4)$
  e) $3(2 - x) - 2(3 - x)$
  f) $2(5a - 1) - 3(2a - 2) + 4(a - 3)$
  g) $-5(a + 3) + 3(1 - a) - (12a - 6)$
  h) $6 + 4(2a - 1) - (11 - 7a)$

13. Simplify each expression. Determine its value when the variable has the given value.
  a) $4a + 7a - 3$ for $a = 3$
  b) $-3m + 21 + 7m$ for $m = -7$
  c) $15(s + 2) - s$ for $s = 0$
  d) $20x - 3 - 6x$ for $x = 2.5$
  e) $8p - 16 - 3p$ for $p = -10$
  f) $4g - 7g - 11g$ for $g = -4$
  g) $-30(c + 1) + 20c$ for $c = 0.1$
  h) $8 - (11 - 5d) - 3d$ for $d = -11$

14. Simplify each expression. Determine its value when $x = 7$, $x = -5$, and $x = 0$.
  a) $9x - 5 - 6x - 2x + 4$
  b) $8x - 2 - 6x - 6$
  c) $-3(x - 1) - (2x - 3)$
  d) $5x - 3(x - 4)$
  e) $-(x - 2) + 4(3 - x)$
  f) $7(1 - x) - 2(3x - 2)$
  g) $2.5x - 3.2 - 1.5x$
  h) $4.2(x - 0.5) - 2.5(x + 0.6)$

15. Simplify each expression.
  a) $m - 2n + 5m - n$
  b) $2a + 3b - c - 3a - b + 5c$
  c) $3x - y + 7 - x + 6y - 7$
  d) $13s - 16r - 4s - 6 + 3r + 10$
  e) $7(-2d - 3e - d + 4) - 6e - 8$
  f) $5(q - 7m + 6q) - (11n + m + 7q)$
  g) $-(a - 5) - 2(3b - 5) + 3(2c - 5)$
  h) $3(11x - 10y - 6x - 6y) - (2x - y)$

Extend your thinking

16. Evaluate each expression for $x = 3$, $y = 2$, and $z = -1$.
  a) $-3xy + 5yz - 2xz + 6xy + yz - 5xz$
  b) $4x^2yz + 5xy^2z - 3xyz - 3x^2yz + 6xyz$

17. Write expressions for the perimeter and the area of each figure.
  a)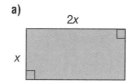
  b)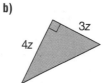

18. a) Do you think all expressions can be simplified? If your answer is no, give an example of an expression that cannot be simplified.
  b) Which of these expressions do you think is the simpler? Give a reason for your answer.
  $$7(x + y + z) \qquad 7x + 7y + 7z$$
  c) Without using the words "simple," "simpler," or "simplest," explain what the word "simplify" means.

The Ideas

Your friend phones you for help in simplifying this expression:
$$3a - 2(a - 1)$$

To simulate that you are talking on the telephone, sit back-to-back with another student. Provide that student with verbal instructions for simplifying the expression.

Write another expression and reverse roles.

Number Tricks

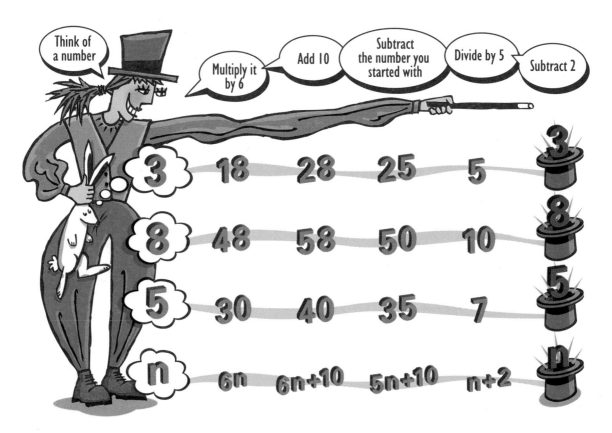

Think of a number · Multiply it by 6 · Add 10 · Subtract the number you started with · Divide by 5 · Subtract 2

Think of a number	Multiply it by 6	Add 10	Subtract the number you started with	Divide by 5	Subtract 2
3	18	28	25	5	3
8	48	58	50	10	8
5	30	40	35	7	5
n	6n	6n+10	5n+10	n+2	n

1. Three examples are given above, each starting with a different number.
   a) Follow the steps to check the calculations.
   b) Choose another natural number and follow the same steps.
   c) Follow the steps again, using a negative integer, and then a decimal.

2. How do you know that the number at the end will always be the number you start with?

3. Change one step in the trick so that everyone will get the same number at the end, no matter what number he or she starts with.

4. Here is another number trick. Follow the steps several times, using a different number each time. Explain why the trick works.
   • Think of a number.
   • Add 2.
   • Multiply by 3.
   • Subtract the number you started with.
   • Divide by 2.
   • Subtract the number you started with.
   • What is your answer?

5. Make up your own number trick, and try it with a friend.

2.4 *SOLVING EQUATIONS USING ALGEBRA TILES*

Developing the Ideas

At the beginning of this chapter, you were asked this question:
A team had 79 points. It had 11 ties. How many wins did it have?
(Page 110, exercise 2c)

To answer this question you solved this equation:

$2w + 11 = 79$

You probably solved this equation by using systematic trial
or inspection.

In the next few sections you will learn an algebraic method
of solving equations like this.

NATIONAL HOCKEY LEAGUE

CENTRAL	WIN	LOSS	TIE	POINTS
	27	10	3	57
Toronto	24	12	4	52
Dallas	20	18	3	43
St. Louis	17	18	4	38
Detroit	16	17	6	38
Chicago	13	23	5	31
Winnipeg				

PACIFIC	WIN	LOSS	TIE	POINTS
	20	12	8	48
Calgary	19	12	7	45
Vancouver	17	15	7	
San Jose				
Edmonton				

▶ ▶ *Using Manipulatives*

To solve equations using algebra tiles, you use a *work chart*.
You can make one simply by drawing a vertical line in the middle
of a piece of paper. You will use the work chart to solve an
equation such as $4x + 2 = 3x + 5$. Put algebra tiles representing
$4x + 2$ on the left side and $3x + 5$ on the right side, like this:

Think:
The expression on the left side must equal the expression on
the right side. For what value(s) of the variable is this true?

To keep both sides equal, you add the same quantity to each side
or you remove the same quantity from each side.
- Start with $4x + 2 = 3x + 5$ on your work chart.
- Remove two 1-tiles from each side. Are both sides equal?
- How many x-tiles could you remove from each side
  and keep both sides equal?
- Can you determine the value of the x-tile
  in this equation?

Recall the Zero Principle that you used to combine like tiles. You will sometimes use this principle when you solve equations with algebra tiles.

There are two other principles you will use.

The Opposites Principle

If two numbers are equal, you can multiply each number by -1 and maintain equality. Similarly, when two sets of tiles are equal, you can flip the tiles in each set and maintain equality.

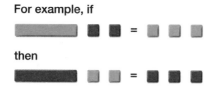

The Sharing Principle

If two numbers are equal, you can divide each of them by the same number and maintain equality. Similarly, when two sets of tiles are equal, if you can divide both sets into the same number of groups, each of these groups will be equal.

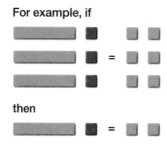

Use algebra tiles and a work chart to solve each equation.

1. $3x - 5 = 2x - 7$ **2.** $4n + 2 = 5n$

3. $3c = 6$ **4.** $2y = -10$

5. $-2 + 5x = 2x + 7$ **6.** $3t - 2 = 6 - t$

▶▶ *Through Guided Examples*

To solve an equation means to determine the value(s) of the variable for which the expressions on both sides of the equals sign represent the same number.

To solve an equation with algebra tiles, use a work chart. Do the same thing to each side, until you have a single variable tile on one side.

Each step in a solution using algebra tiles corresponds to a step in an algebraic solution. To solve an equation using algebra you perform the same operation on each side until you have isolated the variable on one side of the equation.

Example 1

Solve the equation $3x - 2 = x + 4$ using algebra tiles and symbols.

Solution

Using algebra tiles	Using symbols
Step 1	**Step 1**
Start with 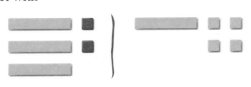	Start with $$3x - 2 = x + 4$$
Step 2	**Step 2**
You want all x-tiles on one side. So, remove one x-tile from each side. 	You want all variables on one side. So, subtract x from each side. $$3x - 2 - x = x + 4 - x$$ $$2x - 2 = 4$$
Step 3	**Step 3**
You want all 1-tiles on the side opposite the x-tiles. So, add two 1-tiles to each side. This creates two pairs of 1-tiles and their opposites on the left side.  By the Zero Principle, this is the same as 	You want all constant terms on the side opposite the variable. So, add 2 to each side. $$2x - 2 + 2 = 4 + 2$$ $$2x = 6$$
Step 4	**Step 4**
You want a single x-tile on the left side. Each side can be arranged into two equal groups. By the Sharing Principle, you need use only one group from each side and still maintain equality. From the tiles, $x = 3$	Divide each side by 2. $$\frac{2x}{2} = \frac{6}{2}$$ $$x = 3$$

Example 2

Solve the equation $2 - 3c = 8$ using algebra tiles and symbols.

Solution

Using algebra tiles	Using symbols
Step 1	**Step 1**
Start with 	Start with $$2 - 3c = 8$$
Step 2	**Step 2**
Since the c-tiles are all on the left side, you want all 1-tiles on the right side. So, remove two 1-tiles from each side. 	You want all constant terms on the side opposite the variable. So, subtract 2 from each side. $$2 - 3c - 2 = 8 - 2$$ $$-3c = 6$$
Step 3	**Step 3**
You want a single c-tile on the left side. Each side can be arranged into three equal groups. By the Sharing Principle, you need use only one group from each side and still maintain equality.  By the Opposites Principle, you can flip all tiles on each side and still maintain equality. You then get a positive c-tile on the left side.  From the tiles, $c = -2$	Divide each side by -3. $$\frac{-3c}{-3} = \frac{6}{-3}$$ $$c = -2$$

Working with Mathematics

Something to talk about

1. When you finish solving an equation, there is one variable tile on one side of the equation. Does it matter if it is on the left side or on the right side? Explain.

2. There is often more than one way to solve an equation using algebra tiles. Illustrate this with an example.

3. In the last step of *Example 2*, all the tiles on each side were flipped. How could you have solved this equation differently to avoid this last step?

4. Are the equations in each pair equivalent? Explain how you know.
   a) $4y = 12$, $y = 3$
   b) $-5k = 25$, $k = -5$
   c) $3x + 15 = 6$, $x + 5 = 2$
   d) $4 - x = -3$, $-4 + x = 3$
   e) $2x = 3 - x$, $6x = 9 - 3x$

Practice

5. a) Write the equation represented by each group of tiles.
   b) Solve each equation using algebra tiles and a work chart.
   c) Record each step using symbols.

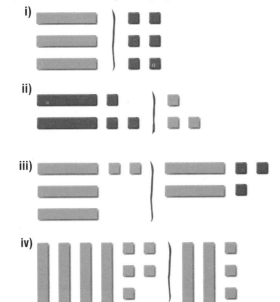

6. Use algebra tiles and a work chart to solve each equation. Record each step using symbols.
   a) $3j = 9$
   b) $4p = -8$
   c) $10 = -2t$
   d) $2b = 10$
   e) $3v = 6$
   f) $4a = 4$
   g) $-4x = -8$
   h) $5 = 3q - 4$
   i) $3r - 2 = 4$
   j) $-2 = -5s + 8$
   k) $6 = 3s + 3$
   l) $5j = 2 + 3j$
   m) $-2 + 4d = -6$
   n) $3 - 4c = -5$

Work together

7. Work with a partner. The pictures below model the steps in the solution of an equation using algebra tiles. Explain what is being done in each step. Record each step using symbols.

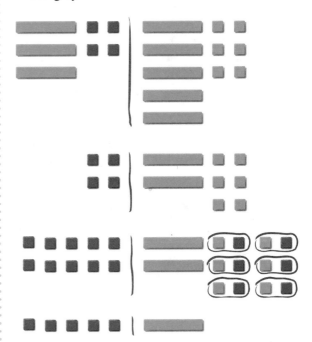

8. Work with a partner. You solve an equation using algebra tiles, and your partner explains the steps. Take turns using the tiles and explaining.
   a) $2x + 1 = -5$
   b) $3a = a + 10$
   c) $-7 = 4r - 3$
   d) $6u - 5 = 13$
   e) $-2 + k = 4k - 5$
   f) $3 + 4s = 9 - 2s$
   g) $5 - h = 2 - 4h$
   h) $-3q - 2 = 7 - 6q$

9. Work with a partner. You solve an equation using algebra tiles, and your partner records the solution using symbols. Take turns using the tiles and recording.

   a) $4m + 1 = 9$ b) $5a + 2 = 3a - 6$
   c) $3 - 2x = 7$ d) $4y - 3 = 6y - 5$
   e) $4v = -2v + 6$ f) $-5b = 6 - 2b$
   g) $2m - 3 = 4m + 3$ h) $5p - 4 = -2p + 3$

On your own

10. Explain the Opposites Principle and the Sharing Principle in your own words. Use algebra tiles and a work sheet to show an example of each principle.

11. Write the equation represented by each group of tiles. Solve each equation using algebra tiles. Record your solution using symbols.

    a)

    b)

    c)

    d)

12. Solve each equation using algebra tiles.
    a) $4x - 5 = 3x$ b) $5g + 4 = 3g$
    c) $2a + 1 = -5$ d) $2 + 3n = 4n$
    e) $3x + 1 = 2x - 4$ f) $4t - 3 = 2t + 3$

13. Solve each equation using algebra tiles. Record the solution using symbols.
    a) $2m + 6 = m$ b) $4x + 2 = 3x$
    c) $5 - 2x = 1$ d) $2b - 3 = b - 5$
    e) $3y + 1 = y + 7$ f) $4k - 2 = 3 - k$

Extend your thinking

14. The area of the shaded region is 9 square units.

    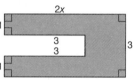

    a) Write an equation to describe the area of the shaded region.
    b) Use algebra tiles to model your equation from part a. Solve the equation.

15. The area of the shaded region is 12 square units.

    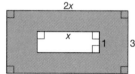

    a) Write an equation to describe the area of the shaded region.
    b) Solve the equation using symbols.

16. When you have solved an equation, how can you check your solution? Develop a method of checking a solution using algebra tiles. Describe your method by illustrating the steps you would follow in at least two examples.

COMMUNICATING

The Ideas

Your friend phones you for help in solving this equation:

$$3x + 7 = x - 5$$

To simulate that you are talking on the telephone, sit back-to-back with another student. Tell that student how to solve the equation.

Write another equation and reverse roles.

Developing the Ideas

▷ ▷ *Through Guided Examples*

When you are familiar with solving equations with algebra tiles, you should try to solve equations using symbols only. Each line in an algebraic solution corresponds to one or more steps using the tiles. You may find that it helps at first to think about the corresponding steps with the tiles.

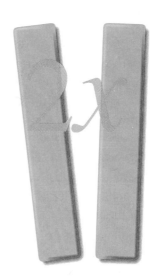

When you have solved an equation, you can check your solution by following these steps:
- Substitute your solution for the variable in both sides of the original equation.
- Simplify both sides of the equation separately. If both sides simplify to the same number, your solution is correct.

Example 1 ·

Solve each equation algebraically. Check your solutions.

a) $3x - 17 = 28$ **b)** $4 - 5k = 8 + k$

Solution

a) $3x - 17 = 28$

Add 17 to each side.

$3x - 17 + 17 = 28 + 17$

$3x = 45$

Divide each side by 3.

$$\frac{3x}{3} = \frac{45}{3}$$

$x = 15$

Check: Substitute 15 for x in each side of the equation.

Left side $= 3(15) - 17$ Right side $= 28$

$= 45 - 17$

$= 28$

Since both sides are equal, $x = 15$ is correct.

b) $4 - 5k = 8 + k$

Add $5k$ to each side.

$4 - 5k + 5k = 8 + k + 5k$

$4 = 8 + 6k$

Subtract 8 from each side.

$4 - 8 = 8 + 6k - 8$

$-4 = 6k$

Divide each side by 6.

$$\frac{-4}{6} = \frac{6k}{6}$$

$k = -\frac{2}{3}$

Check: Substitute $-\frac{2}{3}$ for k in each side of the equation.

Left side $= 4 - 5\left(-\frac{2}{3}\right)$ Right side $= 8 + \left(-\frac{2}{3}\right)$

$= \frac{12}{3} + \frac{10}{3}$ $= \frac{24}{3} - \frac{2}{3}$

$= \frac{22}{3}$ $= \frac{22}{3}$

Since both sides are equal, $k = -\frac{2}{3}$ is correct.

Example 2

The grade 9 students from Westdale High School are
planning a weekend trip to Regina. The bus company
will charge $1416.16 for all transportation costs, including
the driver's salary and accommodations. The cost for
accommodations and admission to the various attractions
the students will visit will be $62.50 per student.

a) Write a formula to determine the total cost of the trip,
C dollars, in terms of the number of students who go
on the trip.

b) The total cost for a group of students was $3978.66.
Substitute 3978.66 for C in your formula to get an
equation. Solve the equation to determine how many
students went.

c) Rearrange your formula so that the accounting office
can figure out how many students went on the trip by
looking at the total cost.

Solution

a) Choose a variable, such as n, to represent the number
of students who go on the trip.
There is a fixed cost of $1416.16.
In addition, there is a cost of $62.50 for each student.
This is $62.5n$ dollars for all students.
Thus, the total cost of the trip, in dollars, is
$C = 1416.16 + 62.5n$

b) $\quad\quad C = 1416.16 + 62.5n$
Substitute 3978.66 for C.
$\quad 3978.66 = 1416.16 + 62.5n$
To solve for n, subtract 1416.16 from each side.
$\quad\quad 2562.5 = 62.5n$
Divide each side by 62.5.
$\quad\quad\quad 41 = n$
Thus, 41 students went on the trip.

c) You want to rearrange the formula so you can solve
for n if you are given a value for C.
First, subtract 1416.16 from each side of the formula.
$$C - 1416.16 = 1416.16 + 62.5n - 1416.16$$
$$C - 1416.16 = 62.5n$$
Divide each side by 62.5.
$$\frac{C - 1416.16}{62.5} = \frac{62.5n}{62.5}$$
The accounting office can use this formula: $n = \dfrac{C - 1416.16}{62.5}$.

Working with Mathematics

Something to talk about

1. a) Would it be possible to solve the two equations in *Example 1* using algebra tiles? Explain your answer.
   b) Would it be possible to solve the equation in *Example 2b* using algebra tiles? Explain.

Practice

2. Solve each equation. Check your solution.
   a) $5j = 15$ b) $4p = -20$
   c) $x + 5 = 9$ d) $c - 5 = -2$
   e) $15 - p = 12$ f) $a + 6 = 8$
   g) $-\frac{v}{2} = -2$ h) $\frac{t}{7} = 1$
   i) $3t = 27$ j) $8 = 15 - s$
   k) $-6 = 3b$ l) $-3s = 9$

3. Solve each equation. Check your solution.
   a) $4v = 12$ b) $j + 27 = 30$
   c) $24 - p = 20$ d) $-4c = -28$
   e) $q + 7 = 11$ f) $36 = -4h$
   g) $-5g = 3$ h) $\frac{c}{7} = 6$

Work together

4. Work with a partner. Take turns solving each equation. Explain each step in the solution to your partner.
   a) $2x - 15 = 27$ b) $3a - 1 = 20$
   c) $12 + 5y = -13$ d) $7p + 11 = -17$
   e) $8z - 42 = 2z$ f) $3f = 12f + 21$
   g) $-3 + x = -4x - 43$ h) $12m - 25 = 4m + 7$
   i) $2e - 6 = -5 - 4e$ j) $24 - 4c = 15 - c$
   k) $6b - 8 = 4 - 3b$ l) $-5p + 9 = 3p - 15$

5. Refer to *Example 2* on page 140.
   a) How much would it cost for a group of 31 students to go on the trip?
   b) How much would it cost for a group of 24 students to go on the trip?
   c) The total cost for a group of students was $3728.66. How many students went?

6. Lester has $53 in savings. Each week he saves another $16. You can represent his total savings with the formula $S = 53 + 16n$, where S is his savings in dollars, and n is the number of weeks.
   a) To determine how much money Lester will have after 3 weeks, substitute 3 for n.
   b) Lester wants to buy a pair of in-line roller skates that cost $165, including all taxes. To determine how many weeks it will take him to save $165, substitute $165 for S. Solve the equation for n.

7. Nasmin has $15 and saves $4.25 per week. Mayumi has $20 and saves $3.50 per week.
   a) For each girl, write a formula showing how much money she will have after n weeks.
   b) Use your formulas to determine how much each girl will have after 5 weeks.
   c) Use your formulas to determine which girl will be the first to have enough money to buy a computer game that costs $49.

8. Write an exercise similar to exercise 6 or 7. Prepare a solution for your exercise. Exchange exercises with a partner. Complete the exercise your partner wrote. Compare your solutions.

9. Raji's car has an average rate of fuel consumption of 8 L/100 km. The gas tank holds 60 L. Whenever Raji buys gas, she fills the tank. So, Raji can calculate the amount of gas left in her car's tank using the formula $F = 60 - 8d$, where F is the amount of fuel, in litres, and d is the distance driven since the last fill-up, in hundreds of kilometres.
   a) Raji has travelled 200 km since her last fill-up. What is the value of d? Use the formula to determine how much gas Raji has left.

b) Raji has travelled 550 km since her last fill-up. What is the value of d? Use the formula to determine how much gas Raji has left.

c) To determine how far Raji can travel on one tank of gas, substitute 0 for F in the formula and solve for d.

10. To rent a certain model of car for one day, a car rental company charges \$28.50 plus an additional charge of 15¢ for every kilometre driven. You can represent this with the formula $C = 28.50 + 0.15d$, where C is the charge, in dollars, and d is the distance driven, in kilometres.

a) To determine the charge for driving 200 km, substitute 200 for d.

b) Your budget allows you \$75 to spend on a rental car for a day. To determine how far the car could be driven for \$75, substitute 75 for C and solve the equation for d.

c) Why do you think the rental cost depends on the distance the car is driven?

11. Solve, and round the answer to the nearest tenth. Compare your solutions.

a) $1.5x - 3.2 = 4.1$

b) $4.7 + 2.3y = 12.4$

c) $2.6k + 7.6 = 1.2k - 8.3$

d) $8.2 - 1.6x = 2.3x - 9.4$

e) $-2.6p + 1.9 = -5.2$

f) $1.1 + 3.2r = 5r + 4.3$

g) $0.9t - 4.8 = 1.4t - 6.3$

h) $4.6w - 4.9 = 3.1 - 0.2w$

On your own

12. Solve each equation. Check your solution.

a) $-4s = -28$ **b)** $11s = 88$

c) $-7a = 91$ **d)** $16c = 24$

e) $23 = 11 - 3r$ **f)** $8 - 3z = -19$

g) $-5r + 14 = 11$ **h)** $13 + 5x = 13$

i) $6k + 5 = 31$ **j)** $12 - t = 22$

k) $5p + 12 = 3p$ **l)** $7p + 9 = 3p$

13. Solve each equation. Check your solution.

a) $7 = 23 - 4x$ **b)** $3a - 10 = 10$

c) $8 - 2z = 5 + 3z$ **d)** $4m + 9 = 2m$

e) $12x + 17 = 10 - 2x$ **f)** $5 - 3k = -4$

g) $5x + 4 = 40$ **h)** $9 - 2a = a + 5$

i) $2 - 4x = 1 - x$ **j)** $3 + 7c = 2c - 3$

k) $2 = 9a - 3$ **l)** $5 - 6n = 2n + 5$

14. The cost, C dollars, of producing a school yearbook is given by the formula $C = 8000 + 9n$, where n is the number of yearbooks printed.

a) What does each term on the right side of the formula represent?

b) The yearbook committee has a budget of \$10 000. To determine the number of yearbooks that can be produced for \$10 000, substitute 10 000 for C and solve the equation for n.

c) How many yearbooks can be produced for \$20 000?

15. Volcanoes and geysers provide striking evidence that Earth's interior is very hot. The formula $T = 10d + 20$ is used to estimate the temperature, T degrees Celsius, at a depth of d kilometres.

a) What does each term on the right side of the formula represent?

b) To estimate the depth where the temperature is 50°C, substitute 50 for T and solve the equation for d.

c) At what depth is the temperature 100°C?

16. The formula for the perimeter P of a rectangle with length l and width w is $P = 2l + 2w$. A rectangular field is 135 m long and requires 450 m of fencing to enclose it.

　a) To determine the width of the field, substitute 450 for P, 135 for l, and solve the equation for w.

　b) Another field is 45 m wide and requires 380 m of fencing. How long is the field?

17. Have you ever seen a flash of lightning, and then heard thunder a few seconds later? A rule of thumb which provides an estimate for the distance to a storm is to count the number of seconds between the lightning and thunderclap and divide by 3. This rule is based on the speed of sound in air being about 330 m/s, which is approximately one-third of a kilometre per second.

　a) Let d represent the distance to the storm, in kilometres, and t represent the time between the lightning and the thunder, in seconds. Express the rule of thumb as a formula.

　b) Suppose the time is 3.5 s. To estimate how far away the storm is, substitute 3.5 for t.

　c) Suppose a storm is 8 km away. Estimate the time between the lightning and the thunder.

Extend your thinking

18. Given the equation $3(x + 2) = x + 2(x + 3)$

　a) Check that $x = 5$, $x = 8$, and $x = -1$ are all solutions of this equation.

　b) Choose any other number and check that it is also a solution of the equation.

　c) Try to solve the equation algebraically. Use the result to explain why every number is a solution of this equation.

　d) Make up another equation like this one, which has infinitely many solutions.

19. Given the equation $3(x + 2) = x + 2(x + 4)$

　a) Choose any number and show that it is *not* a solution of this equation.

　b) Try to solve the equation algebraically. Use the result to explain why the equation has no solution.

　c) Make up another equation like this one, which has no solution.

COMMUNICATING

The Ideas

In your journal, describe the kinds of equations that can be solved with algebra tiles, and give some examples. Also, give some examples of the kinds of equations that would be difficult or impossible to solve with algebra tiles, and explain why.

143

SIMPLIFYING EQUATIONS BEFORE SOLVING

Developing the Ideas

▶ ▶ *Through Discussion*

Later in this chapter you will learn how to use equations to solve problems. The equations are usually slightly more complicated than the equations you have been working with up to now. You need to simplify these equations before you solve them by performing the same operations on each side.

Group 1 | Combining Like Terms

1. What do you think is the first step in solving each equation? Complete this step and continue the solution.

a) $4x + 3x = 35$

b) $6n - 7 - 2n = 21$

c) $4 = 2w + 16 + w - 5$

2. Create two more equations like these and solve them.

Group 2 | Using the Distributive Law

3. What do you think is the first step in solving each equation? Complete this step and continue the solution.

a) $2(x + 3) = 14$

b) $2(3m - 4) = 11$

c) $9 = -3(2t - 7)$

4. Create two more equations like these and solve them.

Group 3 | Solving Equations Involving Fractions

5. Solve each equation. Your first step should be to multiply every term by a common denominator.

a) $\frac{12}{x} = 6$

b) $\frac{b}{3} = 4 + b$

c) $\frac{1}{4}n + \frac{1}{2} = 3$

6. Create two more equations like these and solve them.

All Groups

To the rest of the class, present the solution to one of the equations your group solved. Record the steps on the chalkboard, explaining each step as you write it.

▶ ▶ *Through Guided Examples*

When solving equations, simplify each side before applying the same operation to each side.

Example 1 ....

Solve: $3(a - 3) + 4a + 7 = 5a - 3$

Solution ....

$$3(a - 3) + 4a + 7 = 5a - 3$$

Simplify the left side.

$$3a - 9 + 4a + 7 = 5a - 3$$
$$7a - 2 = 5a - 3$$

Add 2 to each side.

$$7a - 2 + 2 = 5a - 3 + 2$$
$$7a = 5a - 1$$

Subtract $5a$ from each side.

$$7a - 5a = 5a - 5a - 1$$
$$2a = -1$$

Divide each side by 2.

$$\frac{2a}{2} = \frac{-1}{2}$$
$$a = -\frac{1}{2}$$

When an equation contains fractions, multiply each side by a common denominator.

Example 2 ....

Solve and check: $\frac{x}{2} + 1 = \frac{2x}{3} - 3$

Solution ....

$$\frac{x}{2} + 1 = \frac{2x}{3} - 3$$

Multiply each side by a common denominator, 6.

$$6\left(\frac{x}{2} + 1\right) = 6\left(\frac{2x}{3} - 3\right)$$
$$(6)\left(\frac{x}{2}\right) + (6)(1) = (6)\left(\frac{2x}{3}\right) - (6)(3)$$
$$3x + 6 = 4x - 18$$

Subtract 6 from each side.

$$3x + 6 - 6 = 4x - 18 - 6$$
$$3x = 4x - 24$$

Subtract $4x$ from each side.

$$3x - 4x = 4x - 4x - 24$$
$$-x = -24$$

Multiply each side by -1.

$$x = 24$$

Check: Substitute 24 for x in each side of the equation.

Left side $= \frac{24}{2} + 1$ Right side $= \frac{2(24)}{3} - 3$

$$= 12 + 1$$
$$= 13$$

$$= \frac{48}{3} - 3$$
$$= 16 - 3$$
$$= 13$$

Since both sides are equal, $x = 24$ is correct.

Working with Mathematics

Something to talk about

1. The solution of *Example 1* shows one way to solve $3(a - 3) + 4a + 7 = 5a - 3$. What are some other ways to solve this equation?

2. In the solution of *Example 2* both sides were multiplied by a common denominator, 6. Could other common denominators be used? Do you think this equation could be solved without starting by multiplying both sides by a common denominator? Explain.

Practice

3. Refer to the equations you created on page 144. Exchange your equations with a student from another group. Solve the other student's equations. Compare your solutions. Describe any differences.

4. Solve each equation. Check your solution.
   a) $4b - 8b = 24$
   b) $-27 = -9t + 6t + 3$
   c) $13 + 4q = -2q + 12 + q$
   d) $24 - 6j = 36$
   e) $7 + 7k = 2k - 8$
   f) $6s - 30 = 24$
   g) $30 = 6 - 30w$
   h) $4x + 4 = 14x - 6$
   i) $\frac{32}{x} = 4$
   j) $\frac{5}{8}z = -3$
   k) $\frac{m}{4} = \frac{3}{2}$
   l) $-\frac{h}{3} = 12$

5. Solve and round the answers to the nearest tenth.
   a) $2.5x - 4 + 1.2x = 3.5$
   b) $-7.2 = 1.9 - 3.2x - 0.9 - 2.1x$
   c) $5.9 - (3x + 2.4) = 0.5x$
   d) $1.2x + 3.2(2.5 - x) = 40$
   e) $-(5.6x - 2.2) = 3x + 4.7 - 3.6x$
   f) $2.3(x - 1.7) = 4.2(x + 1.3)$

Work together

6. Work with a partner. Take turns solving these equations. Explain each step in your solution to your partner. Check each other's solutions.
   a) $7x - 3x + 5 = 7$
   b) $6 = 4x - x + 9$
   c) $3(n + 2) = 21$
   d) $2(x + 13) = 3(5 - x)$
   e) $-(3d + 4) = 5(2 - d)$
   f) $4(1 - 2j) = 7(2j + 10)$
   g) $\frac{4}{3}d = 12$
   h) $\frac{3}{7}p = \frac{1}{2}$
   i) $\frac{x}{5} = 2 + \frac{x}{3}$
   j) $\frac{3}{4}k - 1 = \frac{1}{3}k$

7. For each equation, decide which of the other two equations is equivalent to it. Explain your choice.
   a) $\frac{3x}{2} + \frac{9}{5} = 12$ b) $5 = \frac{9}{4} - \frac{r}{3}$
   $3x + 9 = 120$ $60 = 27 - 4r$
   $15x + 18 = 120$ $5 = 27 - 4r$

8. Suppose you live in Regina, Saskatchewan and want to call a friend in Singapore. If you call between 8:00 and 16:00, the cost is $4.88 for the first three minutes and $1.22 for each additional minute. You can represent this with the formula $C = 4.88 + 1.22(n - 3)$, where C is the cost in dollars, n is the time in minutes, and n is greater than or equal to 3.
   a) To determine how long you could talk for $10, substitute 10 for C and solve the equation for n.
   b) How long could you talk for $20?
   c) If you have a graphing calculator, graph the equation $y = 4.88 + 1.22(x - 3)$. Set the range so that x is between 3 and 25 and y is between 0 and 40. Trace along the graph to check your answers to parts a and b.

On your own

9. Solve each equation. Check your solution.
   a) $4x + 6x = -20$ b) $5c + 2c + 6 = 34$
   c) $4y - 7y = 18$ d) $50 = 8x - x + 1$
   e) $12 = 2x - 7x - 8$
   f) $-10 = -n + 2 - 2n$
   g) $3x - 2 + x = 5 + 7x - 3$
   h) $2.5x + 1.5x = 6$
   i) $41 = 0.5a + 0.7a - 7$

10. Solve each equation.
   a) $2(x - 4) = 10$ b) $5(x - 6) = -15$
   c) $2(4 - 3m) = 13$ d) $-3(n + 2) = 12$
   e) $7 = -2(-3 - y)$ f) $3(2t + 6) = 0$

11. Solve each equation.
   a) $9x - 1 - 7x - 4 = 5x$
   b) $3(1 - 2y) + y = 2$
   c) $4 = 6 - 2(x + 1)$
   d) $-3(2 - a) - a = 1$
   e) $-2(3n - 1) + 2n = 4$
   f) $2(p + 1) = 3(p - 1)$
   g) $3(3 + 2b) = -2(5 - 4b)$
   h) $3(4x - 1) = 4 - 2(5 - 3x)$

12. Solve each equation.
   a) $\frac{1}{7}x = -8$ b) $13 = \frac{-4}{x}$
   c) $1 - \frac{y}{5} = 3$ d) $\frac{3}{2} = \frac{7}{8}k$
   e) $\frac{x}{2} - 1 = 4$ f) $2 + \frac{n}{3} = 10$
   g) $\frac{x}{4} - \frac{2}{3} = 2$ h) $\frac{a}{3} - 3 = \frac{5}{6}$
   i) $\frac{x}{3} - \frac{3x}{4} = 10$ j) $\frac{5x}{2} - 3 = 8 + \frac{2x}{3}$

13. Keyboarding speed, S, in words per minute, is calculated with the formula $S = \frac{w - 10e}{5}$, where w is the number of words input in 5 min and e is the number of errors.

In keyboarding, a word is equivalent to 5 characters. So, to determine the number of words input, count the number of characters and divide by 5.
   a) Marcus input 275 words in 5 min and made 8 errors. What was his speed?
   b) Sue input 1250 characters in 5 min and had a speed of 40 words/min. How many errors did she make?
   c) Dexter made 3 errors in 5 min and had a speed of 30 words/min. How many words did he input?

Extend your thinking

14. Determine all real numbers that are solutions of each equation. Check that your solutions are correct.
   a) $x^2 - 3 = 6$ b) $a^2 + 3 = 28$
   c) $m^2 - 36 = 64$ d) $x^2 + 5 = 7$
   e) $x^2 + 5 = 5$ f) $x^2 + 5 = 4$

Why do you think the word "all" is included in the above sentence? Why do you think the word "real" is included?

15. Refer to exercise 11 on page 117. Canadian weather data collected before 1970 are often expressed in degrees Fahrenheit.
   a) What would be a rule of thumb for converting Fahrenheit temperatures to Celsius? Express this rule of thumb as a formula.
   b) Determine an exact formula for converting Fahrenheit temperatures to Celsius.
   c) Use a computer to set up a spreadsheet to compare the approximate and exact conversions. When are the results of the approximate formula closest to those of the exact formula?

COMMUNICATING
The Ideas

You could check the solution of an equation by repeating the steps you used to solve it. Explain why you think it is better to substitute your solution into the original equation. Why should both sides be simplified separately when checking?

How Can You Design a Trundle Wheel?

A trundle wheel is a measuring tool. As you roll the wheel along the ground, an odometer displays the distance in metres that the wheel has travelled. The wheel moves forward 1 m for each complete rotation.

Police constable Laureen Tobias Ashbey uses a trundle wheel in her job as a traffic officer. It is one of the most useful tools she has to establish exactly what happened at the scene of an accident. Laureen takes several measurements at the scene, including the length of any skid marks on the road. Using these measurements, she can reconstruct the accident and estimate the speeds of the vehicles involved.

Suppose you are making a trundle wheel. What must the radius of the wheel be, to the nearest tenth of a centimetre?

Understand the problem

- What is a trundle wheel?
- What are you asked to find?

Think of a strategy

- How does the circumference of the wheel compare with the distance it moves in one rotation?
- How are the circumference and the radius of the wheel related?

Carry out the strategy

- Use the formula $C = \pi d$ to find the circumference of the circle, where d is the diameter. If you have a scientific calculator, use the π key; if not, use 3.1416 as an approximation for π.
- Substitute 100 for C and solve the equation for d.
- What is the diameter of the wheel? What is the radius of the wheel, to the nearest tenth of a centimetre?

Look back

- Check your solution.
- Suppose your wheel had a radius that was 0.5 cm too large. How would this affect the distances it measured?
- Suppose another trundle wheel is designed to move forward 2 m for each complete rotation. What must the radius of the wheel be?
- You could also measure distances along the ground with a tape measure. Compare these two methods. What are the advantages and disadvantages of each method?

Communicating the Ideas

In your journal, write a description of this problem and your solution. Include diagrams with your explanation.

Developing the Ideas

▶ ▶ *Through Discussion*

Juice from a vending machine costs 50¢. The vending machine contains $3.50 in dimes and quarters. There are 23 coins in all. How many dimes and how many quarters are there?

Several different ways to solve the problem are suggested below. Each group should choose a method and use it to solve the problem.

| Group 1 | Use systematic trial |

Estimate the numbers of dimes and quarters that you think might be reasonable. What is the value of this many dimes and quarters? Compare with $3.50 and revise your estimate of the numbers of dimes and quarters. Repeat until you have a combination of 23 dimes and quarters that is worth $3.50.

| Group 2 | Use tables |

Make two tables like these:

NUMBER OF DIMES	VALUE OF THE DIMES ($)
0	0
1	0.10
2	0.20
3	0.30
.	.

NUMBER OF QUARTERS	VALUE OF THE QUARTERS ($)
0	0
1	0.25
2	0.50
3	0.75
.	.

Extend your tables for several more rows.
Use your tables to help you solve the problem.

Group 3   Use an equation

Suppose you know how many dimes there are. How would you find the number of quarters? How would you find the value of the dimes? How would you find the value of the quarters?

Let *x* represent the number of dimes. Use your answers to these questions to write expressions in *x* for:

- the number of quarters
- the value of the dimes, in cents
- the value of the quarters, in cents
- the total value of the dimes and quarters, in cents

You know that the total value of the dimes and quarters is 350¢. You can write an equation in *x*. Solve the equation and use the result to solve the problem.

Suppose you let *y* represent the number of quarters. How would the equation change? Would you get the same solution if you solved the new equation? Try it.

Group 4   Reason out the solution

Suppose all 23 coins were dimes. How much money would this be?

How much more money is there? Where does this money come from?

How much more money comes from each quarter? How many quarters are there? How many dimes?

Do you think you could solve the problem in a similar way, by assuming that all 23 coins were quarters? Explain your answer.

Working with Mathematics

Something to talk about

1. What are some of the advantages and disadvantages of each method that was used to solve the problem on page 150? Which method do you prefer?

Work together

2. Solve the problem in two ways.
   1 kg of peanuts costs $4.00.
   1 kg of pecans costs $22.00.
   You want 23 kg of mixed nuts worth $236. How many kilograms of each type of nut should you use?

3. Solve the problem in two ways.
   In one week, Nigel exercised for 23 h and covered 350 km.
   In one hour, he ran 10 km.
   In one hour, he cycled 25 km.
   How much time did he spend running that week?
   How much time did he spend cycling that week?

4. Compare exercises 2 and 3 with the problem on page 150. In what ways are exercises 2 and 3 similar to this problem? In what ways are exercises 2 and 3 different from this problem?

Solve each problem in two ways.

5. A pile of nickels and dimes has a value of $4.50. There are three times as many nickels as dimes. How many nickels and how many dimes are there?

6. The mass of a can and the paint it contains is 3554 g when it is three-quarters full. When it is half full the mass of the can and the paint is 2530 g. What is the mass of the can?

7. Adrian and Jasmine live near a mountain road. There is a viewpoint on the road, higher up the mountain. The two students cycled up to the viewpoint and back. The total travelling time was 3 h. Going up to the viewpoint, they averaged 5 km/h, but returning from the viewpoint they averaged 25 km/h. How far is it to the viewpoint?

Extend your thinking

8. A piggy bank contains 69 coins which are nickels, dimes, and quarters. There are 5 more dimes than nickels, and twice as many quarters as nickels. How much money is in the piggy bank? Solve this problem in at least two ways.

The Ideas

Do you think that some methods of solving a problem are better than others? Do you think there is a "best" way to solve a problem? Be prepared to explain your answers, using a specific problem, in a class discussion.

Keeping Ships Afloat

To keep a freighter balanced and stable in the water, the crew must replace the mass of cargo which is offloaded at each port with sea water. This water is called ballast.

The mass of cargo offloaded is measured in kilograms. The amount of water taken on is measured in litres. How does the first mate know how many litres of water will have the same mass as the cargo that's been offloaded? The answer: use density!

Density is the mass of a unit volume of a substance. Every substance has a characteristic density at a particular temperature. A material with its molecules packed tightly together, like metal, will have a greater density than a material with more space between its molecules, like wood.

The density D of a substance is the quotient of its mass M and its volume V.

We use the formula $D = \dfrac{M}{V}$.

The mass M of a substance is the product of its density D and volume V.

We use the formula $M = DV$.

The volume V of a substance is the quotient of its mass M and its density D.

We use the formula $V = \dfrac{M}{D}$.

1. A tanker is to be loaded with 140 000 t of Kuparuk crude oil from the Alaska North Slope.
   a) The temperature in port when the oil is loaded is 21°C. At this temperature, the density of sea water is 1.030 kg/L. How much sea water must be dumped to allow for this cargo to be loaded?
   b) When the oil is offloaded at its destination, the temperature is only 15°C. At this temperature, the density of sea water is 1.025 kg/L. How much sea water must be taken on as ballast to replace the offloaded oil?

2. a) Kuparuk crude oil has a density of 0.9150 kg/L at 21°C. What is the volume of the oil loaded in exercise 1a?
   b) The density of Kuparuk crude oil at 15°C is only 0.8862 kg/L. What is the volume of the oil offloaded in exercise 1b?

Developing the Ideas

▶ ▶ *Through Discussion*

Problem 1

An electronics store is selling videocassette recorders for $590, with all taxes included. Customers can pay a deposit of $140 and pay the balance in 6 equal monthly payments. What will be the amount of each payment?

Problem 2

Every October, Canine Visions Canada sponsors a national Walk-a-dog-a-thon. The money raised provides blind and visually-impaired Canadians with a free 26-day dog guide handling course.

Last year, Ashok Krishnan and Lisa Crosbie took part in the walk-a-thon. Lisa twisted her ankle during the walk and had to drop out. Ashok completed the walk. Ashok walked 6 km farther than Lisa. Together they walked a total distance of 14 km. How far did Lisa walk?

Work in a group.

1. Try to solve both problems.

2. Several methods for solving problems are described on pages 150 and 151. Did your group use one of these methods?

3. Compare your group's solution to each problem with the solutions from other groups. Did every group solve the problems in the same way?

4. If you haven't done so already, try to solve *Problem 1* using an equation. Suppose you know the monthly payment. How would you calculate the total cost? What is the total cost? Let *p* dollars represent the monthly payment. Write an expression to represent the total cost. Since you know the total cost, write an equation. Solve the equation to obtain the answer to the problem. Check that your answer is correct.

5. If you haven't done so already, try to solve *Problem 2* using an equation.

Suppose you know how far Lisa walked.

How would you determine how far Ashok walked?

What is the total distance they both walked?

Let x kilometres represent the distance Lisa walked.

Write an expression to represent the distance Ashok walked.

Since you know the total distance, write an equation.

Solve the equation to obtain the answer to the problem.

Check that your answer is correct.

▶▶ *Through Guided Examples*

You can solve a problem in many ways. One method is to use an equation.
Follow these steps.
* Use a variable to represent the unknown quantity.
* Express any other unknown quantities in terms of this variable, if possible.
* Write an equation, and solve it.
* State the answer to the problem.
* Check the answer by substituting in the problem.

Example 1

An electronics store is selling videocassette recorders for $590, with all taxes included. Customers can pay a deposit of $140 and pay the balance in 6 equal monthly payments. What will be the amount of each payment?

Solution

Let p dollars represent the monthly payment. Then,

$6 \times$ amount of each payment + deposit = total cost

$$6p + 140 = 590$$
$$6p + 140 - 140 = 590 - 140 \quad \text{◂ Subtracting 140 from each side}$$
$$6p = 450$$
$$\frac{6p}{6} = \frac{450}{6} \quad \text{◂ Dividing each side by 6}$$
$$p = 75$$

Each payment will be $75.

Check: The total of the 6 monthly payments will be $6 \times \$75 = \$450$.
Since the deposit is $140, the total of all payments will be
$450 + $140 = $590.
The solution is correct.

Example 2

Every October, Canine Visions Canada sponsors a national Walk-a-dog-a-thon. The money raised provides blind and visually-impaired Canadians with a free 26-day dog guide handling course. Last year, Ashok Krishnan and Lisa Crosbie took part in the walk-a-thon. Lisa twisted her ankle during the walk and had to drop out. Ashok completed the walk. Ashok walked 6 km farther than Lisa. Together they walked a total distance of 14 km. How far did Lisa walk?

Solution

Let x kilometres represent the distance Lisa walked.

Then, the distance Ashok walked is $(x + 6)$ kilometres.
Since the total distance they walked is 14 km,

$$x + (x + 6) = 14$$
$$2x + 6 = 14$$
$$2x + 6 - 6 = 14 - 6 \quad \text{◄ Subtracting 6 from each side}$$
$$2x = 8$$
$$\frac{2x}{2} = \frac{8}{2} \quad \text{◄ Dividing each side by 2}$$
$$x = 4$$

Lisa walked 4 km.

Check: Ashok walked 4 km + 6 km = 10 km.
The total distance was 4 km + 10 km = 14 km.
The solution is correct.

Working with Mathematics

Something to talk about

1. Suppose *Problem 2* had asked how far Ashok walked. The solution to *Example 2* provides an answer to this problem. Solve the problem by letting *y* kilometres represent the distance Ashok walked and using an equation. Compare your equation with the equation in *Example 2*. What are their similarities and differences?

2. a) What do you think is the answer to this problem? A bottle and a cork cost $1.10. The bottle costs $1 more than the cork. How much does the cork cost?

   b) Solve the problem using an equation, and by reasoning out the solution.

Practice

For each of exercises 3 to 8, write algebraic expressions to complete parts a and b. Use these expressions to write an equation for part c. Solve the equation. Check that your answer satisfies the conditions of the problem.

3. Ravi is 8 years older than Natasha.
   Let Natasha's age be *a* years.
   a) Ravi's age is ▆ years.
   b) The sum of Ravi's and Natasha's ages is ▆ years.
   c) The sum of their ages is 42. Find their ages.

4. The ages of Kirsten and Victor total 27 years. Let *y* years represent Kirsten's age.
   a) Victor's age is ▆ years.
   b) Twice Kirsten's age is ▆ years.
   c) Victor's age plus twice Kirsten's age is 43. Find Kirsten's and Victor's ages.

5. The sum of two numbers is 54. Let *x* represent the smaller number.
   a) The larger number is ▆ .
   b) Twice the smaller number is ▆ .
   c) Twice the smaller number is 9 more than the larger number. Find the two numbers.

6. The combined mass of a dog and a cat is 28 kg. Let the cat's mass be *m* kilograms.
   a) The dog's mass is ▆ kilograms.
   b) Three times the cat's mass is ▆ kilograms.
   c) The dog is three times as heavy as the cat. Find the mass of the dog and of the cat.

7. Sydney's mass is 7.5 kg less than her twin brother Shelby's. Let *s* kilograms represent Shelby's mass.
   a) Sydney's mass is ▆ kilograms.
   b) The sum of their masses is ▆ kilograms
   c) The sum of their masses is 116.5 kg. Find the mass of Sydney and of Shelby.

8. Katie is twice as old as Lana. Let *n* years represent Lana's age.
   a) Katie's age is ▆ years.
   b) Lana's age three years ago was ▆ , and Katie's age three years ago was ▆ .
   c) The sum of their ages 3 years ago was 48. Find the age of Katie and of Lana.

Work together

Solve each problem. Show all your work and check each answer.

9. Find two consecutive numbers with a sum of 273.

10. Members of the school band sold chocolate bars to raise money. Livio sold twice as many bars as Shaun. They sold a total of 48 bars. How many did each boy sell?

11. Marisa and Sandy ran as far as they could in 30 minutes. Sandy ran 2.5 km farther than Marisa. They ran a total distance of 9.5 km. How far did each girl run?

12. Jaquie and her brother Michel entered a weekend fishing derby. The mass of fish Jaquie caught was four times the mass of Michel's catch. Their total catch was 59 kg. What mass of fish did each person catch?

13. The length of a rectangular garden is 7 m longer than the width. The perimeter is 120 m. Find the dimensions of the garden.

14. One number is 0.25 less than another number. The sum of the two numbers is 7.25. What are the numbers?

15. Ms. Durocher bought a dining room suite. She paid $800 down and made 12 equal monthly payments. The total cost was $3800. How much was each payment?

16. Alexia sees a package deal for skis and boots costing $225. The salesperson tells Alexia that the skis cost $60 more than the boots. How much do the skis cost?

17. Barry cut a 72-cm piece of wire into two parts. One part is twice as long as the other. How long is each part?

18. Rashid has 500 cm of trim to frame a banner. If the banner is to be 22 cm wide, how long can it be?

22 cm

19. A salesperson earns $1200 per month plus 5% commission on sales. In one month, she earned $1850. Determine her monthly sales.

20. The washers and dryers at the laundromat accept quarters and loonies only. Zachary has an equal number of quarters and loonies totalling $11.25. How many quarters and how many loonies does he have?

21. A macramé cord with a length of 118 cm is cut into three pieces. One piece is 18 cm longer than the shortest piece. The third piece is three times as long as the shortest piece. How long are the three pieces of cord?

22. The difference between two numbers is 96. One number is nine times the other. How many pairs of numbers can you find that satisfy these conditions? What are the numbers?

23. An airplane travels eight times as fast as a car. The difference in their speeds is 420 km/h. How fast is each vehicle travelling?

On your own

For each of exercises 24 and 25, write algebraic expressions to complete parts a and b. Use these expressions to write an equation for part c. Solve the equation and check your answer.

24. The sum of two numbers is 63. Let k represent the smaller number.
   a) The larger number is ▮ .
   b) Three times the smaller number is ▮ .
   c) Three times the smaller number is 14 more than twice the larger number. Find the two numbers.

25. A tree trunk 12 m long is cut into two pieces. Let p metres represent the length of the shorter piece.
   a) The length of the longer piece is ▮ metres.
   b) One-third of the length of the longer piece is ▮ metres.
   c) The shorter piece is one-third the length of the longer. What are the lengths of the two pieces of tree trunk?

Solve each problem. Show all your work and check each answer.

26. Mary is three years older than Ann, and the sum of their ages is 35. How old is Ann?

27. In a class of 35 students there are 9 more boys than girls. How many girls are there?

28. Tak San earned three times as much as Paul. Together they earned a total of $68. How much did Paul earn?

29. Yvonne has equal numbers of nickels, dimes, and quarters. Their total value is $4.00. How many of each kind of coin does she have?

30. a) In their first season, the Toronto Blue Jays lost 53 more games than they won. They played 161 games. How many games did they win?

b) The Toronto Blue Jays first won the World Series in 1992. That year, they won 34 more games than they lost. They played 162 regular-season games and 12 championship games. How many games did they win in 1992?

31. a) Write a problem using this information, plus any additional information you require.

    i) c represents cost per day, in dollars, and $5c = 12.50$

    ii) k represents the number of kilometres travelled, and $\frac{k}{7} = 560$

    iii) A represents total amount earned, in dollars, and $A - 36 = 200$

  b) Record a solution for each problem.

  c) Exchange your work with another student, and compare solutions.

32. Roy spent $4.20 on a hamburger and a large order of French fries. The hamburger cost 40¢ more than the fries. How much did the hamburger cost?

33. The length of a rectangular swimming pool is 12 m greater than its width. The perimeter of the pool is 96 m. What is the length of the pool?

34. Jamie, Patti, and Brian sold chocolate bars to raise money for a class trip. They sold 91 chocolate bars in total. Jamie sold four times as many chocolate bars as Patti, and Brian sold five fewer bars than Patti. How many chocolate bars did each student sell?

35. Are there four consecutive whole numbers with a sum of 234? If so, what are they?

36. In a cross-country marathon, Sandhu, Tony, and Jesse ran a total of 81 km. Sandhu ran 5 km farther than Jesse. Tony ran 2 km less than Jesse. How far did Sandhu run?

37. Are there five consecutive whole numbers with a sum of 477? If so, what are they?

38. Madhu has 44 cm of trim to put around the edge of a triangular sign. Two sides of the triangle must be 8 cm shorter than the third side. What must the side lengths of the sign be for Madhu to use all the trim?

39. A 200-cm string is cut into four pieces. Two pieces have one length and two pieces have another length. The longer pieces are three times as long as the shorter pieces. How long is each piece of string?

40. For two consecutive integers, the sum of twice the larger and three times the smaller is 242. Find the integers.

41. Alexi and Rob both want to buy a $135 portable CD player. Alexi has $45 and saves $15 per week. Rob has $70 and saves $12.50 per week. Who will be able to buy the CD player first?

42. Alexi and Rob have the same savings and earnings as described in exercise 41. Who would be able to buy a $190 bike first? A $99 jacket?

Extend your thinking

43. Joe has 500 cm of trim to frame a banner. The banner must be between 20 cm and 35 cm wide.

  a) What are the possible lengths the banner could have?

  b) If the width increases by 1 cm, what happens to the length?

  c) Draw a graph of the length of the banner against the width.

The Ideas

Using an equation is only one method to solve a problem. What are some of the advantages and disadvantages of using an equation? Write your ideas in your journal.

Solving Problems with a Spreadsheet

A plane left Halifax, bound for Vancouver, with stops in Ottawa and Winnipeg. In Ottawa, 43 passengers left the plane and 5 others came on. In Winnipeg, half the passengers left the plane and 64 came on. There were 131 passengers on the plane when it left Winnipeg. How many were on the plane when it left Halifax?

Understand the problem

You can solve this problem by systematic trial. Suppose you estimate that 120 passengers were on the plane when it left Halifax. How many passengers were on the plane when it left Ottawa? How many were there when it left Winnipeg?

You could start with other numbers of passengers leaving Halifax and repeat the calculations until you have 131 passengers leaving Winnipeg.

You can do this more easily with a spreadsheet.

Planning the spreadsheet

TEMPLATE DISK

Use a diagram like the one below to help plan your spreadsheet. In this case, the formulas you need have been provided. What do you think each formula in cells B5 and B6 tells the computer to do?

	A	B
1	Plane Problem	
2		
3		Passengers
4	Halifax	120
5	Ottawa	=B4-43+5
6	Winnipeg	=0.5*B5+64

Using the computer

Start your spreadsheet program. Input the information from the spreadsheet shown above.

Move to cell B4 and change the number to 200. What happens to the numbers in cells B5 and B6? Keep changing the number in cell B4 until 131 appears in cell B6. How many passengers were on the plane when it left Halifax?

Look back

Solving a problem by systematic trial with a spreadsheet involves these steps:

Step 1 *Plan the cells you need to solve the problem.*

This is the most important step, because you are designing the spreadsheet to solve your problem. In the example, this step involves deciding that you need a cell for each number of passengers on the plane when it leaves Halifax, Ottawa, and Winnipeg.

Step 2 *Enter numbers and formulas in the cells.*

To complete this step, you must know how to calculate the numbers in the cells. For example, in this problem you must know that the number in cell B5 is found by subtracting 43 from the number in cell B4, then adding 5.

Step 3 *Solve the problem by changing the number in one of the cells.*

By changing the number in cell B4 you were able to solve the problem.

Use a computer to solve these problems.

1. A vending machine contains $3.50 in dimes and quarters. There are 23 coins in all. How many dimes and how many quarters are there? (This is the problem on page 150.)

	A	B	C
1	Dimes and Quarters		
2			
3		Number	Value
4	Dimes		=0.1*B4
5	Quarters	=23-B4	=0.25*B5
6	Total	=B4+B5	=C4+C5

   a) Explain the formulas in columns B and C.

   b) Enter any natural number between 1 and 23 in cell B4.

   c) By entering different numbers in cell B4, solve the problem.

Create your own spreadsheet to solve each of problems 2, 3, and 4.

2. The length of a rectangular pool is 28.5 m greater than its width. The perimeter of the pool is 143.0 m. What are the dimensions of the pool?

3. a) A salesperson earns $1400 per month plus 4% commission on sales. In one month, she earned $1825. Determine her monthly sales.

   b) How much would she have to sell to earn $2000 in a month?

4. Find four consecutive integers such that if the first is increased by 2, the second decreased by 2, the third multiplied by 2, and the fourth divided by 2, the sum of the four resulting numbers is 200.

5. Choose two problems from earlier in this chapter, and solve each problem using a spreadsheet.

Cheetahs can run at speeds of more than 100 km/h.

Developing the Ideas

▶▶ *Through Discussion*

Look at the pictures on this page and the next.

Let *j* centimetres represent Joanne's height.
You write: $j < 180$

Let *v* kilometres per hour represent a cheetah's fastest speed.
You write: $v > 100$

Let *p* represent the percent of passes a good quarterback completes.
You write: $p \geq 50$

Let *r* represent the percent reduction.
You write: $r \leq 70$

These statements are examples of *inequalities*.

SYMBOL	MEANING
>	"is greater than"
<	"is less than"
≥	"is greater than or equal to"
≤	"is less than or equal to"

The inequality $2x < 7x + 15$ states that two times a number is less than seven times the same number, plus 15. Inequalities like this are true for some values of the variable and false for others. To solve such an inequality, you determine the values of the variable for which it is true.

Joanne is less than 180 cm tall.

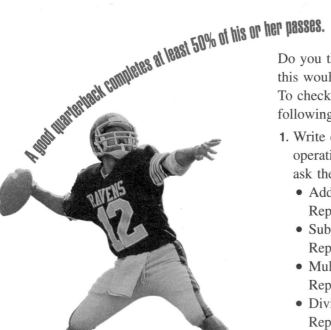

A good quarterback completes at least 50% of his or her passes.

Do you think the steps for solving an inequality such as this would be the same as those for solving equations? To check your answer to this question, complete the following investigation with a partner.

1. Write down an inequality, such as 4 < 8. Apply each operation listed below to your inequality. Each time, ask the question, "Is the inequality still true?"
   - Add the same positive number to each side. Repeat with a negative number.
   - Subtract the same positive number from each side. Repeat with a negative number.
   - Multiply each side by the same positive number. Repeat with a negative number.
   - Divide each side by the same positive number. Repeat with a negative number.

▶ ▶ *Through Guided Examples*

When you multiply or divide both sides of an inequality by the same *negative* number, the inequality is no longer true. To keep the statement true, change the direction of the inequality sign.

For example, 4 < 8, but $-2 \times 4 > -2 \times 8$ because $-8 > -16$

To solve an inequality, you follow the same steps as for solving equations, with one exception — if you multiply or divide both sides by a *negative* number, you must change the direction of the inequality sign.

Example 1 ·

Solve: $2x < 7x + 15$

Solution

$$2x < 7x + 15$$
$$2x - 7x < 7x - 7x + 15 \quad \text{◂ Subtracting } 7x \text{ from each side}$$
$$-5x < 15$$
$$\frac{-5x}{-5} > \frac{15}{-5} \quad \text{◂ Dividing each side by } -5 \text{ and changing } < \text{ to } > \text{ because } -5 < 0$$
$$x > -3$$

The solution of the inequality is all real numbers greater than -3.

This is what you mean by writing $x > -3$.

We can also illustrate the solution to *Example 1* on a number line. An arrow is drawn in the direction "greater than −3." The open dot at −3 indicates that this number is not one of the solutions.

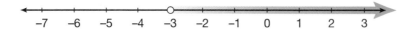

It is impossible to check all the numbers that are solutions of an inequality. To check an inequality, follow these steps:

1. Check that the number obtained is correct. Substitute it in each side of the original inequality. Each side should simplify to the same number.

2. Check the direction of the inequality sign. Choose one solution and substitute it in each side of the original inequality. The results should satisfy the original inequality.

Example 2

Solve, graph, and check: $2 + 4a \geq a - 10$

Solution

$2 + 4a \geq a - 10$

$2 + 3a \geq -10$ ◁ Subtracting a from each side

$3a \geq -12$ ◁ Subtracting 2 from each side

$a \geq -4$ ◁ Dividing each side by 3

Graph the solution on a number line.

The solid dot at −4 indicates that this number is a solution.

Check: **1.** Substitute −4 for a in each side of the inequality.

Left side $= 2 + 4a$ Right side $= a - 10$

$= 2 + 4(-4)$ $= -4 - 10$

$= 2 - 16$ $= -14$

$= -14$

Since both sides are equal, −4 is correct.

2. Substitute any number greater than −4 in each side of the inequality.

Substitute 0 for a in $2 + 4a \geq a - 10$.

Left side $= 2 + 4a$ Right side $= a - 10$

$= 2 + 4(0)$ $= 0 - 10$

$= 2$ $= -10$

Since $2 \geq -10$, the solution is correct.

Working with Mathematics

Something to talk about

1. Compare the last steps in the solutions of *Example 1* and *Example 2*. Explain why the direction of the inequality sign was changed in *Example 1* but not in *Example 2*.

2. State an inequality that is represented by each graph.

a)

b)

c)

d)
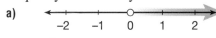

Practice

3. Write an inequality that is represented by each graph. Is -1 a solution to each inequality? How can you tell?

a)

b)

c)

d)

e)

f)

4. Is 7 a solution to each inequality in exercise 3? Is -7?

Work together

5. Graph each inequality.

a) $b > 3$ b) $s < 7$
c) $-2 \leq v$ d) $w \geq -12$
e) $5\frac{1}{2} \geq m$ f) $-3.5 < y$

6. Is 3 a solution to each inequality in exercise 5? Is -3? Explain how you know.

7. Solve and graph each inequality.

a) $5s \geq 25$ b) $7a < -21$
c) $2.5d \leq -10$ d) $\frac{1}{6}x \geq -2$
e) $\frac{1}{4}y > -4$ f) $-\frac{1}{3}p \geq 9$
g) $12 - t \geq 22$ h) $k + 5 \leq 13$
i) $j - 5.6 > 4.4$ j) $x + 5 \geq -4$

8. Is 10 a solution to each inequality in exercise 7? Is -10? Explain your thinking.

9. Solve and check.

a) $3d - 2 \leq -20$ b) $19 - 3h < 7$
c) $3 - 6v < 15$ d) $4a + 11 > -5$
e) $11.5 < -2p + 1.5$ f) $4t + 21 \leq t + 6$
g) $13 - q \leq -5 + 8q$ h) $y + 1 \geq -2 + 3y$
i) $\frac{2}{3}j - 9 \geq 3 + j$ j) $1.1b - 12 < 3b + 7$

10. Solve, graph, and check each inequality.

a) $x + 3 > 2$ b) $2x + 1 \leq 7$
c) $y - 3 \geq -8$ d) $-3x + 2 > 14$
e) $4 - a < 9$ f) $4x - 7 \geq x - 1$
g) $5t - 17 < 19 - 4t$ h) $-2.6p + 13 \leq -5.2$
i) $9 + \frac{1}{3}r > 2r + 4$ j) $10z + 18 \geq -1 - 2z$

11. Each inequality below is followed by a list of numbers. Determine which of the numbers are solutions to the inequality.

a) $3k > 19$ $-2, 0, 8$
b) $4w < 3$ $\frac{1}{2}, 1, 3$
c) $-13 \geq x - 11$ $-5, -3, -1$
d) $9 \leq 15 - f$ $5, -7, 9$
e) $3r < 5r + 12$ $-5, 5, 10$
f) $4g - 12 > -2$ $-2, 0, 3$
g) $q - 3 \leq 2q + 4$ $-10, -5, 0$
h) $-35 - 8s > 6s - 7$ $-6, -2, 2$
i) $13 - 2h \geq 4h - 14$ $1, 4, 8$
j) $-25 + 11c \leq 30 - 11c$ $-3, 2, 5$

12. Each of the 5 essays Gita writes for her English class is worth an equal share of her final mark. She received 75%, 91%, 84%, and 77% on the first four essays. What mark does she need on the fifth essay to have a mean mark of at least 80%?

13. This sign is displayed in a sporting goods store.

a) Let x represent the regular price of an item. Write an expression to describe the sale price.

b) Shaulin has $100 to buy a waterproof jacket. She wants to know the regular price of jackets she can afford. Use your expression from part a to write an inequality. Solve the inequality. Determine the regular price of the jackets Shaulin can afford.

c) Afshar has $175 to buy a ski suit. Determine the regular price of the suits Afshar can afford.

d) Rosie has $17 to buy a hat and mitten set. Determine the regular price of the sets Rosie can afford.

On your own

14. Solve and graph each inequality.

a) $x - 5 \geq -2$ **b)** $9 - y \leq 4$

c) $3x < -6$ **d)** $4c < 11$

e) $-2x > 9$ **f)** $2z + 7 < 5$

g) $12 - 5a \geq -8$ **h)** $10 > 2s + 1$

i) $5 + 3m \leq 10 + m$ **j)** $5g - 2 < 3g + 4$

k) $-7d + 6 \geq 2d - 3$ **l)** $13.5 + 2y < 18.5$

15. Is 3 a solution to each inequality in exercise 14? Is -3?

16. Solve and check.

a) $x + 7 > 2$ **b)** $4x < x - 9$

c) $k + 8 \leq -7$ **d)** $1 - t \geq 4 + t$

e) $13 \leq 1 + \frac{3}{4}x$ **f)** $3.5 - 1.5a \geq 8$

g) $2 - 3a \geq a + 9$ **h)** $39 + 4w \geq 13 - 6w$

i) $-\frac{1}{4}s - 6 < -2$ **j)** $11 - 1.3h < 4.7h - 7$

17. This sign is displayed on a rack of clothing.

a) Let x represent the regular price of an item. Write an expression to describe the sale price.

b) Clarence has $50 to spend on clothes. Write an inequality describing his situation. Solve the inequality. Can Clarence afford to buy a pair of pants with a regular price of $64.99?

c) Joshua has $40 to spend. Can Joshua afford to buy a sweater with a regular price of $54.99?

Extend your thinking

18. In the second part of the check in the solution of *Example 2*, 0 was substituted for *a*. Can you always use 0 when you check the solution of an inequality? If your answer is yes, give a reason for your answer. If your answer is no, give an example of an inequality that cannot be checked by substituting 0 for the variable. Include the solution of the inequality and an explanation why you cannot use 0 to check the solution.

COMMUNICATING

The Ideas

In your journal, write an explanation of how to solve an inequality. Illustrate your explanation with some examples, and be sure to explain why the direction of the inequality sign must sometimes change.

Review

1. Here is a pattern made from toothpicks. Suppose the pattern is continued.

   a) Count the number of squares and the number of toothpicks in each diagram. Record the results in a table.

   b) How many toothpicks would you need to make 4 squares? 5 squares? 10 squares? 50 squares? 100 squares?

   c) Suppose you know the number of squares in one of the diagrams. How would you find the number of toothpicks?

   d) Let *s* represent the number of squares in one of the diagrams. Write an expression for the number of toothpicks. What kind of number is *s*?

   e) If there are 35 squares, how many toothpicks are there?

   f) If there are 100 toothpicks, how many squares are there?

   g) Use your table to draw a graph. How does the graph show the number of toothpicks is related to the number of squares?

2. Take a calendar for any month. Choose any 3 by 3 square of 9 dates on the calendar.

august/août						
M/L	T/M	W/M	T/J	F/V	S/S	S/D
1	2	3	4	5	6	7
8	9	10	11	12	13	14
15	16	17	18	19	20	21
22	23	24	25	26	27	28
29	30	31				

   a) Add the numbers in the four corners. How does the sum compare with the number in the middle? Repeat with other 3 by 3 squares on the same month. Repeat on calendars for other months.

   b) Suppose you know the number in the middle of a 3 by 3 square on the calendar for any month. How would you find the sum of the numbers in the four corners?

   c) Let *n* represent the number in the middle of a 3 by 3 square. Write an expression for the sum of the numbers in the four corners. What are the possible values of *n*?

3. A horse paddock has a width of 10 m.

   a) Calculate the perimeter of the paddock if the length is 15 m and if it is 20 m.

   b) Calculate the perimeter of the paddock for four other lengths. Record the results in a table.

   c) Suppose you know the length of a paddock with width 10 m. How would you find its perimeter?

   d) Let *l* represent the length of the paddock. Write an expression to represent its perimeter. What kind of a number is *l*? What are the possible values of *l*?

   e) If the perimeter of the paddock is 74 m, use the expression to determine its length.

   f) Use the table from part b to draw a graph of perimeter against length.

4. What expression does each group of algebra tiles represent?

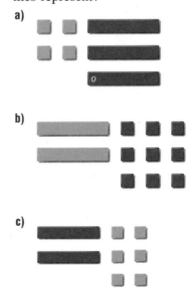

5. Use algebra tiles to represent each expression. Determine the value of the expression when the variable represents 3 and when it represents −2.

a) $4x + 3$ **b)** $3(5 − 2m)$

c) $2(6a + 1)$ **d)** $−4(2s − 5)$

e) $−(4p + 3)$ **f)** $5(1 − 2t)$

g) $−(6c − 8)$ **h)** $6(−2n − 1)$

i) $−12 + 4v$ **j)** $−2(5 + 3d)$

6. Expand using the Distributive Law.

a) $3(2x + 7)$ **b)** $−5(4 + 3n)$

c) $12(4s − 5)$ **d)** $−2(4b − 3)$

e) $−(6p + 10)$ **f)** $\frac{1}{2}(4 − 2t)$

g) $−6(−3c − 5)$ **h)** $1.1(−20 + 4k)$

i) $2(−a + 2)$ **j)** $−\frac{2}{3}(−18 + 6d)$

7. Combine like terms and simplify each expression.

a) $2x + 7 + 3x − 5$

b) $3m − 12 − 7m + 2$

c) $5a + 3b + 8a − 10b$

d) $4y − 11 − 9y + 16$

e) $6s + 5t − 2(3s + 9t)$

f) $−2(4m − 7n) + 3(m − 13n)$

g) $−3(2q − 5) + 8q − 9$

h) $4(−k + \frac{3}{4}) − (5k + 4)$

i) $−(−7.4v − 3.2) − 1.4v − 3.5$

j) $4(6g − 8h) − 3(h − 5g)$

8. Simplify each expression and determine its value when $x = 4$, $x = −3$, and $x = −1$.

a) $5x + 2x$

b) $8x − 3 + 4x + 9$

c) $2x − 7 − 6x + 3$

d) $3x − 2 + 4(x − 5)$

e) $−3(4x + 1) − (−7x − 5)$

f) $2x + 11 − 4(3x + 7)$

g) $5(2x − 3) + 10 − 3x$

h) $−3(2 − x) + 2(5x − 4)$

i) $7(2x − 3) − 3(5 − 2x)$

j) $3(10 − 6x) − (4x + 7)$

9. Solve each equation using algebra tiles.

a) $3x + 2 = 8$

b) $2x − 3 = 1$

c) $7 − 4x = −5$

d) $3x + 4 = 2x − 3$

e) $2x − 5 = 6x + 7$

f) $3x − 1 = 5x − 9$

g) $12 + 4x = 5x + 8$

h) $−3x + 4 = −5x + 10$

i) $−7 − 3x = 8 + 2x$

j) $5 − 7x = −3x + 9$

10. Solve each equation. Check your solution.

a) $2x + 7 = 17$

b) $3 − 2x = 15$

c) $−40 = −4 + 4x$

d) $3x − 2 = 5x + 8$

e) $7 − 5x = 6 + x$

f) $−11 + 6x = −6x + 13$

g) $5x − 3 = 2x + 6$

h) $−3x + 5 = 2x − 10$

i) $−4x + 12 = 2x + 18$

j) $1.4x − 3.6 = 0.8x + 6$

11. When an object falls freely from rest, its approximate speed, v metres per second after t seconds, is given by the formula $v = 9.8t$. This is because acceleration due to Earth's gravity is 9.8 m/s^2.

a) Find the speed of an object after each time.

i) 2 s

ii) 5 s

iii) 8 s

b) Find the time required for the object to reach each speed.

   i) 29.4 m/s   **ii)** 88.2 m/s   **iii)** 137.2 m/s

c) If the object were on the moon, the formula would be $v = 1.63t$. Repeat parts a and b using this formula.

Give the answers to one decimal place.

12. Solve each equation.

a) $5(2x - 3) = 10$

b) $6(-2 - x) = -5(2x + 4)$

c) $-2(1 - x) = -3(2 - x)$

d) $\frac{72}{x} = 8$

e) $\frac{x}{5} = 12$

f) $\frac{3}{4}x = 15$

g) $\frac{x}{3} + 2 = -7$

h) $\frac{x}{6} - 5 = \frac{1}{2}x$

i) $\frac{1}{2}x + \frac{1}{3}x = 10$

j) $\frac{2}{3}x + 9 = \frac{3}{4}x - 6$

13. A parking meter accepts only quarters and dollars. If there are 31 coins with a value of $20.50, how many quarters and how many dollars are there?

14. For two consecutive integers, the sum of the smaller and twice the larger is 38. What are the integers?

15. A Jaguar travelled 1.2 times as fast as a Mercedes. The difference in their speeds was 24 km/h. Find the speed of each car.

16. The length of a rectangle is 5 cm longer than the width. The perimeter is 54 cm. Find the dimensions of the rectangle.

17. An apple orchard is selling baskets of Macintosh and Delicious apples. The orchard has 8 times as many baskets of Macintosh apples as Delicious apples. The orchard has a total of 153 baskets of apples. How many baskets of each type are there?

18. Mrs. Mazza is three times as old as her son, Carmine. In 12 years, Mrs. Mazza will be twice as old. How old is Carmine now?

19. Two numbers differ by 3. The sum of the larger and one-fourth the smaller is 13. What are the numbers?

20. Write an inequality that is represented by each graph.

a)

            -4   -3   -2   -1   0

b)

            -8   -7   -6   -5   -4

c)

            -8   -7   -6   -5   -4

d)

            30   31   32   33   34

e)

            -1   0   1   2   3

21. Is -3 a solution for each inequality in exercise 20? Is 5 a solution? Explain how you know.

22. Solve, graph, and check each inequality.

a) $9 > -2x$

b) $3y + 8 < 17$

c) $21 - 5x \geq 11$

d) $61 \leq 13a - 4$

e) $4.5m - 1.5 > 18$

f) $-3x + 8 < 5 - 7x$

g) $2h + 4 \geq -1 + 3h$

h) $-9r + 16 < -11$

i) $-9 + 4f \geq 3.3f - 4.1$

j) $\frac{1}{2}b - 5 < 4 - b$

Investigating a Card Trick

You will need a deck of 52 playing cards. In this trick, aces count as 1, and jacks, queens, and kings count as 10. Shuffle the cards as much as you like before you start.

Step 1

Hold the pack face down and deal the top card face up on the table. Continue to deal cards face up on top of this one. To determine the number of cards to deal, subtract the value of the card on the table from 13. For example, if the first card is a queen, deal three more cards; if it is a 5, deal eight more cards. Set the pile of cards off to the side, face down.

Step 2

Repeat *Step 1*, and set the new pile off to the side, face down. Keep repeating *Step 1* until you run out of cards.

At the end you will probably not have enough cards to finish the last pile. If this happens, hold the cards that are left face down.

Step 3

Ask a friend to choose any three piles, and to turn over the top card on two of those piles. Pick up the other piles. Add the cards to those you are already holding. It does not matter if you shuffle them.

There will now be three piles on the table, with the top card turned over on two of the piles.

Step 4

Deal some cards from those you are holding. To determine how many cards to deal, add the values of the two cards you see on the table, and add 10 to the result.

Ask your friend to turn over the top card on the third pile. The value of this card should be equal to the number of cards that you have in your hand!

ACTIVITY 1

Do this trick a few times with a friend, until you are familiar with it.

ACTIVITY 2

To understand why the trick works, let *a*, *b*, and *c* represent the values of the top three cards on the three piles your friend chose in *Step 3*. Develop an expression for the number of cards in each of the three piles. Use these expressions to develop a formula for the number of cards you are holding just before you start dealing cards in *Step 4*.

What is the least number of piles that you can have on the table at the end of *Step 2*? What is the greatest?

ACTIVITY 3

The number 13 plays an important role in *Steps 1* and *2*. Suppose this number is replaced by 14. How can the instructions for the trick be slightly modified so that the outcome is the same? Try numbers other than 13 and 14. In each case, develop a formula for the number of cards you are holding just before you start dealing cards in *Step 4*.

In *Step 3*, ask your friend to choose four piles instead of three piles. How can the instructions for the trick be slightly modified so that the outcome is the same? Try numbers other than 3 and 4.

COMMUNICATING

The Ideas

Write a brief report to summarize the results of your investigations. Include an explanation of why the trick works, and what happens if you change the trick as suggested in *Activity 3*.

Cumulative Review

1. Add each pair of numbers.
   a) 4 and 7   **b)** 4 and −7
   c) −4 and 7   **d)** −4 and −7
   e) 7 and −2   **f)** 10 and −4
   g) 2 and −8   **h)** −5 and −9

2. For each pair in exercise 1, subtract the second number from the first.

3. Determine each product or quotient.
   a) $4 \times (-3)$ **b)** $(-25) \div (-5)$
   c) $(-8) \times (-6)$ **d)** $(-4) \times 4$
   e) $\dfrac{-18}{9}$ **f)** $\dfrac{-24}{-8}$

4. Predict the sign of each expression. Do not calculate the answer.
   a) $39.4 \times (-4.5) \times (-7.5) \times (-3.0)$
   b) $(-58.7) \times 49.3 \times (-3.8) \times 3.2$
   c) $\dfrac{4.5 \times 8.3}{-15}$
   d) $\dfrac{93.5 - 104.8}{-25}$
   e) $\dfrac{-1}{4} \times \dfrac{2}{-3} \times \dfrac{-9}{-5}$

5. Use a calculator to evaluate each expression in exercise 4.

6. Jacques works as a server at a restaurant. Last year he reported earnings of $11 070.00 from his hourly wage, plus $2800 from tips. What percent of Jacques' total income was earned from tips?

7. Draw a square 25 cm by 25 cm. Suppose you increase each side by 20%.
   a) Determine the perimeter of the enlarged square.
   b) What is the percent increase in the area of the square?

8. Draw a square 25 cm by 25 cm. Suppose you decrease each side by 20%.
   a) Determine the perimeter of the reduced square.
   b) What is the percent decrease in the area of the square?
   c) Compare your answer to part b with your answer to exercise 7b. Explain any similarities or differences.

9. Each graph shows the positions of a car relative to a measuring device at various times. The four graphs represent four different situations.

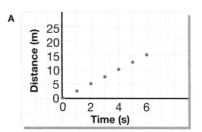

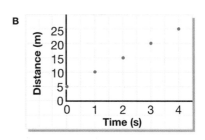

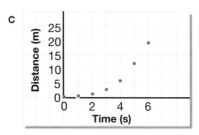

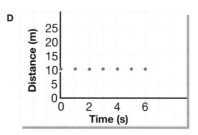

   a) In situation A, what was the distance travelled after 2 s?
   b) In situation B, what was the distance travelled in each 1-s time interval?
   c) In which situation was the car not moving? Explain how you know.
   d) In which situations was the car moving at a constant speed? Explain how you know.
   e) In which situation was the car gaining speed? Explain how you know.

10. Make a scatterplot of these data. Describe any relationship you find.

Name	Average egg size (g)	Average time to hatch (days)
Black-capped chickadee	16	12.0
Common loon	89	28.5
Common raven	50	19.5
Eastern bluebird	21	13.0
Great grey owl	54	24.5
Grey jay	29	17.0
Killdeer	37	26.0
Marbled murrelet	60	28.5
White pelican	90	32.5
Willow ptarmigan	43	21.5

11. a) The data below show the scoring record of one lacrosse player. Graph the data.

Games played	2	4	8	10
Goals scored this season	0	1	2	3
Games played	12	14	16	18
Goals scored this season	4	4	6	6

  b) Does it make sense to join the points in this graph? Explain.

12. Explain why each statement is misleading.
  a) A cure for the common cold has been found. In a recent test, 300 people with a cold took a new medication. After five days, their colds were gone.
  b) There are nearly 1 500 000 unemployed people, yet the "Help Wanted" advertisements fill several pages in most newspapers. This shows that the unemployed are not interested in working.

13. A paper bag contains 5 blue marbles and 8 yellow marbles. One marble is removed at random.
  a) What are the possible outcomes?
  b) Are the outcomes equally likely? Explain.
  c) What is the probability of each outcome?

14. A paper bag contains 5 blue marbles and 8 yellow marbles. Tina removes 1 marble and records the colour. She replaces the first marble, selects another, and records the colour. She repeats the process a third time
  a) What are the possible outcomes?
  b) Are the outcomes equally likely? Explain.
  c) What is the probability of each outcome?

15. In euchre, players play only with the 9, 10, jack, queen, king, and ace of all four suits. At the start of a game, four euchre players each cut the deck to select the dealer.
  a) What is the probability all players choose a 9 when they cut the deck?
  b) What is the probability all players choose an ace when they cut the deck?
  c) Suppose the first player to cut the deck turns up a king. What is the probability the other three players also select a king?

16. Expand each expression.
  a) $4(a + 5)$ **b)** $3(a - 2)$
  c) $5a(a + 7)$ **d)** $2a(9 - 3a)$
  e) $-2(5 - 2a)$ **f)** $-a(3a - 5)$

17. Evaluate each expression in exercise 16 for $a = -2$.

18. Simplify each expression. Determine its value when $p = 3$, $q = -2$, and $r = -1$.
  a) $5p + 3q + 4p + q$
  b) $8q + 5p - 6q - p + 3q$
  c) $3r - 2p - 5q + r - 2p + 3q$
  d) $5r + 5q - 7q - q - 3r$
  e) $r + 3p + 2r - p$
  f) $q - 7p - 5q + 3q + 5p$

19. Show how you solve each equation with algebra tiles. Record the solution using symbols.
  a) $4k + 8 = 2k$ **b)** $3x - 6 = 4x$
  c) $9 - 4p = 1$ **d)** $2b - 3 = b + 7$
  e) $6 + 2y = -10$ **f)** $4a - 2 = 8 - k$

20. Solve, graph, and check each inequality.
  a) $b < -5$ **b)** $k - 7 > 4$
  c) $g + 3 > 2g$ **d)** $4g - 5 < 3g$

CONGRUENCE AND SIMILARITY

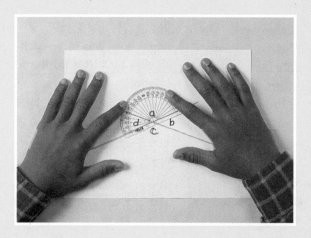

Start With What You Know

Since humans first constructed buildings, they have used geometric ideas such as symmetry, parallelism, and perpendicularity in their designs. These concepts are evident in buildings from all cultures and ages. Four famous buildings are shown on these pages.

One of the great architectural wonders of the world is the Parthenon, built by the ancient Greeks between 448 B.C. and 432 B.C.

1. In each photograph:
   a) Identify as many geometric figures as you can.
   b) Identify pairs of parallel lines and pairs of perpendicular lines. Does any photograph not contain parallel or perpendicular lines?
   c) Describe any symmetry you see.

2. Look for pairs of equal angles. Explain how you know they are equal.

3. Each building contains parts that have the same size and shape. Describe as many of these parts as you can.

4. Does any building contain parts that have the same shapes with different sizes? Describe these parts.

The spectacular palace at Versailles, France, was constructed between 1669 and 1685. The photograph shows the Royal Chapel of the palace.

This is the dome of a mosque in Cordoba, Spain. The mosque was designed over 1000 years ago by Muslim architects.

Another wonder of the architectural world is the Taj Mahal in India. This building was constructed between 1632 and 1654.

3.1 CONSTRUCTING TRIANGLES USING COMPASSES AND RULER

Developing the Ideas

Archimedes was probably the greatest mathematician of ancient times. He lived in Syracuse, which is in present-day Sicily. Archimedes was also a great inventor. Over 2200 years ago, he designed catapults with adjustable ranges. Huge rocks, with masses of several tonnes, were tossed at invading Roman ships. Archimedes' catapults and other ingenious inventions helped the Greeks hold off invading Roman forces for almost three years.

Some of the tools for geometric construction used by Archimedes were the compasses and the straightedge. A straightedge is a piece of wood, metal, or plastic with a straight edge — similar to a ruler without markings. In this section, you will use these tools to draw figures and solve problems.

▶▶ *Through Activities*

ACTIVITY 1

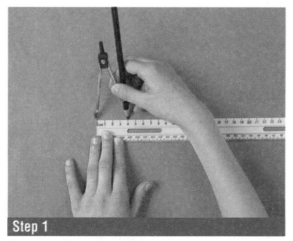

Step 1

Set your compasses to 4 cm.

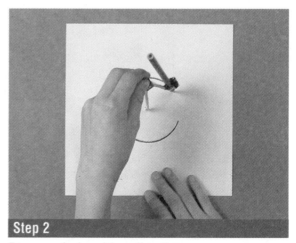

Step 2

Draw a circle with radius 4 cm.

1. Label the centre of the circle P. Label any point Q on the circle.
   a) How far is Q from P? How do you know?
   b) How far is any point on the circle from P? Explain how you know.
   c) Is there any point 4 cm from P that is not on the circle?
       Explain how you know.

ACTIVITY 2

Follow the steps to construct a triangle with sides of lengths 10 cm,
8 cm, and 6 cm.

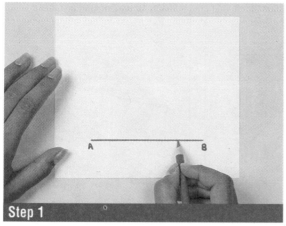

Step 1

Draw a line segment 10 cm long. Label it AB.

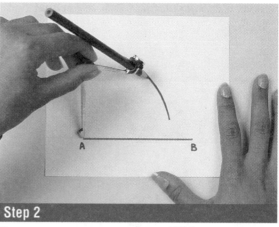

Step 2

Set your compasses to 8 cm. With compasses
point on A, draw an arc.

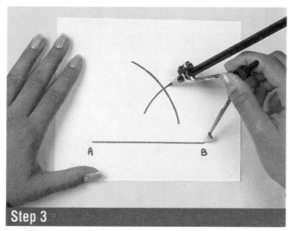

Step 3

Set your compasses to 6 cm. With compasses
point on B, draw an arc to intersect the first
arc you drew.

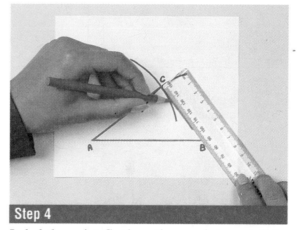

Step 4

Label the point C where the arcs intersect. Join
AC and CB. You have drawn △ABC. Label
each side of the triangle with its length.

1. Compare your triangle with those of other students. Do all the triangles
look the same?

2. Use ruler and compasses to draw a triangle with each set of sides.
   a) 5 cm, 6 cm, 7 cm
   b) 10 cm, 10 cm, 10 cm
   c) 6 cm, 10 cm, 14 cm
   d) 8.5 cm, 8.5 cm, 6.0 cm
   e) 9.5 cm, 5.5 cm, 5.5 cm
   f) 6.5 cm, 6.5 cm, 6.5 cm

Keep these triangles. You will use them later on page 188.

We can classify triangles by the lengths of their sides.

A triangle with three equal sides is an *equilateral triangle*. 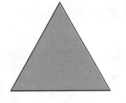	A triangle with at least two equal sides is an *isosceles triangle*. 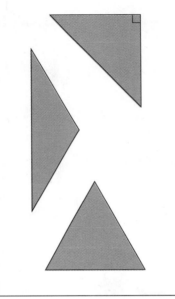	A triangle with no equal sides is a *scalene triangle*. 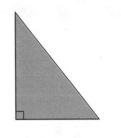

- For each triangle you drew in *Activity 2*, write whether it is equilateral, isosceles, or scalene.

BOGGLE YOUR MIND

Trace the isosceles triangle on the right. Glue your tracing onto a piece of cardboard. Cut out the tracing along the white lines. You now have five pieces. Use all five pieces to form each of the figures shown below. What other figures can you form using all five pieces?

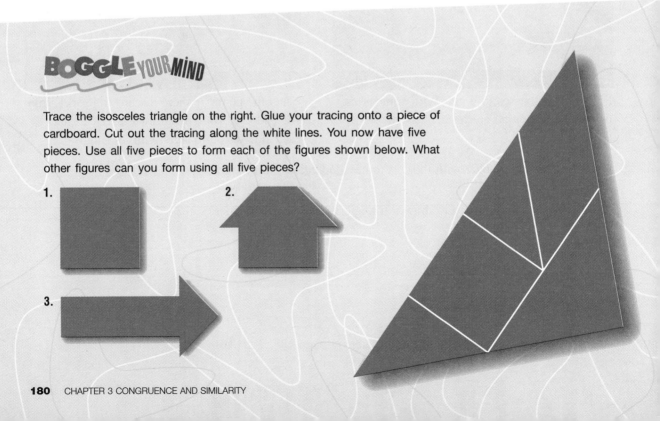

1.

2.

3.

Working with Mathematics

Something to talk about

1. A circle with centre A and radius 4 cm is drawn. Are there any points inside this circle that are 4 cm from A? Explain how you know.

2. Is it possible to construct a triangle with sides of lengths 5 cm, 8 cm, and 21 cm? If your answer is yes, construct the triangle. If your answer is no, explain why it cannot be constructed.

3. Explain how you find out whether three certain lengths can be the lengths of the sides of a triangle.

Practice

4. Classify each triangle as scalene, isosceles, or equilateral. Use a ruler if necessary.

a)
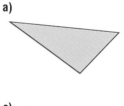

b)

c)
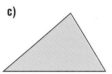

d)

e)
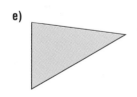

f)

5. Use a ruler and compasses. Construct a triangle for each set of side lengths. Identify each type of triangle you constructed.
   a) 8 cm, 8 cm, 8 cm
   b) 12.5 cm, 9.0 cm, 12.5 cm
   c) 16 cm, 12 cm, 20 cm
   d) 10.0 cm, 5.5 cm, 13.5 cm
   e) 12 cm, 10 cm, 6 cm
   f) 5 cm, 12 cm, 13 cm

Work together

6. On a sheet of paper, construct the largest equilateral triangle you can. Measure the lengths of the sides of the triangle. Compare your triangle with those of your classmates. How can you tell who drew the largest triangle?

7. On a sheet of paper, construct the largest isosceles triangle you can. Measure the lengths of the sides of the triangle. Compare your triangle with those of your classmates. How can you tell who drew the largest triangle?

8. Construct a triangle with sides of lengths 10 cm, 8 cm, and 4 cm. Compare your triangle with those of your classmates. Are the triangles the same shape? Did anyone's triangle have a different shape?

On your own

9. Points P and Q are 9 cm apart. A third point R is 7 cm from P and 5 cm from Q. Using ruler and compasses, locate the two possible positions of R. Join P and Q to the two points R. Describe the diagram.

10. Is an equilateral triangle also an isosceles triangle? Explain your answer.

Extend your thinking

11. Obtain a paper strip with two parallel sides. Construct an isosceles triangle by folding the strip.

COMMUNICATING

The Ideas

In your journal, sketch each triangle below and explain how you identify it.
   a) scalene triangle
   b) isosceles triangle
   c) equilateral triangle

Investigating the Medians of a Triangle

Sometimes we discover patterns in geometric figures that make us wonder *why*. Why is the circumference of a circle always π times the diameter, no matter how large or small the circle is? And why do the medians of a triangle … whoops … this is something you can discover using software like *The Geometer's Sketchpad*.

A *median* of a triangle is the line segment that joins a vertex to the midpoint of the opposite side.

In the diagram, D is the midpoint of side AC. The line segment BD is a *median* of △ABC.

Start *The Geometer's Sketchpad*.

Construct a triangle using the Line Segment tool.

Choose the Selection tool. Select one side of the triangle by clicking on it. The two black squares on the line segment show that it has been selected.

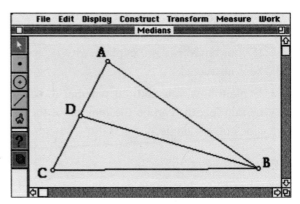

From the Construct menu, select the Point At Midpoint command. This places a point at the midpoint of the line segment you selected. Hold down the shift key and select the point at the opposite vertex by clicking on it. From the Construct menu, select the Segment command.

This constructs the median from the vertex to the midpoint of the selected side.

Follow the procedure above to construct the other two medians of the triangle. Describe what you discover about the three medians of the triangle.

Do you think this property is true for all triangles?

To find out, click and drag one vertex of the triangle to create other triangles. Does this property of medians apply to all these triangles?

Write a statement that describes this interesting property of medians.

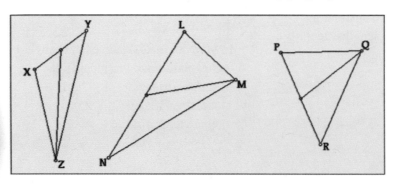

. . . . 3.2 CONSTRUCTING TRIANGLES USING RULER AND PROTRACTOR

Developing the Ideas

In this section, you will use a ruler and a protractor to construct triangles. You have probably used a protractor to measure angles.

There are circular protractors where the scale is marked from 0° to 360°.

There are semicircular protractors where the scale is marked from 0° to 180°.

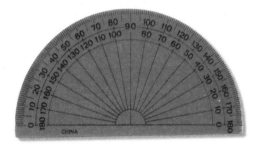

Most protractors have two scales. The scale we use depends on how we place the protractor on the angle.

In the following activities, you will learn how to use a semicircular protractor to construct a triangle.

Binney and Smith is Canada's only crayon manufacturer. Every day, the company produces 1.15 million crayons. How many crayons would Binney and Smith produce in a year? Suppose you lay these crayons in a line end-to-end. Would the line be long enough to stretch around the world?

ACTIVITY 1

Work with a partner.

Follow the steps to construct a triangle with two angles of 68° and 32°, so that the side between these angles has length 7 cm.

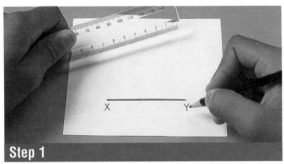

Step 1

Draw a line segment 7 cm long. Label it XY.

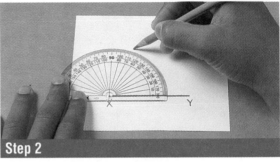

Step 2

Place the centre of the protractor at X. Use the inner scale. Mark a point on the paper at 68°.

Step 3

Use a ruler to draw the line through X and the point. Extend the line beyond the point.

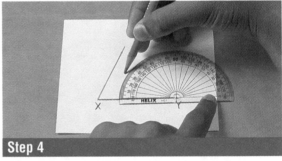

Step 4

Place the centre of the protractor at Y. Use the outer scale. Mark a point on the paper at 32°.

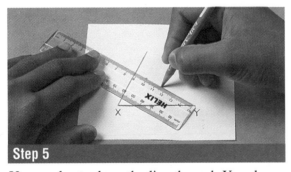

Step 5

Use a ruler to draw the line through Y and the point. Extend the line to intersect the line through X.

Step 6

Label Z as the intersection of the line through X and the line through Y.

You have drawn △XYZ. Label the triangle with the given angles and length.

1. Compare your triangle with those of other students. Do all the triangles look the same?

Work with a partner.

Follow the steps to construct a triangle with two sides of lengths
7 cm and 5 cm, and an angle of 44° between these sides.

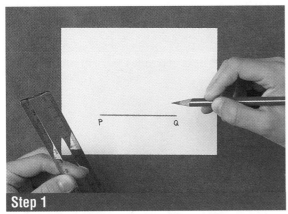

Step 1

Draw a line segment 7 cm long. Label it PQ.

Step 2

Place the centre of the protractor at P. Use the
inner scale. Mark a point on the paper at 44°.

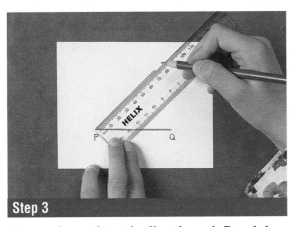

Step 3

Use a ruler to draw the line through P and the
point. Extend the line beyond the point.

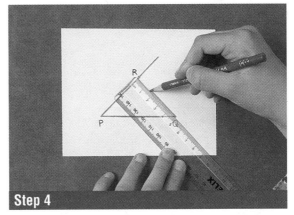

Step 4

With a ruler, measure 5 cm from P along the
line you drew. Mark a point, and label it R.
Join QR.

You have drawn △PQR. Label the triangle with the given lengths and angle.

1. Compare your triangle with those of other students. Do all the triangles
   look the same?

ACTIVITY 3

Work in a group.

1. Construct each triangle.

a) Side 6 cm between angles 36° and 46°   **b)** Angle 96° between sides 7.5 cm and 6.5 cm

c) Side 7.4 cm between angles 53° and 53°   **d)** Angle 114° between sides 5.7 cm and 4.6 cm

e) Side 8.3 cm between angles 124° and 14°   **f)** Angle 60° between sides 7.9 cm and 7.9 cm

g) Side 9.2 cm between angles 72° and 82°   **h)** Angle 75° between sides 5.4 cm and 5.4 cm

i) Side 10.4 cm between angles 60° and 60°   **j)** Angle 108° between sides 6.8 cm and 9.7 cm

2. Compare each triangle you constructed in exercise 1 with those of other students. For each set of measurements, are all the triangles the same? If they are not the same, explain how they are different.

▶▶ *Through Instruction*

We classify angles by their measures.

An angle measuring less than 90° is an *acute angle*. 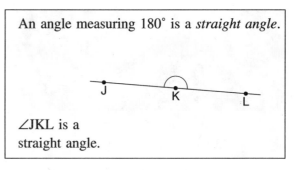 ∠ABC is an acute angle.	An angle measuring 90° is a *right angle*. ∠DEF is a right angle.
An angle measuring more than 90° and less than 180° is an *obtuse angle*. ∠GHI is an obtuse angle.	An angle measuring 180° is a *straight angle*. ∠JKL is a straight angle.

We can use the types of angles in a triangle to classify triangles.

A triangle with three acute angles is an *acute triangle*. 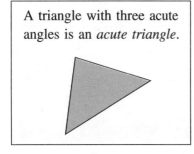	A triangle with a right angle is a *right triangle*. 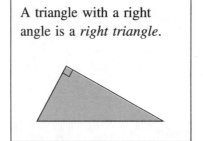	A triangle with an obtuse angle is an *obtuse triangle*. 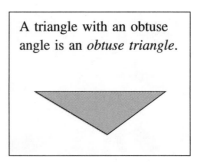

• For each triangle you drew in *Activity 3*, write whether it is acute, right, or obtuse.

Working with Mathematics

Something to talk about

1. Tell whether each angle is right, acute, obtuse, or straight. Explain how you know.

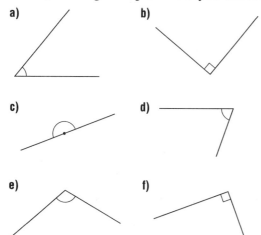

a)   b)

c)   d)

e)   f)

Practice

2. Tell whether each triangle is acute, right, or obtuse. Explain how you know.

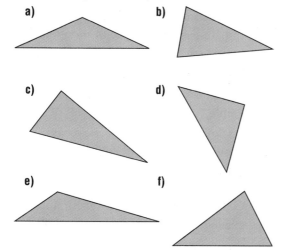

a)   b)

c)   d)

e)   f)

3. Name as many acute angles as you can in this diagram.

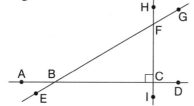

4. Use a ruler and a protractor. Construct a triangle for each set of measurements. Identify each type of triangle you constructed.
   a) angle 60° between sides 7 cm and 7 cm
   b) side 7.1 cm between angles 30° and 45°
   c) side 12.7 cm between angles 63° and 63°
   d) angle 74° between sides 5.3 cm and 9.6 cm
   e) angle 117° between sides 6.4 cm and 5.8 cm
   f) side 8.5 cm between angles 90° and 53°

5. Refer to the triangles in exercise 2. Find an example of each type.
   a) an obtuse scalene triangle
   b) an acute isosceles triangle
   c) a right scalene triangle
   d) an obtuse isosceles triangle
   e) an acute scalene triangle
   f) a right isosceles triangle

Work together

6. a) Trace this diagram. Draw a triangle whose vertices are on the dots.

   b) How many kinds of triangles can you draw in this way? Identify each triangle.
   c) Compare your triangles with those of your partner. Did you draw all possible triangles?

7. a) State whether it is possible for a triangle to be drawn:
      i) with 2 equal sides and 1 right angle
      ii) with 2 equal sides and 1 obtuse angle
      iii) with 3 equal sides and 1 right angle
      iv) with no equal sides and 3 equal angles
   b) Draw each triangle in part a that can be drawn. Compare your triangles with those of your partner.

8. A tunnel is to be constructed through a mountain. The surveyor drew line segment XY to represent the tunnel. She measured the distances to X and Y from a point Z. She found that ZX is 500 m and ZY is 700 m. Angle XZY is 125°.

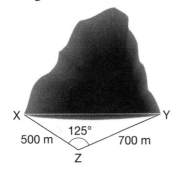

Complete this exercise to construct a scale drawing to measure the length of the tunnel XY. Use a scale of 1 cm to represent 100 m.
a) i) How long will the line segment XZ be in your drawing?
ii) How long will the line segment YZ be in your drawing?
b) Construct △XYZ using the measures from part a.
c) Measure XY in centimetres.
d) How long is the tunnel in metres?

On your own

9. a) Name one acute angle and one obtuse angle in each diagram.

i)

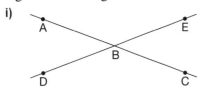

ii)

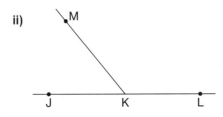

iii)

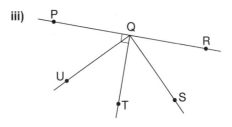

b) Compare your answers with those of another student. Did you select the same angles?

10. a) Construct a triangle with sides of lengths 3 cm, 4 cm, and 5 cm.
b) Classify the triangle in two ways.

11. Look at the equilateral triangles you constructed in *Activity 2*, page 179. How else can you classify each triangle?

12. Look at the isosceles triangles you constructed in *Activity 2*, page 179. How else can you classify each triangle?

13. a) Draw an example of each triangle, if possible.
 i) an acute isosceles triangle
 ii) an obtuse isosceles triangle
 iii) a right isosceles triangle
b) Compare each triangle with those drawn by other students. How are the triangles the same? How are the triangles different?

14. a) Draw an example of each triangle, if possible.
 i) a right scalene triangle
 ii) an obtuse scalene triangle
 iii) an acute scalene triangle
b) Compare each triangle with those drawn by other students. How are the triangles the same? How are the triangles different?

15. Draw an example of each triangle, if possible.
a) an obtuse equilateral triangle
b) a right equilateral triangle

16. A sailor wants to know her distance from a lighthouse. She measures the angle to the lighthouse when she is at point B. She then proceeds due west a distance of 1000 m. She measures the angle to the lighthouse from point A. She sketches the diagram below.

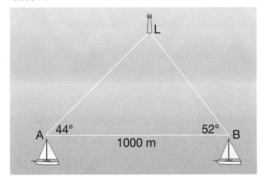

Use a scale drawing to find how far the sailor is from the lighthouse when she is at point B.

17. Measure the angles of each equilateral triangle you drew in *Activity 2*, page 179. Measure the angles of any other equilateral triangles in the text or in your notebook. Compare your results with those of other students. What do you notice?

18. Measure the angles of each isosceles triangle you constructed in *Activity 2*, page 179. Measure the angles of any other isosceles triangles in the text or in your notebook. Compare your results with those of other students. What do you notice?

Extend your thinking

19. A line segment representing the height of a triangle is called an *altitude*.
  a) How many altitudes does every triangle have?
  b) Draw a triangle in which all the altitudes have the same length. What kind of triangle is it?
  c) Draw a triangle in which only two altitudes have the same length. What kind of triangle is it?
  d) Are the altitudes of every triangle inside the triangle? Explain your answer.
  e) Is it possible for a side of a triangle to be an altitude? Explain your answer.

20. A line segment joining a vertex of a triangle to the midpoint of the opposite side is called a *median*.
  a) How many medians does every triangle have?
  b) Draw a triangle in which all the medians have the same length. What kind of triangle is it?
  c) Draw a triangle in which only two medians have the same length. What kind of triangle is it?
  d) Are the medians of every triangle inside the triangle? Explain your answer.
  e) Is it possible for a side of a triangle to be a median? Explain your answer.

COMMUNICATING

The Ideas

Look through magazines and newspapers. Cut out examples of angles and triangles. Label each angle with its type. Label each triangle with its type, in more than one way if possible. Post these pictures on a bulletin board display in your classroom.

Developing the Ideas

Two figures are *congruent* if they are identical in size and shape.
No two things are exactly alike. However, when we say that two
figures are congruent, we mean that they are so close to being identical
that we cannot tell the difference between them.

▷ ▶ *Through Activities*

ACTIVITY 1

Follow these steps to make congruent copies of a figure.

Step 1

Fold a piece of paper in half.

Step 2

Fold the paper in half again.

Step 3

Fold the paper in half a third time.

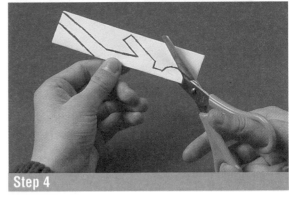

Step 4

Along the fold line, draw a figure or object on
your paper. Cut out the figure.

1. Describe any symmetry in your figures.

To check that two of the figures are congruent, place one on top of
another so they coincide. You should find that they overlap so that one
figure is completely covered by the other. Two figures coincide like this
only if they have the same size and shape. Checking that two figures
coincide is one way to verify that they are congruent.

2. How many congruent figures did you make?

ACTIVITY 2

We can extend the idea of congruence to line segments and angles.

1. Use tracing paper to determine which line segment is congruent to XY.

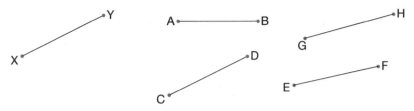

2. Use tracing paper to determine which angle is congruent to ∠XYZ.

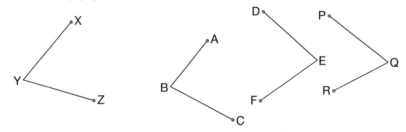

3. Use tracing paper to determine which triangle is congruent to △PQR.

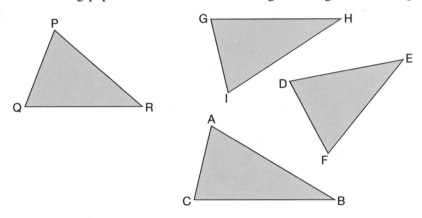

4. Check your answers to exercises 1 to 3 with other students. If you do not agree on the answers, try to find the mistakes.

5. a) In exercise 1, how could you find which line segment is congruent to XY without tracing?

b) In what way are congruent line segments *equal?*

6. a) In exercise 2, how could you find which angle is congruent to ∠XYZ without tracing?

b) In what way are congruent angles *equal?*

7. a) In exercise 3, how could you find which triangle is congruent to △PQR without tracing?

b) If you know that two triangles are congruent, what can you say about their sides and their angles?

Work in a group. You will need a protractor.

1. Draw two lines that intersect. Label the angles as shown.

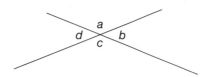

2. Measure the angles. Record the answers. What do you notice?

3. Repeat exercises 1 and 2 for a different pair of intersecting lines.

4. Compare your results with those of the other students in your group.

5. Did you find pairs of congruent angles?

6. Write a statement about the measures of the angles formed by two intersecting lines.

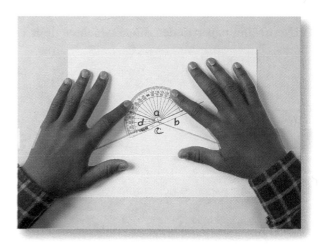

▶ ▶ *Through Instruction*

When two lines intersect, four angles are formed.

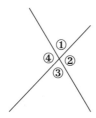

∠① and ∠③ are called *opposite* angles.

∠② and ∠④ are also opposite angles.

From *Activity 3*, you should have discovered this fact.

• • • • • • • • •

When two lines intersect, the opposite angles are congruent.

In the diagram above, ∠① = ∠③

$$∠② = ∠④$$

Working with Mathematics

Something to talk about

1. Explain what is meant by each statement.
   a) AB is congruent to CD.
   b) ∠ABC is congruent to ∠DEF.
   c) △ABC is congruent to △XYZ.

2. a) When is a photocopy of a figure congruent to the original figure?
   b) When is a photocopy of a figure not congruent to the original figure?

3. Is every line segment of length 5 cm congruent to all other line segments of length 5 cm? Explain your answer.

4. Explain how you could find whether two circles are congruent without placing one over the other.

5. Explain why congruence is important in the manufacture of these items.
   a) loonie dollars
   b) a duplicate house key
   c) soft drink containers
   d) golf balls

6. a) Do two congruent triangles have the same area? Explain.
   b) Are all triangles with the same area congruent? Explain.

7. a) Do two congruent triangles have the same perimeter? Explain.
   b) Are all triangles with the same perimeter congruent? Explain.

8. The diagram shows △ABC and △DEF. ∠ABC and ∠DEF both have a measure of 45°.
   a) Is ∠ABC congruent to ∠DEF? Explain.
   b) Is △ABC congruent to △DEF? Explain.

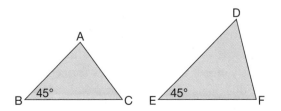

Practice

9. Measure each angle. Find two angles that are congruent.

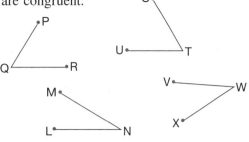

10. Each diagram shows congruent triangles. Name the equal angles and the equal sides.

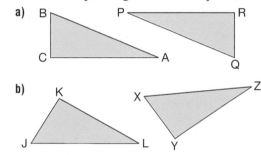

11. Measure each line segment. Find two congruent segments.

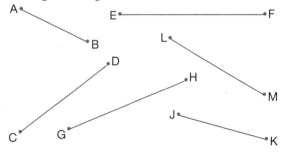

12. Find the measure of each angle represented by *x*. Explain your answers.

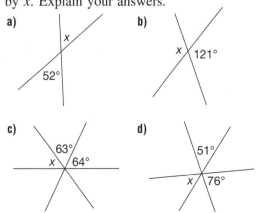

Work together

13. In each diagram, are the triangles congruent? If they are, explain why.

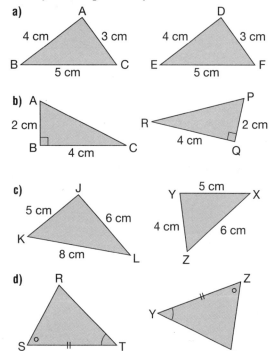

14. Only one pair of triangles in this set is congruent. By measuring with a ruler or protractor, find the matching pair.

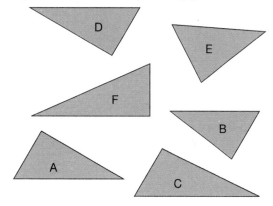

15. **a)** Construct a large rectangle similar to this. Draw the diagonals of your rectangle.

b) Measure the angles formed where the diagonals intersect. What do you notice?

c) Compare your answers to part b with those of your partner. Write a statement about the angles formed by the diagonals of a rectangle.

d) How could you have answered part c without drawing a rectangle?

On your own

16. Find the measure of each angle represented by *a*. Explain your answers.

a)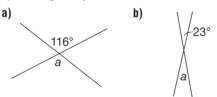

b)

c)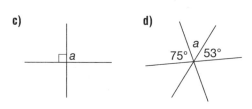

d)

e)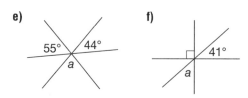

f)

17. **a)** Construct a large square similar to this. Draw the diagonals.

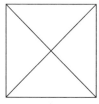

b) Measure the angles formed where the diagonals intersect. What do you notice?

c) Compare your answers to part b with those of another student. Write a statement about the angles formed by the diagonals of a square.

d) How does this statement compare with the one you wrote in exercise 15?

18. Mei Lin has three keys and a duplicate set. When her key chain broke, the keys were mixed. Use tracing paper to match each key with its duplicate.

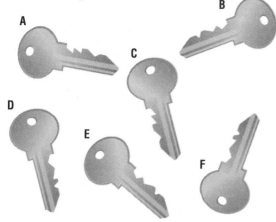

a) Write a pair of letters to match each key with its duplicate.

b) Which keys can be matched without flipping the tracing paper?

19. Use tracing paper to identify as many pairs of congruent triangles as you can. For each pair, name the angles and the sides that are equal.

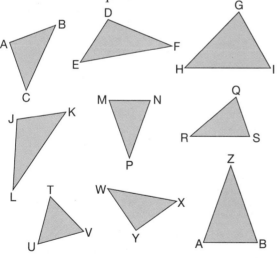

20. Make several tracings of this 4 by 3 rectangle. The diagram shows one way to divide the rectangle into two congruent parts by joining the dots with lines parallel to the sides. How many other ways can you find?

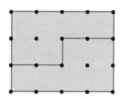

21. Recall that a triangle with at least two equal sides is an isosceles triangle. Construct three different isosceles triangles. Record the measures of the angles of each triangle.

a) Describe any pattern you discover in the measures of the angles opposite the congruent sides.

b) For each triangle, draw a line of symmetry. What can you say about the two figures formed by the line of symmetry?

c) Fold your paper along the line of symmetry. Verify that the line of symmetry divides the isosceles triangle into two congruent figures. Does the line of symmetry bisect the angle? Explain how you know.

Extend your thinking

22. In each figure, find as many pairs of congruent triangles as you can.

a) 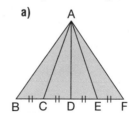   **b)**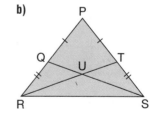

The Ideas

In your journal, explain what *congruence* is. Draw diagrams to show congruent segments, congruent angles, and congruent triangles.

Fingerprints

THE SKIN OF YOUR FINGERS HAS A UNIQUE PATTERN of ridges. No two sets of fingerprints are alike, even those of identical twins. Secretions are produced by glands under the surface of the skin and released through holes called pores. When you touch something, these secretions cause you to leave behind an invisible copy of your fingerprint pattern.

Fingerprints are one of the best ways to identify people. Fingerprint records are used to identify criminals, and dead or injured people. If the fingerprint of an unknown person is congruent to a fingerprint on record, then the unknown person can be identified. The system for classifying fingerprints is based on two things: class and ridges.

There are ten classes. These are shown below.

Ulnar loop (right hand)

Radial loop (right hand)

Double loop

Whorl

Arch

Tented arch

Lateral pocket loop

Central pocket loop

Composite

Accidental

There are five ridge characteristics.
These are shown below.

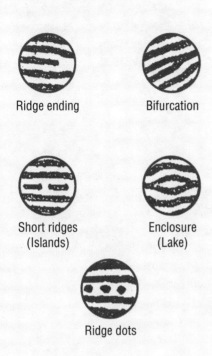

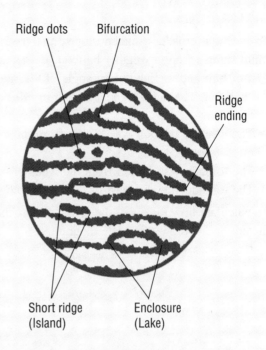

Matching prints have the same class, and the same number of ridges between shapes.

Complete the following exercises to classify your thumb print using these diagrams. You need an ink pad, blank paper, and a magnifying glass.

Work with a partner.

1. Lightly roll your right thumb face down over the ink pad. Slowly roll your thumb onto a blank piece of paper. Record your name underneath.

2. Make notes under the print to answer these questions.
   a) What is the class?
   b) Are there any identifying marks like cuts or scars?
   c) Are there any bifurcations, islands, or lakes?
   d) Count the ridges from the centre shape outwards to a new shape.
   e) Draw a sketch of the general shape.

3. Make a new thumb print on another piece of paper. Exchange prints with your partner. Repeat exercise 2 for your partner's print.

4. With your partner, compare your notes for both thumb prints.
   a) How well did you agree on your classification?
   b) What difficulties did you have in classifying the prints?

Mathematics & Science

Linking Ideas

Developing the Ideas

▶ ▶ *Through Discussion*

To locate a tornado, a meteorologist analyzed radio signals from a weather balloon. It was due east of him and inclined at an angle of 40° above the horizon. The radio signals gave him this information:

- The weather balloon was 20 km from the meteorologist.
- The tornado was 16 km from the weather balloon.
- The tornado was due east of the meteorologist.

To calculate how far away the tornado was, the meteorologist drew this scale diagram.

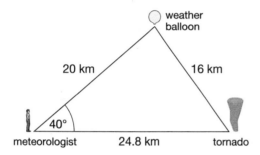

He measured the length of the third side on his triangle and concluded that the tornado was 24.8 km due east of him.

However, the tornado reached the meteorologist much sooner than he expected. How were his calculations incorrect?

We assume the information received from the weather balloon was correct.

Did the meteorologist draw a correct diagram?

Did the meteorologist make an error in measuring the third side of the triangle?

In *Activity 1*, you will draw a scale diagram to check.

ACTIVITY 1

You will need a ruler, a protractor, and compasses.

Step 1

Use a scale of 1 cm to represent 2 km.

On your diagram, how long should you draw the line segment:

a) joining the meteorologist to the balloon?

b) joining the balloon to the tornado?

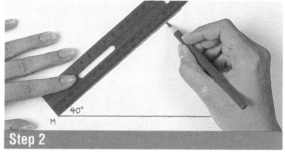

Step 2

Draw a line segment to represent the line between the meteorologist M and the tornado. Use a protractor to construct an angle of 40° at M.

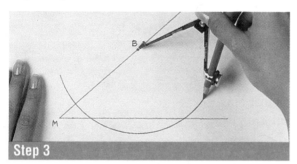

Step 3

Measure 10 cm along the line from M to the balloon B. Set your compasses to 8 cm. Place the compasses point on B and draw a circle.

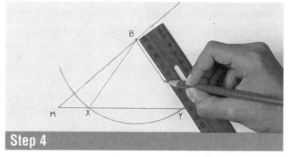

Step 4

Join B to each point where the circle intersects the line through M and the tornado. Label these points X and Y.

1. Measure MX and MY. What are the two possible distances that the tornado was from the meteorologist?

2. Which triangle should the meteorologist have drawn to model the position of the tornado?

3. How far away was the tornado when the meteorologist received the information from the balloon?

4. What further information did the meteorologist need before he drew his scale diagram?

Activity 1 illustrates that two different triangles can be drawn when certain measurements of a triangle are given.

Are there cases where only one triangle can be drawn when certain measurements are given? You will investigate this in *Activity 2*.

ACTIVITY 2

Work with a partner. You will need compasses, a protractor, and a ruler.

For each exercise, you are given the same measurements for two triangles. Use these measurements to try to construct two triangles that are not congruent.

1. AB = 6 cm, BC = 8 cm, AC = 12 cm   DE = 6 cm, EF = 8 cm, DF = 12 cm
   Can you draw △ABC so that it is not congruent to △DEF?

2. ∠G = 65°, ∠H = 85°, ∠I = 30°   ∠J = 65°, ∠K = 85°, ∠M = 30°
   Can you draw △GHI so that it is not congruent to △JKM?

3. NP = 8 cm, PQ = 5 cm, ∠P = 50°   RS = 8 cm, ST = 5 cm, ∠S = 50°
   Can you draw △NPQ so that it is not congruent to △RST?

4. UV = 7 cm, UW = 4 cm, ∠V = 30°   XY = 7 cm, XZ = 4 cm, ∠Y = 30°
   Can you draw △UVW so that it is not congruent to △XYZ?

5. ∠BAC = 62°, ∠ABC = 80°, BA = 6 cm   ∠EDF = 62°, ∠DEF = 80°, ED = 6 cm
   Can you draw △ABC so that it is not congruent to △DEF?

6. Compare your results with those of other students. Which measurements of a triangle would you have to be given so that only one triangle can be drawn?

▶ ▶ *Through Instruction*

From your work with *Activity 2*, you should have found that only one triangle can be drawn if the following measurements are given.

- the lengths of the three sides

- the lengths of two sides and the measure of the angle between them

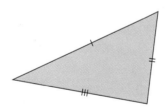

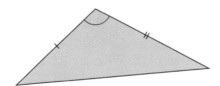

- the measures of two angles and the length of the side between them

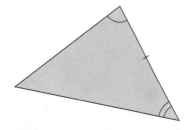

When considering whether two triangles are congruent, we do not need to know all the measurements of both triangles. If the given information about the triangles matches any of the three descriptions at the bottom of page 200, we know the triangles are congruent.

Example ··

Is each pair of triangles congruent? If they are, list the equal sides and the equal angles.

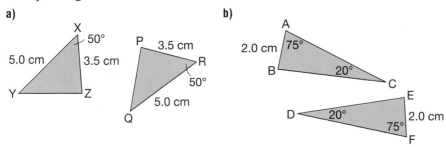

a)

b)

Solution

a) For each triangle, the lengths of two sides and the measure of the angle between them are given. These measures are equal in both triangles.

YX = QR = 5.0 cm
XZ = RP = 3.5 cm
∠X = ∠R = 50°

Since only one triangle can be drawn with these measurements, the triangles are congruent.
The other equal parts are:
YZ = QP, ∠Y = ∠Q, and ∠Z = ∠P

b) For each triangle, the length of one side and the measures of two angles are given. These measures are equal in both triangles.

AB = FE = 2.0 cm
∠A = ∠F = 75°
∠C = ∠D = 20°

We can use the sum of the angle measures of a triangle to find the measures of ∠B and ∠E.

∠B = 180° − 75° − 20°   ∠E = 180° − 75° − 20°
= 85°   = 85°

So, ∠B = ∠E

This means that for each triangle, the measures of two angles and the length of the side between them are equal.

Since only one triangle can be drawn with these measurements, the triangles are congruent.
The other equal parts are:
AC = FD and BC = ED

Working with Mathematics

Something to talk about

1. How many different triangles can be constructed from three straws of different lengths?

2. Both these triangles have angle measures of 30°, 65°, and 85°.

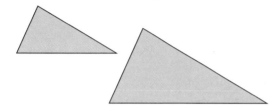

  a) Do the triangles have the same shape?

  b) Are the triangles congruent?

  c) Suppose we know that two triangles have equal pairs of angles. Are the triangles congruent?

3. In each pair of diagrams, △ABC is congruent to △DEF. Find the values of *x*, *y*, and *z*.

  a)

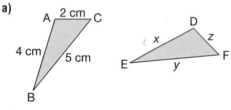

  b)

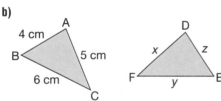

Practice

4. In the diagram, △ABC is congruent to △DEF. Find each measure.

  a) DE   **b)** ∠B   **c)** EF

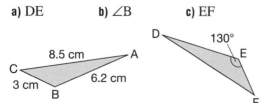

5. In the diagram, △ABC is congruent to △XYZ. Find each measure.

  a) XZ   **b)** ∠X   **c)** ∠Y   **d)** ∠B

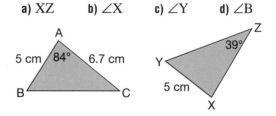

Work together

6. Which of the triangles in the box is congruent to each given triangle?

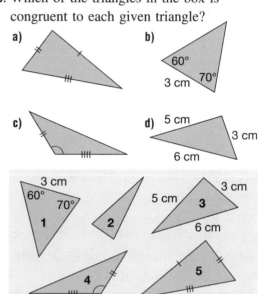

7. In the diagram, is △ABC congruent to △PQR? Give reasons for your answers.

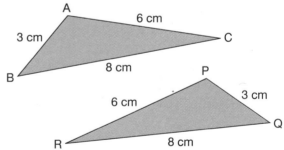

8. Is each pair of triangles congruent? If they are, list the equal sides and the equal angles.

  a)

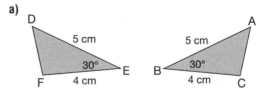

b)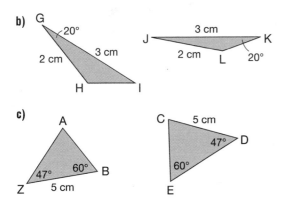

c)

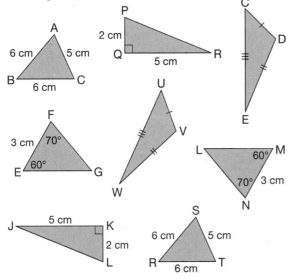

On your own

9. If you have access to a computer and *The Geometer's Sketchpad* software, load the sketch entitled SSA (Macintosh version) or SSA.GSP (Windows version), which comes with the program. Follow the instructions on the screen to construct two triangles that are not congruent. Try some of the other congruence sketches.

10. List as many pairs of congruent triangles as you can. Explain why each pair is congruent.

11. Each diagram shows congruent triangles. Find the values of *x* and *y*.

a)

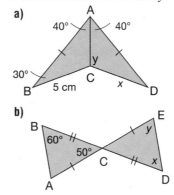

b)

12. In △PQR and △STU, ∠P = ∠S, ∠Q = ∠T, and QR = TU. Are △PQR and △STU congruent? Give reasons for your answer.

13. Suppose you are shown two triangles that look congruent.
   a) Suppose you could cut out the triangles. How could you check they are congruent?
   b) Suppose you could not cut out the triangles. How could you check they are congruent?

Extend your thinking

14. When the angles in one polygon have the same measures as the angles in another polygon, we say the two polygons are *equiangular.* Here are two quadrilaterals that are equiangular.

   a) Do equiangular quadrilaterals have the same shape? Are they congruent?
   b) Do equiangular triangles have the same shape? Are they congruent?
   c) What additional information do we need to determine whether two equiangular triangles are congruent?

COMMUNICATING

The Ideas

Look through newspapers and magazines for examples of congruent triangles. Display these pictures on a bulletin board in your classroom.

Developing the Ideas

▶ ▶ *Through Discussion*

How can we tell whether two figures of different sizes have the same shape? One of these logos has a distinctly different shape from the other two. How can we determine whether the two logos that look alike actually have the same shape?

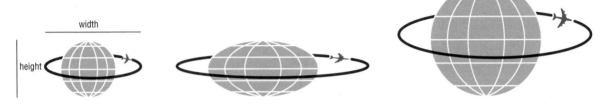

1. For each logo, measure the height and the width.
Calculate its height-to-width ratio to one decimal place.

2. What do you discover?

Repeat these measurements with the rectangles below.

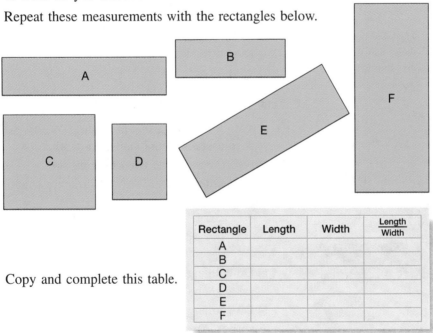

Copy and complete this table.

Rectangle	Length	Width	$\frac{\text{Length}}{\text{Width}}$
A			
B			
C			
D			
E			
F			

3. Measure and record the length and width of each rectangle.

4. Calculate and record the length : width ratio for each rectangle.
Write the ratio as a decimal.

5. Which two rectangles have the same length : width ratio?

We say that two rectangles that have the same length : width ratio are *similar*. Similar rectangles have the same shape but not necessarily the same size.

6. Which of the rectangles are similar? Explain.

Similar is the mathematical word meaning *same shape*. If two rectangles are similar, the ratio of the lengths of any two sides of one rectangle is equal to the ratio of the lengths of the corresponding sides of the other rectangle.

$$\frac{AB}{BC} = \frac{A'B'}{B'C'}$$

We can extend the concept of similarity to polygons.

If two polygons are similar, then the ratio of the lengths of any two sides of one polygon is equal to the ratio of the lengths of the corresponding sides of the other polygon.

The following examples show how we use this property of similar figures. We can calculate the unknown length of one side of a figure if we know the length of one of its sides and the lengths of corresponding sides of a similar figure.

Example 1 ·······················

These two rectangles are similar. Determine the length of side FG.

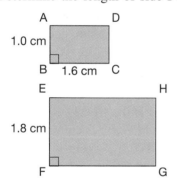

Solution ·······························

Since the rectangles are similar, the ratio of any two sides of EFGH is equal to the ratio of the corresponding sides of ABCD. We write a proportion.
$$\frac{FG}{EF} = \frac{BC}{AB}$$
Substitute the lengths we know.
$$\frac{FG}{1.8} = \frac{1.6}{1.0}$$
Solve the proportion. Multiply each side by 1.8.

FG = 1.8 × 1.6
     = 2.88

FG is about 2.9 cm long.

Example 2 ·······················

These two octagons are similar. Determine the length of diagonal B'F'.

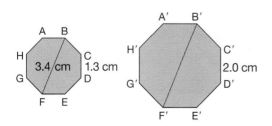

Solution ·······························

Since the octagons are similar, we can write a proportion relating corresponding segments.
$$\frac{B'F'}{C'D'} = \frac{BF}{CD}$$
Substitute the lengths we know.
$$\frac{B'F'}{2.0} = \frac{3.4}{1.3} \qquad \text{Multiply each side by 2.0.}$$
$$B'F' = \frac{3.4 \times 2.0}{1.3}$$
$$\doteq 5.23$$

B'F' is approximately 5.2 cm long.

Working with Mathematics

Something to talk about

1. Explain how you can find out whether two rectangles have the same shape.

2. What does it mean when two figures are said to be *similar*?

3. Each side of the hexagon on the right is twice as long as the corresponding side of the hexagon on the left. Are the hexagons similar? Explain your answer.

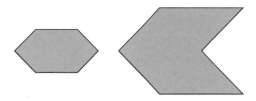

4. Recall that figures that can be made to coincide are *congruent*. Are congruent figures similar? Explain your answer.

Practice

5. Name pairs of similar figures. List their corresponding sides.

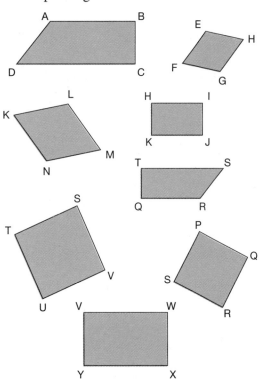

Work together

6. a) Calculate the length-to-width ratio for each rectangle.

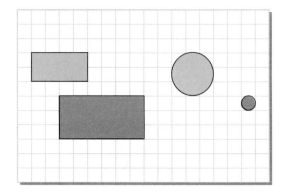

b) Are the rectangles similar?

c) How many times as great as the length of the blue rectangle is the length of the red rectangle?

d) Are the two circles similar? Explain your answer.

7. a) Draw parallelogram ABCD, where AB = 7 cm, BC = 3 cm, and ∠ABC = 110°.

b) Draw parallelogram PQRS, where PQ = 10.5 cm, QR = 4.5 cm, and ∠PQR = 110°.

c) Are the parallelograms similar? How do you know?

8. a) Draw rectangle EFGH, where EF = 3.5 cm and FG = 5.7 cm.

b) Draw rectangle TUVW, where TU = 10.5 cm and UV = 13.1 cm.

c) Are the rectangles similar? How do you know?

9. Each pair of figures are similar. Determine the length of AC.

a)

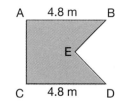

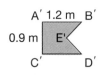

b)

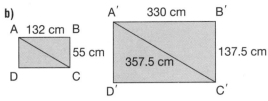

On your own

10. Which rectangle has the same shape as the yellow rectangle? Explain how you know.

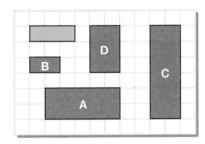

11. A photocopy machine is set to reduce all dimensions to 77% of their original sizes. This picture of the Canadian flag is copied on the machine.

a) Measure the flag. What is its length-to-width ratio?

b) What is the length-to-width ratio of the photocopy?

c) What is the length of the flag on the photocopy?

d) What is the width of the flag on the photocopy?

e) Calculate the areas of the flag and its photocopy.

f) Write the area of the photocopy as a fraction of the area of the flag. Express this fraction as a percent, to the nearest whole number.

Extend your thinking

12. a) An enlargement of a rectangle makes every dimension k times as large as the original, where k is greater than 1. The perimeter of the original rectangle is p. What is the perimeter of the enlarged rectangle?

b) The area of the original rectangle is A. What is the area of the enlarged rectangle?

The Ideas

In your journal, explain what is meant by the statement that two figures are similar. Are all rectangles similar? Explain your answer. Are all squares similar? Explain your answer.

Developing the Ideas

▷ ▶ *Through Activities*

In the previous section, we learned that two figures that have the same shape but not necessarily the same size are similar. To test rectangles for similarity, we calculated their length-to-width ratios. Rectangles with the same length-to-width ratio are similar.

In *Activity 1*, you will identify similar triangles.

ACTIVITY 1

1. Measure the sides of each triangle. Write each length to the nearest 0.5 mm.

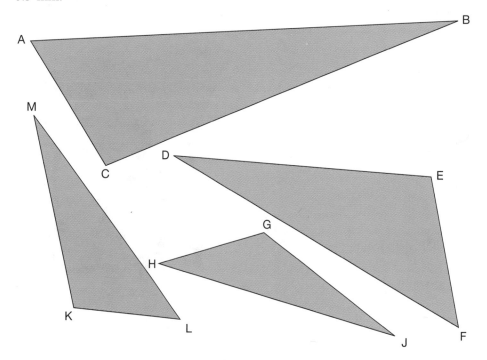

2. Arrange the lengths of the sides of each triangle in order from longest to shortest.

3. Write the lengths of the sides of each triangle as a three-term ratio.

4. For each triangle, divide each term of the ratio by the last term of the ratio. That is, write an equivalent ratio with last term 1. Where necessary, round the quotient to 2 decimal places.

5. Identify the two triangles that have the same three-term ratio.

6. Identify the two triangles that are similar.

7. Compare your results with those of other students. Did all of you find the same two similar triangles?

ACTIVITY 2

1. Draw any △ABC. Measure the angles.

2. Measure the lengths of the sides of △ABC.

3. Multiply each length in step 2 by 1.5.

4. Construct △EFG with side lengths equal to those in step 3.

5. Measure the angles of △EFG.

6. Record your results in two tables.

Triangle ABC

Side	Length		Angle	Measure
AB			A	
BC			B	
CA			C	

Triangle EFG

Side	Length		Angle	Measure
EF			E	
FG			F	
GE			G	

7. Are the two triangles you drew similar? How do you know?

8. What do you notice about the angle measures in the two triangles?

9. Compare your results with those of other students. Did all of you get the same answers to the questions in steps 7 and 8?

▶ ▶ *Through Discussion*

In *Activity 1*, you should have discovered that △FDE and △LMK have side lengths that reduce to the same three-term ratio.

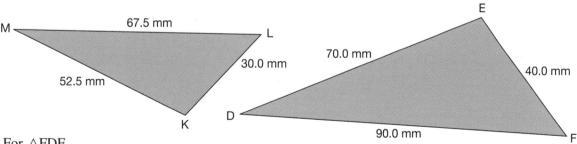

For △FDE

FD : DE : EF = 90.0 : 70.0 : 40.0

        = 2.25 : 1.75 : 1   ◁ Dividing each term by 40.0

For △LMK

LM : MK : KL = 67.5 : 52.5 : 30.0

        = 2.25 : 1.75 : 1   ◁ Dividing each term by 30.0

We say that two triangles, △FDE and △LMK, are similar if

FD : DE : EF = LM : MK : KL

This equation of two three-term ratios can also be written in fraction form.

$$\frac{FD}{LM} = \frac{DE}{MK} = \frac{EF}{KL}$$

In *Activity 2*, you should have discovered that corresponding angles in the triangles you drew had equal measures. The triangles you drew may have looked like this.

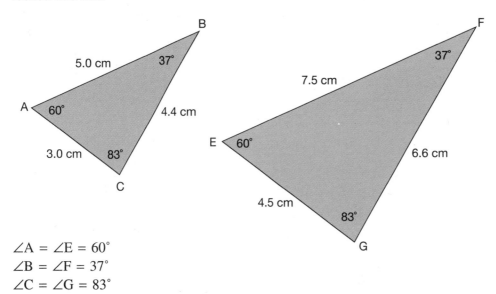

$\angle A = \angle E = 60°$
$\angle B = \angle F = 37°$
$\angle C = \angle G = 83°$

If you know two triangles are similar, then their corresponding angles are equal. Conversely, if two triangles have corresponding angles equal, then the triangles are similar.

▶ ▶ *Through Guided Examples*

We can use the fact that similar triangles have corresponding angles equal to calculate the measures of angles in triangles.

Example 1 ·

Find the measures of $\angle A$, $\angle B$, and $\angle C$.

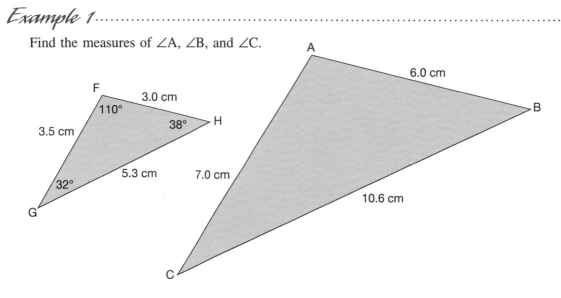

Solution

Check to see if the triangles are similar.

The ratios of corresponding sides are:

$\dfrac{AB}{FH} = \dfrac{6.0}{3.0}$, or 2; $\qquad \dfrac{BC}{HG} = \dfrac{10.6}{5.3}$, or 2; $\qquad \dfrac{AC}{FG} = \dfrac{7.0}{3.5}$, or 2

Since the ratios of corresponding sides are equal, the triangles are similar. That is, △FHG is similar to △ABC. Since the triangles are similar, corresponding angles are equal.

$\angle A = \angle F = 110°$

$\angle B = \angle H = 38°$

$\angle C = \angle G = 32°$

In *Example 1*, notice the triangles are described so that corresponding angles appear in the same order. That is, we write △A̱ḆC̱ and △F̱H̱G̱ because $\angle A = \angle F$; $\angle B = \angle H$; and $\angle C = \angle G$.

We can use the ratios written as fractions to calculate the length of a side of a triangle if we know the length of one of its sides, and the lengths of the corresponding sides of a similar triangle.

Example 2

△ABC is similar to △RPQ. Find the lengths of RP and AC.

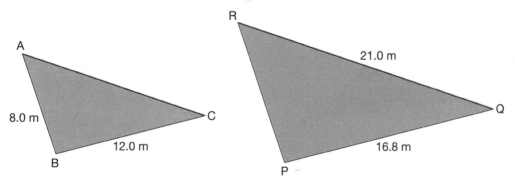

Solution

△RPQ is similar to △ABC, so the ratios of corresponding sides are equal.

$\dfrac{RP}{AB} = \dfrac{PQ}{BC} = \dfrac{RQ}{AC}$

Substitute the given lengths.

$\dfrac{RP}{8.0} = \dfrac{16.8}{12.0} = \dfrac{21.0}{AC}$

To find RP, use the first two fractions above.

$\dfrac{RP}{8.0} = \dfrac{16.8}{12.0}$

Multiply each side by 8.0.

$RP = \frac{16.8}{12.0} \times 8.0$

$ = 11.2$

RP is 11.2 m.

To find AC, use the second and third fractions above.

$\frac{21.0}{AC} = \frac{16.8}{12.0}$

Invert these fractions.

$\frac{AC}{21.0} = \frac{12.0}{16.8}$

Multiply each side by 21.0.

$AC = 21.0 \times \frac{12.0}{16.8}$

$ = 15.0$

AC is 15.0 m.

Some similar triangles are found in composite figures, as illustrated by the following example. We can show these triangles are similar by finding pairs of equal corresponding angles.

Example 3 . . . .

For each figure below, show that △DEF is similar to △DGH.

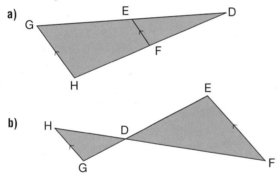

a)

b)

Solution

a) Since EF is parallel to GH,

$\angle DFE = \angle DHG$ — corresponding angles

$\angle DEF = \angle DGH$ — corresponding angles

∠D is common to both triangles.

$\angle EDF = \angle GDH$

Since the corresponding angles in the two triangles are equal, △DEF is similar to △DGH.

b) Since EF is parallel to HG,

$\angle DEF = \angle DGH$ — alternate angles

$\angle DFE = \angle DHG$ — alternate angles

Also, $\angle EDF = \angle GDH$ — opposite angles

Since the corresponding angles in the two triangles are equal, △DEF is similar to △DGH.

Working with Mathematics

Something to talk about

1. Explain how you can find out if two triangles are similar.

2. a) Are similar triangles congruent? Explain.
   b) Are congruent triangles similar? Explain.

Practice

3. Which triangle is similar to △ABC? Explain.

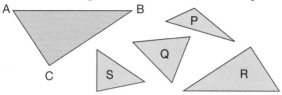

4. For each pair of similar triangles, list the corresponding sides and angles.

a)

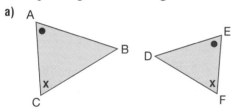

b)

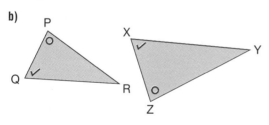

5. Each pair of triangles are similar. In each case, state the measures of the angles that are not marked.

a)

b)

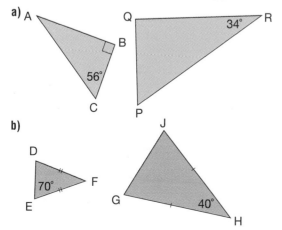

c)

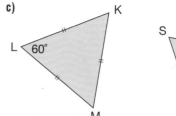

Work together

6. Explain why each pair of triangles are similar. Find the values of x and y.

a)   **b)**

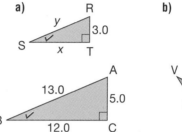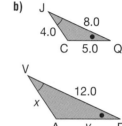

7. Suppose you are shown two triangles that appear to have the same shape. Describe two different ways to find out whether the triangles are similar.

8. State the ratios of the corresponding sides of each pair of similar triangles. Find each value of x.

a) △XYZ is similar to △PQR.

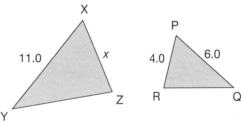

b) △TNC is similar to △EQS.

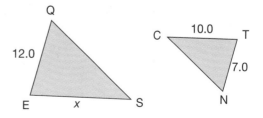

9. State which triangles are similar. Find the values of *x* and *y*.

a)

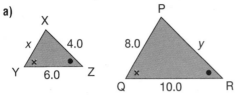

b)

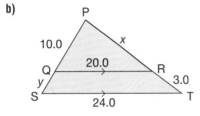

10. For each diagram, name two similar triangles. Find the length of CE.

a)   **b)**

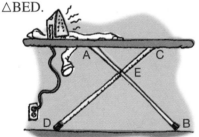

11. For this picture of an ironing board, explain how you know that △AEC is similar to △BED.

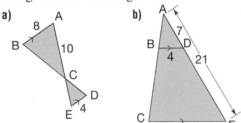

On your own

12. Explain why each pair of triangles are similar. Find the values of *x* and *y*.

a)   **b)**

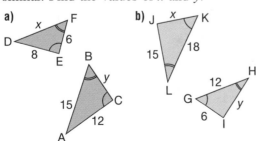

13. Name a pair of similar triangles in each diagram. Explain how you know the triangles are similar.

a)   **b)**

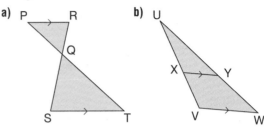

14. Look at the figure in exercise 13a. Suppose you know the length of PR is 8.0 cm, RQ is 6.5 cm, and PQ is 8.7 cm.

a) Could you find the lengths of QT, ST, and QS?

b) If you answered yes to part a, explain how you would find the lengths of the sides of △QST. If you answered no to part a, explain why you could not find the lengths.

15. For each diagram, name two similar triangles. Find the values of *x* and *y*.

a)   **b)**

c)

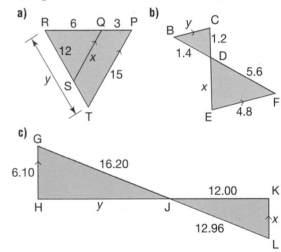

16. In each diagram, the triangles are similar. For each pair of triangles, write the ratio of sides that is equal to $\dfrac{AB}{BC}$.

a)

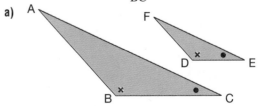

b)

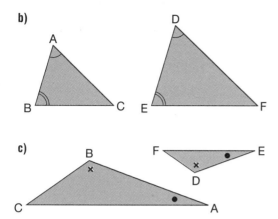

c)

17. The two triangles in each diagram are similar. Find each length represented by x.

a)

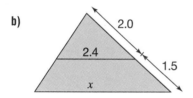

b)

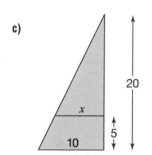

c)

18. Measure AD, AB, AE, and AC. Is △ABC similar to △ADE? Explain.

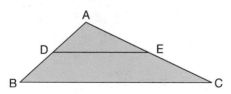

Extend your thinking

19. Name a pair of similar triangles in this figure. Explain how you know the triangles are similar.

20. In each figure, name a pair of similar triangles. Explain how you know they are similar. Find the values of x and y.

a)

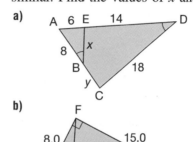

b)

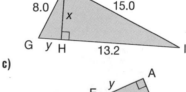

c)

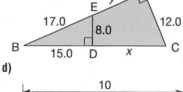

d)

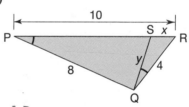

COMMUNICATING

The Ideas

In your journal, write a few sentences to explain whether each statement is true or false. Give examples to support your answers.

a) All similar triangles are congruent.

b) All congruent triangles are similar.

Is a Laser Gun Better for Catching Speeders than a Radar Gun?

A radar gun is used by a police officer to catch speeding motorists. A beam of microwave radiation is directed at an approaching car. This beam spreads out as it travels away from the gun. At a distance of 300 m from the gun, the beam has spread out approximately 32 m. The frequency of the signal, when it reflects off a car and returns to the gun, indicates the speed of the car.

Police officers in New York State have started to use laser guns to catch speeding motorists. The gun emits infrared radiation. This beam does not spread out as much as a radar beam. At a distance of 300 m from the gun, the radiation has spread out approximately 0.9 m.

A radar gun can be used at a range of 200 m. The New York State troopers claim that a laser gun is more effective for controlling speeders. Do you agree? Why?

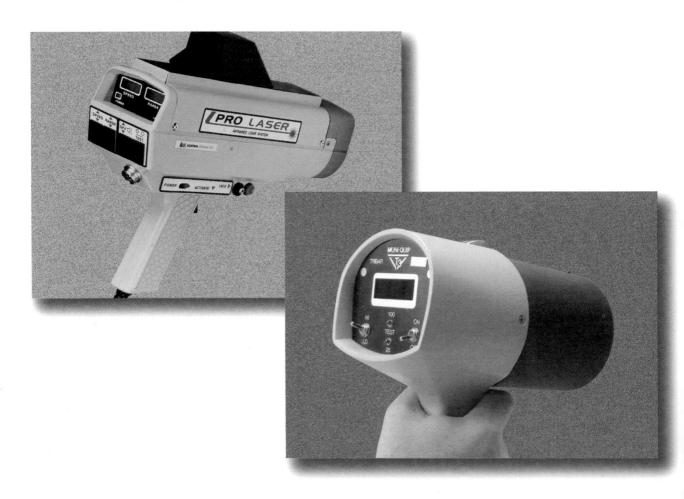

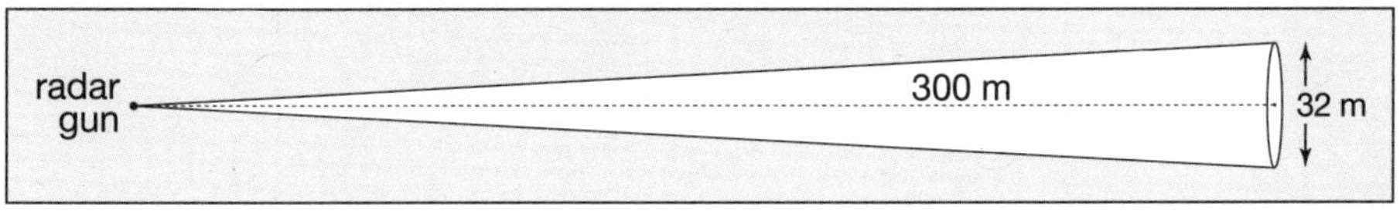

Diagram of radar gun and beam

Diagram of laser gun and beam

Understand the problem

- What are the two types of guns used by police to catch speeders?
- What is meant by one type of gun being "more effective"?
- At a range of 300 m, how many cars could be "caught" in each beam? How many cars could be "caught" in each beam at a range of 200 m?

Think of a strategy

- Use the information for the spread of each beam at 300 m. For each gun, draw a diagram to show the spread at 200 m.

Carry out the strategy

- Use similar triangles. A gun will be the vertex of an isosceles triangle. The equal sides of the triangle will be the edges of the beam.
- What is the length of the base of each triangle when its height is 200 m?

Look back

- At 200 m, how many lanes of traffic would be in the "field of vision" of a radar gun? Could a police officer determine which car was speeding if there was a car in each lane?
- When using a laser gun, would the police officer have the same difficulty? Explain your answer.
- Could the speed of a particular car at a distance of 500 m be determined using a laser gun? How could the police officer be sure she had the right car?
- Some companies sell speed trap detectors to warn drivers they are approaching a speed trap. The companies claim the detector usually alerts the driver that the speed trap is there, before the speed of the car is known by the police officer. This allows the driver to slow down. Why do you think it might be more difficult for a speed trap detector to warn a speeding motorist of a laser trap than a radar trap?

Communicating the Ideas

In your journal, explain why a laser gun is better for catching speeders than a radar gun is.

Developing the Ideas
▶▶ *Through Guided Examples*

Sometimes we wish to know the height of a tree or building, or the distance across a river or pond. None of these heights or distances can be measured directly. We can use similar triangles to calculate the desired height or distance.

Example 1···

The dimensions of the front of a church are shown in the photograph.
Use these dimensions to calculate the slant height AC of the roof.

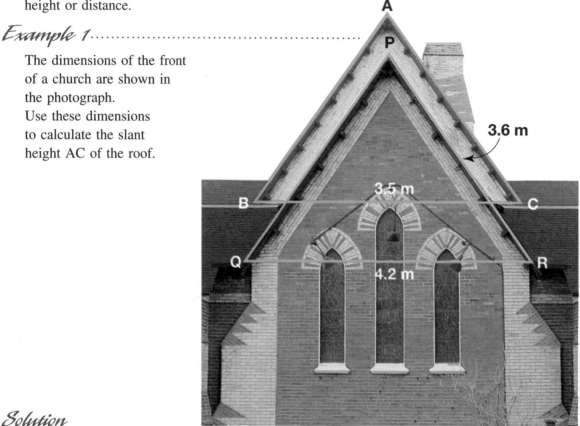

Solution

It appears that AC is parallel to PR, and BA is parallel to QP.
AC and AB intersect the horizontal line BC.
PR and PQ intersect the horizontal line QR. This means that
∠ACB = ∠PRQ and
∠ABC = ∠PQR

So, the third angles in the triangles must be equal.
That is, ∠BAC = ∠QPR
Since corresponding angles are equal,
△ABC is similar to △PQR.
Write the ratio of corresponding sides.
$$\frac{AB}{PQ} = \frac{AC}{PR} = \frac{BC}{QR}$$
Substitute the known lengths.
$$\frac{AB}{PQ} = \frac{AC}{3.6} = \frac{3.5}{4.2}$$

Use the second and third fractions.

$$\frac{AC}{3.6} = \frac{3.5}{4.2}$$

Multiply each side by 3.6.

$$AC = \frac{3.5 \times 3.6}{4.2}$$
$$= 3.0$$

The slant height of the roof is about 3.0 m.

Example 2 ···

A scorecard shows these distances on
the fifteenth hole of a golf course.

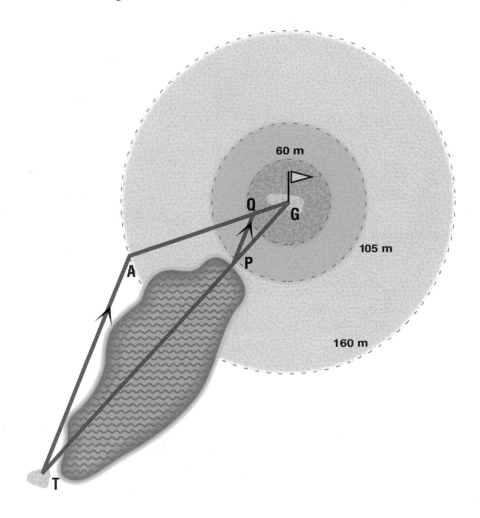

A golfer plans to hit her ball across the pond, from T to P. To find how
far this is, she makes a sketch. The golfer sketches a line segment from
P, parallel to TA, to meet AG at Q. The card indicates the distance QG is
60 m.

a) What is the distance TG from the golfer to the hole?

b) What is the distance TP across the pond?

Solution

a) We can use similar triangles to find TG. The golfer knows that GP is 105 m, QG is 60 m, and GA is 160 m.

Since PQ is parallel to TA,

∠GPQ = ∠GTA ◂ corresponding angles

∠GQP = ∠GAT ◂ corresponding angles

Also, ∠G is common to both triangles.

Since corresponding angles are equal, △GQP is similar to △GAT.

Write the ratios of corresponding sides.

$$\frac{GQ}{GA} = \frac{GP}{GT} = \frac{QP}{AT}$$

Substitute the known lengths.

$$\frac{60}{160} = \frac{105}{GT} = \frac{QP}{AT}$$

Use the first two fractions.

$$\frac{60}{160} = \frac{105}{GT}$$

Invert the fractions.

$$\frac{160}{60} = \frac{GT}{105}$$

Multiply each side by 105.

$$\frac{105 \times 160}{60} = GT$$

$$GT = 280$$

The distance from the golfer to the hole is 280 m.

b) The distance across the pond is

$$TP = GT - GP$$
$$= 280 \text{ m} - 105 \text{ m}$$
$$= 175 \text{ m}$$

Notice that the golfer can calculate the distance TP, even though the golf card only shows distances from points within 160 m of the green.

Working with Mathematics

Not all drawings are to scale.

Something to talk about

1. In *Example 1*, how do we know that the third angles in two triangles are equal, after we have shown that two other pairs of corresponding angles are equal?

2. a) What information do you need about the side lengths of two triangles to know whether the triangles are similar?
   b) What information do you need about the angles of two triangles to know whether the triangles are similar?

3. What information would you need to ensure there is a pair of similar triangles in each figure below?

a)
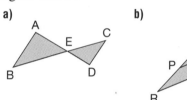

b)

Practice

4. State which triangles are similar. Find the values of *x* and *y*.

a)
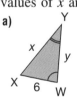
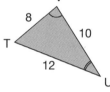

b)
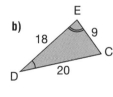
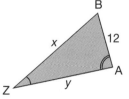

c)
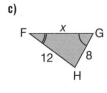

5. In each figure, state which triangles are similar, then find the value of *x*.

a)
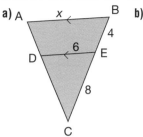

b)
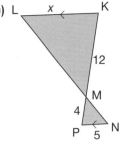

c)
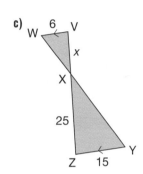

d)
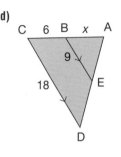

Work together

6. To find the distance PQ across a farm pond, Marty marks out points R and S so that RS is parallel to PQ. By measuring, she finds that RS = 5.7 m, OP = 19.5 m, and OS = 4.2 m. What is the distance PQ?

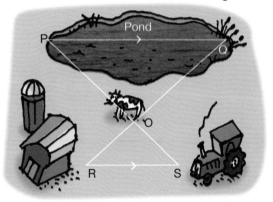

7. Two trees cast shadows as shown. How tall is the evergreen tree?

8. How far is it across the river?

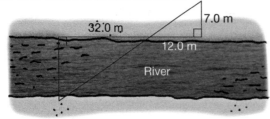

9. How high are the two supports x and y for the conveyor?

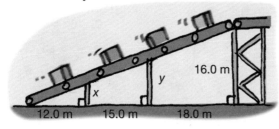

10. The shadow of a telephone relay tower is 32.0 m long on level ground. At the same time, a boy 1.8 m tall casts a shadow 1.5 m long. What is the height of the tower?

11. Karen is 37.5 m from a church. She finds that a pencil, 4.8 cm long, which is held with its base 60 mm from her eye, just blocks the church from her sight. How high is the church?

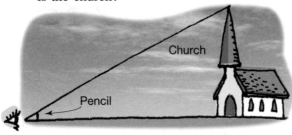

On your own

12. In each figure, state which triangles are similar. Find the values of x and y.

a)

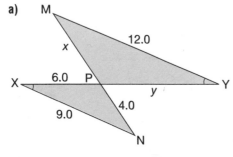

b)

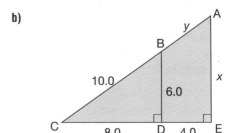

13. To find the distance AB across a pond, surveyors measured the distances shown in the figure. Use these distances to calculate the distance AB.

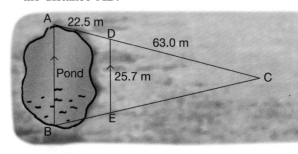

14. To find the distance across a river, Elinka uses the sketch and the measurements shown below. Find the distance across the river.

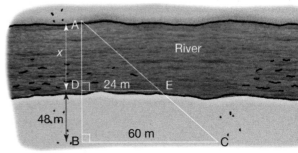

15. To calculate the height of a building, Rudolf uses the height of a pole and the length of the shadows cast by the pole and the building, as shown in the diagram. How tall is the building?

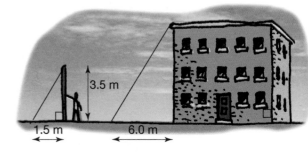

16. Ioana drew the diagram below to determine the length of a bridge over a river. Find the length of the bridge.

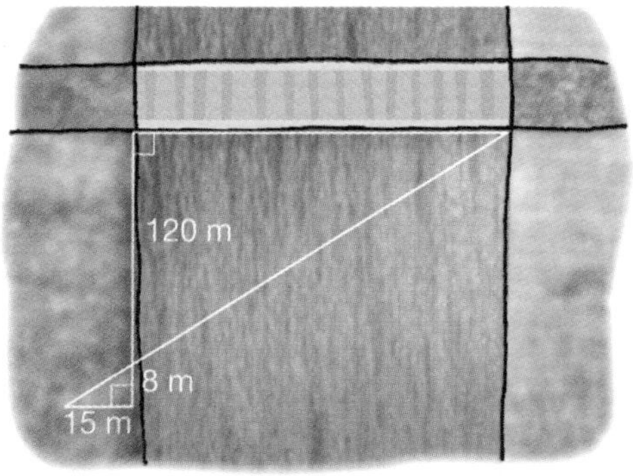

17. A pole 3.8 m high casts a shadow that measures 1.3 m. A nearby tree casts a shadow 7.8 m long. Find the height of the tree.

18. Monique made a scale drawing of her triangular vegetable garden. Two sides of the garden are 7 m and 9 m. The angle between these sides is 75°. Monique's drawing was a triangle with side lengths 14.0 cm and 18.0 cm, with an angle of 75° between them. She drew the third side, then measured it. It was 19.7 cm long. What is the length of the third side of the vegetable garden?

Extend your thinking

19. To determine the height of a tree, Jerry places a 2-m rod 24 m from the tree. He finds that he can align the top of the rod with the top of the tree when he stands 1.9 m from the rod. Jerry's eyes are 1.6 m from the ground. What is the height of the tree?

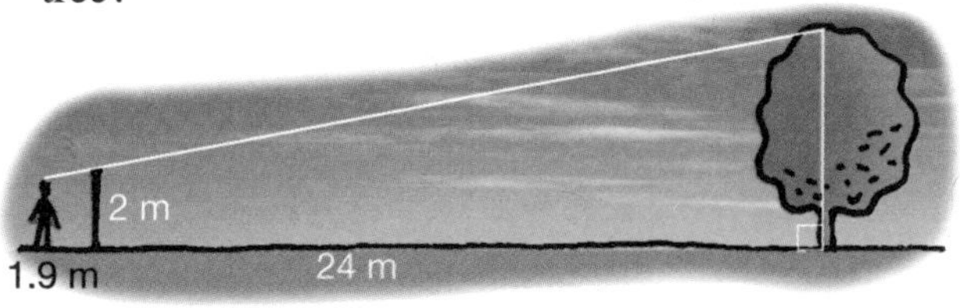

20. The diagram below shows the floor plan of an auditorium. It has 26 rows. Only the first row and every fifth row after the first are shown. There are 60 seats in the first row. The rows are 1 m apart.

a) How many seats are there in Row F? Row K? Row P? Row U? Row Z?

b) Estimate the total number of seats in the auditorium.

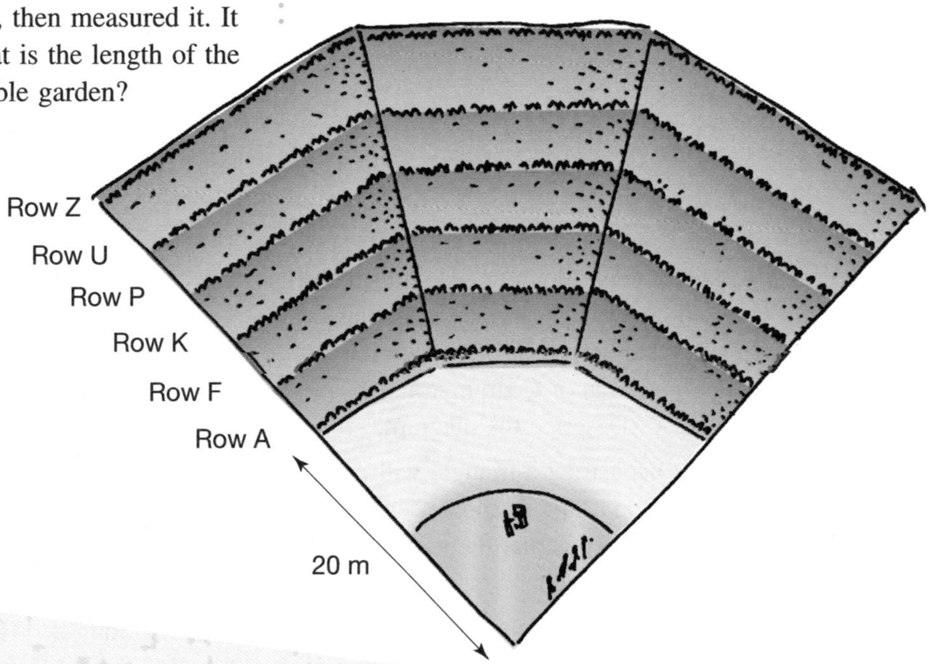

COMMUNICATING The Ideas

In your journal, describe how similar triangles can be used to calculate distances that cannot be measured. Illustrate your explanation with an example.

Review

1. Explain each term.

   a) parallel   **b)** line of symmetry

   c) perpendicular   **d)** altitude

   e) median   **f)** vertex

   g) congruent   **h)** similar

2. Use a ruler and compasses to draw each figure.

   a) a circle with radius 6.5 cm

   b) a triangle with side lengths 6.0 cm, 4.0 cm, and 7.5 cm

   c) a triangle with sides 5 cm, 8 cm, 5 cm

   d) a circle with radius 4 cm

   e) a triangle with sides 8 cm, 15 cm, 17 cm

3. Determine whether each triangle is equilateral, isosceles, or scalene. Explain your answers.

a)    **b)**

c) 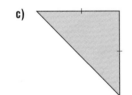   **d)**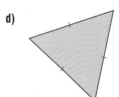

4. Points A and B are 10.0 cm apart. A third point C is 6.0 cm from A and 7.5 cm from B. Use a ruler and compasses to locate the two possible positions of C. Join A and B to the two points C. Describe the diagram.

5. Is it possible to construct a triangle with side lengths 6.5 cm, 9.0 cm, and 11.5 cm? If your answer is yes, construct the triangle. If your answer is no, explain.

6. a) Draw each type of triangle.

     i) scalene   **ii)** right

   b) Construct the medians of each triangle.

   c) In each case, how many medians did you draw?

7. Use a ruler and a protractor to draw each triangle.

   a) angle 74° between sides 7.3 cm and 4.6 cm

   b) side 8.7 cm between angles 57° and 64°

   c) side 10.4 cm between angles 105° and 37°

   d) angle 124° between sides 5.1 cm and 8.5 cm

8. Determine whether each triangle is acute, right, or obtuse.

a)    **b)**

c) 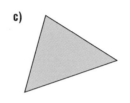   **d)**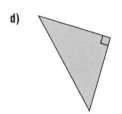

9. Draw each type of triangle.

   a) right isosceles

   b) acute equilateral

   c) obtuse scalene

   d) right scalene

   e) obtuse isosceles

10. At the 8th hole of a golf course, the tee T is 190 m from the hole, H. Craig hits his tee shot 25° to the left. The ball lands at C, 90 m from the tee. Use a scale drawing where 1 cm represents 10 m.

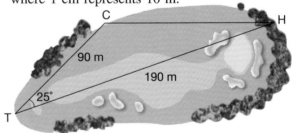

   a) How long is TC in the scale drawing?

   b) How long is TH in the scale drawing?

   c) Construct △CTH to scale.

   d) Measure CH.

   e) Find the distance Craig has to hit the ball to reach the hole.

11. What conditions are needed to determine whether two triangles are congruent?

12. Which triangle is congruent to △ABC? Explain your answer.

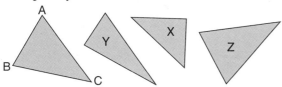

13. Name the equal angles and the equal sides in each pair of congruent triangles.

a)

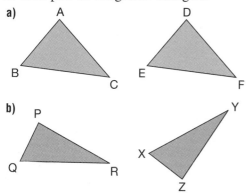

b)

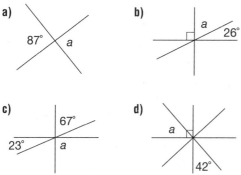

14. Find the measure of each angle represented by *a*. Explain your answers.

a)   **b)**

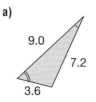

87° *a*

c)   **d)**

67°

23° *a*

15. In △ABC and △XYZ, ∠A = ∠X, BC = YZ, and ∠C = ∠Z. Are △ABC and △XYZ congruent? Give reasons for your answer.

16. Each diagram shows congruent triangles. Find the value of *x*.

a)

9.0

7.2

3.6   *x*

b)

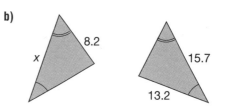

8.2   15.7

x

13.2

17. Which triangle is similar to △DEF? Explain your answer.

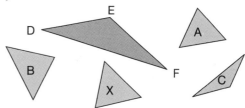

18. Use similar triangles to find each value of *a*.

a)   **b)**

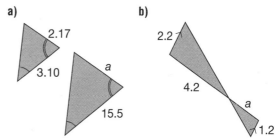

2.17   2.2

3.10   *a*   4.2

15.5   *a*

1.2

19. In this diagram of compasses, explain how you know that △PST is similar to △PQR.

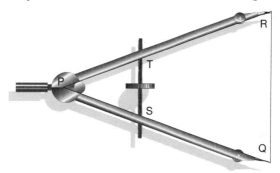

20. How far is it across the pond? The diagram is not to scale.

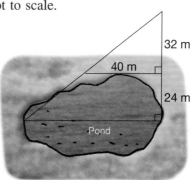

32 m

40 m

24 m

Pond

In Search of the Centre of a Triangle

Where is the centre of a triangle?

The centre of a triangle is in some sense the *average* or typical position of all the points in the triangle. When you studied data management, you learned that there are three kinds of average: the mean, the median, and the mode. You might expect that when you look for the centre of a triangle, you will find different definitions of centre.

In this project, you will investigate four different centres for a triangle.

ACTIVITY 1

Draw a large scalene triangle on chart paper.

Construct the three medians of your triangle.

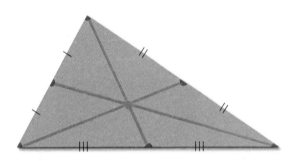

Recall *Linking Ideas* on page 182. You discovered that the three medians intersect at a point. This point is called the *centroid* of the triangle. It is one kind of centre.

Cut out the triangle. Demonstrate that the centroid is the point where the triangle can be balanced on the point of a pencil.

The centroid divides each median into line segments. Measure both segments of one of the medians. What is the ratio of the length of the longer segment to the length of the shorter segment? Check the other medians to see if the same ratio applies to them.

ACTIVITY 2

Copy the triangle you drew in *Activity 1*.

Construct the altitudes of the triangle.

The altitudes intersect at the *orthocentre*.

ACTIVITY 3

Copy the triangle you drew in *Activity 1*. Construct the perpendicular bisectors of the three sides of the triangle. The perpendicular bisectors intersect at a point. This point is called the *circumcentre*.

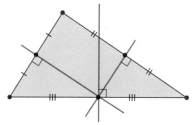

Set your compasses so that their radius is the distance from the circumcentre to one of the vertices. Draw a circle with centre at the circumcentre.

What do you observe about the centre? Why is the centre of the circle called the circumcentre?

The circle you have drawn is called the *circumcircle*. Label it on your triangle. Look up the meaning of the prefix *circum*. Explain why the circle is given this name.

The circumcentre is equidistant from all the vertices of the triangle. Explain how you know this.

ACTIVITY 4

Copy the triangle you drew in *Activity 1*. Draw the bisectors of all three angles. They meet at a point called the *incentre*.

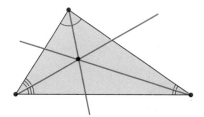

Set your compasses so that their radius is the shortest distance from the incentre to one of the sides. Draw a circle with centre at the incentre. Label it the *incircle*.

What property has the incircle?

What property has the incentre?

ACTIVITY 5

For the last time, copy the triangle from *Activity 1*.

Complete all the previous constructions on this triangle. Label the centroid C, the circumcentre T, the incentre I, and the orthocentre O.

Which three centres lie in a straight line?

ACTIVITY 6

Which centre would you choose if you want a point that is:
a) equidistant from the vertices?
b) equidistant from the sides?
c) the centre of gravity of the triangle?

The Ideas

Write a brief report about the various kinds of centres that triangles have. Include illustrations. Also, include an explanation for the point you would choose as the centre of the triangle.

RIGHT TRIANGLE CALCULATIONS

WHAT'S COMING UP?

DEPARTMENTS

Start With What You Know

To do these exercises you will need a ruler, a protractor, and a calculator.

1. An extension ladder is leaning against a wall. The scale diagram below shows that the base of the ladder is 3.2 m from the wall. The top of the ladder reaches 10 m up the wall.

Scale: 1 cm to 2 m

a) Use your protractor to measure the angle formed by the ladder and the ground.

b) Measure the length of the hypotenuse AB. Use the scale to determine the length of the ladder.

2. Some aerial fire ladders can reach heights of several storeys. The scale diagram below shows a fire ladder inclined at an angle of 77°. Its base is placed 11 m from a building.

Scale: 1 cm to 10 m

a) Measure the length of DF. Use the scale to determine how high up the wall the ladder reaches.

b) Measure the length of the hypotenuse ED. About how long is the ladder?

In this chapter, you will learn a way to solve problems like these using only calculations, without using scale diagrams.

3. In each diagram, the lengths of two sides of a right triangle are given. Use the Pythagorean Theorem to calculate the length of the third side, to the nearest tenth of a centimetre.

a)

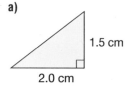

1.5 cm

2.0 cm

b)

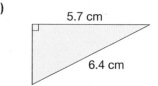

5.7 cm

6.4 cm

4. In each diagram, there are two similar triangles. Determine the value of x, to the nearest tenth of a centimetre.

a)

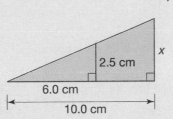

b)

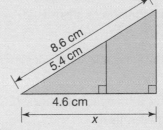

5. Solve for x.

a) $\frac{x}{5} = 9$ **b)** $\frac{x}{0.625} = 2.4$ **c)** $\frac{3}{x} = 8$ **d)** $\frac{7.6}{x} = 0.514$

6. In $\triangle ABC$, BC is half as long as AB.

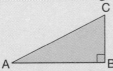

a) If AB = 6 cm, how long is BC?

b) If BC = 5 cm, how long is AB?

c) Recall that the *legs* of a right triangle are the two shorter sides. What are the legs of $\triangle ABC$?

Developing the Ideas

▶ ▶ *Through an Activity*

You will need 1-cm grid paper and a protractor.

Work with a partner.

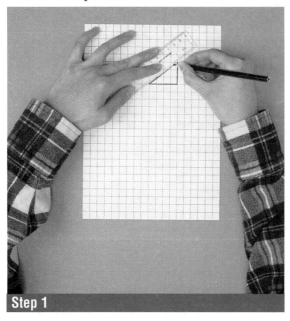

Step 1

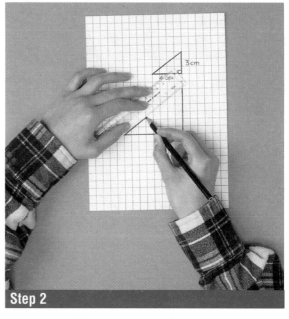

Step 2

Along the lines of the grid paper, draw a triangle so that one side is 3 cm, another side is 4 cm, and the angle between them is 90°.

Repeat Step 1 for a triangle with sides 6 cm and 8 cm, with an angle of 90° between them.

1. Repeat Step 1 for a triangle with sides 9 cm and 12 cm, with an angle of 90° between them.

2. Repeat Step 1 for a triangle with sides 12 cm and 16 cm, with an angle of 90° between them.

3. Use your protractor to measure the other two angles of each triangle. What do you notice?

4. Compare your results with those of other students. Did all of you get the same answers?

5. How are your triangles related?

Keep these diagrams for use later.

In the preceding *Activity*, you drew four similar triangles. The illustration on the right shows many similar right triangles. The diagram below shows four similar right triangles overlapping in the same way. If you cut out the triangles you drew in the *Activity*, you could overlap them the same way. To check that the triangles are similar, we find the ratios of corresponding sides. We use the sides that are opposite ∠A and the sides that are adjacent to ∠A.

$$\frac{BC}{AC} = \frac{3 \text{ cm}}{4 \text{ cm}} = 0.75 \qquad \frac{DE}{AE} = \frac{6 \text{ cm}}{8 \text{ cm}} = 0.75$$

$$\frac{FG}{AG} = \frac{9 \text{ cm}}{12 \text{ cm}} = 0.75 \qquad \frac{HI}{AI} = \frac{12 \text{ cm}}{16 \text{ cm}} = 0.75$$

The ratios are all equivalent. They depend only on the measure of ∠A, and not on the size of the triangles. We call this ratio the *tangent* of ∠A, and write it as tan A.

• • • • • • • • •

If ∠A is an acute angle in a right triangle, then

$$\tan A = \frac{\text{length of side } \textit{opposite } \angle A}{\text{length of side } \textit{adjacent} \text{ to } \angle A}$$

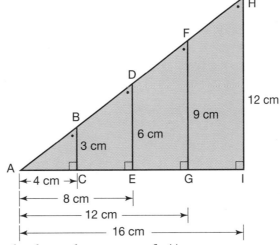

Although the tangent of an angle is defined as a ratio, you can think of it as a number that compares the two shorter sides (or legs) of a right triangle.

For example, in the overlapping triangles above, tan A = 0.75.

This means that in any of the triangles in the diagram, the side opposite ∠A is 0.75 times as long as the side adjacent to ∠A.

▶ ▶ *Through Guided Examples*

To determine tangents of angles, you need a scientific calculator. Your calculator must be in degree mode. To check this, enter 45 and press TAN .

• If your calculator displays 1, it is in degree mode.
• If your calculator does not display 1, you must put it in degree mode.

On some calculators you can do this using DRG . If necessary, consult your manual or ask another student or your teacher to help you put your calculator in degree mode.

Example 1 ....

Determine tan 32°, rounded to 4 decimal places. Draw a diagram to explain the meaning of the result.

Solution

Be sure your calculator is in degree mode.

Press: **32 TAN** to display: **0.624869351**

Rounded to 4 decimal places, tan 32° = 0.6249
We say: "The tangent of 32° is 0.6249."

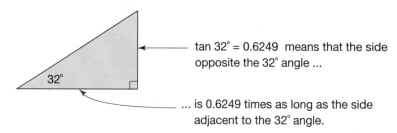

tan 32° = 0.6249 means that the side opposite the 32° angle ...

... is 0.6249 times as long as the side adjacent to the 32° angle.

You can use the tangent ratio to calculate unknown sides in a right triangle.

Example 2 ....

In △ABC, ∠C = 90°, ∠A = 27°, and AC = 5.0 cm. Calculate the length of BC to the nearest tenth of a centimetre.

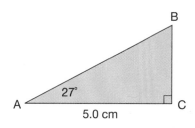

Solution ....

$\dfrac{BC}{AC}$ = tan 27°   ◁ Substitute for AC.

$\dfrac{BC}{5.0}$ ≐ 0.5095   ◁ Press: 27 TAN

BC ≐ 5.0 × 0.5095   ◁ Then press: × 5 =

   ≐ 2.5476

In this triangle, BC ≐ 2.5 cm

Example 3..

In △PQR, ∠R = 90°, ∠P = 27°, and QR = 5.0 cm. Calculate the length of PR to the nearest tenth of a centimetre.

Solution

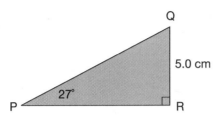

$$\frac{QR}{PR} = \tan 27° \quad \text{◄ Substitute for QR.}$$

$$\frac{5.0}{PR} \doteq 0.5095 \quad \text{◄ Press: 27 } \boxed{\text{TAN}}$$

$$0.5095 \times PR \doteq 5.0 \quad \text{◄ Multiplying each side by PR, and transposing sides}$$

$$PR \doteq \frac{5.0}{0.5095} \quad \text{◄ Dividing each side by 0.5095}$$

$$\doteq 9.8130 \quad \text{◄ Then press: } \boxed{\frac{1}{x}} \boxed{\times} \boxed{5} \boxed{=}$$

In this triangle, PR ≐ 9.8 cm

Compare the results of *Examples 2* and *3*.
In *Example 2*, the length of BC is approximately one-half the length of AC.
In *Example 3*, the length of QR is approximately one-half the length of PR.

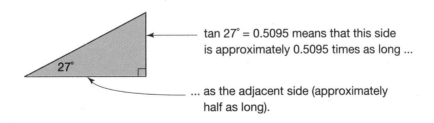

tan 27° = 0.5095 means that this side is approximately 0.5095 times as long ...

... as the adjacent side (approximately half as long).

The keying sequences are for the *TEXAS INSTRUMENTS TI-34* calculator. Other calculators may have different keying sequences. Refer to your calculator's manual to find out.

Example 4 ···

A guy wire supports a tower. The wire forms an angle of 57° with level ground. The wire is attached to the ground 16.5 m from the base of the tower.

a) At what height is the guy wire attached to the tower?

b) How long is the guy wire?

Solution

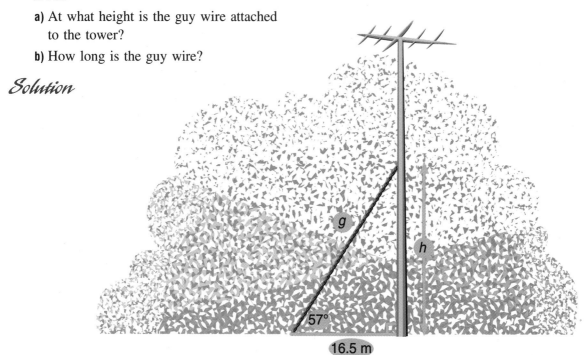

a) Let h metres represent the height at which the guy wire is attached to the tower.

$$\frac{h}{16.5} = \tan 57°$$

$$\frac{h}{16.5} \doteq 1.5398$$

$$h \doteq 16.5 \times 1.5398$$

$$\doteq 25.4077$$

The guy wire is attached to the tower at a height of approximately 25.4 m.

b) Let g metres represent the length of the guy wire.
Use the Pythagorean Theorem.

$g^2 = 16.5^2 + 25.4^2$ ◄ Press: AC/ON 16.5 x^2 + 25.4 x^2 =

$\quad = 272.25 + 645.16$

$\quad = 917.41$

$g = \sqrt{917.41}$ ◄ Then press: $\sqrt{x}$

$\quad \doteq 30.2887$

The guy wire is approximately 30.3 m long.

Working with Mathematics

Something to talk about

1. a) Why are the triangles in the diagram on page 233 similar?

   b) Check that in any of the triangles in the diagram on page 233 the side opposite ∠A is 0.75 times as long as the side adjacent to ∠A.

2. In *Example 1*, tan 32° ≐ 0.625, or $\frac{5}{8}$. Refer to the diagram on page 234. Which of the following statements are true?

   a) The opposite side is approximately $\frac{5}{8}$ of the adjacent side.

   b) The opposite side is approximately $\frac{5}{8}$ of the hypotenuse.

   c) The adjacent side is approximately $\frac{5}{8}$ of the opposite side.

   d) The adjacent side is approximately $\frac{8}{5}$ of the opposite side.

3. Your calculator displays 1 when you press 45 [TAN]. Why do you think this shows your calculator is in degree mode?

4. *Example 2* was solved using the tangent of ∠A, which was the given angle. You can also solve it using the tangent of ∠B.

   a) What is the measure of ∠B?

   b) Solve *Example 2* using tan B instead of tan A.

   c) How does your solution compare with the solution of *Example 2* given on page 234?

5. In right △ABC, AC is the hypotenuse and ∠B = 90°. The length of each side of the triangle is described by the small letter that matches the capital letter of the opposite angle.

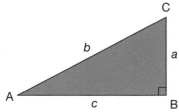

Which of these statements are true?

   a) tan A is the number you multiply *c* by to calculate *a*.

   b) tan A is the number you divide *a* by to calculate *c*.

   c) tan C is the number you multiply *a* by to calculate *c*.

   d) tan C is the number you divide *c* by to calculate *a*.

Practice

6. In each triangle, name the side:

   a) opposite ∠A   b) adjacent to ∠A

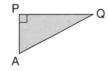 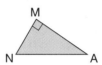

7. In each triangle in exercise 6,

   a) what ratio is used to describe tan A?

   b) state the tangent ratio for the other acute angle in each triangle.

8. Draw △ABC in which ∠B = 90° and tan A has each value.

   a) $\frac{5}{9}$ b) $\frac{3}{7}$ c) $\frac{4}{11}$ d) $\frac{12}{5}$

9. Find tan C for each triangle in exercise 8.

10. Find each value to 3 decimal places.

   a) tan 35°   b) tan 49°   c) tan 65°   d) tan 80°

11. Calculate tan A and tan B.

   a)
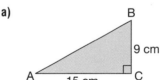

   b)
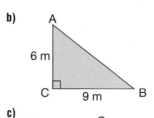

   c)
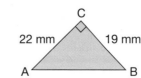

Work together

12. a) Use your calculator to determine each value to 3 decimal places.

    i) tan 20°   **ii)** tan 37°

    iii) tan 55°   **iv)** tan 71°

b) Choose one ratio in part a. Draw a diagram to explain the meaning of the result.

13. Use your calculator to check that the tangent of 25° is approximately 0.4663.

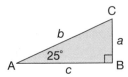

Decide which of the statements below about △ABC are true. If any statements are not true, correct them.

a) If $c = 1$, then $a = 0.4663$.

b) If $c = 100$, then $a = 46.63$.

c) The length of a is 0.4663 times the length of c.

d) The length of c is 2.1445 times the length of a.

14. In △DEF, calculate the length of DE for each given angle.

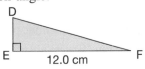

    a) ∠F = 18°   **b)** ∠F = 36°

    c) ∠D = 33°   **d)** ∠D = 9°

15. In △PQR, calculate the length of PQ for each given angle.

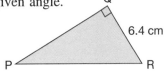

    a) ∠P = 15°   **b)** ∠P = 65°

    c) ∠R = 70°   **d)** ∠R = 45°

16. The foot of a ladder is on level ground 1.2 m from a wall. The angle formed by the ladder and the ground is 77°.

a) Calculate how high up the wall the ladder reaches.

b) Calculate the length of the ladder.

17. The top of a communications tower is 450 m above sea level. From a ship at sea, its angle of elevation is 4°. The diagram is not to scale.

a) How far is the ship from the tower?

b) Suppose the angle of elevation were 8°. How far would the ship be from the tower?

18. In △ABC, ∠C = 90° and AC = 1.

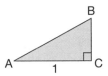

a) Determine the length of BC to 1 decimal place for each value of ∠A.

    i) 15° **ii)** 30° **iii)** 45° **iv)** 60° **v)** 75°

b) Describe what tan A represents on this diagram.

c) Do you think this idea could be used to define the tangent of an acute angle in a right triangle? Explain your answer.

On your own

19. a) Use your calculator to determine each value to 3 decimal places.

    i) tan 30°   **ii)** tan 44°

    iii) tan 63°   **iv)** tan 86°

b) Choose one ratio in part a. Draw a diagram to explain the meaning of the result.

20. In △JKL, calculate the length of JK for each given angle.

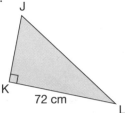

    a) ∠L = 24°   **b)** ∠L = 75°

    c) ∠J = 50°   **d)** ∠J = 22°

21. In △XYZ, ∠Z = 90° and ZY = 2.8 m. Calculate the length of ZX for each given angle.

a) ∠X = 15° **b)** ∠X = 40°
c) ∠Y = 75° **d)** ∠Y = 50°

22. To measure the height of clouds, or "ceiling" at night, airport controllers shine a light vertically. They measure the angle of elevation of the spot of light on the clouds. The diagram is not to scale.

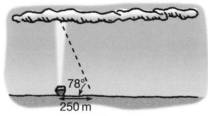

a) How high are the clouds in the diagram?
b) Suppose the angle of elevation were 85°. How high would the clouds be?

23. A gorge with a rectangular cross section is 65 m wide. The angle of depression of a bottom corner when viewed from the opposite edge is 70°.

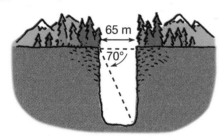

a) How deep is the gorge?
b) Suppose the angle of depression were 80°. How deep would the gorge be?

24. Calculate each value of *x*.

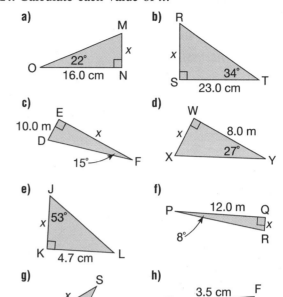

Extend your thinking

25. In isosceles △ABC, AB = AC, ∠B = 70°, and BC = 4 cm. Calculate the area and the perimeter of the triangle.

26. Your calculator should have a TAN⁻¹ function. To use it, you may need to press 2nd TAN.
   a) Enter the following keystrokes and record the results.
   i) 0.6248694 TAN⁻¹   **ii)** 1.5398 TAN⁻¹
   b) Compare the results in part a with the calculations in *Example 1* and *Example 4*. What do you think the TAN⁻¹ key does?
   c) Predict what the result would be if you press: 1 TAN⁻¹. Use your calculator to check your prediction.

COMMUNICATING
The Ideas

How would you explain to someone the meaning of the tangent of an angle? Write an explanation in your journal, and include one or more diagrams.

Explain why the tangent of an angle is useful. Make up one or two examples to illustrate your explanation.

Developing the Ideas

▶▶*Through Discussion*

Recall the four triangles you drew in the preceding section.

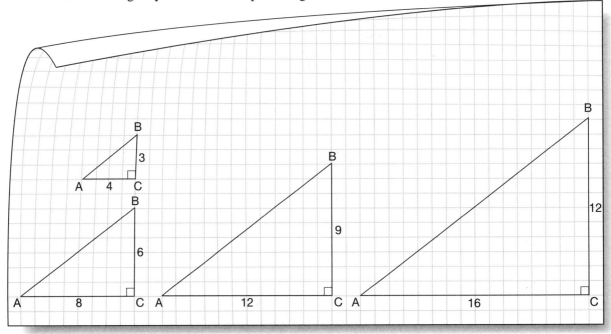

1. **a)** For each triangle, what is the ratio $\dfrac{BC}{AC}$?

   b) What do we call this ratio?

2. For each triangle, what is the measure of $\angle A$? How did you determine this angle?

3. How is the measure of $\angle A$ related to the ratio $\dfrac{BC}{AC}$?

Instead of using a protractor to determine the measure of $\angle A$, we could calculate it using the tangent of $\angle A$. In *Example 1*, you will learn how to do this.

▶▶*Through Guided Examples*

Example 1...

Use the fact that $\tan A = \dfrac{3}{4}$. Calculate the measure of $\angle A$ in the four triangles above.

Solution

Be sure your calculator is in degree mode.

Press: **3** ÷ **4** = TAN⁻¹ to display: **36.86989765**

To the nearest degree, $\angle A = 37°$

Example 2 ···

     i) Draw a diagram to explain what each statement below means.

     ii) Calculate $\angle A$ to the nearest degree.

     iii) Explain how tan A relates to $\angle A$.

       a) $\tan A = \dfrac{5}{8}$ **b)** $\tan A = 1.319$

Solution

    a) i) Draw a right triangle. Label one acute angle, $\angle A$.
        The side opposite $\angle A$ has length 5 units.
        The side adjacent to $\angle A$ has length 8 units.

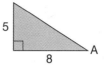

     ii) Express $\dfrac{5}{8}$ as a decimal.

       Press: **5** ÷ **8** = **TAN⁻¹** to display: **32.00538321**
       To the nearest degree, $\angle A = 32°$

    iii)

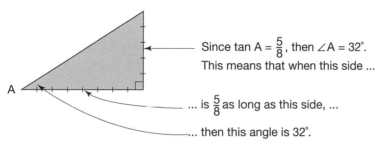

Since $\tan A = \dfrac{5}{8}$, then $\angle A = 32°$.
This means that when this side ...

... is $\dfrac{5}{8}$ as long as this side, ...

... then this angle is 32°.

    b) i) We can write $\tan A = 1.319$ as $\tan A = \dfrac{1.319}{1}$.
        Draw a right triangle. Label one acute angle, $\angle A$.
        The side opposite $\angle A$ has length 1.319 units.
        The side adjacent to $\angle A$ has length 1 unit.

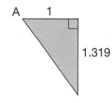

     ii) Press: **1.319** **TAN⁻¹** to display: **52.83241068**
       To the nearest degree, $\angle A = 53°$

    iii)

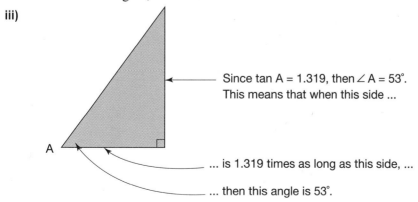

Since $\tan A = 1.319$, then $\angle A = 53°$.
This means that when this side ...

... is 1.319 times as long as this side, ...

... then this angle is 53°.

If you know the lengths of the two legs in a right triangle, you can use the tangent ratio to calculate the angles.

Example 3

In right $\triangle ABC$:

a) calculate $\tan A$, and $\angle A$ to the nearest degree

b) calculate $\tan C$, and $\angle C$ to the nearest degree

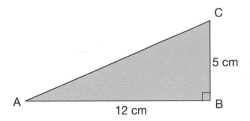

Solution

a) The side opposite $\angle A$ is BC. The adjacent side is AB.

$$\tan A = \frac{BC}{AB}$$
$$= \frac{5}{12}$$ ◁ Press: 5 ÷ 12 =
$$\doteq 0.4166$$ ◁ Then press: TAN⁻¹
$$\angle A \doteq 22.6198°$$

$\angle A$ is 23° to the nearest degree.

b) The side opposite $\angle C$ is AB. The adjacent side is BC.

$$\tan C = \frac{AB}{BC}$$
$$= \frac{12}{5}$$ ◁ Press: 12 ÷ 5 =
$$= 2.4$$ ◁ Then press: TAN⁻¹
$$\angle C \doteq 67.3801°$$

$\angle C$ is 67° to the nearest degree.

We can check the results of *Example 3.*
The sum of the angles in $\triangle ABC$ should be 180°.

$$23° + 67° + 90° = 180°$$

Working with Mathematics

Something to talk about

1. a) In *Example 3*, how are ∠A and ∠C related? Explain.
   b) How are tan A and tan C related? Explain.
   c) Do you think relationships like these would be true for all right triangles?

Practice

2. Determine ∠A to the nearest degree.
   a) tan A = 0.250   b) tan A = 0.709
   c) tan A = 1.365   d) tan A = 3.271
   e) tan A = 0.549   f) tan A = 0.933
   g) tan A = 2.050   h) tan A = 4.556

3. Determine ∠A to the nearest degree.
   a) tan A = $\frac{1}{2}$ b) tan A = $\frac{2}{5}$
   c) tan A = $\frac{4}{3}$ d) tan A = $\frac{5}{4}$
   e) tan A = $\frac{3}{4}$ f) tan A = $\frac{3}{5}$
   g) tan A = $\frac{5}{2}$ h) tan A = $\frac{10}{7}$

4. In each triangle:
   a) calculate tan A, and ∠A to the nearest degree
   b) calculate tan C, and ∠C to the nearest degree
   c) check that the sum of the three angles is 180°

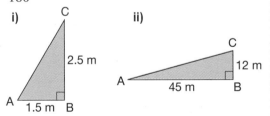

5. In △PQR, calculate tan R and ∠R to the nearest degree for each given length.
   a) PQ = 12.8 cm
   b) PQ = 9.6 cm
   c) PQ = 4.8 cm

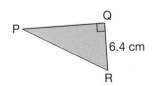

6. In △JKL, calculate tan K and ∠K to the nearest degree for each length of JL.
   a) 8.0 m   b) 12.0 m   c) 14.0 m   d) 21.0 m

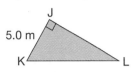

Work together

7. An extension ladder is leaning against a wall. The base of the ladder is 2.5 m from the wall. The top of the ladder reaches 10 m up the wall.
   a) Calculate the measure of the angle formed by the ladder and the ground.
   b) Calculate the length of the ladder.

8. A rectangle measures 6 cm by 3 cm.
   a) Calculate the measures of the two acute angles formed at one vertex by one of the diagonals.
   b) Calculate the measures of the angles of intersection of the diagonals.

9. Look at exercise 17 on page 238. Suppose the ship is 10 km from the communications tower. Calculate the angle of elevation of the top of the tower as seen from the ship.

On your own

10. Calculate tan A and ∠A to the nearest degree, then calculate tan B and ∠B to the nearest degree. Check the results by showing that the sum of the three angles in each triangle is 180°.
   a)

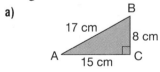

   b)

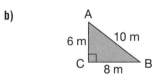

   c)

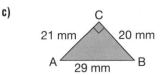

11. In △DEF, calculate tan F and ∠F to the nearest degree, for each given length.
   a) DE = 3.0 cm
   b) DE = 6.0 cm
   c) DE = 9.0 cm

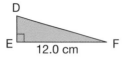

12. A guy wire supports a tower. The wire is attached to the tower at a height of 25.0 m. The guy wire is attached to the ground 8.4 m from the base of the tower. Calculate the measure of the angle formed by the guy wire and the ground.

13. You will need three sheets of paper, a ruler, and a protractor.
   a) Measure the length and the width of the paper.
   b) On one sheet, use your ruler to draw the diagonal (below left). Calculate the measure of the angle formed by the diagonal and the bottom side of the paper.
   c) Take another sheet and fold it in half. Draw a line from one corner to the midpoint of the opposite side (below centre). Calculate the measure of the angle formed by this line and the bottom side of the paper.

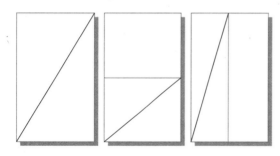

d) Take a third sheet and fold it in half the other way. Draw a line from one corner to the midpoint of the top side (below right). Calculate the measure of the angle formed by this line and the bottom side of the paper.
e) Use your protractor to check your answers to parts b, c, and d.

Extend your thinking

14. An isosceles △PQR has a base QR of length 10 cm and a height of 4 cm. Calculate the measures of the three angles of the triangle.

15. The diagram shows squares arranged side by side to form two rectangles at right angles to each other. The rectangles can be lengthened by adding more squares.

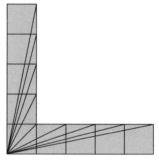

a) Calculate the angle of elevation of each angle shown.
b) How many squares would be needed on the vertical rectangle to have an angle of elevation greater than each angle?
   i) 80°   ii) 85°   iii) 88°   iv) 89°
c) How many squares would be needed on the horizontal rectangle to have an angle of elevation less than each angle?
   i) 10°   ii) 5°   iii) 2°   iv) 1°

The Ideas

In your journal, explain how you can use the tangent of an angle to calculate the measures of acute angles in a right triangle if you know the lengths of two of the three sides. Include the case in which the given sides are the two legs, and also the case in which the given sides are the hypotenuse and one leg.

What Is Wrong with These Diagrams?

Four pieces are arranged to form an 8 by 8 square, like this:

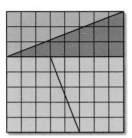

The same four pieces can be arranged to form a 13 by 5 rectangle:

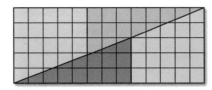

What is the area of the square?   What is the area of the rectangle?

The areas of the square and the rectangle are not equal. How can this happen?

Understand the problem

- Why should the area of the square and the rectangle be equal?
- What are you asked to do?

Think of a strategy

- Calculate some of the angles in the second diagram.

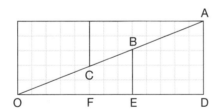

Carry out the strategy

- In △AOD, you know the lengths of AD and OD. Use this information to calculate ∠AOD.
- Calculate ∠BOE and ∠COF the same way.
- What do you notice about the results?

Look back

- The area of the square is 64 square units. The area of the rectangle is 65 square units. Where did the extra square unit come from?

Communicating the Ideas

In your journal, explain how you can show that the area of the square and the area of the rectangle are different.

4.3 THE SINE AND COSINE RATIOS IN RIGHT TRIANGLES

Developing the Ideas

▶▶ *Through an Activity*

You will need the triangles you constructed in the *Activity* on page 232.

1. Label each triangle ABC, with ∠C as the right angle, AC the longer leg, and BC the shorter leg.

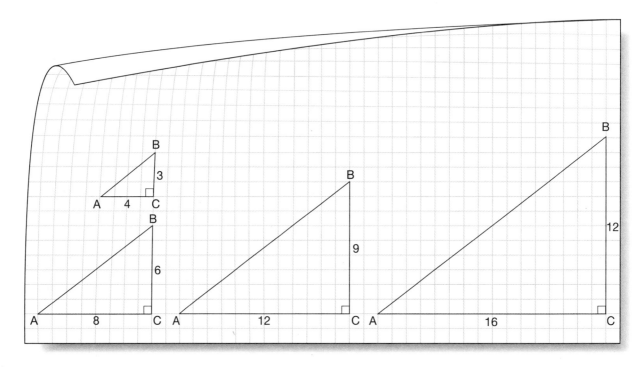

2. For each triangle, measure the length of the hypotenuse AB.

3. For each triangle, write the ratio $\frac{BC}{AB}$. Express the ratio in simplest form where possible. What do you notice?

4. For each triangle, write the ratio $\frac{AC}{AB}$. Express the ratio in simplest form where possible. What do you notice?

5. Compare your results for steps 3 and 4 with those of other students. Did all of you get the same results?

6. Explain why the ratios in step 3 are the same, and the ratios in step 4 are the same.

▶▶ *Through Instruction*

In the previous section, the tangent ratio was defined in a right triangle in terms of the sides opposite and adjacent to an acute angle. Since a triangle has three sides, there are additional ratios involving the hypotenuse. You investigated these ratios in the preceding activity.

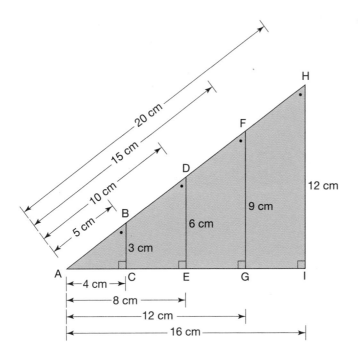

These are the ratios of the sides opposite ∠A
and the hypotenuse:

$\dfrac{BC}{AB} = \dfrac{3 \text{ cm}}{5 \text{ cm}}$ $\qquad$ $\dfrac{DE}{AD} = \dfrac{6 \text{ cm}}{10 \text{ cm}}$

$\quad = 0.6$ $\qquad\qquad\quad = 0.6$

$\dfrac{FG}{AF} = \dfrac{9 \text{ cm}}{15 \text{ cm}}$ $\qquad$ $\dfrac{HI}{AH} = \dfrac{12 \text{ cm}}{20 \text{ cm}}$

$\quad = 0.6$ $\qquad\qquad\quad = 0.6$

The ratios are all equivalent. We call this ratio
the *sine* of ∠A, and we write it as sin A.

These are the ratios of the sides adjacent to ∠A
and the hypotenuse:

$\dfrac{AC}{AB} = \dfrac{4 \text{ cm}}{5 \text{ cm}}$ $\qquad$ $\dfrac{AE}{AD} = \dfrac{8 \text{ cm}}{10 \text{ cm}}$

$\quad = 0.8$ $\qquad\qquad\quad = 0.8$

$\dfrac{AG}{AF} = \dfrac{12 \text{ cm}}{15 \text{ cm}}$ $\qquad$ $\dfrac{AI}{AH} = \dfrac{16 \text{ cm}}{20 \text{ cm}}$

$\quad = 0.8$ $\qquad\qquad\quad = 0.8$

The ratios are all equivalent. We call this ratio
the *cosine* of ∠A, and we write it as cos A.

• • • • • • • • •

If ∠A is an acute angle in a right triangle, then

$$\sin A = \frac{\text{length of side } opposite \text{ } \angle A}{\text{length of hypotenuse}}$$

$$\cos A = \frac{\text{length of side } adjacent \text{ to } \angle A}{\text{length of hypotenuse}}$$

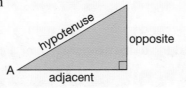

Although the sine and cosine of an angle are defined as ratios, you
can think of them as numbers that compare the shorter sides of a right
triangle with the hypotenuse.

For example, in the overlapping triangles above, sin A = 0.6
This means that in any of the triangles in the diagram, the side *opposite*
∠A is 0.6 times as long as the hypotenuse.

Similarly, cos A = 0.8

This means that in any of the triangles in the diagram, the side *adjacent*
to ∠A is 0.8 times as long as the hypotenuse.

Be sure your calculator is in degree mode.

Example 1 ···

Determine sin 32° and cos 32°, rounded to 4 decimal places. Draw a diagram to explain the meaning of the results.

Solution

Press: **32** SIN to display: **0.529919264**

Press: **32** COS to display: **0.848048096**

Rounded to 4 decimal places, sin 32° = 0.5299
We say: "The sine of 32° is 0.5299."

Also cos 32° = 0.8480
We say: "The cosine of 32° is 0.8480."

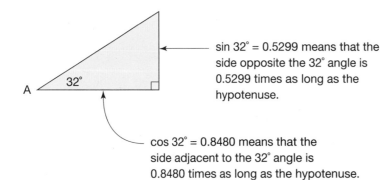

sin 32° = 0.5299 means that the side opposite the 32° angle is 0.5299 times as long as the hypotenuse.

cos 32° = 0.8480 means that the side adjacent to the 32° angle is 0.8480 times as long as the hypotenuse.

Example 2 ···

In right △PQR, ∠R = 90°, ∠P = 24°, and PQ = 7.5 cm. Calculate the lengths of RQ and PR to the nearest tenth of a centimetre.

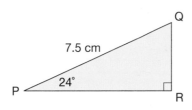

Solution

$$\frac{RQ}{PQ} = \sin 24°$$ 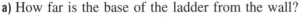 Press: 24 SIN

$$\frac{RQ}{7.5} \doteq 0.4067$$

$$RQ \doteq 7.5 \times 0.4067$$ Then press: × 7.5 =

$$\doteq 3.0505$$

$$\frac{PR}{PQ} = \cos 24°$$ Press: 24 COS

$$\frac{PR}{7.5} \doteq 0.9135$$

$$PR \doteq 7.5 \times 0.9135$$ Then press: × 7.5 =

$$\doteq 6.8515$$

In this triangle, RQ is 3.1 cm and PR is 6.9 cm to the nearest tenth of a centimetre.

Example 3

A 6.1-m ladder leans against a wall. The angle formed by the ladder and the ground is 71°.

a) How far is the base of the ladder from the wall?

b) How far up the wall does the ladder reach?

Solution

a) Let b metres represent the distance from the base of the ladder to the wall. The ladder, with length 6.1 m, forms the hypotenuse of a right triangle.

$$\frac{b}{6.1} = \cos 71°$$

$$\frac{b}{6.1} \doteq 0.3255$$

$$b \doteq 6.1 \times 0.3255$$

$$\doteq 1.9859$$

The base of the ladder is approximately 2.0 m from the wall.

b) Let h metres represent the distance the ladder reaches up the wall.

$$\frac{h}{6.1} = \sin 71°$$

$$\frac{h}{6.1} \doteq 0.9455$$

$$h \doteq 6.1 \times 0.9455$$

$$\doteq 5.7676$$

The ladder reaches approximately 5.8 m up the wall.

Working with Mathematics

Something to talk about

1. Check that in any of the triangles in the diagram on page 247:
   a) the side opposite ∠A is 0.6 times as long as the hypotenuse
   b) the side adjacent to ∠A is 0.8 times as long as the hypotenuse

2. In right △ABC, AC is the hypotenuse and ∠B = 90°.

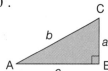

   Which of these statements are true?
   a) sin A is the number you multiply *a* by to calculate *b*.
   b) sin A is the number you multiply *b* by to calculate *a*.
   c) sin A is the number you divide *a* by to calculate *b*.
   d) sin A is the number you divide *b* by to calculate *a*.

3. In *Example 2*, one angle and the hypotenuse were given. The lengths of the other two sides were determined. That is, all three sides are now known.
   a) What theorem relates the three sides of a right triangle?
   b) Use this theorem to check the answers to *Example 2*.

Practice

4. In each triangle, name the side:
   a) opposite ∠A   **b)** adjacent to ∠A
   c) that is the hypotenuse

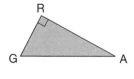

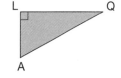

5. For each triangle in exercise 4, what ratio is used to express each value?
   a) sin A   **b)** cos A

6. For the triangles in exercise 4, what ratio is used to express each value?
   a) sin G   **b)** cos G   **c)** sin Q   **d)** cos Q

7. Use your calculator. Determine the sine and cosine of each angle to 4 decimal places.
   a) 76°   **b)** 43°   **c)** 19°   **d)** 81°   **e)** 62°
   f) 14°   **g)** 47°   **h)** 71°   **i)** 9°   **j)** 28°

8. Find each value of *x*.
   a)   **b)**

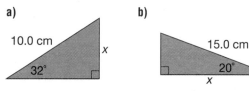

   c)   **d)**

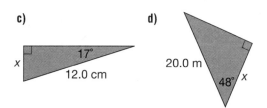

9. In △ABC, ∠B = 90° and AC = 25.0 m. Find AB and BC for each angle.
   a) ∠A = 15°   **b)** ∠C = 65°

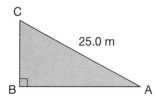

10. In △PQR, ∠Q = 90° and PQ = 15.0 cm. Find PR and QR for each angle.
    a) ∠P = 40°   **b)** ∠R = 61°

Work together

11. **a)** Use your calculator to determine each value to 3 decimal places.
       i) sin 30°   **ii)** cos 22°   **iii)** sin 78°   **iv)** cos 71°
    b) Choose one ratio in part a. Draw a diagram to explain the meaning of the result.

12. Use your calculator to check that the sine of 25° is approximately 0.4226. Decide which of the statements below about △ABC are true. Correct the other statements to make them true.

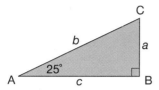

   a) If $b = 1$, then $c = 0.4226$.
   b) If $b = 10\ 000$, then $a = 4226$.
   c) The length of a is 0.4226 times the length of b.
   d) The length of b is 2.3662 times the length of c.

13. In △ABC, ∠B = 90° and AC = 25.0 m. Calculate the lengths of AB and BC for each given angle.
   a) ∠A = 31°   b) ∠C = 78°

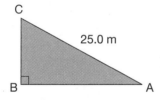

14. A 10.0-m ladder leans against a vertical wall at an angle of 73°.

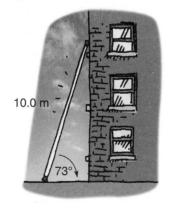

   a) Calculate the height the ladder reaches up the wall.
   b) Calculate the distance from the foot of the ladder to the wall.

15. In △ABC, ∠C = 90° and the hypotenuse AB = 1.

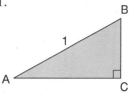

   a) Determine the lengths of AC and BC to 3 decimal places, for each value of ∠A.
      i) 15°   ii) 30°   iii) 45°   iv) 60°   v) 75°
   b) Describe what cos A and sin A represent in this diagram.
   c) Do you think this idea could be used to define the cosine and the sine of an acute angle in a right triangle? Explain your answer.

On your own

16. Use your calculator to check that the cosine of 25° is approximately 0.9063. Decide which of the statements below about △ABC are true. Correct the other statements to make them true.

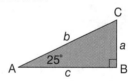

   a) If $b = 1$, then $c = 0.9063$.
   b) If $b = 10\ 000$, then $a = 9063$.
   c) The length of a is 0.9063 times the length of c.
   d) The length of b is 1.1034 times the length of c.

17. a) Use your calculator to determine each value to 3 decimal places.
      i) sin 58°   ii) cos 40°   iii) cos 60°   iv) sin 18°
   b) Choose one ratio in part a. Draw a diagram to explain the meaning of the result.

18. In △PQR, ∠Q = 90° and PQ = 15.0 cm. Calculate the lengths of PR and QR for each given angle.
   a) ∠P = 58°   b) ∠R = 42°

19. A kite has a string 180 m long. The string makes an angle of 41° with the ground. Determine the height of the kite.

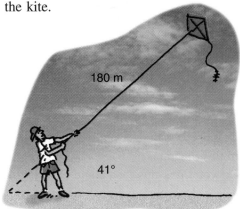

20. A snow plow has a 3.2-m blade set at an angle of 25°. How wide a path will the snow plow clear?

21. A storm causes some 14.0-m hydro poles to lean over. One pole leans at an angle of 72° to the ground. How high is the top of the pole from the ground?

22. Calculate the perimeter of △PQR.

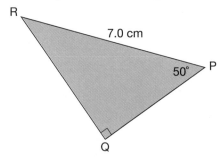

Extend your thinking

23. Use your calculator to check that the cosine of 60° is exactly 0.5.

   a) Use this diagram of an equilateral triangle to explain why cos 60° = 0.5.

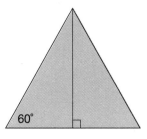

   b) What other trigonometric ratio is exactly 0.5?

24. a) What do you think the $\boxed{\text{SIN}^{-1}}$ and $\boxed{\text{COS}^{-1}}$ keys on your calculator do? Use some examples to check your predictions.

   b) Predict what the result would be if you press: **0.5** $\boxed{\text{SIN}^{-1}}$. Use your calculator to check your prediction.

The Ideas

How would you explain to someone what is meant by the sine and the cosine of an angle? Write an explanation in your journal, including some diagrams.

Explain why the sine and the cosine of an angle are useful. Make up some examples to illustrate your explanation.

Developing the Ideas

▶ ▶ *Through Discussion*

Recall the four triangles you drew and labelled in previous sections.

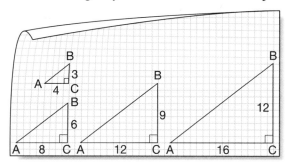

1. **a)** For each triangle, what is the ratio $\dfrac{BC}{AB}$?

   b) What do we call this ratio?

2. For each triangle, what is the measure of $\angle A$? How did you determine this angle?

3. How is the measure of $\angle A$ related to the ratio $\dfrac{BC}{AB}$?

4. **a)** For each triangle, what is the ratio $\dfrac{AC}{AB}$?

   b) What do we call this ratio?

5. How is the measure of $\angle A$ related to the ratio $\dfrac{AC}{AB}$?

Instead of using a protractor to determine the measure of $\angle A$, we could calculate it using the sine of $\angle A$ or the cosine of $\angle A$. In *Example 1*, you will learn how to do this.

▶ ▶ *Through Guided Examples*

Example 1 ....

Calculate the measure of $\angle A$ in the four triangles above using the fact that:

a) $\cos A = \dfrac{4}{5}$ **b)** $\sin A = \dfrac{3}{5}$

Solution

Be sure your calculator is in degree mode.

a) Press: **4** ÷ **5** = cos⁻¹ to display: **36.86989765**
   To the nearest degree, $\angle A = 37°$

b) Press: **3** ÷ **5** = sin⁻¹ to display: **36.86989765**
   To the nearest degree, $\angle A = 37°$

You can use your calculator to find the measure of an angle in a right triangle when you know the lengths of the hypotenuse and one leg.

Example 2

i) Draw a diagram to explain what each statement below means.

ii) Calculate ∠A to the nearest degree.

iii) Explain how cos A relates to ∠A and how sin A relates to ∠A.

    a) $\cos A = \dfrac{3}{4}$ **b)** $\sin A = \dfrac{3}{7}$

Solution

a) i) Draw a right triangle. Label one acute angle, ∠A.
The side adjacent to ∠A has length 3 units.
The hypotenuse has length 4 units.

ii) Express $\dfrac{3}{4}$ as a decimal: $\dfrac{3}{4} = 0.75$

Press: .75 $\boxed{\cos^{-1}}$ to display: **41.40962211**
To the nearest degree, ∠A = 41°

iii)

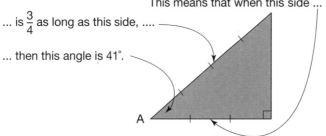

Since $\cos A = \dfrac{3}{4}$, then ∠A = 41°.
This means that when this side ...

... is $\dfrac{3}{4}$ as long as this side, ...

... then this angle is 41°.

b) i) Draw a right triangle. Label one acute angle, ∠A.
The side opposite ∠A has length 3 units.
The hypotenuse has length 7 units.

ii) Express $\dfrac{3}{7}$ as a decimal, then use the method of part a.

Press: **3** $\boxed{\div}$ **7** $\boxed{=}$ $\boxed{\text{SIN}^{-1}}$ to display: **25.37693352**
To the nearest degree, ∠A = 25°

iii)

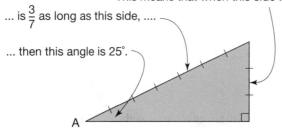

Since $\sin A = \dfrac{3}{7}$, then ∠A = 25°.
This means that when this side ...

... is $\dfrac{3}{7}$ as long as this side, ...

... then this angle is 25°.

If you know the lengths of the hypotenuse and one leg of a right triangle,
you can use the sine or cosine ratios to calculate the angles.

Example 3..

In right △ABC:

a) calculate sin A, and ∠A to the nearest degree

b) calculate cos A, and ∠A to the nearest degree

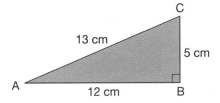

Solution

a) The side opposite ∠A is BC. The hypotenuse is AC.

$$\sin A = \frac{BC}{AC}$$

$$= \frac{5}{13}$$

Press: 5 ÷ 13 =

$$\doteq 0.3846$$

Then press: SIN⁻¹

$$\angle A \doteq 22.6198°$$

∠A is 23° to the nearest degree.

b) The side adjacent to ∠A is AB.

$$\cos A = \frac{AB}{AC}$$

$$= \frac{12}{13}$$

Press: 12 ÷ 13 =

$$\doteq 0.9230$$

Then press: COS⁻¹

$$\angle A \doteq 22.6198°$$

∠A is 23° to the nearest degree.

BOGGLE YOUR **MIND**

You're probably familiar with the classical
tangram set. It consists of 7 pieces that fit
together to form a square. These pieces
can be arranged to form outlines of animals,
people, and geometric figures. But did you
know that a tangram set doesn't have to be
square? You can make or buy a set that
forms a circle, an oval, or even a heart!

Trace the 2 circles on the right. Cut out your
tracings along the white lines. Use all 7
pieces to form each of the figures shown.

Working with Mathematics

Something to talk about

1. a) In *Example 3*, calculate sin C and ∠C, then cos C and ∠C to the nearest degree.
b) How are ∠A and ∠C related?
c) How are these ratios related? Explain.
  i) sin C and cos A
  ii) cos C and sin A
d) Do you think relationships like these would be true for all right triangles?

Practice

2. Determine ∠A to the nearest degree.
a) sin A = 0.602   **b)** cos A = 0.777
c) sin A = 0.956   **d)** cos A = 0.225
e) sin A = 0.200   **f)** cos A = 0.271
g) cos A = 0.872   **h)** sin A = 0.930

3. Use your calculator to calculate each ∠A to the nearest degree.
a) $\sin A = \frac{2}{3}$ **b)** $\cos A = \frac{1}{4}$ **c)** $\cos A = \frac{5}{8}$
d) $\sin A = \frac{3}{7}$ **e)** $\cos A = \frac{4}{5}$ **f)** $\sin A = \frac{2}{9}$

4. Determine ∠A to the nearest degree.
a) $\cos A = \frac{1}{3}$ **b)** $\sin A = \frac{1}{4}$ **c)** $\sin A = \frac{1}{2}$
d) $\cos A = \frac{3}{4}$ **e)** $\sin A = \frac{4}{5}$ **f)** $\cos A = \frac{3}{7}$
g) $\sin A = \frac{5}{8}$ **h)** $\cos A = \frac{8}{9}$ **i)** $\cos A = \frac{5}{6}$

5. Determine ∠K to the nearest degree.
a) cos K = 0.425   **b)** sin K = 0.367
c) sin K = 0.519   **d)** cos K = 0.785
e) sin K = 0.910   **f)** cos K = 0.612

Work together

6. Calculate sin A and ∠A. Calculate sin C and ∠C. Check the results by showing that the sum of the three angles in each triangle is 180°.
a)
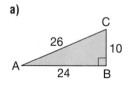
b)
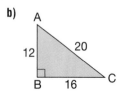

c)
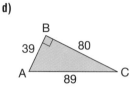
d)

7. a) In △DEF, find:
  i) sin D and ∠D   **ii)** cos F and ∠F
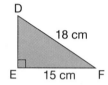

b) How are ∠D and ∠F related?
c) How are sin D and cos F related?
d) How are sin F and cos D related?

8. Calculate ∠A in each triangle.
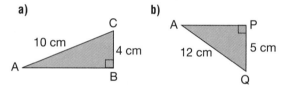
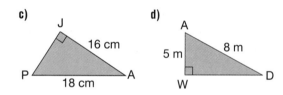

9. In △ABC, ∠B = 90° and AC = 25.0 cm. Calculate ∠A and ∠C for each length.
  a) BC = 10.0 cm   **b)** AB = 17.0 cm

10. In right △PQR, ∠Q = 90°, PR = 4.0 cm, and QR = 3.0 cm. Find the measures of ∠P and ∠R to the nearest degree, and the length of PQ to the nearest centimetre.

11. A guy wire is 15 m long. It supports a television tower. The wire is fastened to the ground 9.6 m from the base of the tower.
  a) Calculate the measure of the angle formed by the guy wire and the ground.
  b) How far up the tower is the guy wire?

12. You may have noticed that all the sine and cosine values in these problems are numbers between 0 and 1. Explain why this is so.

On your own

13. Calculate ∠A in each triangle.

a)

b)

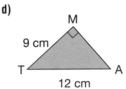

c)

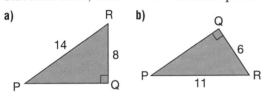

d)

14. Calculate sin P, then ∠P to 1 decimal place.

a)

b)

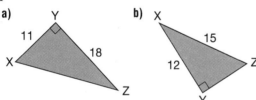

15. For each triangle in exercise 14, determine the measure of ∠R.

16. Calculate cos X, then ∠X to 1 decimal place.

a)

b)

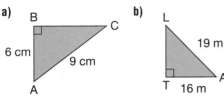

17. For each triangle in exercise 16, determine the measure of ∠Z.

18. In △PQR, ∠Q = 90° and PQ = 15.0 cm. Determine the measures of ∠P and ∠R for each length.

 a) PR = 28.0 cm   **b)** QR = 25.0 cm

19. A 6.0-m ladder is leaning against a wall. The base of the ladder is 1.8 m from the wall.

 a) Calculate the measure of the angle formed by the ladder and the ground.

 b) How high up the wall does the ladder reach?

20. A storm causes some 15.0-m hydro poles to lean over. The top of one of these poles is 12.0 m above the ground. Calculate the measure of the angle between this pole and the ground.

21. Determine the measures of all the angles in isosceles triangles ABC and DEF.

a)

b)

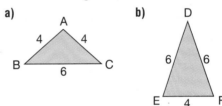

Extend your thinking

22. A 20-m telephone pole was broken as shown. How high above the ground is the break?

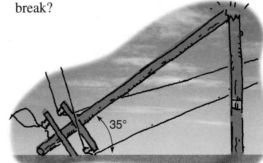

The Ideas

In your journal, explain how you can use the sine or the cosine of an angle to calculate the acute angles in a right triangle if you know the lengths of two of the three sides. Include the case in which the given sides are the hypotenuse and one leg, and also the case in which the given sides are the two legs.

Gondola Lifts

A gondola lift may generally be assumed to follow the hypotenuse of a right triangle. The lift begins at the lower terminal and ends at the upper terminal. If you know the elevations of these terminals above sea level, and the length of the cable, you can calculate the average angle of inclination of the lift.

Upper terminal

Lower terminal

Average angle of inclination

Data for three gondola lifts in Banff and Jasper National Parks are given here.

Banff Sulphur Mountain Gondola Lift

Lower terminal: 1583 m
Upper terminal: 2286 m
Length of track: 1561 m

Lake Louise Gondola

Lower terminal: 1532 m
Upper terminal: 2036 m
Length of track: 3353 m

Jasper Tramway

Lower terminal: 1408 m
Upper terminal: 2500 m
Length of track: 2000 m

Calculate the average angle of inclination for each gondola lift.

WORKING WITH RIGHT TRIANGLES

Developing the Ideas

The work you have been doing in this chapter is part of a branch of mathematics known as *trigonometry* (which means "triangle measurement"). The tangent, sine, and cosine ratios are called *trigonometric ratios*.

▷ ▶ *Through Guided Examples*

If you know an acute angle and the length of one side of a right triangle, you can use a trigonometric ratio to calculate the length of a second side.

Example 1 ....

In △XYZ, XY = 4.5 m, ∠Y = 90°, and ∠X = 28°. Calculate the length of YZ to the nearest tenth of a metre.

Solution

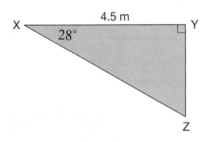

YZ is the side opposite the 28° angle.
XY is adjacent to the 28° angle.
We use the tangent ratio.

$\frac{YZ}{4.5} = \tan 28°$

$YZ \doteq 4.5 \times 0.5317$

$ \doteq 2.3926$

To the nearest tenth of a metre, YZ = 2.4 m

Get 6 toothpicks and some Plasticine
or tape to hold them together.
Use the 6 toothpicks to make
4 equilateral triangles.

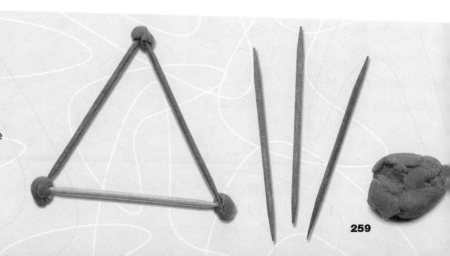

Trigonometry was originally developed to solve problems in navigation. Since then, it has been applied to a wide range of problems in mathematics, science, and industry.

Example 2

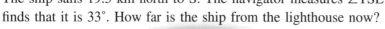

When a ship is at T, the navigator observes a lighthouse L on the shore. The ship sails 19.5 km north to S. The navigator measures $\angle$TSL and finds that it is 33°. How far is the ship from the lighthouse now?

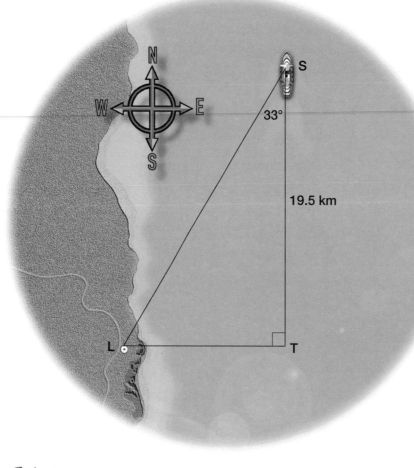

Solution

TS is the side adjacent to the 33° angle.
SL is the hypotenuse.
We use the cosine ratio.

$$\frac{19.5}{SL} = \cos 33°$$

$$\frac{19.5}{SL} \doteq 0.8386$$

$$0.8386 \times SL \doteq 19.5$$

$$SL \doteq \frac{19.5}{0.8386}$$

$$\doteq 23.2510$$

The ship is now approximately 23.3 km from the lighthouse.

If you know the lengths of two sides of a right triangle, you can use a trigonometric ratio to determine one of the acute angles.

Example 3 ·

A truck travels 6 km up a mountain road. The change in height is 1250 m. What is the angle of inclination of the road?

Solution

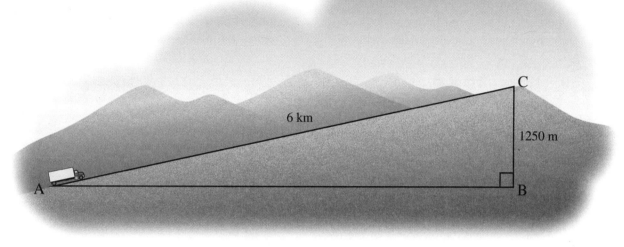

Let ∠A represent the angle of inclination of the road. The length of the road is 6 km, or 6000 m.

Since the given sides are the hypotenuse and the side opposite ∠A, we use the sine ratio.

$$\sin A = \frac{1250}{6000}$$
$$\doteq 0.2083$$
$$\angle A \doteq 12°$$

The angle of inclination of the road is approximately 12°.

BOGGLE YOUR MIND

The surface area of all the windows at the National Gallery of Canada is 28 680 m². It is estimated that a 10 m² window can be cleaned in 2 min. At this rate, how many hours would it take to clean all the windows in the gallery?

Working with Mathematics

Something to talk about

1. Describe two different ways you could calculate each measure.
   a) in *Example 1*, the length of XZ
   b) in *Example 2*, the distance TL
   c) in *Example 3*, the distance AB

2. What trigonometric ratio can be used when you know the lengths of each pair of sides?
   a) the opposite side and the hypotenuse
   b) the adjacent side and the opposite side
   c) the hypotenuse and the adjacent side

3. In △ABC, ∠A = 38°, ∠B = 90°, and AB = 17.3 cm. Which trigonometric ratio would you use to find each length?
   a) BC   b) AC

4. In exercise 3, what are the lengths of BC and AC?

Practice

5. In each triangle, the lengths of two sides are given. Calculate the measures of the two acute angles.
   a)
   b)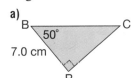

6. In each triangle, one acute angle and the length of one side are given. Calculate the lengths of the other two sides.
   a)
   b)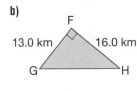

7. Calculate the measures of all unknown angles and sides in these triangles.
   a)
   b)

8. Calculate the measures of all unknown angles and sides in these triangles.
   a)
   b)
   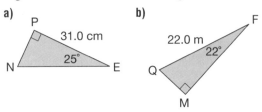

Work together

9. In the diagram, an observer at O is directly opposite a tree at A on the other side of a river. Another tree at B, on the same side of the river as O, is 30 m from O. ∠B = 64° and ∠O = 90°. Calculate the distance from O to A.

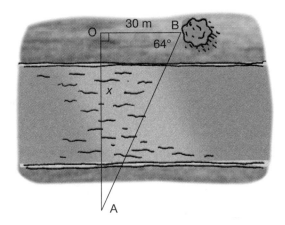

10. A radio tower is 350 m high. The sun's rays make an angle of 39° with the ground. Calculate the length of the tower's shadow.

11. The diagonal of a rectangle is 12 cm long. It makes an angle of 32° with one of the sides. Calculate the length of the rectangle.

12. Solve these two problems in as many different ways as you can:

    Problem 1 The sides of an equilateral triangle are 10.0 cm long. Calculate the lengths of the altitudes, to the nearest millimetre.

    Problem 2 The altitudes of an equilateral triangle are 10.0 cm long. Calculate the lengths of the sides, to the nearest millimetre.

On your own

13. In $\triangle XYZ$, $XY = 9.0$ m, $\angle Y = 90°$, and $\angle Z = 36°$. Find the lengths of the other two sides, and the measure of the third angle.

14. Sharif is flying a kite on a string that is 130 m long. The string makes an angle of 34° with the ground. How high is the kite?

15. The diagram below shows a house designed for solar heating. Calculate the length l of the solar collectors.

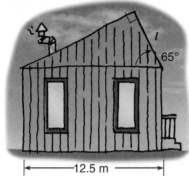

16. The sun's rays are at an angle of 38° to the ground. A tree casts a shadow 42 m long. Calculate the height of the tree.

17. A guy wire supporting a TV tower joins the tower 50 m above the ground to an anchor point 25 m from the base. Calculate the length of the wire, and the measure of the angle it makes with the ground.

18. The diagonal of a rectangle is 15 cm long. It makes a 20° angle with one of the sides. Calculate the width of the rectangle.

19. A rectangle measures 16 cm by 12 cm. Calculate the measure of the acute angle formed by the intersection of its diagonals.

20. An airplane is flying at a speed of 52.0 m/s. It increases its altitude at the rate of 8.0 m/s. At what angle is it climbing?

21. Only one of these three statements about a right triangle is true. Which one is it? Explain why it is true, and why the other two statements are not true.

    Statement 1 If the base is twice as long as the height, then the triangle has 30° and 60° angles.

    Statement 2 If the hypotenuse is twice as long as one of the legs, then the triangle has 30° and 60° angles.

    Statement 3 If one side is twice as long as another side, then the triangle has 30° and 60° angles.

Extend your thinking

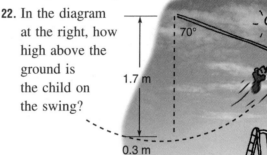

22. In the diagram at the right, how high above the ground is the child on the swing?

23. Calculate the perimeter of a regular pentagon that is inscribed in a circle with radius 10 cm.

COMMUNICATING The Ideas

Make up two problems to explain your answers to these two questions. Record the problems and your solutions in your journal.

- Suppose you know an acute angle and the length of one side of a right triangle. How can you determine the lengths of the other two sides?
- Suppose you know the lengths of two sides of a right triangle. How can you determine the measures of its acute angles?

Using Regular Polygons to Estimate π

The ancient Greek mathematician, Archimedes, was one of the greatest mathematicians who ever lived. In about 240 B.C., he determined an accurate approximation to π. His method is related to exercise 23 on page 263. Recall you calculated the perimeter of a regular pentagon that is inscribed in a circle with radius 10 cm. The diagram for that exercise is reproduced here, but the radius has been changed to 0.5 cm.

Since the pentagon has 5 sides, $\angle\text{BON} - \dfrac{360°}{2 \times 5}$, or $36°$.

Then,

$$\frac{\text{NB}}{\text{OB}} = \sin 36°$$

$$\frac{\text{NB}}{0.5} \doteq 0.587\ 785\ 252$$

$$\text{NB} \doteq 0.5 \times 0.587\ 785\ 252$$

$$\doteq 0.293\ 892\ 626$$

The perimeter of the pentagon is
$10 \times 0.293\ 892\ 626$ cm $= 2.938\ 926\ 26$ cm

1. Calculate the circumference of the circle on page 264. Use the π key on your calculator, or if it does not have one, use π ≐ 3.141 592 65.

   a) How does the perimeter of the pentagon compare with the circumference of the circle?

   b) Repeat the above calculations for a regular polygon with 12 sides. How does the perimeter of this polygon compare with the circumference of the circle?

2. You can use a spreadsheet to calculate the perimeter of a regular polygon for any number of sides. Start a new document in a spreadsheet program, and enter the information below.

TEMPLATE DISK

	A	B
1	Number of sides	12
2	Angle BON	
3	Length of OB	0.5
4	Length of AB	
5	Perimeter of polygon	

   a) In cell B2, type this formula: = 180/B1
   In cell B4, type: = 2*B3*SIN(B2*PI()/180)
   In cell B5, type: = B1*B4
   Format cells B2, B4, and B5 to show several decimal places. Widen column B if necessary.

   b) In the formula in cell B4, notice that the angle in cell B2 is multiplied by PI()/180. The computer needs to do this so that it is working with angles in degrees. Explain the formulas in cells B2, B4, and B5.

3. a) Check that the number in cell B5 agrees with your result from exercise 1b.

   b) Use your spreadsheet to determine the perimeter of a polygon with each number of sides.

   i) 20   ii) 100   iii) 1000   iv) 100 000

   c) How would the perimeter of the polygon with 100 000 sides compare with the circumference of the circle?

   d) How do you think the perimeter of the polygon with 100 000 sides compares with π?

4. When Archimedes performed his work over 2000 years ago, he did not have a calculator or a computer to do the calculations. Instead, he used sophisticated mathematical techniques. He showed that π was slightly greater than $3\frac{10}{71}$. Use your spreadsheet to estimate the number of sides in the polygon Archimedes used.

Review

1. In each diagram, name:
   a) the side opposite ∠L
   b) the side adjacent to ∠L
   c) the side opposite ∠M
   d) the side adjacent to ∠M
   e) the hypotenuse

   i) 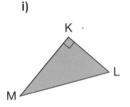   ii)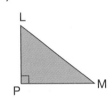

2. Find each value to 4 decimal places.
   a) tan 10°   b) tan 25°   c) tan 33°
   d) tan 67°   e) tan 79°   f) tan 84°

3. Determine the measure of ∠J to the nearest degree.
   a) tan J = 0.425   b) tan J = 1.534
   c) tan J = $\frac{5}{3}$ d) tan J = $\frac{7}{10}$
   e) tan J = 3.271   f) tan J = 7.115

4. Find the sine and cosine of each angle to 4 decimal places.
   a) 13°   b) 44°   c) 23°
   d) 74°   e) 30°   f) 56°

5. Determine the measure of ∠S to the nearest degree.
   a) sin S = 0.788   b) sin S = 0.731
   c) cos S = $\frac{3}{5}$ d) sin S = $\frac{5}{8}$
   e) cos S = 0.899   f) sin S = 0.122

6. In △EFG, calculate the length of FG for each given angle.

   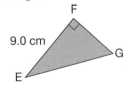

   9.0 cm

   a) ∠E = 20°   b) ∠E = 39°
   c) ∠G = 56°   d) ∠G = 75°

7. In △JKL, for each given length, calculate tan L and ∠L to the nearest degree.

   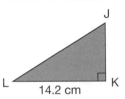

   14.2 cm

   a) JK = 7.1 cm   b) JK = 18.0 cm
   c) JK = 5.4 cm   d) JK = 9.6 cm

8. In △VWX, for each given length, find ∠W and ∠X to the nearest degree.
   a) VW = 12.0 cm   b) VX = 16.0 cm
   c) VX = 14.6 cm   d) VW = 5.0 cm

   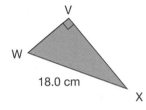

   18.0 cm

9. Calculate sin F, then ∠F to 1 decimal place.
   a)   b)

   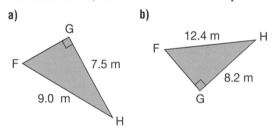

10. For each triangle in exercise 9, determine the measure of ∠H.

11. Calculate each value of x to 1 decimal place.
    a)   b)

    c)   d)

    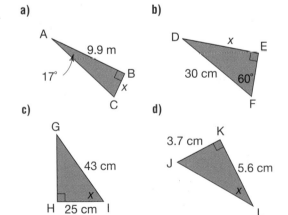

12. Calculate the measures of all unknown angles and sides in these triangles.

a)

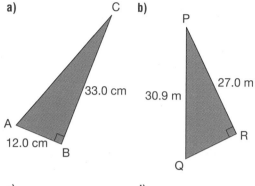

b)

c)

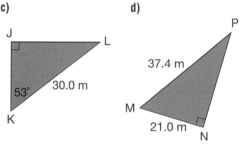

d)

e)

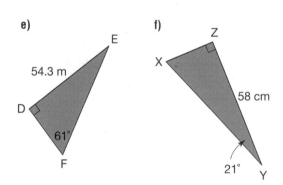

f)

13. Francesco is flying a kite on a string 150 m long. The string makes an angle of 68° with the ground. Suppose Francesco is holding the end of the kite string 2 m above the ground. How high is the kite?

14. The longest side of a rectangle is 22.0 cm. The diagonal of the rectangle makes an angle of 32° with this side.
   a) Calculate the width of the rectangle.
   b) Calculate the length of the diagonal.

15. The sun's rays are at an angle of 42° to the ground. A hydro pole casts a shadow 18 m long. Calculate the height of the pole.

16. A roller coaster climbs vertically 60 m at an angle of 25° from the lowest to the highest point of the track. It then plunges over the high point to begin the ride. Calculate the length of track that brings the roller coaster from the ground to the highest point.

17. A water ski ramp floats on the surface of a lake. The ramp rises 1.5 m above the water at its highest point. The edge of the ramp along the level surface of the water is 5.0 m. Find the length of the ramp, *y*. What is the value of *x*?

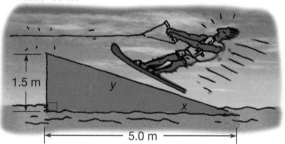

18. The foot of a 6.0-m ladder is on a level patio 1.5 m from the wall, against which it leans.
   a) Find the angle formed by the ladder and the ground.
   b) Calculate how high up the wall the ladder reaches.
   c) Suppose the ladder slips another 0.5 m from the wall. Repeat parts a and b for this situation.

19. Determine the measures of all the angles in isosceles △RST and △VWX, to the nearest degree.

a)

b)

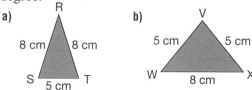

Measuring Inaccessible Heights

Astronomers use trigonometry to measure distances to the moon and stars. You can use trigonometry in a similar way to measure inaccessible heights such as the height of a building.

Work with a partner.

ACTIVITY 1

Making a clinometer

Follow the steps below to make a *clinometer*. You will need a rectangular piece of corrugated cardboard, a metre stick, some tape, a needle and some thread, and a small object to hang from the thread.

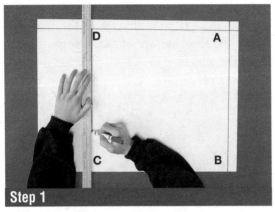

Step 1

Use the metre stick to draw lines near two edges of the cardboard. Measure the distance AB (to the nearest 0.1 cm). Draw another line CD so that ABCD is a square.

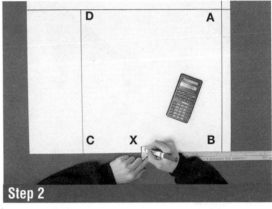

Step 2

Suppose ∠BAX = 30°. Calculate the distance BX to the nearest 0.1 cm. Make a mark on the edge of the cardboard, and label it 30°. Repeat for angles of 5°, 10°, 15°, ... up to 40°.

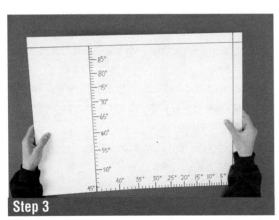

Step 3

Repeat Step 2 for angles of 1°, 2°, 3°, ... up to 44°, but do not label the marks. This gives a scale from 0° to 45° along BC. Make the same scale from 90° to 45° along DC as shown.

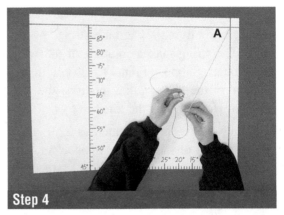

Step 4

Use the needle to pull the thread through the cardboard at A. Secure it on the back with tape. Attach a small object, such as a nut, to the other end of the thread.

To use your clinometer, hold it at an angle as shown. Let the object hang down in front of the scales you made. Look along the top edge of the cardboard. Have your partner read the angle of inclination of the clinometer from the scales.

ACTIVITY 2

Measuring the length of your step

You will need a measuring tape to do this activity.

- Go outside and mark two points in an open area. Measure the distance between these points.
- Walk from one point to the other, counting the number of steps you take. Repeat this a few times. Find the mean number of steps you took to walk from one point to the other.
- You now know the distance you walked, and the mean number of steps you took to walk that distance. Use this information to calculate the mean length of your step.

ACTIVITY 3

Measuring the height of an object

To do this activity, you will need your clinometer from *Activity 1*.

- Find a building, a tree, or some other object whose height you want to measure.
- Stand at a convenient location. Sight along the top edge of the clinometer to line it up with the top of the object. Ask your partner to read the angle of elevation from the scale on the clinometer.
- Pace off the distance to the base of the object. Use your result from *Activity 2* to calculate this distance d metres.
- Use a trigonometric ratio to calculate the height h metres of the object, relative to the level of your eyes. Add the height of your eyes above the ground to determine the height of the object.
- Determine the heights of some other objects.

The Ideas

Write a report that summarizes the results of your investigations. Include diagrams and your calculations in your report.

Cumulative Review

1. For each of the following expressions:
   i) record the key strokes you use to evaluate the expression
   ii) evaluate the expression in a different way and record the key strokes
   iii) explain why one method uses fewer key strokes than the other
   a) $(14.7 - 8.2) \times (42.8 + 14.3)$
   b) $(96.3 - 59.7) \times (15.9 - 7.5)$
   c) $\dfrac{1.5}{5.8 - 10.4}$
   d) $\dfrac{4.9 - 7.7}{3.2 \times (14.3 - 15)}$

2. The table shows the winning times for the women's 200-m race at the Olympic Summer Games.

Year	Time (s)	Winner
1948	24.4	Francina Blankers-Koen
1952	23.7	Marjorie Jackson
1956	23.4	Betty Cuthbert
1960	24.0	Wilma Rudolph
1964	23.0	Edith McGuire
1968	22.58	Irena Szewinska
1972	22.40	Renate Stecher
1976	22.37	Bärbel Eckert
1980	22.03	Bärbel Wöckel (Eckert)
1984	21.81	Valerie Brisco-Hooks
1988	21.34	Florence Griffith Joyner

   a) Plot the data. Construct a line of best fit.
   b) Predict the winning time for the women's 200-m race at the 1992 Summer Games. Find the winning time in an almanac or database. How close was your prediction?

3. A hospital nursery receives 3 newborn infants one morning. What is the probability they are all boys?

4. A busy city hospital receives an average of 5 newborns every day during the months of April, May, and June. Estimate the number of days in these months when the hospital might expect to receive 5 girls.

5. Combine like terms. Evaluate when $x = 4$ and $y = -3$.
   a) $2x + 5x - 3x$
   b) $7y - 8y + y$
   c) $x + x + y + x + y$
   d) $3x + 4x + 2x - 4x - y$
   e) $7x - 5y - 5x - 2y + 4y$
   f) $2y - 3x + 5y + 5x - 7y + x$

6. Solve and check.
   a) $4b - 7 = 3b + 8$
   b) $2k + 3 = -7$
   c) $4(t - 1) = 6$
   d) $3j - 7 = 5j - 1$
   e) $5(2 + w) = -4 - 2w$
   f) $7t - 3 = t - 3$

7. Two consecutive numbers have a sum of 31. What are the numbers?

8. Solve, graph, and check each inequality.
   a) $4b < 8$
   b) $2g + 1 > -7$
   c) $-3k < 5$
   d) $10 > -3t + 1$

9. Name the congruent triangles in each diagram. Explain how you know they are congruent. List pairs of corresponding equal sides.
   a)
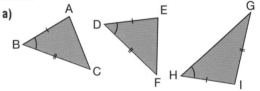
   b)
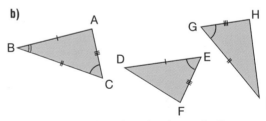

10. Name the similar triangles in each diagram. Explain how you know they are similar.
   a)   b)
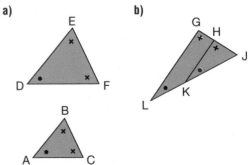

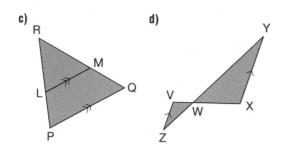

c)

R
M
L
Q
P

d)

Y
V
W
X
Z

11. Use a scale diagram. Determine each value of x.

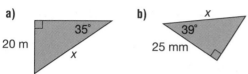

a)

35°
20 m
x

b)

x
39°
25 mm

12. Determine the distance across the pond.

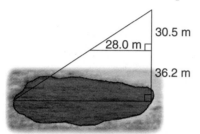

30.5 m
28.0 m
36.2 m

13. Find each value to 4 decimal places.

a) $\sin 28°$ b) $\cos 16°$ c) $\tan 55°$

d) $\cos 51°$ e) $\sin 35°$ f) $\tan 74°$

14. Determine $\angle P$ to the nearest degree.

a) $\tan P = 0.878$ b) $\sin P = 0.325$

c) $\sin P = \dfrac{3}{5}$ d) $\cos P = \dfrac{5}{8}$

e) $\tan P = 1.15$ f) $\cos P = 0.5$

15. In $\triangle JKL$, calculate the length of JK for each given angle.

a) $\angle L = 22°$

b) $\angle L = 33°$

c) $\angle K = 58°$

d) $\angle K = 65°$

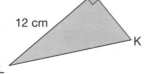

J
12 cm
K
L

16. Calculate sin F, then $\angle F$ to 1 decimal place.

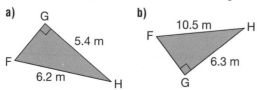

a)

G
5.4 m
F
6.2 m
H

b)

10.5 m
F
H
6.3 m
G

17. Calculate each value of x to 1 decimal place.

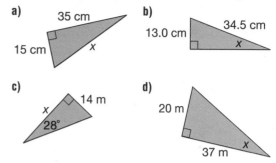

a)

35 cm
15 cm
x

b)

34.5 cm
13.0 cm
x

c)

14 m
x
28°

d)

20 m
37 m
x

18. Calculate the measures of all unknown angles and sides in these triangles.

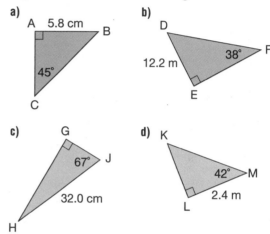

a)

A   5.8 cm   B
45°
C

b)

D
38°   F
12.2 m
E

c)

G
67°   J
32.0 cm
H

d)

K
42° M
2.4 m
L

19. The longest side of a rectangle is 24 cm. Its diagonal makes an angle of 35° with this side.

a) Calculate the width of the rectangle.

b) Calculate the length of the diagonal.

20. A child flying a kite has released 120 m of string. The string makes an angle of 70° with the ground. The child is holding the end of the kite string about 1 m above the ground. About how high is the kite?

21. A building 42.0 m high casts a shadow 53.5 m long. Determine the angle between the sun's rays and the ground at the time the shadow measurement was taken.

POWERS AND ROOTS

WHAT'S COMING UP?

DEPARTMENTS

Start With What You Know

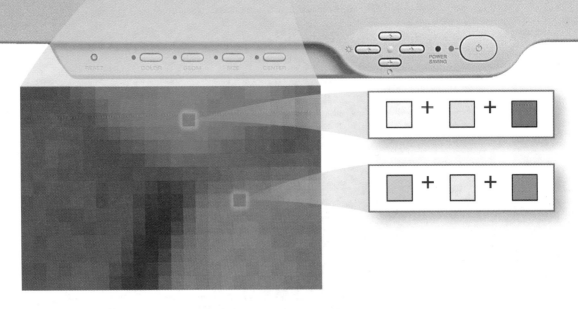

Modern computer monitors can display images with photographic quality. The images are formed by combining different tones of red, green, and blue. Computers are designed so that there are 256 different tones of red, 256 different tones of blue, and 256 different tones of green. This means that the number of different colours a monitor can display is $256 \times 256 \times 256$, or 256^3. The number 256^3 is an example of a *power*.

1. a) What does 256^3 mean? Identify the *base* and the *exponent* of this power.
   b) Use your calculator to multiply $256 \times 256 \times 256$.
   c) Another way to evaluate this power is to use the y^x key on a scientific calculator. Press: **256** y^x **3** $=$
   Does the result agree with your answer in part b?

2. a) What does 2^3 mean?
   b) What does 3^2 mean?
   c) Explain how these pictures illustrate 2^3 and 3^2.

3. Explain what each power means. Write it in decimal form.
   a) 10^3
   b) 3^3
   c) $(-5)^4$
   d) -5^4
   e) 5^4
   f) $-(-5)^4$
   g) 9^3
   h) $(-3)^2$

4. To display the colour red, a computer needs 8 bits of information. There are 2^8 ways the computer can store 8 bits of information. The computer also needs 8 bits of information to display blue, and 8 bits of information to display green.
   a) What does 2^8 mean? Check that $2^8 = 256$.
   b) What does the product $2^8 \times 2^8 \times 2^8$ mean?
   c) Explain how the product in part b relates to the introductory sentences at the top of page 274.

5. Use the Pythagorean Theorem to calculate the length of the third side of each triangle. Round the answer to one decimal place.
   a)
   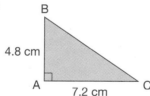
   b)
   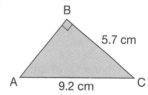

6. The dimensions of a typical computer monitor are 28 cm by 21 cm. Calculate the length of the diagonal.

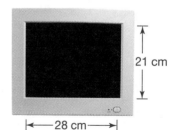

7. Write as a power of 10.
   a) one million
   b) one billion
   c) one trillion

8. Write in scientific notation.
   a) 2.8 million
   b) 28 million
   c) 280 million
   d) 6 billion
   e) 60 billion
   f) 600 billion

9. Write the number of colours a computer monitor can display in two ways.
   a) using the word "million"
   b) in scientific notation

Developing the Ideas

▶▶*Through an Activity*

Powers are defined in terms of repeated multiplication. Do you think powers would have some special properties when they are multiplied or divided? Complete this activity to find out.

Multiplying powers

1. Copy and complete this table.

	Product of powers	Product form	Power form
	$10^2 \times 10^3$	$10 \times 10 \times 10 \times 10 \times 10$	10^5
a)	$10^3 \times 10^4$		
b)	$10^2 \times 10^6$		
c)	$5^4 \times 5^5$		
d)	$5^3 \times 5^1$		
e)	$2^2 \times 2^9$		

2. Extend the table to include five more examples.

3. Based on your results, state a rule for multiplying two powers of 10. Explain why your rule works. Modify the rule to multiply two powers with a different base.

4. Can you use your rule to multiply the powers 2^3 and 3^5? Explain.

Dividing powers

1. Copy and complete this table.

	Quotient of powers	Product form	Power form
	$10^5 \div 10^3$	$\dfrac{10 \times 10 \times 10 \times 10 \times 10}{10 \times 10 \times 10}$	10^2
a)	$10^8 \div 10^5$		
b)	$10^7 \div 10^3$		
c)	$5^{10} \div 5^4$		
d)	$5^5 \div 5^4$		
e)	$9^8 \div 9^3$		

2. Extend the table to include five more examples.

3. Based on your results, state a rule for determining the quotient of two powers of 10. Explain why your rule works. Modify the rule for powers with a different base.

4. Can you use your rule to simplify $5^7 \div 10^4$? Explain.

In the preceding *Activity*, you used the definitions of powers to discover some properties of operations with powers. Now we will explain these properties.

Multiplying powers with positive exponents

Since n^3 means $n \times n \times n$ and n^4 means $n \times n \times n \times n$, we know that

$$n^3 \times n^4 = n \times n \times n \times n \times n \times n \times n$$
$$= n^7$$

Observe that the powers n^3 and n^4 have the same base. We can obtain the product $n^3 \times n^4$ by adding the exponents:

$$n^3 \times n^4 = n^{3+4}$$
$$= n^7$$

1. Do you think we would get similar results if the exponents were different from 3 and 4? What kinds of numbers can the exponents be?

2. Do you think we would get similar results with a different base?

• • • • • • • • •

Exponent Law for a Product of Powers

To multiply powers with the same base, keep the base and add the exponents:

$$n^a \times n^b = n^{a+b}$$

Dividing powers with positive exponents

Since n^5 means $n \times n \times n \times n \times n$ and n^3 means $n \times n \times n$, we know that

$$n^5 \div n^3 = \frac{n \times n \times n \times n \times n}{n \times n \times n}$$
$$= n^2$$

Observe that the powers n^5 and n^3 have the same base. We can obtain the quotient $n^5 \div n^3$ by subtracting the exponents:

$$n^5 \div n^3 = n^{5-3}$$
$$= n^2$$

3. Do you think we would get similar results if the exponents were different from 5 and 3? What kinds of numbers can the exponents be?

4. Do you think we would get similar results with a different base?

• • • • • • • • •

Exponent Law for a Quotient of Powers

To divide powers with the same base, keep the base and subtract the exponents:

$$n^a \div n^b = n^{a-b} \qquad n \neq 0$$

5. In the conclusion above, why is it stated that $n \neq 0$?

Working with Mathematics

Something to talk about

1. Explain the difference between each pair of powers.

   a) 3^2 and 2^3 **b)** 3^4 and 4^3

2. How could each expression be written in a shorter way?

   a) $7^5 \times 7^3$ **b)** $23^{12} \times 23^7$
   c) $16^9 \div 16^4$ **d)** $8^{23} \div 8^{11}$

3. **a)** A wheat field is 10^5 m long and 10^3 m wide. What is its perimeter and area?
   b) A second field, 10 000 m wide, has an area of 10^9 m^2. How long is it?

4. **a)** The tallest tree in the world is about 10^2 m tall. The highest mountain is about 10^4 m. About how many times as high as the tree is the mountain?

   b) Earth's diameter is about 10^7 m. The diameter of the largest known star is 10^{12} m. About how many times as great as the diameter of Earth is the diameter of the largest star?

Practice

5. Express each number as a power of 10.

   a) 1000   **b)** 10 000
   c) 100 000 000   **d)** 1 000 000
   e) 100 000   **f)** 1 000 000 000 000

6. Write each product as a power.

   a) $3^4 \times 3^6$ **b)** $7^4 \times 7^7$
   c) $(-5)^{16}(-5)^9$ **d)** $(2.1)^5(2.1)^{11}$
   e) $(-8)^2(-8)^3(-8)$ **f)** $(-1.7)^4(-1.7)^2(-1.7)$
   g) $\left(\frac{2}{5}\right)^8\left(\frac{2}{5}\right)^{14}$ **h)** $\left(\frac{3}{11}\right)^{21}\left(\frac{3}{11}\right)^{15}$

7. Write each quotient as a power.

   a) $3^8 \div 3^3$ **b)** $2^{16} \div 2^7$
   c) $8^{20} \div 8^5$ **d)** $\dfrac{1.5^{18}}{1.5^6}$
   e) $\dfrac{6^8}{6^2}$ **f)** $\dfrac{(-2)^7}{(-2)^3}$

8. Simplify.

   a) $\dfrac{2^3 \times 2^5}{2^6}$ **b)** $\dfrac{3 \times 3^7}{3^2 \times 3^2}$
   c) $\dfrac{(-5)^{41} \times (-5)^{19}}{(-5)^{50}}$ **d)** $\dfrac{7^{14}}{7^3 \times 7^4}$

Work together

9. Write each expression as a power.

   a) $10^3 \times 10^2$ **b)** $10^8 \times 10^5$
   c) $10^{12} \times 10^4$ **d)** $10^6 \div 10^2$
   e) $10^7 \div 10^2$ **f)** $10^{15} \div 10^3$
   g) $(-4)^{12} \times (-4)^5$ **h)** $3^3 \times 3^8$
   i) $7.2^5 \times 7.2^7$ **j)** $(-5)^7 \div (-5)^5$
   k) $1.2^6 \div 1.2^3$ **l)** $9^4 \times 9^4$

10. **a)** List the powers of 2 up to 2^8. Evaluate each power.
    b) Use your answers from part a. Evaluate each expression without multiplying or dividing.

    i) 16×16 **ii)** 32×4
    iii) $256 \div 8$ **iv)** $128 \div 32$

11. Evaluate.

    a) $(-2)^1$ **b)** $(-2)^2$ **c)** $(-2)^3$ **d)** $(-2)^4$
    e) $(-2)^5$ **f)** $(-2)^6$ **g)** $(-2)^7$ **h)** $(-2)^8$

12. **a)** Describe when $(-2)^n$ will be positive.
    b) Describe when $(-2)^n$ will be negative.

On your own

13. Write each product as a power.

    a) $10^4 \times 10^5$ **b)** $10^8 \times 10$
    c) $10^4 \times 10^6$ **d)** $10^{11} \times 10^3$
    e) $10^6 \times 10^2$ **f)** $10^2 \times 10^7$
    g) $10^3 \times 10^5$ **h)** $10^3 \times 10^5 \times 10^7$
    i) $10^8 \times 10 \times 10^2$ **j)** $10^4 \times 10^2 \times 10^9$

14. Write each expression as a power.

    a) $10^{10} \div 10^3$ **b)** $10^{11} \div 10^6$
    c) $\dfrac{10^9}{10^2}$ **d)** $\dfrac{10^{12}}{10^8}$
    e) $10^5 \div 10^3$ **f)** $10^7 \div 10^4$

15. Write each expression as a power.

   a) $3^3 \times 3^2$ b) $9^4 \div 9^2$

   c) $(-8)^7 \div (-8)^4$ d) $(-2)^4 \times (-2)^3$

   e) $5^4 \div 5$ f) $2^2 \times 2^3 \times 2$

   g) $4^3 \div 4^5$ h) $7^5 \div 7^3$

   i) $11^4 \times 11^3$ j) $5.2^{10} \div 5.2^3$

   k) $(-3)^{11} \div (-3)^6$ l) $\dfrac{8.3^9}{8.3^2}$

16. Write each expression as a power.

   a) $\dfrac{10^5 \times 10^2}{10^3}$ b) $\dfrac{2^7 \times 2^3}{2^4}$

   c) $\dfrac{3^{12}}{3 \times 3^6}$ d) $\dfrac{(-5)^9 \times (-5)}{(-5)^4}$

   e) $\dfrac{6^7 \times 6^{11}}{6^8 \times 6^2}$ f) $\dfrac{(-1)^{10}}{(-1)^5 \times (-1)}$

17. Astronomers estimate that there are about 10^{11} galaxies in the universe. They also estimate that each galaxy contains about 10^{11} stars. About how many stars are there in the universe?

18. Use guess and check to determine the value of n.

   a) $n^3 = 27$ b) $n^5 = 32$

   c) $n^2 = 0.25$ d) $n^3 = 125$

   e) $2^n = 8$ f) $3^n = 81$

   g) $(-3)^n = -27$ h) $2^n = 64$

Extend your thinking

19. a) What is the magic sum for this magic square? Add any row, column, or diagonal.

8	1	6
3	5	7
4	9	2

   b) Change this magic square so that the product of the numbers in any row, column, or diagonal is the same. What is the magic product for your square?

COMMUNICATING The Ideas

To *multiply* two powers with the same base you *add* the exponents. For example, to multiply $10^2 \times 10^4$, you add $2 + 4$, and write 10^6.

What are some other examples in mathematics where you carry out one operation by performing a different operation? In your journal, list your ideas, with examples.

Good News Travels Fast

In the 1970s, there was a TV commercial that used the mathematical idea of doubling to promote shampoo! In the commercial, a woman described how she had used a new shampoo and was so pleased with the results that she told two friends about it. Each of these people told two friends, who told two friends, and so on.

Suppose each step of this process took one day. That is, on day 1, the first woman used the shampoo. On day 2, she told two friends, who then used the shampoo. On day 3, each friend told two friends, who then used the shampoo, and so on. Suppose this process could continue indefinitely, with each person telling two friends who had not heard about the shampoo. How many days would it take until more than one million people had tried the shampoo?

Understand the problem

- How many people would be told about the shampoo on day 3? On day 4?
- How would you calculate the total number of people who had tried the shampoo from day 1 to a particular day?
- What are you asked to find?

Think of a strategy

- Make a table showing the number of people who hear about the shampoo on each of the first 10 days and the total number of people who had tried the shampoo. Look for a pattern in the table.

Carry out the strategy

- Copy and complete a table like this.
- What is the pattern in the numbers in the second column?
- Each number in the third column should be one less than a power of 2. Express each number in the third column in this form. How is the exponent in the power of 2 related to the day number?
- What is the smallest power of 2 that is greater than 1 000 000?
- On what day does the number in the third column exceed 1 000 000?

Day	Number who hear about the shampoo that day	Total number who have tried the shampoo
1	1	1
2	2	$1 + 2 = 3$
3	$2^2 = 4$	$3 + 4 = 7$
4	$2^3 = 8$	$7 + 8 = 15$
5		
6		
7		
8		
9		
10		

Look back

- Write a formula in terms of n for the number of people who have tried the shampoo after n days.

  Use the formula to calculate the number of people who would have used the shampoo in the first 20 days and in the first 25 days.
- Do you think that the number of people who have tried a new product would double each day in real life? Explain.
- Suppose you started with the number one million and divided it in half, then divided the answer in half, and so on. How many divisions would you have to perform until the number you get is less than 1?

Communicating the Ideas

In your journal, describe the doubling process that was suggested in the TV commercial. Tell how many days it would take for more than one million people to have tried the shampoo if the process could continue indefinitely. Describe how you were able to calculate the number of days.

5.2 ZERO AND NEGATIVE EXPONENTS

Developing the Ideas

▶▶ *Through Instruction*

Powers are defined using repeated multiplication: 2^3 means $2 \times 2 \times 2$.

Powers such as 2^0 and 2^{-3} have no meaning according to this definition. It does not make sense to multiply 0 twos together, or to multiply -3 twos together. To give meaning to powers such as 2^0 and 2^{-3}, we define zero and negative exponents so that the exponent laws are satisfied.

Meaning of a zero exponent

Consider these two ways to evaluate $2^3 \div 2^3$.

By applying the power law:

$$\frac{2^3}{2^3} = 2^{3-3}$$
$$= 2^0$$

By evaluating the powers first:

$$\frac{2^3}{2^3} = \frac{8}{8}$$
$$= 1$$

Comparing these results, we define: $2^0 = 1$

We could use any number (except 0) for the base, and obtain the same result. We define a power with a zero exponent as follows.

Zero Exponent

x^0 is defined to be equal to 1, that is, $x^0 = 1$ $(x \neq 0)$.

Meaning of a negative exponent

Consider these two ways to evaluate $2^2 \div 2^5$.

By applying the power law:

$$\frac{2^2}{2^5} = 2^{2-5}$$
$$= 2^{-3}$$

By evaluating the powers first:

$$\frac{2^2}{2^5} = \frac{4}{32}$$
$$= \frac{1}{8}$$
$$= \frac{1}{2^3}$$

Comparing these results, we define: $2^{-3} = \frac{1}{2^3}$

We would get similar results with other numbers for the base and the exponents. We define a power with a negative integer exponent as follows.

Negative Integer Exponent

x^{-n} is defined to be the reciprocal of x^n, that is, $x^{-n} = \frac{1}{x^n}$ $(x \neq 0)$.

You can now evaluate a power with any integer exponent.

Example 1

Evaluate each power.

a) 5^{-2} **b)** $(-3)^{-1}$

Solution

a) $5^{-2} = \dfrac{1}{5^2}$

$\quad = \dfrac{1}{25}$

b) $(-3)^{-1} = \dfrac{1}{(-3)^1}$

$\quad\quad\quad = \dfrac{1}{-3}$

$\quad\quad\quad = -\dfrac{1}{3}$

Example 2

Use a scientific calculator to evaluate each power. Explain each result.

a) 2^{-4} **b)** $(-3)^{-4}$

Solution

a) Press: 2 $\boxed{y^x}$ 4 $\boxed{+/-}$ $\boxed{=}$ to display: **0.0625**

This is the reciprocal of 2^4. That is, $2^{-4} = \dfrac{1}{2^4}$

$\quad\quad\quad\quad\quad\quad\quad\quad = \dfrac{1}{16}$

$\quad\quad\quad\quad\quad\quad\quad\quad = 0.0625$

b) Press: 3 $\boxed{+/-}$ $\boxed{y^x}$ 4 $\boxed{+/-}$ $\boxed{=}$ to display: **0.012345679**

This is the reciprocal of $(-3)^4$, or 81. That is, $(-3)^{-4} = \dfrac{1}{(-3)^4}$

$\quad\quad\quad\quad\quad\quad\quad\quad\quad\quad = \dfrac{1}{81}$

$\quad\quad\quad\quad\quad\quad\quad\quad\quad\quad = 0.012\ 345\ 679$

We can use the exponent laws to simplify expressions involving zero and negative exponents.

Example 3

Write as a single power, then evaluate each expression.

a) $4^{-5} \times 4^3$ **b)** $\dfrac{6^2}{6^{-1}}$ **c)** $\dfrac{3^4 \times 3^{-1}}{3^{-2}}$

Solution

a) $4^{-5} \times 4^3 = 4^{-5\,+\,3}$

$\quad\quad\quad\quad\quad = 4^{-2}$

$\quad\quad\quad\quad\quad = \dfrac{1}{4^2}$

$\quad\quad\quad\quad\quad = \dfrac{1}{16}$

b) $\dfrac{6^2}{6^{-1}} = 6^{2\,-\,(-1)}$

$\quad\quad\quad = 6^3$

$\quad\quad\quad = 216$

c) $\dfrac{3^4 \times 3^{-1}}{3^{-2}} = \dfrac{3^{4\,+\,(-1)}}{3^{-2}}$

$\quad\quad\quad\quad\quad = \dfrac{3^3}{3^{-2}}$

$\quad\quad\quad\quad\quad = 3^{3\,-\,(-2)}$

$\quad\quad\quad\quad\quad = 3^5$

$\quad\quad\quad\quad\quad = 243$

Working with Mathematics

Something to talk about

1. **a)** Explain the meanings of 4^3 and 4^{-3}. How are these expressions similar? How are they different?

   b) Explain the meanings of 4^3 and -4^{-3}. How are these expressions similar? How are they different?

   c) Explain the meanings of $(-4)^3$ and -4^{-3}. How are these expressions similar? How are they different?

2. Evaluate each power.

   a) 1^1 **b)** 1^{-1} **c)** $(-1)^1$ **d)** $(-1)^{-1}$

   e) -1^1 **f)** -1^{-1} **g)** $-(-1)^1$ **h)** $-(-1)^{-1}$

Practice

3. Evaluate each power.

   a) 3^{-1} **b)** 2^{-2} **c)** 7^{-1}

   d) 5^{-2} **e)** 3^{-3} **f)** 6^{-2}

4. Evaluate each power.

   a) -3^{-1} **b)** -2^{-2} **c)** -7^{-1}

   d) -5^{-2} **e)** -3^{-3} **f)** -6^{-2}

5. Evaluate.

   a) 2^3 **b)** 2^{-3} **c)** -2^3 **d)** -2^{-3}

   e) $(-2)^3$ **f)** $(-2)^{-3}$ **g)** $-(-2)^3$ **h)** $-(-2)^{-3}$

6. Evaluate.

   a) $\dfrac{1}{2^{-1}}$ **b)** $\dfrac{1}{3^{-2}}$ **c)** $\dfrac{1}{5^{-2}}$

   d) $\dfrac{1}{2^{-3}}$ **e)** $\dfrac{-1}{4^{-2}}$ **f)** $\dfrac{-1}{10^{-4}}$

7. Evaluate.

   a) $\dfrac{-1}{2^{-1}}$ **b)** $\dfrac{-1}{3^{-2}}$ **c)** $\dfrac{-1}{5^{-2}}$

   d) $\dfrac{-1}{2^{-3}}$ **e)** $\dfrac{1}{4^{-2}}$ **f)** $\dfrac{1}{10^{-4}}$

8. Evaluate.

   a) 0.2^{-1} **b)** 0.25^{-2} **c)** 0.5^{-3}

   d) $(-2)^0$ **e)** 1.5^{-1} **f)** $\left(\dfrac{2}{3}\right)^{-2}$

9. Simplify.

   a) $10^4 \times 10^{-7}$ **b)** $3^{-5} \times 3^{-2}$

   c) $5^{-6} \div 5^2$ **d)** $(-2)^{-5} \times (-2)^{12}$

   e) $4^8 \div 4^{-3}$ **f)** $(-7)^{-3} \div (-7)^{10}$

Work together

10. **a)** Describe the pattern:
    $$3^3, 3^2, 3^1, 3^0, 3^{-1}, 3^{-2}, \ldots$$

    b) Write each number in the pattern as a decimal.

    c) Write the next two numbers in the pattern as powers and as decimals.

11. Evaluate each power.

    a) 2^{-4} **b)** 4^{-2} **c)** 10^{-2} **d)** 5^0

    e) $(-3)^0$ **f)** $(-3)^{-1}$ **g)** $(-5)^{-2}$ **h)** 7^{-3}

12. Evaluate each power.

    a) -2^{-3} **b)** -4^{-2} **c)** -10^{-2} **d)** -5^0

    e) $-(-3)^0$ **f)** $-(-3)^{-1}$ **g)** $-(-5)^{-2}$ **h)** -7^{-3}

13. Write as a single power, then evaluate each expression.

    a) $10^3 \times 10^{-2}$ **b)** $2^{-6} \times 2^2$

    c) $(-7)^{-2} \times (-7)^5$ **d)** $5^{-1} \times 5^{-2}$

    e) $3^{-4} \times 3^5$ **f)** $3^2 \div 3^{-2}$

    g) $\dfrac{2^{-1}}{2^3}$ **h)** $\dfrac{(-3)^{-4}}{(-3)^{-2}}$

    i) $10^{-2} \div 10^2$ **j)** $3^{-3} \times 3^2 \times 3^{-1}$

    k) $\dfrac{2^5}{2^{-1}} \times \dfrac{2^{-3}}{2^2}$ **l)** $\dfrac{4}{4^{-2}} \times \dfrac{2^{-2}}{2^2}$

14. Use guess and check to determine each value of n.

    a) $n^{-2} = \dfrac{1}{9}$ **b)** $n^{-4} = \dfrac{1}{625}$ **c)** $n^{-5} = \dfrac{1}{32}$

    d) $3^n = \dfrac{1}{27}$ **e)** $4^n = \dfrac{1}{16}$ **f)** $7^n = \dfrac{1}{343}$

On your own

15. **a)** Describe this pattern:
    $$2^3, 2^2, 2^1, 2^0, 2^{-1}, 2^{-2}, \ldots$$

    b) Write each number in the pattern as a decimal.

    c) Write the next two numbers in the pattern as powers and as decimals.

16. Evaluate each power.

    a) -3^3 **b)** 3^2 **c)** -3^1 **d)** 3^0

    e) -3^{-1} **f)** 3^{-2} **g)** -3^{-3} **h)** 3^{-4}

17. Evaluate each power.

    a) $(-4)^3$ **b)** $-(-4)^2$ **c)** $(-4)^1$ **d)** $-(-4)^0$

    e) $(-4)^{-1}$ **f)** $-(-4)^{-2}$ **g)** $-(-4)^{-3}$ **h)** $(-4)^{-4}$

18. Write each power as a decimal.

  a) 10^3 **b)** 10^2 **c)** 10^1 **d)** 10^0

  e) 10^{-1} **f)** 10^{-2} **g)** 10^{-3} **h)** 10^{-4}

19. Evaluate each power.

  a) 8^{-2} **b)** 4^{-3} **c)** 2^{-6} **d)** $(-2)^0$

  e) 5^{-3} **f)** 6^{-2} **g)** $(-2)^{-4}$ **h)** $(-3)^{-5}$

20. Two powers are given. Determine which one is greater. Explain your answer. Check with a calculator.

  a) $2^{-3}, 3^{-2}$ **b)** $2^{-4}, 4^{-2}$ **c)** $2^{-5}, 5^{-2}$

21. Use your calculator to evaluate each power. Explain the result.

  a) 4^{-5} **b)** 5^{-4} **c)** 7^{-3}

  d) $(-5)^{-6}$ **e)** $(-6)^{-3}$ **f)** 1.2^{-10}

22. Write as a single power, then evaluate each expression. Explain any patterns you find.

  a) $2^3 \times 2^3$ **b)** $2^3 \times 2^2$

  c) $2^3 \times 2^1$ **d)** $2^3 \times 2^0$

  e) $2^3 \times 2^{-1}$ **f)** $2^3 \times 2^{-2}$

  g) $2^3 \times 2^{-3}$ **h)** $2^3 \times 2^{-4}$

23. Write as a single power, then evaluate each expression. Explain any patterns you find.

  a) $\dfrac{2^3}{2^3}$ **b)** $\dfrac{2^3}{2^2}$ **c)** $\dfrac{2^3}{2^1}$ **d)** $\dfrac{2^3}{2^0}$

  e) $\dfrac{2^3}{2^{-1}}$ **f)** $\dfrac{2^3}{2^{-2}}$ **g)** $\dfrac{2^3}{2^{-3}}$ **h)** $\dfrac{2^3}{2^{-4}}$

24. Use the laws of exponents to evaluate each expression.

  a) $3^2 \times 3^{-1}$ **b)** $5^3 \times 5^{-2}$

  c) $10^{-3} \times 10^{-2}$ **d)** $4^2 \times 4^{-2} \times 4^3$

  e) $2^{-6} \times 2^{-2} \times 2^5$ **f)** $(-1)^1 \times (-1)^2 \times (-1)^3$

  g) $\dfrac{7^{-1}}{7^3}$ **h)** $\dfrac{6^{-2}}{6^{-3}}$

i) $\dfrac{(-3)^0}{(-3)^{-1}}$ **j)** $\dfrac{3^2}{3^{-1}} \times \dfrac{3^{-4}}{3^0}$

k) $\dfrac{5^2}{5^0} \times \dfrac{5^{-1}}{5^3}$ **l)** $\dfrac{2^5}{2^3} \times \dfrac{4^{-1}}{4^{-2}}$

25. Evaluate.

  a) $4^0 \times 4^{-3}$ **b)** $11^3 \div 11^{-1}$ **c)** $9^0 \div 9^{-4}$

  d) $6^{-5} \times 6^3$ **e)** $3^{-1} \div 3^{-4}$ **f)** $5^{-7} \times 5^{10}$

26. Evaluate.

  a) $\dfrac{8^5 \times 8^{-11}}{8^{-3}}$ **b)** $\dfrac{3^{-3}}{3^5 \times 3^{-2}}$

  c) $\dfrac{(-2)^9 \times (-2)^{-6}}{(-2)^2}$ **d)** $\dfrac{2^7}{2^{-2}} \times \dfrac{2^{-4}}{2^3}$

  e) $\dfrac{4^5}{4^2} \times \dfrac{2^6 \times 2^{-4}}{2^{-1}}$ **f)** $\dfrac{3^7}{3^3} \times \dfrac{9^{-2} \times 9^3}{9^2 \times 9^0}$

27. Use guess and check to determine each value of n.

  a) $n^{-2} = \dfrac{1}{25}$ **b)** $n^{-3} = \dfrac{1}{8}$ **c)** $n^{-4} = \dfrac{1}{81}$

  d) $2^n = \dfrac{1}{4}$ **e)** $2^n = \dfrac{1}{64}$ **f)** $5^n = \dfrac{1}{625}$

Extend your thinking

28. There is only one integer n such that $n^n = \dfrac{1}{4}$. What is the integer?

29. Two students were discussing the meaning of -2^{-4}. Their discussion went as follows.

Jean-Marc: I think it means $(-2)^{-4}$. Using my calculator, I get 0.0625.

Ruda: I think it means $-(2^{-4})$. Using my calculator, I get -0.0625.

With which student do you agree? Explain.

30. There are only two different positive integers m and n such that $m^{-n} = n^{-m}$. What are these integers?

COMMUNICATING

The Ideas

Is a power with a negative exponent always negative? Is it always positive? Or, is it sometimes negative and sometimes positive? Make up some examples to investigate these questions. Write your answers in your journal and include your examples.

Developing the Ideas

▶ ▶ *Through Instruction*

Powers of products

We can use the meaning of a positive integer exponent to tell what an expression such as $(2 \times 3)^3$ means.

$(2 \times 3)^3$ means $(2 \times 3) \times (2 \times 3) \times (2 \times 3)$.

Hence, $(2 \times 3)^3 = (2 \times 3) \times (2 \times 3) \times (2 \times 3)$
$$= 2 \times 3 \times 2 \times 3 \times 2 \times 3$$
$$= 2 \times 2 \times 2 \times 3 \times 3 \times 3$$
$$= 2^3 \times 3^3$$

We would get similar results for other numbers inside the brackets or a different exponent. We can write an exponent law for a power of a product.

• • • • • • • • •

Exponent Law for a Power of a Product

$(xy)^n = x^n y^n$ (n is any integer.)

Powers of quotients

Similarly, we can tell what an expression such as $\left(\frac{3}{4}\right)^5$ means.

$\left(\frac{3}{4}\right)^5$ means $\frac{3}{4} \times \frac{3}{4} \times \frac{3}{4} \times \frac{3}{4} \times \frac{3}{4}$.

Hence, $\left(\frac{3}{4}\right)^5 = \frac{3}{4} \times \frac{3}{4} \times \frac{3}{4} \times \frac{3}{4} \times \frac{3}{4}$
$$= \frac{3 \times 3 \times 3 \times 3 \times 3}{4 \times 4 \times 4 \times 4 \times 4}$$
$$= \frac{3^5}{4^5}$$

We would get similar results for other numbers inside the brackets or a different exponent. We can write an exponent law for a power of a quotient.

• • • • • • • • •

Exponent Law for a Power of a Quotient

$\left(\frac{x}{y}\right)^n = \frac{x^n}{y^n}$ (n is any integer, $y \neq 0$.)

Powers of powers

Similarly, we can tell what an expression such as $(2^4)^3$ means.

Hence, $(2^4)^3 = 2^4 \times 2^4 \times 2^4$
$$= 2^{4+4+4}$$
$$= 2^{12}$$

Observe that the exponent of 2^{12} is the product of the exponents in the expression $(2^4)^3$. That is, $(2^4)^3 = 2^{4 \times 3}$

We would get similar results if we use other exponents or another number for the base. We can write an exponent law for a power of a power.

• • • • • • • • • •

Exponent Law for a Power of a Power

$(x^m)^n = x^{mn}$ (m and n are any integers.)

▶▶ *Through Guided Examples*

You can use the exponent laws to simplify expressions involving powers. Since powers involving negative exponents were defined to satisfy the exponent laws, we can use these laws for any integer exponents.

Example 1 .... *Solution* ....

Write each expression as a product of powers.

a) $(5 \times 4)^6$ **b)** $(3 \times 2)^{-4}$

a) $(5 \times 4)^6 = 5^6 \times 4^6$ **b)** $(3 \times 2)^{-4} = 3^{-4} \times 2^{-4}$

Example 2 .... *Solution* ....

Write as a quotient of powers.

a) $\left(\dfrac{3}{5}\right)^4$ **b)** $\left(\dfrac{4}{7}\right)^{-3}$

a) $\left(\dfrac{3}{5}\right)^4 = \dfrac{3^4}{5^4}$ **b)** $\left(\dfrac{4}{7}\right)^{-3} = \dfrac{4^{-3}}{7^{-3}}$

Example 3 .... *Solution* ....

Write as a power.

a) $(4^2)^5$ **b)** $(2^{-2})^3$

a) $(4^2)^5 = 4^{2 \times 5}$ **b)** $(2^{-2})^3 = 2^{(-2) \times 3}$
$ = 4^{10}$ $\phantom{(2^{-2})^3} = 2^{-6}$

Example 4 .... *Solution* ....

Simplify each expression.

a) $(3^8 \div 3^{12})^4$

b) $(4^{-3} \times 4^{10})^{-2}$

c) $(45^3)^{-2} \times (45^2)^{-1}$

a) $(3^8 \div 3^{12})^4 = (3^{8-12})^4$
$\phantom{(3^8 \div 3^{12})^4} = (3^{-4})^4$
$\phantom{(3^8 \div 3^{12})^4} = 3^{(-4) \times 4}$
$\phantom{(3^8 \div 3^{12})^4} = 3^{-16}$

b) $(4^{-3} \times 4^{10})^{-2} = (4^{-3+10})^{-2}$
$\phantom{(4^{-3} \times 4^{10})^{-2}} = (4^7)^{-2}$
$\phantom{(4^{-3} \times 4^{10})^{-2}} = 4^{7 \times (-2)}$
$\phantom{(4^{-3} \times 4^{10})^{-2}} = 4^{-14}$

c) $(45^3)^{-2} \times (45^2)^{-1} = 45^{3 \times (-2)} \times 45^{2 \times (-1)}$
$\phantom{(45^3)^{-2} \times (45^2)^{-1}} = 45^{-6} \times 45^{-2}$
$\phantom{(45^3)^{-2} \times (45^2)^{-1}} = 45^{-6 + (-2)}$
$\phantom{(45^3)^{-2} \times (45^2)^{-1}} = 45^{-8}$

Working with Mathematics

Something to talk about

1. Explain what each expression means.

   a) $(3 \times 2)^4$ b) $\left(\dfrac{3}{2}\right)^4$ c) $(3^2)^4$

   d) $(7 \times 5)^{10}$ e) $\left(\dfrac{1}{8}\right)^5$ f) $[(-2)^6]^2$

Practice

2. Write as a product of powers.

   a) $(5 \times 2)^3$ b) $(5 \times 2)^2$ c) $(5 \times 2)^1$

   d) $(5 \times 2)^0$ e) $(5 \times 2)^{-1}$ f) $(5 \times 2)^{-2}$

3. Write as a product or a quotient of powers.

   a) $(2 \times 5)^{-2}$ b) $(9 \times 3)^{-4}$ c) $(5 \times 7)^{-3}$

   d) $\left(\dfrac{2}{3}\right)^{-2}$ e) $\left(\dfrac{1}{2}\right)^{-4}$ f) $\left(\dfrac{4}{3}\right)^{-3}$

4. Write as a power.

   a) $(2^3)^{-2}$ b) $(3^{-2})^4$ c) $(4^{-3})^2$

   d) $(5^2)^{-4}$ e) $(8^{-5})^0$ f) $(7^{-2})^{-1}$

Work together

5. Use the laws of exponents to write each expression as a product or a quotient of powers.

   a) $(7 \times 3)^2$ b) $(6 \times 5)^4$ c) $(10 \times 3)^5$

   d) $\left(\dfrac{4}{5}\right)^2$ e) $\left(\dfrac{2}{7}\right)^4$ f) $\left(\dfrac{1}{2}\right)^3$

6. Use the laws of exponents to write each expression as a power.

   a) $(4^3)^2$ b) $(7^4)^2$ c) $(3^6)^2$

   d) $(10^3)^4$ e) $(3^2)^6$ f) $[(-10)^2]^3$

7. In exercise 1, you explained the meaning of each expression below. Use your calculator to evaluate each expression in two different ways:

   i) do the operations in brackets first

   ii) use the exponent laws

   Compare the results to see if they are equal.

   a) $(3 \times 2)^4$ b) $\left(\dfrac{3}{2}\right)^4$ c) $(3^2)^4$

   d) $(7 \times 5)^{10}$ e) $\left(\dfrac{1}{8}\right)^5$ f) $[(-2)^6]^2$

8. Use guess and check. Find each value of n.

   a) $(n^2)^2 = 16$

   b) $(n^2)^3 = 729$

   c) $(n^5)^2 = 1024$

On your own

9. Write each expression as a product or a quotient of powers.

   a) $(6 \times 2)^3$ b) $(3 \times 7)^5$

   c) $(9 \times 5)^4$ d) $\left(\dfrac{3}{5}\right)^5$

   e) $\left(\dfrac{1}{3}\right)^3$ f) $\left(\dfrac{3}{2}\right)^{10}$

10. Write as a power.

    a) $(4^3)^2$ b) $(2^5)^5$

    c) $(3^6)^3$ d) $(3^5)^4$

    e) $[(-2)^3]^4$ f) $[(-3.5)^4]^2$

11. Write as a quotient of powers.

    a) $\left(\dfrac{3}{4}\right)^3$ b) $\left(\dfrac{3}{4}\right)^2$ c) $\left(\dfrac{3}{4}\right)^1$

    d) $\left(\dfrac{3}{4}\right)^0$ e) $\left(\dfrac{3}{4}\right)^{-1}$ f) $\left(\dfrac{3}{4}\right)^{-2}$

12. Write as a power.

    a) $(3^3)^3$ b) $(3^3)^2$ c) $(3^3)^1$

    d) $(3^3)^0$ e) $(3^3)^{-1}$ f) $(3^3)^{-2}$

13. Write as a product or a quotient of powers.

    a) $(2 \times 3)^{-3}$ b) $(5 \times 4)^{-2}$

    c) $(6 \times 2)^{-4}$ d) $\left(\dfrac{3}{7}\right)^{-3}$

    e) $\left(\dfrac{1}{3}\right)^{-2}$ f) $\left(\dfrac{5}{8}\right)^{-4}$

14. Write as a power.

    a) $(2^3)^{-2}$ b) $(5^2)^{-1}$

    c) $(3^{-5})^{-2}$ d) $(4^0)^{-2}$

    e) $[(-2)^2]^{-3}$ f) $[(-4)^3]^{-2}$

15. Simplify.

    a) $(7^5 \times 7^3)^2$ b) $(3^2 \times 3^6)^2$

    c) $(8^3 \times 8^5)^7$ d) $(2^3 \times 2^{-6})^4$

    e) $(4^2 \times 4^3)^5$ f) $(11^{-6} \times 11^4)^{-3}$

    g) $(5^4 \times 5^6)^2$ h) $(9^{-3} \times 9^8)^6$

    i) $(25^5 \times 25^{-3})^{-3}$ j) $(2.8^2 \times 2.8^{-3})^{-5}$

16. Simplify.

    a) $(3^8 \div 3^4)^2$ b) $(7^6 \div 7^8)^5$

    c) $(4^7 \div 4^3)^3$ d) $(12^4 \div 12^9)^{-4}$

    e) $(5^{11} \div 5^8)^6$ f) $(2^6 \div 2^9)^{-3}$

    g) $(6^4 \div 6^{-2})^5$ h) $(16^2 \div 16^{-3})^{-3}$

    i) $(10^5 \div 10^{-1})^{-2}$ j) $(3.5^6 \div 3.5^7)^{-1}$

17. Simplify

a) $(3^2)^3 \times (3^4)^2$

b) $(6^5)^2 \div (6^2)^3$

c) $(7^3)^2 \times (7^8)^2$

d) $(15^3)^4 \div (15^{-6})^{-2}$

e) $(8^{-5} \times 8^{13})^{-4}$

f) $(4^{-2})^{-3} \div (4^{-6})^{-2}$

g) $(51^{-3})^{-5} \div (51^{-4})^6$

h) $(29^{-6})^3 \times (29^7)^{-2}$

i) $(101^{-8})^{-4} \div (101^{-7})^{-5}$

18. Use guess and check to determine each value of n.

a) $(n^2)^2 = 81$ b) $(n^2)^3 = 64$ c) $(n^2)^2 = 625$

Extend your thinking

19. Write these numbers in order from least to greatest.

2^{5555} 3^{4444} 4^{3333} 5^{2222}

20. Karol and Yashida were discussing the meaning of 2^{3^2}. Their discussion went as follows:

Karol: I think 2^{3^2} should mean $(2^3)^2$.

Yashida: I think 2^{3^2} should mean $2^{(3^2)}$.

a) Use the rules for the order of operations to simplify $(2^3)^2$ and $2^{(3^2)}$. Are the results the same?

b) Many years ago, mathematicians agreed that, in an expression such as 2^{3^2}, the exponents should be evaluated starting at the top. Using this convention, evaluate each power.

i) 3^{2^2} ii) 2^{2^3} iii) 2^{3^4}

c) Evaluate the powers in this pattern. How many can you evaluate before the calculator shows an error message?

$2^2, 2^{2^2}, 2^{2^{2^2}}, 2^{2^{2^{2^2}}}, 2^{2^{2^{2^{2^2}}}}, \ldots$

d) Find out how your calculator evaluates 2^{3^2}. Does your calculator's method agree with the mathematicians' definition?

COMMUNICATING

The Ideas

In your journal, explain why you add the exponents when you write $2^4 \times 2^3$ as a power, and why you multiply the exponents when you write $(2^4)^3$ as a power.

It has been estimated that the number $2^{2^{2^{2^2}}}$ is so large that it can never be calculated. The answer would require the age of the universe in computer time, and the space of the universe to hold the printout.

Mathematicians have calculated that $2^{2^{2^2}}$ is a number with 19 729 digits. Estimate the number of pages of this book that would be needed to print this number.

Powers of 2

Use only the table of powers of 2 to complete exercises 1 to 5.

$2^{25} = 33\ 554\ 432$	$2^8 = 256$	$2^{-9} = 0.001\ 953\ 125$
$2^{24} = 16\ 777\ 216$	$2^7 = 128$	$2^{-10} = 0.000\ 976\ 562\ 5$
$2^{23} = 8\ 388\ 608$	$2^6 = 64$	$2^{-11} = 0.000\ 488\ 281\ 25$
$2^{22} = 4\ 194\ 304$	$2^5 = 32$	$2^{-12} = 0.000\ 244\ 140\ 625$
$2^{21} = 2\ 097\ 152$	$2^4 = 16$	$2^{-13} = 0.000\ 122\ 070\ 312\ 5$
$2^{20} = 1\ 048\ 576$	$2^3 = 8$	$2^{-14} = 0.000\ 061\ 035\ 156\ 25$
$2^{19} = 524\ 288$	$2^2 = 4$	$2^{-15} = 0.000\ 030\ 517\ 578\ 125$
$2^{18} = 262\ 144$	$2^1 = 2$	$2^{-16} = 0.000\ 015\ 258\ 789\ 062\ 5$
$2^{17} = 131\ 072$	$2^0 = 1$	$2^{-17} = 0.000\ 007\ 629\ 394\ 531\ 25$
$2^{16} = 65\ 536$	$2^{-1} = 0.5$	$2^{-18} = 0.000\ 003\ 814\ 697\ 265\ 625$
$2^{15} = 32\ 768$	$2^{-2} = 0.25$	$2^{-19} = 0.000\ 001\ 907\ 348\ 632\ 812\ 5$
$2^{14} = 16\ 384$	$2^{-3} = 0.125$	$2^{-20} = 0.000\ 000\ 953\ 674\ 316\ 406\ 25$
$2^{13} = 8192$	$2^{-4} = 0.062\ 5$	$2^{-21} = 0.000\ 000\ 476\ 837\ 158\ 203\ 125$
$2^{12} = 4096$	$2^{-5} = 0.031\ 25$	$2^{-22} = 0.000\ 000\ 238\ 418\ 579\ 101\ 562\ 5$
$2^{11} = 2048$	$2^{-6} = 0.015\ 625$	$2^{-23} = 0.000\ 000\ 119\ 209\ 289\ 550\ 781\ 25$
$2^{10} = 1024$	$2^{-7} = 0.007\ 812\ 5$	$2^{-24} = 0.000\ 000\ 059\ 604\ 644\ 775\ 390\ 625$
$2^9 = 512$	$2^{-8} = 0.003\ 906\ 25$	$2^{-25} = 0.000\ 000\ 029\ 802\ 322\ 387\ 695\ 312\ 5$

1. Determine each answer without doing the arithmetic.
   a) 4096×256 **b)** $256 \times 128 \times 64$ **c)** $65\ 536 \div 2048$
   d) $\dfrac{262\ 144 \times 8192 \times 512}{16\ 384 \times 64}$ **e)** 64^3 **f)** 4^{10}

2. a) Find as many patterns as you can in the final digits of the powers of 2.
   b) Explain why the patterns occur.

3. Determine each answer without doing the arithmetic.
   a) 0.125×0.0625 **b)** $131\ 072 \times 0.007\ 812\ 5$
   c) $256 \times 0.003\ 906\ 25$ **d)** $0.015\ 625 \div 0.0625$
   e) $16\ 384 \div 0.031\ 25$ **f)** $0.003\ 906\ 25 \div 4096$
   g) 0.25^5 **h)** 0.125^4

4. a) Use the table of powers of 2 to create a table of powers of 4.
   b) Create a table of powers of 8.

5. a) Find a power of 2 that is very close to a power of 10.
   Write the result in the form $2^m \doteq 10^n$.
   b) Estimate each power below as a power of 10.
   Use a calculator to check your results.
      i) 2^{30} **ii)** 2^{40} **iii)** 2^{50}

Half-life on a Spreadsheet

IN APRIL 1986, THERE WAS AN ACCIDENT AT A NUCLEAR POWER PLANT IN CHERNOBYL. The atmosphere was contaminated with radioactive material including iodine-131. This substance has a half-life of about 8 days. This means that every 8 days, half of the iodine decays to a form that is not radioactive.

What if 100 g of iodine-131 were released? How long would it take for less than 1 g to remain?

You can develop a simple spreadsheet model to analyze this situation. Set up your spreadsheet as shown and answer the questions below.

TEMPLATE DISK

	A	B
1	Radioactive decay	
2		
3	Remaining iodine-131	Time units in days
4		0
5	=A4*0.5	=B4+8

1. **a)** What does each formula in cells A5 and B5 tell the computer to do?
   b) Enter 100 in cell A4 to indicate that 100 g is the mass of iodine-131 released. What values does the computer display in cells A5 and B5?

2. Copy the formulas in cells A5 and B5 to the next 20 cells below. Some of the cells in column A may display answers in scientific notation, such as 7.62939453125e−6. To avoid this, you can widen column A and change its format to display numbers as fixed decimals to 10 places. Use your spreadsheet to determine how many days it would take for the iodine-131 to decay to less than 1 g.

3. In how many days will 1000 g of iodine-131 decay to less than 1 g? Change the spreadsheet to answer this question.

4. In cell C5 enter the formula =A5/1000. This tells the computer to calculate and display the quotient of the amount of iodine-131 left after 1 time unit and the initial amount. Copy this formula to all the rows in column C. What pattern do you notice?

Mathematics & Technology

Linking Ideas

5.4 POWER EXPRESSIONS INVOLVING VARIABLES

Developing the Ideas

Through Instruction

In the previous sections we developed several exponent laws.

Here is a summary of the exponent laws for integer exponents.

Exponent law description	Algebraic representation
To multiply powers with the same base, add the exponents.	$n^a \times n^b = n^{a+b}$
To divide powers with the same base, subtract the exponents.	$n^a \div n^b = n^{a-b}, n \neq 0$
To determine the power of a power, multiply the exponents.	$(n^a)^b = n^{ab}$
The power of a product is equal to the product of the powers.	$(m \times n)^a = m^a \times n^a$
The power of a quotient is equal to the quotient of the powers.	$\left(\frac{m}{n}\right)^a = \frac{m^a}{n^a}, n \neq 0$

We have also developed meanings for zero and negative exponents.

x^0 is defined to be equal to 1.

$x^0 = 1, x \neq 0$

x^{-n} is defined to be the reciprocal of x^n.

$x^{-n} = \frac{1}{x^n}, x \neq 0$

We applied the exponent laws to simplify numerical expressions. We can also use the exponent laws to simplify algebraic expressions involving powers, as shown in the examples that follow.

Through Guided Examples

Example 1

Simplify.

a) $(4x^3y^2)(5x^2y^4)$ **b)** $\frac{6a^5b^3}{3a^2b^2}$ **c)** $\left(\frac{x^2}{z^3}\right)^2$

Solution

a) $(4x^3y^2)(5x^2y^4)$ means $4 \cdot x^3 \cdot y^2 \cdot 5 \cdot x^2 \cdot y^4$.

We can multiply in any order.

$$\begin{aligned}(4x^3y^2)(5x^2y^4) &= 4 \cdot x^3 \cdot y^2 \cdot 5 \cdot x^2 \cdot y^4 \\ &= 4 \cdot 5 \cdot x^3 \cdot x^2 \cdot y^2 \cdot y^4 \\ &= 20x^5y^6\end{aligned}$$

b) $\dfrac{6a^5b^3}{3a^2b^2}$ means $\dfrac{6}{3} \times \dfrac{a^5}{a^2} \times \dfrac{b^3}{b^2}$

$\dfrac{6a^5b^3}{3a^2b^2} = \dfrac{6}{3} \times \dfrac{a^5}{a^2} \times \dfrac{b^3}{b^2}$

$\qquad = 2a^3b$

c) $\left(\dfrac{x^2}{z^3}\right)^2$ means $\dfrac{x^2}{z^3} \times \dfrac{x^2}{z^3}$

$\left(\dfrac{x^2}{z^3}\right)^2 = \dfrac{x^2}{z^3} \times \dfrac{x^2}{z^3}$

$\qquad = \dfrac{x^4}{z^6}$

The same methods apply if some of the exponents are negative integers.

Example 2 ....

Simplify.

a) $c^{-3} \cdot c^5$ **b)** $m^2 \div m^{-3}$ **c)** $(a^{-2})^{-3}$

Solution

a) $c^{-3} \cdot c^5 = c^{-3\,+\,5}$

$\qquad\qquad = c^2$

b) $m^2 \div m^{-3} = m^{2\,-\,(-3)}$

$\qquad\qquad\quad = m^5$

c) $(a^{-2})^{-3} = a^{(-2)\,\times\,(-3)}$

$\qquad\qquad = a^6$

Example 3 ....

Simplify.

a) $(3a^3b^{-2})(15a^2b^5)$ **b)** $\dfrac{42x^{-1}y^4}{7x^3y^{-2}}$ **c)** $(a^{-3}b^2)^3$

Solution

a) $(3a^3b^{-2})(15a^2b^5) = 3 \cdot a^3 \cdot b^{-2} \cdot 15 \cdot a^2 \cdot b^5$

$\qquad\qquad\qquad\qquad = 3 \cdot 15 \cdot a^3 \cdot a^2 \cdot b^{-2} \cdot b^5$

$\qquad\qquad\qquad\qquad = 45a^5b^3$

b) $\dfrac{42x^{-1}y^4}{7x^3y^{-2}} = \dfrac{42}{7} \times \dfrac{x^{-1}}{x^3} \times \dfrac{y^4}{y^{-2}}$

$\qquad\qquad\quad = 6 \cdot x^{-1\,-\,3} \cdot y^{4\,-\,(-2)}$

$\qquad\qquad\quad = 6x^{-4}y^6$

c) $(a^{-3}b^2)^3 = a^{-9}b^6$

In *Example 3b*, we could have used the fact that $x^{-4} = \dfrac{1}{x^4}$ to write the answer in the form $\dfrac{6y^6}{x^4}$. However, unless otherwise stated, we will leave all answers in the form ax^by^c, where b and c are integers.

Working with Mathematics

Something to talk about

1. Explain what each expression means.

   a) $n^5 \times n^{-2}$ b) $\dfrac{n^5}{n^{-2}}$ c) $(n^5)^{-2}$

2. An algebraic expression is given, followed by four numerical expressions. Simplify the algebraic expression. What does this tell you about the values of the numerical expressions?

   a) $n^5 \times n^{-2}$ $2^5 \times 2^{-2}, 7^5 \times 7^{-2}, 12^5 \times 12^{-2},$
   $(-3)^5 \times (-3)^{-2}$

   b) $\dfrac{x^2}{x^{-3}}$ $\dfrac{3^2}{3^{-3}}, \dfrac{5^2}{5^{-3}}, \dfrac{10^2}{10^{-3}}, \dfrac{(-2)^2}{(-2)^{-3}}$

   c) $(y^3)^{-2}$ $(5^3)^{-2}, (2^3)^{-2}, (9^3)^{-2}, [(-4)^3]^{-2}$

Practice

3. Simplify each expression.

   a) $m^3 \times m^2$ b) $a^6 \times a^4$ c) $s^5 \times s^7$

   d) $e^{14} \div e^3$ e) $y^4 \div y^2$ f) $j^8 \div j^5$

   g) $b^{12} \times b^8$ h) $r^3 \times r^7$ i) $p^6 \div p^{11}$

4. Simplify each expression.

   a) $(-a)^5 \times (-a)^4$ b) $(-b)^7 \div (-b)^{11}$

   c) $(-m)^{11} \times (-m)^5$ d) $(-f)^6 \div (-f)^9$

   e) $(-t)^4 \times (-t)^{13}$ f) $(-z)^8 \div (-z)^3$

   g) $(-g)^7 \div (-g)^{13}$ h) $(-v)^4 \times (-v)^3$

   i) $(-d)^3 \div (-d)^9$ j) $(-x)^5 \times (-x)^2$

5. Simplify.

   a) $w^{-4} \times w^9$ b) $(-h)^4 \div (-h)^6$

   c) $(-s)^7 \div (-s)^{-5}$ d) $a^{-7} \div a^3$

   e) $(-f)^{-8} \times (-f)^5$ f) $(-c)^{-6} \div (-c)^9$

   g) $(-y)^{-8} \times (-y)^3$ h) $n^{-11} \div n^5$

   i) $(-b)^{-4} \div (-b)^{-10}$ j) $y^{-3} \times y^7$

Work together

6. Use the laws of exponents to write each expression as a power.

   a) $n^3 \times n^2$ b) $n^3 \times n^1$ c) $n^3 \times n^0$

   d) $n^3 \times n^{-1}$ e) $n^3 \times n^{-2}$ f) $n^3 \times n^{-3}$

7. Write each expression as a power.

   a) $(x^{-3})^2$ b) $(x^{-3})^1$ c) $(x^{-3})^0$

   d) $(x^{-3})^{-1}$ e) $(x^{-3})^{-2}$ f) $(x^{-3})^{-3}$

8. Write as a power.

   a) $x^{-2} \cdot x^3$ b) $m^{-3} \cdot m^{-1}$

   c) $x^5 \cdot x^{-1} \cdot x^{-3}$ d) $\dfrac{x^{-4}}{x^2}$

   e) $\dfrac{y^3}{y^{-2}}$ f) $\dfrac{c}{c^{-2}}$

   g) $(x^{-2})^3$ h) $(y^{-1})^{-2}$

   i) $(a^4)^{-1}$ j) $b^4 \cdot b^{-3} \cdot b^2$

   k) $\dfrac{x^{-2}}{x^4}$ l) $(x^{-1}y^2)^{-1}$

9. Simplify.

   a) $\dfrac{x^3y^5}{x^2y^4}$ b) $\dfrac{m^6n^3}{m^4n^3}$

   c) $\dfrac{a^8b^4}{a^6b^7}$ d) $\dfrac{c^2d^8}{c^5d^{11}}$

   e) $\dfrac{p^{12}q^7}{p^6q^9}$ f) $\dfrac{j^{-8}k^5}{j^4k^{-3}}$

   g) $\dfrac{r^{-4}s^{-6}}{r^{-5}s^{-3}}$ h) $\dfrac{u^7v^2}{u^{-3}v^{-8}}$

   i) $\dfrac{e^{-4}f^5g^{-8}}{e^{-6}f^{-9}g^2}$ j) $\dfrac{m^{-7}n^6}{m^{-3}n^{-2}}$

10. Simplify each expression.

    a) $\dfrac{36a^4b^{-2}}{12a^2b^3}$ b) $\dfrac{36a^3b^{-2}}{12a^3b^2}$

    c) $\dfrac{36a^2b^{-2}}{12a^4b^1}$ d) $\dfrac{36ab^{-2}}{12a^5b^0}$

    e) $\dfrac{36a^0b^{-2}}{12a^6b^{-1}}$ f) $\dfrac{36a^{-1}b^{-2}}{12a^7b^{-2}}$

11. Simplify.

    a) $(3x^3y^2)(6x^2y^4)$ b) $(8m^2n^{-1})(2m^{-3}n^{-2})$

    c) $(9a^{-1}b^0)(5a^4b^{-3})$ d) $\dfrac{30c^5d^4}{6c^3d}$

    e) $\dfrac{24x^3y^{-2}}{8x^{-1}y^3}$ f) $\dfrac{6p^{-2}q^3}{12pq^{-1}}$

    g) $(n^2)^{-2}$ h) $(ab^{-3})^2$

    i) $(x^3y^{-1})^{-3}$ j) $(4m^5n)(7m^{-4}n^{-3})$

    k) $\dfrac{6x^{-2}y^0}{8x^2y^{-2}}$ l) $(a^{-1}b^3)^{-1}$

12. Evaluate each expression for $n = 2$.

    a) $(n^{-1})^2$ b) $n^{-3} \times n^{-1}$ c) $n^{-2} \times n^6$

    d) $\dfrac{n^{-1}}{n^2}$ e) $\dfrac{n^{-2}}{n^{-1}}$ f) $\dfrac{(n^{-2})^3}{n^{-8}}$

13. Simplify, then determine the value of each expression when $a = -2$ and $b = 3$.

    a) a^2b^3 b) $a^{-2}b^2$

    c) $a^{-3}b^{-2}$ d) $\dfrac{a^7b^9}{a^6b^7}$

    e) $\dfrac{10a^{-3}b^{12}}{5a^{-5}b^{14}}$ f) $\dfrac{-27a^8b^{-10}}{-9a^9b^{-9}}$

g) $\dfrac{16a^{-5}b^{-8}}{-8a^{-6}b^{-9}}$ h) $\dfrac{-24a^{17}b^4}{-6a^{18}b^4}$

i) $\dfrac{-36a^5b^{-3}}{-12a^6b^{-5}}$ j) $\dfrac{12a^3b^{-3}}{-18a^5b^2}$

On your own

14. Use the laws of exponents to write each expression as a power.

a) $\dfrac{x^3}{x^2}$ b) $\dfrac{x^3}{x^1}$ c) $\dfrac{x^3}{x^0}$

d) $\dfrac{x^3}{x^{-1}}$ e) $\dfrac{x^3}{x^{-2}}$ f) $\dfrac{x^3}{x^{-3}}$

15. Write each expression as a power.

a) $c^5 \cdot c^{-2}$ b) $c^4 \cdot c^{-1}$ c) $c^3 \cdot c^0$

d) $c^2 \cdot c$ e) $c \cdot c^2$ f) $c^0 \cdot c^3$

16. Simplify.

a) $a^6 \cdot a^{-2}$ b) $y^4 \cdot y^{-4}$

c) $d^6 \cdot d^{-2} \cdot d^{-5}$ d) $\dfrac{m^5}{m^{-5}}$

e) $\dfrac{a^{-3}}{a^{-3}}$ f) $\dfrac{b^{-8}}{b^{-3}}$

g) $(m^{-3})^2$ h) $(c^3)^{-3}$

i) $(x^2y^{-3})^2$ j) $p^{-1} \cdot p^7 \cdot p^6$

k) $\dfrac{t^4}{t^{-7}}$ l) $(a^{-2}b^2)^{-2}$

17. Write as a power.

a) $c^{-4} \times c^9$ b) $m^{-3} \times m^{-2}$

c) $x^3 \cdot x^{-2} \cdot x^{-4}$ d) $\dfrac{n^4}{n^{-1}}$

e) $\dfrac{a^{-3}}{a^{-2}}$ f) $\dfrac{z^{-3}}{z^{-3}}$

g) $(k^3)^3$ h) $(r^4)^{-1}$

i) $(x^{-3})^{-2}$ j) $(a^2b^3)^2$

k) $\left(\dfrac{x^4}{y^2}\right)^3$ l) $\left(\dfrac{m^2}{n^{-1}}\right)^2$

18. Simplify.

a) $(7a^4b^3)(5a^{-1}b^2)$ b) $(7c^{-2}d)(9c^4d^{-3})$

c) $(6x^{-5}y^{-1})(8x^0y^{-1})$ d) $\dfrac{52x^2y^{-2}}{13x^{-1}y}$

e) $\dfrac{51c^{-2}d^6}{17c^0d^{-1}}$ f) $\dfrac{28a^{-4}b^{-2}}{12a^4b^{-3}}$

g) $(2p^3)^{-2}$ h) $(x^{-2}y^{-1})^3$

i) $(a^4b^{-2})^{-1}$ j) $(12m^{-2}n^{-3})(5m^7n^{-3})$

k) $\dfrac{48r^{-1}s^3}{16r^4s^{-5}}$ l) $(p^{-3}q^2)^{-2}$

19. Simplify, then evaluate each expression for $x = -2$.

a) $x^3 \cdot x^2$ b) $\dfrac{x^3}{x^2}$ c) $(x^3)^2$

d) $x^{-1} \cdot x^{-2}$ e) $\dfrac{x^{-1}}{x^{-2}}$ f) $(x^{-1})^{-2}$

Extend your thinking

20. Simplify.

a) $45x^{-3} \div 5x^5 \times 3x^{-7}$

b) $4a^{-7} \times 12a^{-5} \div 8a^{-4}$

c) $(2x^2y^2)^{-1} \div (2x^2y)^{-2}$

d) $\left(\dfrac{p^2}{q}\right)^{-3} \div \dfrac{q}{p^6}$

e) $\left(\dfrac{2x^2}{3y}\right)^{-3} \div \dfrac{1}{x}$

f) $\left(\dfrac{a^2b}{c^3}\right)^{-3} \times \left(\dfrac{a^5b^{-2}}{c^3}\right)^{-1}$

COMMUNICATING

The Ideas

In your journal, explain the meaning of each expression:

- $x^2 \cdot x^{-3}$
- $\dfrac{x^2}{x^{-3}}$
- $(x^2)^{-3}$

Show how you would simplify each expression.

BOGGLE YOUR MIND

A single CD-ROM disk, less than 13 cm across, can contain the names, addresses, and telephone numbers of all the people in Canada, with room to spare. What if the telephone company stopped printing a separate telephone directory for each community, and produced a single CD-ROM disk for the entire country? Do you think this would be a good idea? Why?

Developing the Ideas

▷ ▶ *Through Guided Examples*

Many problems involve numbers in scientific notation. Your scientific calculator has a key for entering numbers in scientific notation. This key is probably [EE] or [EXP]. We will use the *TEXAS INSTRUMENTS TI-34* calculator, where the key is [EXP]. If your calculator is different, check your manual to find out how to work with numbers in scientific notation.

Example 1 ···

Earth's diameter is about 1.27×10^4 km.
The sun's diameter is about 1.39×10^6 km.
Suppose we shrink Earth to the size of the small circle below.
We then compare Earth with the sun.

a) How many times as great as the diameter of Earth is the diameter of the sun?

b) What would the diameter of the sun be on this scale?

Solution

a) Divide the sun's diameter by Earth's diameter to determine how many times as great the sun is.

$$\frac{\text{Diameter of the sun}}{\text{Diameter of Earth}}$$

$$= \frac{1.39 \times 10^6}{1.27 \times 10^4}$$

$$\doteq 109$$

Press: **1.39** [EXP] **6** [÷] **1.27** [EXP] **4** [=]
to display: **109.4488189**
Do not clear the display.

The sun's diameter is about 109 times Earth's diameter.

b) Measure the diameter of the circle. It is about 1.2 cm.

Diameter of sun
$= 109 \times 1.2$ cm
$\doteq 130$ cm

Then press: [×] **1.2** [=]
to display: **131.3385827**

On this scale, the sun's diameter is about 130 cm, or 1.3 m.

Example 2

Diatoms are a primary source of food in the sea. They are tiny one-celled plants that live in shells. A diatom measures about 5×10^{-4} mm across. Suppose diatoms were placed side by side. How many diatoms would be needed to stretch along Canada's Pacific coastline, which measures about 7000 km?

Solution

Express 7000 km in millimetres.

$1 \text{ km} = 1000 \text{ m}$
$\qquad = 1\ 000\ 000 \text{ mm}$
$\qquad = 10^6 \text{ mm}$

$7000 \text{ km} = 7000 \times 10^6 \text{ mm}$
$\qquad = 7.0 \times 10^3 \times 10^6 \text{ mm}$
$\qquad = 7.0 \times 10^9 \text{ mm}$

To calculate how many diatoms are needed to stretch this far, divide the distance by the width of a diatom.

$$\frac{7.0 \times 10^9}{5 \times 10^{-4}} = 1.4 \times 10^{13}$$

Press: 7 [EXP] 9 [÷] 5 [÷] [EXP] 4 [+/−] [=]
to display: **1.4^{13}**

It would require about 1.4×10^{13} diatoms to stretch all along Canada's Pacific coastline.

Working with Mathematics

Something to talk about

1. Explain the keystrokes you would use to do the following operations on your calculator.
   a) $(5.9 \times 10^5) \times (4.7 \times 10^{-8})$
   b) $(3.5 \times 10^9) \div (8.7 \times 10^{-5})$
   c) $(2.4 \text{ million}) \times (6.5 \text{ million})$
   d) $1 \div (5 \text{ billion})$

2. Scientific calculators may display results differently. What do you think each display below means?
   a) Calculator 1

   i)

        2.5 12   6.25–10

   ii)

   b) Calculator 2

   i)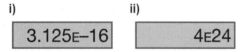

       3.125E–16   4E24

   ii)

   c) Calculator 3

   i)

      4.33333E22   5.E–40

   ii)

3. Refer to *Example 1*. Suppose the small circle represents the sun. How would you calculate the size of the circle that represents Earth?

4. Refer to *Example 2*. Calculate the number of diatoms needed to cover each distance. Explain each answer.
   a) a line 1 mm long
   b) a line 1 km long
   c) Canada's ocean coastline, 241 402 km

Practice

5. Simplify.
   a) $3 \times 10^7 \times 4 \times 10^8$
   b) $1.4 \times 10^{10} \times 3.7 \times 10^{14}$
   c) $9.8 \times 10^{11} \times 1.3 \times 10^4$
   d) $3.6 \times 10^3 \times 5.9 \times 10^6$
   e) $1.2 \times 10^{13} \times 4.7 \times 10^9$
   f) $4.1 \times 10^{26} \times 3.2 \times 10^9$

6. Simplify.
   a) $\dfrac{3.72 \times 10^{10}}{1.47 \times 10^8}$ b) $\dfrac{4.9 \times 10^4}{7.0 \times 10^3}$
   c) $\dfrac{8.43 \times 10^4}{3.7 \times 10^2}$ d) $\dfrac{9.3 \times 10^{12}}{3.3 \times 10^7}$
   e) $\dfrac{2.43 \times 10^{-7}}{2.3 \times 10^{-4}}$ f) $\dfrac{2.55 \times 10^{-9}}{3.0 \times 10^{-15}}$

Work together

7. a) How many pages of this book together will make a thickness of 1 cm? Calculate the thickness of one page of this book.
   b) Plastic food wrap has a thickness of approximately 2.5×10^{-3} cm. We would like to compare this with the thickness of one page in this book. Suppose we enlarge a cross section of the paper so that it has the thickness shown. How thick would the plastic food wrap be on this scale?

8. On a television program about sea otters, the following statements were made:
   - One square centimetre of a sea otter's fur contains about 20 000 hairs.
   - A sea otter has about 8 billion hairs.
   a) Write these two numbers in scientific notation.
   b) Calculate the area of a sea otter's body, in square centimetres.
   c) Express your answer to part b in square metres. Does the result seem reasonable? Explain.

9. A magazine article reported that about 100 billion aluminum beverage cans are made each year in North America. Suppose these cans are piled one on top of another. Carry out measurements and calculations to determine how high this stack would be.

On your own

10. The volume of Earth is about 1.1×10^{12} km^3.
    a) The volume of the sun is about 1.3×10^6 times as great as the volume of Earth. Calculate the volume of the sun.
    b) The volume of Earth is about 49 times the volume of the moon. Calculate the volume of the moon.

11. The mass of Earth is about 6.0×10^{24} kg.
    a) The mass of the sun is about 3.3×10^5 times the mass of Earth. Calculate the mass of the sun.
    b) The mass of Earth is about 81 times the mass of the moon. Calculate the mass of the moon.

12. One human hair has a diameter of about 1.0×10^{-4} m. Spiders can make strands of silk with a diameter of about 5.0×10^{-6} m. We would like to compare spider silk with human hair. Suppose we enlarge a cross-section of spider silk so that it is the size of this circle.

    a) How many times as great as the diameter of spider silk is the diameter of human hair?
    b) What would be the diameter of a cross-section of hair on this scale?

13. Use the *Moon and Planets* database from the data disk. Find the information you need to answer each question.

    DATA DISK

    a) The nearest star is about 2.7×10^5 times as far from the sun as Earth is. How far is the nearest star from the sun?
    b) The mass of the heaviest known star, Eta Carinae, is about 6.23×10^8 times as great as the mass of Mars. What is the mass of Eta Carinae?
    c) The diameter of the largest known star, Betelgeuse, is about 1.35×10^4 times as great as the diameter of Uranus. What is the diameter of Betelgeuse?

14. In 1977, two spacecraft named Voyager 1 and Voyager 2 were launched to visit the outer planets, which they did in the 1980s. These spacecraft have now travelled so far they have left the solar system. Voyager 2 is travelling at 58 000 km/h, and 296 000 years from now it will reach Sirius, the brightest star in the sky. How far away is Sirius?

Extend your thinking

15. Sirius has a companion star known as Sirius B. This star is about the size of Earth, but its mass is almost the same as the mass of the sun. Carry out calculations to estimate the mass of 1 cm^3 of matter from Sirius B. Use the information from exercises 10 and 11. Does the result seem reasonable? Explain.

16. In 1938, physicist Sir Arthur Eddington estimated the number of particles in the universe to be 33×2^{259}. Use your calculator to express this number in scientific notation.

COMMUNICATING

The Ideas

Suppose two numbers in scientific notation are multiplied, and the product is written in scientific notation. How is the power of 10 in the product related to the powers of 10 in the two original numbers? Answer this question in your journal, and illustrate your answer with some examples.

5.6 *ESTIMATING SQUARE ROOTS*

Developing the Ideas

▶▶*Through Discussion*

Chinese New Year's Day is celebrated on the first day of the lunar calendar. To ensure that the new year brings prosperity and good health, dances are performed for 15 days. The man in the square photographs below is taking part in a parade held in Vancouver for Chinese New Year. The banner he carries is red because this colour signifies good luck and happiness.

The photograph on the right is an enlargement of the one on the left — its area is exactly twice as large. How can you find the side length of the photograph on the right without measuring?

5 cm

5 cm

1. What is the area of the photograph on the left?

2. **a)** What is the area of the photograph on the right?
   b) Is it possible that its side length is 10 cm?

3. Without using your calculator, estimate the side length of the photograph on the right, to the nearest tenth of a centimetre.

4. Suppose two other enlargements are made of the first photograph. Their areas are 3 times as great and 4 times as great respectively. Without using your calculator, estimate the side lengths of these photographs to the nearest tenth of a centimetre.

Recall that when we square a number, we multiply it by itself:

$$7^2 = 49$$
$$(-7)^2 = 49$$

Since $7 \times 7 = 49$, we say that 7 is a square root of 49, and we write $\sqrt{49} = 7$.
Since $(-7) \times (-7) = 49$, another square root of 49 is -7.
When the radical sign, $\sqrt{}$, is used, it indicates only the positive square root.

All positive numbers have square roots. Those that have square roots which are natural numbers are called *perfect squares*. For example, 25 is a perfect square because one of its square roots is 5.

Number, n	0	1	4	9	16	25	36	49	64	81	100
Square root, $\sqrt{n}$	0	1	2	3	4	5	6	7	8	9	10

You can estimate the square roots of numbers that are not perfect squares. To estimate $\sqrt{50}$ and $\sqrt{75}$, think of the perfect squares near 50 and 75:

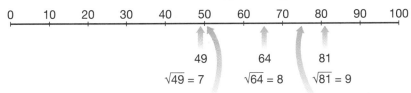

49
$\sqrt{49} = 7$

64
$\sqrt{64} = 8$

81
$\sqrt{81} = 9$

50 is between 49 and 64, and is much closer to 49.
Hence, $\sqrt{50}$ is between 7 and 8, and is probably much closer to 7.
We estimate $\sqrt{50}$ to be about 7.1.

75 is between 64 and 81, and is a little closer to 81.
Hence, $\sqrt{75}$ is between 8 and 9, and is probably a little closer to 9.
We estimate $\sqrt{75}$ to be about 8.6.

BOGGLE YOUR MIND

The Hermitage art gallery in St. Petersburg, Russia has nearly 3 million works of art and historical artifacts on display. What if it takes an average of 15 s to look at each item? How many days would it take to view the entire collection?

Working with Mathematics

Something to talk about

1. Which of the three estimates is closest to the square root? Explain your answer.
   - a) $\sqrt{13}$ 3.4   3.5   3.6
   - b) $\sqrt{20}$ 4.4   4.5   4.6
   - c) $\sqrt{85}$ 9.2   9.3   9.4

2. A student estimated $\sqrt{50}$ as follows:
   "Since 50 is halfway between 0 and 100, $\sqrt{50}$ should be halfway between 0 and 10. Therefore, $\sqrt{50}$ should equal 5."
   Is this reasoning correct? Explain your answer.

3. Which square roots are between 8 and 9? Explain how you know.

$$\sqrt{67} \qquad \sqrt{91} \qquad \sqrt{78}$$
$$\sqrt{62} \qquad \sqrt{84} \qquad \sqrt{80}$$

4. Abhena made a sketch on a square piece of paper with sides 15 cm long. She wants to mount it on a piece of poster board twice the area of the paper. How would you estimate the length of each side of the poster board? What is your estimate?

5. Suppose the sketch in exercise 4 is enlarged so that its area is 3 times as great as the original. Estimate the length of each side of the enlargement.

Practice

6. Which of the square roots listed below are between each pair of numbers?
   - a) 3 and 4   b) 7 and 8   c) 11 and 12
   - d) 10 and 11   e) 13 and 14   f) 18 and 19

$$\sqrt{11}, \sqrt{52}, \sqrt{61}, \sqrt{14}, \sqrt{330}, \sqrt{360},$$
$$\sqrt{320}, \sqrt{257}, \sqrt{190}, \sqrt{140}, \sqrt{171},$$
$$\sqrt{118}, \sqrt{110}, \sqrt{130}, \sqrt{80}, \sqrt{35}$$

7. What are the square roots of each number?
   - a) 4   b) 9   c) 49
   - d) 81   e) 121   f) 64

8. What are the square roots of each number?
   - a) $\frac{1}{16}$ b) $\frac{1}{25}$ c) $\frac{16}{25}$
   - d) $\frac{4}{9}$ e) $\frac{25}{49}$ f) $\frac{64}{81}$

9. Estimate each square root to one decimal place.
   - a) $\sqrt{76}$ b) $\sqrt{86}$ c) $\sqrt{117}$
   - d) $\sqrt{140}$ e) $\sqrt{45}$ f) $\sqrt{105}$

10. Determine each square root.
    - a) $\sqrt{144}$ b) $\sqrt{14\ 400}$
    - c) $\sqrt{1\ 440\ 000}$ d) $\sqrt{1.44}$
    - e) $\sqrt{0.0144}$ f) $\sqrt{0.000\ 144}$

11. Determine each square root.
    - a) $\sqrt{1\ 210\ 000}$ b) $\sqrt{12\ 100}$
    - c) $\sqrt{121}$ d) $\sqrt{1.21}$
    - e) $\sqrt{0.0121}$ f) $\sqrt{0.000\ 121}$

12. a) Determine two values that satisfy $m^2 = 36$.
    b) Determine two values that satisfy $p^2 = 75$, to two decimal places.
    c) Determine two values that satisfy $t^2 = 4.9$, to two decimal places.

Work together

13. Simplify each expression. Estimate the result where necessary.
    - a) $\sqrt{25} + \sqrt{49}$
    - b) $25 + \sqrt{49}$
    - c) $\sqrt{25} + 49$
    - d) $\sqrt{25} \times \sqrt{49}$
    - e) $\sqrt{25 + 49}$
    - f) $\sqrt{25 \times 49}$
    - g) $\sqrt{25 + \sqrt{49}}$
    - h) $\sqrt{\sqrt{25} + 49}$
    - i) $\sqrt{\sqrt{25} + \sqrt{49}}$

14. Find the length of the side of a square with each area. Round to one decimal place where necessary.
    - a) 400 cm^2 b) 0.25 m^2
    - c) 90 cm^2 d) 150 cm^2
    - e) 300 cm^2 f) 25 000 m^2

15. Explain why each answer in exercise 14 involves only the positive square root.

16. Joel has a square garden with area 230 m².
    a) How long is each side of Joel's garden, to the nearest centimetre?
    b) How much fencing would be needed to enclose the entire garden?

17. A decorator installs a square carpet in a banquet room, to cover 60% of the hardwood floor area. The room is 5 m by 5 m. What are the dimensions of the carpet?

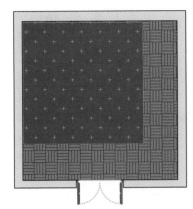

18. What are the square roots of each number?
    a) 36   b) 100   c) 400
    d) 1   e) $\frac{1}{4}$ f) $\frac{1}{9}$

19. Estimate each square root to one decimal place.
    a) $\sqrt{40}$ b) $\sqrt{97}$ c) $\sqrt{30}$ d) $\sqrt{65}$

20. Simplify each expression. Estimate the result where necessary.
    a) $\sqrt{64} + \sqrt{36}$
    b) $\sqrt{64 + 36}$
    c) $64 + \sqrt{36}$
    d) $\sqrt{64} \times \sqrt{36}$
    e) $\sqrt{64 + \sqrt{36}}$
    f) $\sqrt{\sqrt{64} + \sqrt{36}}$

21. a) Use a calculator to find each square root.
    i) $\sqrt{3}$ ii) $\sqrt{300}$
    iii) $\sqrt{30\ 000}$ iv) $\sqrt{3\ 000\ 000}$
    v) $\sqrt{0.03}$ vi) $\sqrt{0.0003}$
    b) Look at the results in part a. Try to explain the pattern.

22. a) Determine two values that satisfy each equation. Give answers to two decimal places where necessary.
    i) $n^2 = 81$ ii) $k^2 = 0.25$
    iii) $x^2 = 96$ iv) $z^2 = \frac{4}{49}$
    v) $y^2 = 38$ vi) $q^2 = 5$
    b) Explain why each equation in part a has two possible solutions.

On your own

23. Rajeet bought a square carpet with an area of 15 m². What are the approximate dimensions of the carpet?

24. Louis enlarges a 6-cm square photograph to twice its original area. What are the approximate dimensions of the enlargement?

25. Write the two square roots of each number.
    a) 8100   b) 6400   c) 900
    d) 12 100   e) 0.25   f) 0.01

26. a) A square has one vertex at (0,0) and an area of 49 square units. Find possible coordinates of the other vertices of the square.

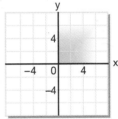

    b) A square has one vertex at (0, 0) and an area of 64 square units. Find possible coordinates of the other vertices of the square.
    c) A square has one vertex at (2, 3) and an area of 16 square units. Find possible coordinates of the other vertices of the square.

27. Estimate each square root to one decimal place.
    a) $\sqrt{5}$ b) $\sqrt{12}$
    c) $\sqrt{32}$ d) $\sqrt{69}$

28. The area of a square is given. Estimate the length of a side to the nearest millimetre.

a) 45 cm²   b) 54 cm²

c) 72 cm²   d) 86 cm²

29. Simplify each expression. Estimate the result where necessary.

a) $\sqrt{16 + 9}$

b) $\sqrt{16} + \sqrt{9}$

c) $\sqrt{16 - 9}$

d) $\sqrt{16} - \sqrt{9}$

e) $\sqrt{16} \times \sqrt{9}$

f) $\sqrt{\sqrt{16} + \sqrt{9}}$

30. a) Suppose you know the area of a square. How could you find its perimeter?

b) Write a formula relating the perimeter P and the area A of a square.

c) Find the perimeter of the square with each area. Estimate the result where necessary.

i) 26 cm²   ii) 64 cm²

iii) 78 m²   iv) 3.8 m²

31. Solve each equation. Give answers to two decimal places where necessary.

a) $x^2 = 100$ b) $8.1 = k^2$

c) $d^2 = 144$ d) $120 = p^2$

e) $s^2 = 94$ f) $y^2 = 0.01$

g) $6.25 = n^2$ h) $m^2 = 7.5$

i) $m^2 + 5 = 30$ j) $q^2 - 10 = 90$

Extend your thinking

32. a) Use a calculator to find each square root.

i) $\sqrt{2}$

ii) $\sqrt{20}$

iii) $\sqrt{200}$

iv) $\sqrt{2000}$

v) $\sqrt{20\ 000}$

vi) $\sqrt{200\ 000}$

b) Look at the results in part a. Try to explain the pattern.

33. What happens when you use the $\sqrt{}$ key on a calculator to evaluate the square root of a negative integer such as −3? Explain.

34. A square has one vertex at (0,0) and an area of 25 square units. Find possible coordinates of the other vertices of the square.

35. a) Suppose you know the diameter of a circle. How could you find its area?

b) Write a formula for the area A of a circle in terms of its diameter d.

c) Suppose you know the area of a circle. How could you find its diameter?

d) Write a formula for the diameter of a circle in terms of its area.

e) Find the diameter of the circle with each area. Give each answer to one decimal place.

i) 22 cm²   ii) 33 cm²

iii) 40 cm²   iv) 5 m²

COMMUNICATING

The Ideas

Look at the square roots in these exercises. Some of the square roots are less than the original numbers, while others are greater than the original numbers. How can you tell if the square root of a number is greater than or less than the number? Record your ideas in your journal, with examples.

Can You Make One Large Square from Two Small Ones?

You will need a pair of scissors and two identical square pieces of paper or cardboard. Your challenge is to cut the squares into smaller pieces and arrange all the pieces to form one large square.

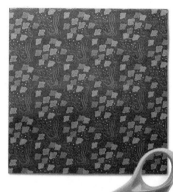

Understand the problem

- What are you asked to do?
- Can the pieces overlap? Do they have to overlap?

Think of a strategy

- Try cutting the squares into as few pieces as possible.
- Try cutting the squares into parts that are congruent.
- Try arranging the pieces to form a symmetrical pattern in the large square.
- If one method does not work, you will need to start again with two new squares.

Carry out the strategy

- Suppose you fold each square into two congruent parts, as shown, and then cut along the fold line. Can you arrange the four rectangles to form one large square?
- Is there another way you could fold each square into two congruent parts?
- If you then cut along the fold lines, can you form a large square using the four pieces?

Look back

- Can you find another solution to this problem?

Suppose the side length of each small square is 1 unit.
- What is the area of each small square?
- What is the area of the large square?
- How long is each side of the large square?

Communicating the Ideas

In your journal, write a description of this problem. Include diagrams to illustrate your solution.

Developing the Ideas

▶▶ *Through Discussion*

Earlier in your study of mathematics, you encountered these sets of numbers

Natural numbers, N	**Rational numbers, Q**
1, 2, 3, 4, 5,...	Numbers that can be expressed in fractional form
Integers, I	Examples:
... −3, −2, −1, 0, 1, 2, 3,...	$\frac{2}{3}$ $\frac{-9}{4}$ $\frac{5}{-7}$ $\frac{-1}{-2}$ 1.32 5.8 −2

1. Express each rational number in decimal form.
Use a calculator if necessary.

a) $\frac{3}{8}$ b) $\frac{7}{12}$ c) $\frac{-23}{16}$ d) $\frac{7}{-8}$

e) $\frac{37}{11}$ f) $\frac{53}{99}$ g) $\frac{17}{222}$ h) $\frac{22}{7}$

Look at the results for exercise 1. The decimals in the quotients always terminate or repeat. You can see why by looking at paper-and-pencil division calculations such as these:

In this example, the remainder must be less than 8. Since a remainder of 0 occurs, the division terminates.

```
    0.375
8)3.000
    2 4
    ──
      60
      56
      ──
       40
       40
       ──
        0
```

We write $\frac{3}{8}$ = 0.375, which is a terminating decimal.

In this example, the remainders must be less than 12. Since we get a remainder that occurred previously, the division repeats.

```
     0.583
12)7.000
     6 0
     ──
      1 00
        96
        ──
         40
         36
         ──
          4
```

We write $\frac{7}{12}$ = 0.58333333..., which is a repeating decimal.

One of these two cases will occur when any rational number is expressed in decimal form. Therefore, when a rational number is expressed in decimal form, the digits either terminate or repeat.

2. Only three of the numbers below are rational numbers.
   a) Which ones do you think they are?
   b) Why are the others not rational numbers?
      Do you think they are numbers?
         i) 1.010203040506070809010011101201301...
         ii) −238.418773
         iii) 3.141592653589793238462643383279502884419...
         iv) 88175.47547547547547547547547547547475...
         v) 47.444444438383838383838382220974449072...
         vi) −0.0792188367584920007839783978397839...

3. We use *bar notation* to indicate a repeating decimal. For example, $2.4\overline{35}$ means $2.4353535353535353535353535...$

a) Write a few digits of each number without using bar notation.

   i) $4.\overline{9}$ ii) $17.\overline{02}$ iii) $-8.51\overline{273}$

b) Write the two repeating decimals in exercise 2b using bar notation.

c) What are two advantages of bar notation?

If you use a calculator to calculate $\sqrt{2}$, you will obtain something like $1.414\ 213\ 562$.

To check this, you can multiply $1.414\ 213\ 562$ by $1.414\ 213\ 562$.

But the product has more digits than most calculators can handle. Using a computer, the exact value of this product is:

$1.414\ 213\ 562 \times 1.414\ 213\ 562 = 1.999\ 999\ 998\ 944\ 727\ 844$

Since the product is not exactly 2, we say that $1.414\ 213\ 562$ is an *approximation* to $\sqrt{2}$. We write $\sqrt{2} \doteq 1.414\ 213\ 562$. Using a computer, we can calculate more accurate approximations to $\sqrt{2}$, such as:

$\sqrt{2} \doteq 1.414\ 213\ 562\ 373\ 095\ 048\ 801\ 688\ 724\ 209\ 698\ 078\ 569\ 671\ 875\ 376\ 94$

No matter how many digits we calculate for $\sqrt{2}$, we will never determine its exact value, and we will never find a pattern of digits that repeats.

This means that $\sqrt{2}$ cannot be expressed in fractional form $\frac{m}{n}$, where m and n are integers. That is, $\sqrt{2}$ is not a rational number. $\sqrt{2}$ is called an irrational number.

· · · · · · · · ·

> Any number that cannot be expressed in the form $\frac{m}{n}$, where m and n are integers ($n \neq 0$), is an *irrational number*. In decimal form, the digits of an irrational number neither terminate nor repeat. The set of numbers is denoted $\overline{Q}$.

Examples of rational numbers	**Examples of irrational numbers**
Terminating decimals	Decimals that neither terminate nor repeat
-2.875 3.0	$-2.718\ 281\ 828\ 459\ 045\ 235\ 36...$
$7.231\ 875\ 622\ 945$ 8.45×10^{-7}	$1.010\ 010\ 001\ 000\ 010\ 000\ 010...$
Repeating decimals	$-357.575\ 757\ 575\ 757\ 877\ 233...$
$-2.333\ 333\ 333\ 333\ 333\ 333\ 33...$	$\sqrt{5} \doteq 2.236\ 067\ 977\ 499\ 789\ 696\ 41$
$0.\overline{7}$	$-\sqrt{31.5} \doteq -5.612\ 486\ 080\ 160\ 912\ 078\ 38$
$3.\overline{142\ 857}$	
$5.121\ 212\ 121\ 212\ 121\ 212\ 12...$	
$-23.059\ 723\ 116\ \overline{894\ 5}$	

All the numbers shown above are *real numbers*. The set of real numbers consists of all the rational numbers and all the irrational numbers — that is, all numbers that can be expressed in decimal form.

Working with Mathematics

Something to talk about

1. A calculator was used to approximate $\sqrt{3}$. It displayed 1.732 050 8.
   a) Is 1.732 050 8 rational or irrational?
   b) Is $\sqrt{3}$ rational or irrational?
   c) Can a number be both rational and irrational?

2. A student wrote the formula for the circumference of a circle in the form $\pi = \frac{C}{d}$. The student claimed that this proved that π is a rational number. Do you agree with this reasoning?

3. Does each number appear to be rational or irrational? Why is the phrase "appear to be" used in this question?
   a) 1.253 253 253 253 253 253 253 253...
   b) 0.147 474 747 474 747 457 883 312...
   c) 72.041 000 000 019 875 198 751 987...
   d) −0.121 232 123 432 123 454 321 234...

Practice

4. Classify each number as natural, integer, rational, or irrational. Explain your reasoning. (Some numbers may belong to more than one set.)
   a) $\frac{1}{4}$ b) −4   c) 4.99
   d) $-5\frac{3}{8}$ e) 8   f) 3^{-2}

5. Which of these numbers appear to be rational?
   a) 2.547 483 271...   b) 27.216 216 2...
   c) −13.478 197 435...   d) 43.304 004 00...
   e) −7.428   f) −0.453 562 5710...

6. Give examples of two rational numbers between each pair of numbers.
   a) 3.0, 3.5   b) −6.5, −6.1
   c) 1.2, 1.25   d) 2.628, 2.629
   e) $-4.17, -4.1\overline{7}$ f) $7.\overline{45}, 7.45$

7. Which of these numbers are not rational?
   a) $\sqrt{5}$ b) $\sqrt{5} + \sqrt{11}$ c) $\sqrt{5 + 11}$
   d) $\sqrt{11 - 5}$ e) $\sqrt{11} \times \sqrt{5}$ f) $\sqrt{11 \times 5}$

8. Which of these numbers are irrational?
   a) $\sqrt{21}$ b) $\sqrt{64}$ c) $\sqrt{135}$
   d) $\sqrt{1.44}$ e) $\sqrt{0.9}$ f) $\sqrt{0.04}$

On your own

9. Classify each number as natural, integer, rational, or irrational. Some of the numbers will belong to more than one set.
   a) $\frac{3}{5}$ b) $0.\overline{25}$ c) −7
   d) 23 517   e) $\sqrt{25}$ f) 2^{-1}
   g) 3×10^9 h) 2.4×10^{-6} i) $-2\frac{1}{4}$
   j) $\sqrt{7}$ k) 3.14   l) $-875.02\overline{97}$

10. Which of these numbers are irrational?
    a) $\sqrt{3}$ b) $-\sqrt{3}$ c) $6 + \sqrt{3}$
    d) $6 - \sqrt{3}$ e) $\sqrt{6 + 3}$ f) $\sqrt{6 - 3}$
    g) $\sqrt{63}$ h) $\sqrt{36}$ i) $\sqrt{6 \times 3}$

11. Only three of the numbers below are rational. Which ones are they? For each of the other numbers, explain why it is irrational.
    a) $\sqrt{9} + 7$ b) $\sqrt{9} - 7$ c) $9 + \sqrt{7}$
    d) $9 - \sqrt{7}$ e) $\sqrt{9 + 7}$ f) $\sqrt{9 - 7}$
    g) $\sqrt{9} + \sqrt{7}$ h) $\sqrt{9} - \sqrt{7}$ i) $\sqrt{9 \times 7}$

Work together

12. Give examples of two rational and two irrational numbers between the numbers in each pair.
    a) 2.47, 2.61   b) −4.825, −4.82
    c) $1.1\overline{47}$, 1.15   d) $\frac{3}{8}, \frac{4}{9}$
    e) $7.\overline{323}$, 7.323   f) $1.\overline{6}$, 1.7

13. You can use envelopes to show how different sets of numbers are related. You will need five envelopes of different sizes, and 30 small pieces of cardboard or paper.

Write each of these numbers on a small piece of cardboard.

6, 0, –2, –99, $\frac{2}{3}$, 2^{10}, 3×10^6,

2.4×10^9, $\sqrt{2}$, $\frac{12}{7}$, π, $\sqrt{900}$, 2.13,

2^{-1}, –1, 5.8×10^{-6}, $-\sqrt{2}$, 75%,

10^{-3}, 0.762, $32.\overline{6}$, $-\frac{1}{2}$, $-17.0\overline{298}$,

22^{22}, 3 355 432, 63.172 844,

1.212 211 222 111 222 211 111...,

150 million, 2.5 billion,

–17.002 900 290 029 002 900 290 029…

Label each of the four envelopes with one of the descriptions below. Think carefully about the size of each envelope as you label it. Place the numbers into the envelopes.

Natural numbers
N
1, 2, 3 …

Integers
I
… –3, –2, –1, 0, 1, 2, 3, …

Rational numbers
Q
Terminating decimals
Repeating decimals

Irrational numbers
Q̄
Decimals that neither terminate nor repeat

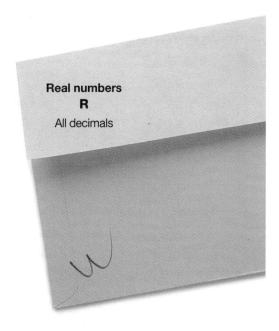

Follow this rule:

Each number must be inside every envelope containing a set of numbers to which it belongs.

For example, since –2 is an integer, –2 must be inside envelope I. Since $-2 = \frac{-2}{1}$, –2 is a rational number, and must also be inside envelope Q.

Label the fifth envelope as shown. Place all the numbers in this envelope!

Real numbers
R
All decimals

Extend your thinking

14. Is the sum of two irrational numbers always an irrational number? If your answer is no, give an example to support your answer.

The Ideas

Suppose you have a number with many decimal places.

a) If you see a repeating pattern, can you be certain that the number is a rational number?

b) If you do not see a repeating pattern, can you be certain that the number is an irrational number?

Record your ideas in your journal. Include some examples to illustrate your conclusions.

Revisiting the Pythagorean Theorem

The Pythagorean Theorem relates the areas of the squares on the sides of a right triangle.

The Pythagorean Theorem is important because people use it to calculate the length of a side of a right triangle if they know the lengths of the other two sides. Ancient texts reveal that many centuries ago, different civilizations knew this property of right triangles.

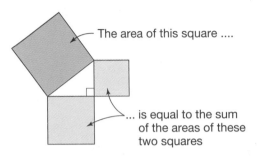

The area of this square ....

... is equal to the sum of the areas of these two squares

Egypt, 2000 B.C.

The ancient Egyptians may have constructed square pyramids using a knotted rope to form a triangle with sides of lengths 3, 4, and 5 units.

Babylonia, 1700 B.C.

Clay tablets show that the ancient Babylonians knew how to calculate the length of the diagonal of a square.

Greece, 540 B.C.

Although it had been known for centuries, the Pythagorean Theorem is named after the Greek philosopher, Pythagoras, who was the first to prove that this theorem applies to all right triangles.

China, 200 B.C.

About the time of the Han period, the Chinese text Chòu-peï contains a discussion of the Pythagorean Theorem based on the diagram at the right.

1. Calculate the length of the third side of each triangle. Give each answer to one decimal place where necessary.

a)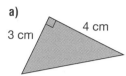
4 cm
3 cm

b)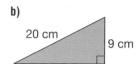
20 cm
9 cm

c)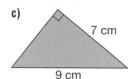
7 cm
9 cm

2. Calculate the length of the diagonal of each rectangle. Give each answer to one decimal place where necessary.

a)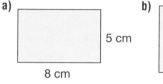
5 cm
8 cm

b)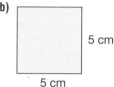
5 cm
5 cm

c)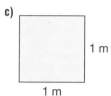
1 m
1 m

3. a) Calculate the areas of the three squares in the diagram below.
   b) Calculate the lengths of the sides of the squares.
   c) What patterns can you find in the results?

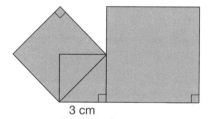
3 cm

4. In the diagram from Chòu-peï on page 310, suppose the small square in the middle has an area of 1 cm². Without using the Pythagorean Theorem, calculate the side length of the large square.

5. An archaeologist measures a pyramid. She finds that the base is a square with a side length of 90 m. The slant height is 60 m. Calculate the height of the pyramid to the nearest metre.

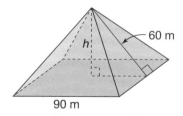
60 m
h
90 m

6. a) Get a cardboard box. Measure its length, width, and height.
   b) Calculate the lengths of the diagonals of the faces of the box.
   c) What do you think is meant by the *body diagonal* of the box? Use the Pythagorean Theorem to calculate the length of the body diagonal of the box.
   d) Use a ruler or a tape measure to check your results.

Review

1. Write each product as a power.
   a) $3^5 \times 3^2$ b) $(-2)^4(-2)^3$
   c) $-2^3 \times 2^5$ d) $15^3 \times 15^2$
   e) $18^{18} \times 18^3$ f) $(-24)^5(-24)^{11}$

2. Write each quotient as a power.
   a) $4^5 \div 4^3$ b) $3^8 \div 3^6$
   c) $7^6 \div 7^5$ d) $\dfrac{12^8}{12^8}$
   e) $\dfrac{16^3}{16^2}$ f) $\dfrac{25^{15}}{25^{12}}$

3. a) Can you apply the laws of exponents to simplify $5^4 \times 4^5$? Explain.
   b) Can you apply the laws of exponents to simplify $9^2 \div 27^2$? Explain.

4. What does each power mean? Evaluate each power.
   a) 5^3 b) 3^5 c) 5^{-3}
   d) 3^{-5} e) $(-5)^3$ f) $(-3)^5$
   g) $(-5)^{-3}$ h) $(-3)^{-5}$ i) 3^0

5. Which is the greater number in each pair?
   a) 8^3, 5^4 b) 8^{-3}, 5^{-4}
   c) 6^3, 4^4 d) 6^{-3}, 4^{-4}
   e) 9^2, 2^6 f) 9^{-2}, 2^{-6}

6. There is only one power of 5 between 1000 and 10 000. Which number is it?

7. Use the laws of exponents to write each expression as a product or quotient of powers.
   a) $(4 \times 5)^3$ b) $(3 \times 4)^{-2}$
   c) $(12 \div 3)^5$ d) $(27 \div 9)^{-3}$
   e) $(12 \times 7)^2$ f) $\left(\dfrac{-5}{2}\right)^4$
   g) $\left(\dfrac{24}{28}\right)^{-5}$ h) $\left(\dfrac{-56}{84}\right)^3$

8. Use the laws of exponents to write each expression as a single power.
   a) $(5^2)^2$ b) $(8^3)^4$
   c) $(12^5)^2$ d) $(9^3)^{-1}$
   e) $[(-5)^2]^3$ f) $[(-3)^4]^{-2}$

9. Use a calculator. Evaluate each expression two different ways:
   i) by doing the operations in the brackets first
   ii) by using the exponent laws
   Compare the results to confirm they are equal.
   a) $(3 \times 5)^4$ b) $\left(\dfrac{2}{5}\right)^3$ c) $(4^3)^4$
   d) $(4 \times 2)^3$ e) $(56 \div 7)^2$ f) $(2^5)^5$

10. Write each expression as a power.
    a) $10^4 \times 10^9$ b) $7.3^5 \times 7.3^3$
    c) $(-12)^6 \times (-12)^8$ d) $8^7 \div 8^2$
    e) $9.4^{-4} \div 9.4^{-11}$ f) $(-3)^8 \div (-3)^{-5}$
    g) $(3^2)^2$ h) $\dfrac{6.25^8}{6.25^3}$
    i) $\dfrac{8^6 \times 8^4}{8^3}$ j) $\dfrac{2^5}{2^3 \times 2^8}$
    k) $\dfrac{4^{-3} \times 4^{10}}{4^5 \times 4^{-2}}$ l) $\dfrac{(-7)^2 \times (-7)^9}{(-7)^3 \times (-7)^4}$

11. Simplify each algebraic expression.
    a) $m^5 \times m^9$ b) $3s^{-6} \times 8s^8$
    c) $\dfrac{21a^{-4}}{-7a^{10}}$ d) $(-j)^6 \div (-j)^9$
    e) $-12r^{-5} \times 6r^{-11}$ f) $(-p)^7 \div (-p)^{-16}$
    g) $(a^2b^2)^3$ h) $(3q^2)^2$
    i) $(2x^3y^5)^2$ j) $5(v^2y^{-3})^{-1}$

12. Simplify.
    a) $\dfrac{15c^5d^8}{5c^3d^6}$ b) $\dfrac{8f^{-4}g^3}{-12f^6g^{-7}}$
    c) $\dfrac{-15s^3t^{-4}}{-5s^{-2}t^{-8}}$ d) $\dfrac{(-m)^5n^3}{(-m)^7n^{-3}}$
    e) $\dfrac{27p^{-6}q^{-4}}{-3p^{-2}q^{-8}}$ f) $\dfrac{(-a)^7(-b)^{-4}}{(-a)^{-2}(-b)^{-9}}$

13. Refer to *Example 1* on page 296. The moon is about 3.84×10^5 km from Earth.
    a) How many times as great as the diameter of Earth is the distance to the moon?
    b) Suppose Earth is the size of the circle in *Example 1*. How far away would the moon be on this scale?

14. Refer to *Example 1* on page 296. The sun is about 1.5×10^9 km from Earth.
    a) How many times as great as the diameter of Earth is the distance to the sun?

b) Suppose Earth is the size of the circle in *Example 1*. How far away would the sun be on this scale?

15. One diatom has a mass of about 1×10^{-12} g. It is estimated that 1 L of sea water contains as many as 1×10^7 diatoms. Determine the mass of the diatoms in 1 L of sea water.

16. During the last 60 years, more than 8.5×10^7 Monopoly games have been sold worldwide.
    a) Find out how much play money there is in a Monopoly game.
    b) How much Monopoly money has been printed during the last 60 years?
    c) The world population is about 5.5 billion. Suppose all this Monopoly money were distributed evenly among all the people on Earth. What would be the value of each person's share?

17. One grain of grass pollen has an estimated mass of 5×10^{-9} g. How many pollen grains are there in 1 g of grass pollen?

18. A unit for measuring astronomical distances is the light-year, which is the distance light travels in one year. The speed of light is 3×10^8 m/s. Calculate the approximate number of:
    a) metres in one light-year
    b) kilometres in one light-year

19. The Andromeda galaxy is the farthest heavenly body that can be seen with the naked eye. Its distance from Earth is about 2.3 million light-years. Calculate the distance to the Andromeda galaxy in each unit.
    a) kilometres   **b)** metres

20. Write the two square roots of each number.
    a) 36   **b)** 400   **c)** 441
    d) 256   **e)** 0.49   **f)** 0.01

21. Estimate each square root to one decimal place.
    a) $\sqrt{18}$ **b)** $\sqrt{35}$ **c)** $\sqrt{87}$
    d) $\sqrt{107}$ **e)** $\sqrt{150}$ **f)** $\sqrt{210}$

22. Simplify each expression. Estimate the result where necessary.
    a) $\sqrt{4} + \sqrt{81}$ **b)** $\sqrt{4 + 81}$
    c) $\sqrt{81} - \sqrt{4}$ **d)** $\sqrt{81 - 4}$
    e) $\sqrt{4} \times \sqrt{81}$ **f)** $\sqrt{4 \times 81}$
    g) $\sqrt{81 + \sqrt{4}}$ **h)** $\sqrt{\sqrt{81} - \sqrt{4}}$

23. **a)** Find the perimeter of a square with area 49 cm².
    b) Find the approximate perimeter of a square with area 150 cm².

24. Does each number appear to be rational or irrational? Explain.
    a) 2.147 474 474 474…
    b) −6.132 133 134…
    c) 72.041 296 478…
    d) 0.165 165 516 555…
    e) −2.236 067 977 749…
    f) −4.317 495

25. Classify each number as natural, integer, rational, or irrational. Some numbers will belong to more than one set.
    a) $\frac{4}{5}$ **b)** $0.2\overline{17}$
    c) −6   **d)** $\sqrt{225}$
    e) 6.121 121 12...   **f)** 1.8×10^{-4}
    g) 4.76×10^3 **h)** $\sqrt{27}$

26. Give examples of two rational numbers between the numbers in each pair.
    a) 3.65, 3.69
    b) −1.476, −1.47
    c) $0.3\overline{97}$, 0.4
    d) $-5.3\overline{76}$, $-5.3\overline{7}$
    e) $\frac{8}{9}$, $\frac{9}{10}$
    f) 2.236 067…, 2.236 071 23…

Designing a Scale Model of the Solar System

The Voyager 2 spacecraft was launched in 1977 on a journey
of discovery that took over 10 years to complete. Its goal was
to travel to the outer planets of our solar system: Jupiter,
Saturn, Uranus, and Neptune. The cameras and scientific
equipment it carried have provided information about these
planets as well as stunning photos like those you see here.

The Apollo 11 spacecraft launched in 1969 reached the moon in only
4 days. Why did it take the Voyager so long to complete its journey?

The answer lies in the vast distances which separate the planets.
One way to visualize the incredibly large is to design a scale model of
the solar system.

ACTIVITY 1

Before you can begin to design your model, you will need to
collect some data about the solar system.

The diameter of the sun is about 1.40×10^9 m.

DATA DISK

Do some research to find the mean diameter of each planet in our solar
system and its distance from the sun, in metres. This information can be
found in the *Moon and Planets* database on the data disk. Express each
measurement in scientific notation.

ACTIVITY 2

Obtain a spherical object to represent the sun. Measure and record
the diameter of this object. Calculate how many times as small as
the diameter of the sun is the diameter of your object. This figure
establishes the scale for your model.

ACTIVITY 3

Use the scale established in *Activity 2*. Calculate the diameters
of the objects you would need to represent the planets in your
scale model. Think of as many objects as you can with these diameters.
As you do this, keep in mind:
* There will probably not be objects with the exact diameters you
  require. Use other objects whose diameters are approximations of
  the diameters you require.
* If the diameters of the objects are too small, you may need a
  larger object to represent the sun. Conversely, if the diameters of
  the objects are too large, you may need a smaller object for the sun.

ACTIVITY 4

Use the scale established in *Activity 2*. Calculate the distances from the sun to the objects that represent the planets in your model. Try to visualize where they would be in relation to your sun.

ACTIVITY 5

After the sun, the moon is the celestial body which has the most influence on Earth. The moon has a diameter of about 3.5×10^6 m and is about 3.8×10^8 m from Earth. About how far from Earth would the moon be in your model? How does this compare with the distance from Earth to one of the planets visited by Voyager 2?

ACTIVITY 6

Research to find more information about the Voyager 2 spacecraft, its journey, and the planets it visited. Some questions you may wish to research include:

How was Voyager 2 powered and how was its flight path controlled?

What scientific equipment was on board the craft? How was the information it gathered sent to Earth?

What new information did we learn about the outer planets and their moons?

What happened to the Voyager spacecraft after it reached Neptune in 1989?

ACTIVITY 7

Construct a scale drawing showing the sun and planets as circles. You could use a Draw program that allows you to draw circles with a given radius or diameter. Since the sun is much larger than any of the planets, you might want to show only part of the sun on your drawing.

COMMUNICATING
The Ideas

Write a brief report describing how you would create a scale model of our solar system. Summarize the results of your research and investigations. Include tables and drawings.

POLYNOMIALS

WHAT'S COMING UP?

DEPARTMENTS

Linking Ideas

Minds on Math Project

Start With What You Know

Packaging is important in the food industry. If the surface area of a can of food can be reduced, without changing its volume, the packaging is cheaper and costs are reduced.

In earlier grades, you learned formulas for the surface area and volume of a cylinder. Working with formulas involves some of the skills you will apply in this chapter when working with polynomials.

The surface area A of a cylinder is given by $A = 2\pi rh + 2\pi r^2$, and the volume V of a cylinder is given by $V = \pi r^2 h$, where r represents radius and h represents height.

Each can in the photograph above has radius 4.1 cm. For these cylinders, the formulas above can be expressed in terms of h only.

- $A \doteq 25.8h + 105.6$
- $V \doteq 52.8h$

Use these formulas to complete exercise 1.

1. a) Calculate the surface areas and volumes of cans with radii 4.1 cm and heights of 7.6 cm, 9.0 cm, and 14.9 cm.
   b) Calculate the height of a can with radius 4.1 cm and surface area 363.6 cm^2. What is the volume of this can?
   c) Suppose a manufacturer doubles the height of a can. Would the surface area double? Would the volume double? Explain how you know.

3.4 cm

3.0 cm

5.0 cm

Each can shown here has a height of 12.0 cm. For these cylinders, the formulas for surface area and volume can be expressed in terms of r only.

- $A \doteq 75.4r + 6.28r^2$
- $V \doteq 37.7r^2$

Use these formulas to complete exercise 2.

2. a) Calculate the surface area and the volume of each can shown.
   b) Suppose a manufacturer doubled the radius of a can. Would the surface area double? Would the volume double? Explain how you know.

All the cans on a supermarket shelf arrived at the store in cartons. Cans of Cloverleaf tuna are sometimes packaged in cartons of 24. The cans are arranged in 2 layers. Each layer is 4 cans long and 3 cans wide.

Recall that 2, 3, and 4 are factors of 24 and $2 \times 3 \times 4 = 24$.

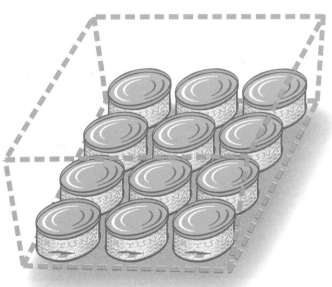

3. a) Suppose the carton containing the tuna had different dimensions.
   i) How many different ways could the tuna be arranged in the carton?
   ii) Use the answer to part i to list as many sets of three factors of 24 as you can.
   b) Other cans of Cloverleaf tuna are packaged in cartons of 48. Repeat part a for this carton.

6.1 THE CONCEPT OF A POLYNOMIAL

Developing the Ideas

▶▶ *Through Instruction*

Jennifer brought some money home from her vacation in the United States. She had some Canadian and some U.S. bills.

To calculate the amount of money she has, Jennifer adds the U.S. money: $20 + $10 + $10 + $5 + $1 = $46 U.S. and the Canadian money: $10 + $5 + $5 = $20 Can

The terms which represent Canadian money are *like* terms. They can be combined into a single value. Similarly, the terms which represent U.S. money are like terms. However, a term that represents Canadian money and a term that represents U.S. money are unlike terms. They cannot be combined into a single value.

We can say only that Jennifer has $46 U.S. and $20 Can.

In an earlier chapter, you worked with like and unlike terms in the form of algebra tiles.

Recall:
This tile is called a 1-tile.

It measures 1 unit on each side.
It has an area of 1 square unit.

This tile is called a variable-tile.
We call it an x-tile.

It measures 1 unit by x units.
It has an area of x square units.

We now add a new algebra tile:

This tile is a square measuring x units on each side.
It has an area of $x \times x$ or x^2 square units.

Since x is a variable, we cannot combine the areas of a 1-tile, an x-tile, and an x^2-tile to form a single term. That is, these tiles represent unlike terms.

How would we represent the tiles shown below?

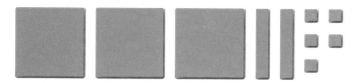

We think: 3 x^2-tiles + 2 x-tiles + 5 1-tiles
We write: $3x^2 + 2x + 5$

▶▶ *Through Discussion*

There are special names for terms and combinations of terms.
Look at the table below. Answer each question in the last column.

All of these are monomials.	None of these is a monomial.	Which of these is a monomial?
$3x^2$ $4x$ $-6m^3$ $7x^2y$ $-\frac{1}{2}bc$	$3x + 4$ $4y^2 - y$ $\frac{-2}{z}$	$3x + 2$ $\frac{-5y^2}{x}$ $-6xy$

All of these are binomials.	None of these is a binomial.	Which of these is a binomial?
$3x + 7$ $2y^2 - y$ $4 - x^4$ $\frac{1}{2}z^3 - 4zy$	$3x^5$ $x^2 - 5x + 7$ $+1$ $\frac{1}{a} + \frac{1}{b}$	$\frac{1}{2}x^2 - 4xy$ $-2x^2y^3$ $3a^2 - 2a + 4$ $\frac{1}{a} - 5$

All of these are trinomials.	None of these is a trinomial.	Which of these is a trinomial?
$3x^4 + 7x - 6$ $4ab - 2bc + c^3$ $1 - 4x - 3y^2$	$5x^4 - 2xy$ $3a + 7$ $6x^3 - \frac{2}{y^2} + 2z$	$1 - 2x^5 + \frac{1}{x}$ -4 $x^2 - 3a^2 + 4$ $x^2 + \frac{1}{y^2} - x$

All of these are polynomials.	None of these is a polynomial.	Which of these is a polynomial?
$-3xy$ $3a^3 - 5z^2 - 14$ $11 - d^2$ $3x^3 - 5x + y - 7$	$4a^2 - \frac{2}{b} + 1$ $\frac{-2}{z}$ $\frac{1}{x}$	$2x^2 + \frac{3y}{x} - 4y^3$ $3x + 2$ $\frac{-5y^2}{-x}$

A *polynomial* is one term or the sum of two or more terms.
A *monomial* is a polynomial with one term.
A *binomial* is a polynomial with two terms.
A *trinomial* is a polynomial with three terms.

The term $3x^2$ has *coefficient* 3. The trinomial $3x^2 - 2x + 5$ contains coefficients 3 and -2; the number 5 is a *constant term*. The variable is x.

In a polynomial, exponents that occur with variables are whole numbers. Since $\frac{1}{x} = x^{-1}$, $\frac{1}{x}$ is not a polynomial.

▶▶ Using Manipulatives

We represented the polynomial $3x^2 + 2x + 5$ using algebra tiles. This polynomial has terms that have positive coefficients. We can also represent a polynomial such as $3x^2 - 2x + 5$, which has a term with a negative coefficient. We flip the two x-tiles.

We see: $3x^2 - 2x + 5$
We think: 3 x^2-tiles, 2 flipped x-tiles, and 5 1-tiles
We display:

1. Represent each polynomial using algebra tiles.
    a) $-3x^2 + 1$ **b)** $6 - x$ **c)** $3x^2 - x - 4$ **d)** 5   **e)** $4x$

▶▶ Through a Guided Example

We can combine algebra tiles to form a rectangle.
We can write the area and the perimeter of the rectangle as a polynomial.

Example ....

Write polynomials that represent the perimeter and area of each rectangle.

a)

b)

Solution

a) The rectangle comprises 5 x-tiles.
  Its length is 5.
  Its width is x.
  The perimeter is $x + 5 + x + 5 = 2x + 10$
  The area is $5 \times x = 5x$

b) The rectangle comprises 3 x^2-tiles.
  Its length is $3x$.
  Its width is x.
  The perimeter is $x + 3x + x + 3x = 8x$
  The area is $3x \times x = 3x^2$

Working with Mathematics

Something to talk about

1. How much money is represented?

2. Explain how adding money in the same currency is similar to adding like terms.

3. Which of these expressions are polynomials? Give reasons.

a) $5x - 3$ **b)** $6x + 7x^2 - 1$

c) $2x + 3y - x^2$ **d)** $2 + \dfrac{1}{x}$

e) 3 **f)** $-\dfrac{4}{y^2}$

4. State whether each expression is a monomial, a binomial, or a trinomial. Give reasons.

a) $3x + 4$ **b)** $-x^2$

c) $-2 - y^2$ **d)** 10

e) $5 - 2x + 3y$ **f)** $4x$

g) $5x^2 + 4y^2 + x$ **h)** $-3 - y$

5. For each display of tiles, state a polynomial that represents the total area.

a)

b)

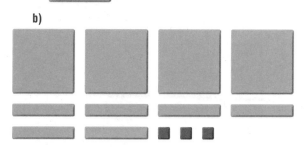

c)

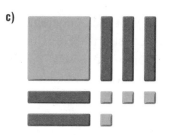

d)

e)

Practice

6. Which of the following expressions are polynomials?

a) $2x + 3$ **b)** $5x^2 - 2x + 1$

c) $3 + \dfrac{2}{x}$ **d)** $xy - 4x + 3$

e) 7 **f)** $\dfrac{2}{3}a$

g) $7\sqrt{x}$ **h)** $x\sqrt{7}$

7. State whether each expression is a monomial, a binomial, or a trinomial.

a) $2x + 3$ **b)** $5xy$

c) $7 - a - 3a^2$ **d)** $-k^2$

e) 43 **f)** $7a - 4b$

8. State the coefficient in each term.

a) $14x$ **b)** $7y^2$ **c)** a

d) $-b^2$ **e)** πr^2 **f)** $\sqrt{3}m^3n$

9. State the constant term in each polynomial.

a) $5x^2 - 2x + 6$ **b)** $-x^2y - 5$

c) $7 - 3x - 2y$ **d)** $\dfrac{1}{2}m^2 - \dfrac{2}{5} + 5m$

e) $7x^2 - 5y^2$ **f)** $\dfrac{x}{2}$

10. State the coefficients in each polynomial. Identify the constant term if there is one.

   a) $6p + 2q + 3$ **b)** $a - 2b + 9c$

   c) $1.8C + 32$ **d)** $2\pi r$

   e) $7x^2 - 3xy - 9$ **f)** $4.9s^3 - 1.2s^2 - 0.5s + 2$

11. State the like terms.

   a) $5a$, $3b$, $5c$, a^2, $-a$, $3d$, $3e$

   b) $4x$, $3y^2$, $4z$, $2y$, y^2, $4w$

   c) $9g$, $6h$, $9g^2$, $\frac{1}{9}g$, $\frac{1}{6}h^2$, g^2

   d) 16, d^2, d, f, -8, $0.5d$, $7d^3$

12. Evaluate $3n + 4$ for each value of n.

   a) 1 **b)** 3 **c)** 4 **d)** -1

13. Evaluate $3x - 5$ for each value of x.

   a) 0 **b)** 1 **c)** -1 **d)** 7

Work together

14. Use algebra tiles to represent each polynomial. Take turns to explain how you did it.

   a) $x^2 + 3x + 2$ **b)** $2x^2 + x + 7$

   c) $-2x^2 - 3$ **d)** $2x^2 - 5x - 4$

   e) $-x^2 - 3x + 2$ **f)** $x^2 - 4x$

15. Write a polynomial that represents the perimeter of each rectangle.

   a)

   b)

   c)

16. Write a polynomial that represents the area of each rectangle in exercise 15.

17. Represent each rectangle using algebra tiles.

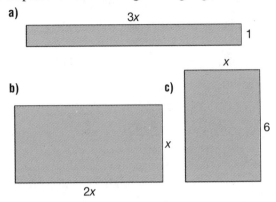

   a) $3x$ by 1

   b) $2x$ by x

   c) x by 6

18. For each rectangle in exercise 17, write a polynomial that represents its perimeter and a polynomial that represents its area.

On your own

19. a) Write an example of an algebraic expression which is *not* a polynomial.

   b) Write an example of a polynomial which does not use the variable x.

20. Write a polynomial that represents the perimeter of each rectangle.

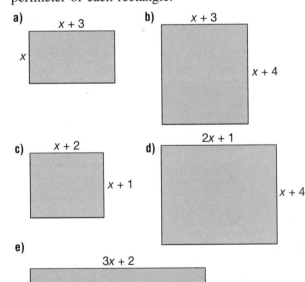

   a) x by $x + 3$

   b) $x + 3$ by $x + 4$

   c) $x + 2$ by $x + 1$

   d) $2x + 1$ by $x + 4$

   e) $3x + 2$ by $x + 3$

21. Substitute into the polynomials in exercise 20 to find the perimeter of each rectangle when $x = 4$ cm.

22. Substitute into the polynomials in exercise 20 to find the perimeter of each rectangle when $x = 1.5$ m.

23. **a)** Write a polynomial that represents the area of a square of side length $2s$.

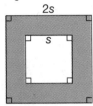

2s

s

b) Write a polynomial that represents the area of:
   i) the large square
   ii) the small square
   iii) the shaded region

c) Find the area of each figure in part b when $s = 2.5$ cm.

24. The formula gives the temperature in an oven, T degrees Celsius, n minutes after it has been turned on.

$T = -n^2 + 30n + 20$, for $n < 14$

Find each temperature.
a) 7 min after the oven was turned on
b) 10 min after the oven was turned on

25. The formula gives the stopping distance d metres for a car travelling at v kilometres per hour. $d = 0.20v + 0.015v^2$

Find the stopping distance for each speed.
a) 50 km/h   **b)** 100 km/h

Extend your thinking

26. **a)** Write a polynomial that represents the circumference of a circle with diameter $2x$ (below left).

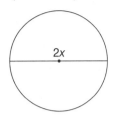

2x

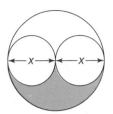

x   x

b) Write a polynomial that represents the perimeter of the shaded region (above right).

c) Write a polynomial that represents the area of each small circle, and a polynomial that represents the area of the large circle (above right).

d) Write a polynomial that represents the area of the shaded region.

e) Create a similar problem of your own. Modify the shading in the figure above, or adapt one of the figures below.

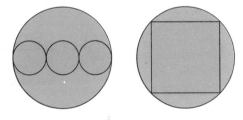

COMMUNICATING
The Ideas

The prefixes mono-, bi-, tri-, and poly- mean one, two, three, and many respectively.

a) In your journal, list some other words that contain these prefixes. Then consult your dictionary to extend your list.

b) Are there any other prefixes for one, two, three or many?

POLY

The Search for a Polynomial to Generate Prime Numbers

A prime number is any whole number, greater than 1, that is divisible by only itself and 1. Since the discovery of prime numbers, mathematicians have attempted to find a polynomial for generating them.

In 1772, the great Swiss mathematician, Leonhard Euler, devised the polynomial $n^2 - n + 41$ for the generation of primes.

We will use a spreadsheet to check that this polynomial does generate primes.

TEMPLATE DISK

1. Set up the spreadsheet as shown.
   Enter different numbers, up to 10, in cell A2.
   Are all the numbers generated in cell B2 primes?

	A	B
1	N	Euler's polynomial
2		=A2*A2-A2+41

2. Enter several other numbers, up to 40, in cell A2. Use your calculator to check that each number in cell B2 is prime.

3. **a)** Enter 41 in cell A2.
   b) What is 41^2?
   c) Does Euler's polynomial generate a prime number when $n = 41$?

In 1879, E.B. Escott devised the polynomial $n^2 - 79n + 1601$. We'll insert this polynomial on the spreadsheet beside Euler's polynomial.

	A	B	C
1	N	Euler's polynomial	Escott's polynomial
2		=A2*A2-A2+41	=A2*A2-79*A2+1601

4. Test Escott's polynomial for several values of N. Use your calculator to check if each number in cell C2 is prime.

5. Compare the numbers in column C with those in column B.
   a) Do you notice any similarities?
   b) What patterns can you find in the numbers in column C?

6. **a)** Enter 80 in cell A2. Show that the number in cell C2 is *not* prime.
   b) Find another value of N for which the number in cell C2 is not prime.

7. Adapt the spreadsheet to find a value of n for which each of the following polynomials does *not* produce a prime number.
   a) $n^2 + n - 1$ **b)** $n^2 - n + 17$ **c)** $n^2 - n + 41, n \neq 41$

Currently, there is no known polynomial that produces *only* prime numbers. There is also no known polynomial that will produce all the prime numbers.

Mathematics & Technology

Linking Ideas

Developing the Ideas

Polynomials, like numbers, can be added and subtracted. To add two polynomials, we combine like terms. Recall how you combined like terms in Chapter 2. The only difference now is that we include x^2-tiles.

▶ ▶ *Using Manipulatives*

We can use algebra tiles to add polynomials.
Suppose we add $2x^2 + 3x + 1$ and $-x^2 + 2x - 4$.

We write: We display:

$(2x^2 + 3x + 1) + (-x^2 + 2x - 4)$

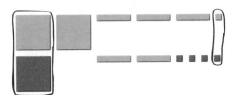

We think:
Combine like terms. Use the Zero Principle. Each pair of opposite tiles forms a 0-pair. 1 x^2-tile, 5 x-tiles, and 3 flipped 1-tiles remain.
From the tiles, $(2x^2 + 3x + 1) + (-x^2 + 2x - 4) = x^2 + 5x - 3$

1. Use algebra tiles to add each pair of polynomials.
  a) $(x^2 + 2x - 1) + (2x^2 + 3x + 3)$
  b) $(3x^2 - x + 5) + (x^2 - 2x - 4)$
  c) $(-2x^2 - 3x - 4) + (-2x^2 - 5x - 1)$
  d) $(x^2 - 2x - 4) + (-x^2 + 2x + 4)$

2. a) How are the polynomials in exercise 1d alike?
  b) How are the polynomials different?

You should have discovered that $x^2 - 2x - 4$ and $-x^2 + 2x + 4$ have a sum of 0. Polynomials that have a sum of 0 are called *opposites*. Recall that flipping the tiles representing $x^2 - 2x - 4$ gives its opposite, $-x^2 + 2x + 4$. We can use this to subtract one polynomial from another.

Suppose we subtract $-2x^2 + x - 9$ from $3x^2 + 5x - 6$.
We write: $(3x^2 + 5x - 6) - (-2x^2 + x - 9)$
We think: We display:
Flip the tiles representing $(-2x^2 + x - 9)$.

Combine like terms. Use the Zero Principle.
5 x^2-tiles, 4 x-tiles, and 3 1-tiles remain.
From the tiles,
$(3x^2 + 5x - 6) - (-2x^2 + x - 9) = 5x^2 + 4x + 3$

3. Use algebra tiles to perform each subtraction.
  a) $(-x^2 + 5x + 4) - (2x^2 + 3x + 3)$
  b) $(3x^2 + 4) - (x^2 + 2)$

▶▶ *Through Guided Examples*

To add polynomials, we group like terms and simplify.

Example 1

Simplify. $(-2x^2 + 6x - 7) + (3x^2 - x - 2)$

Solution

$(-2x^2 + 6x - 7) + (3x^2 - x - 2) = -2x^2 + 6x - 7 + 3x^2 - x - 2$

$$= -2x^2 + 3x^2 + 6x - x - 7 - 2 \quad \triangleleft \text{ Grouping like terms}$$
$$= x^2 + 5x - 9$$

When we subtract a polynomial from itself, we get zero.
For example, $(x^2 - 2x - 4) - (x^2 - 2x - 4) = 0$

We get the same result if we add the polynomial and its opposite.
For example, $(x^2 - 2x - 4) + (-x^2 + 2x + 4) = 0$

So, to subtract a polynomial, we add its opposite.

Example 2

a) Simplify. $(3x^2 + 5x - 6) - (-2x^2 + x - 9)$

b) Find the value of the polynomial when:

  i) $x = 2$ **ii)** $x = -1$

Solution

a) $(3x^2 + 5x - 6) - (-2x^2 + x - 9)$
$= (3x^2 + 5x - 6) + (2x^2 - x + 9) \quad \triangleleft \text{ The opposite of } -2x^2 + x - 9$
$= 5x^2 + 4x + 3$

b) **i)** When $x = 2$, the value of the polynomial is:

$5(2)^2 + 4(2) + 3 = 5(4) + 8 + 3$
$$= 20 + 11$$
$$= 31$$

  ii) When $x = -1$, the value of the polynomial is:

$5(-1)^2 + 4(-1) + 3 = 5(1) - 4 + 3$
$$= 5 - 1$$
$$= 4$$

Recall that some polynomials cannot be represented with algebra tiles.
We use the above principles to combine these polynomials.

Example 3

Simplify. $(3x^4 - 2x^2 + 3x - 9) - (x^2 - 4x + 2)$

Solution

$(3x^4 - 2x^2 + 3x - 9) - (x^2 - 4x + 2) = (3x^4 - 2x^2 + 3x - 9) + (-x^2 + 4x - 2)$
$$= 3x^4 - 3x^2 + 7x - 11$$

Working with Mathematics

Something to talk about

1. Show each polynomial using algebra tiles. Then flip the tiles and state its opposite.
   a) $3x^2 + 7$
   b) $2x^2 - 5x + 3$
   c) $-4n^2 + 3n - 5$

2. What is the sum of a polynomial and its opposite?

3. Is there a polynomial which is equal to its opposite? Explain.

4. a) State the opposite of the polynomial $3x^2 - 2x - 1$.
   b) Then state the opposite of your answer.
   c) What do you discover?
   d) Do you think this is true for all polynomials? Explain.

5. a) Suppose you have a display of algebra tiles representing a polynomial. How do you obtain the tile display for the opposite polynomial?
   b) How do you determine the opposite of a polynomial without using algebra tiles?

6. State each subtraction as an addition.
   a) $(3x^2 + 5) - (2x^2 + 1)$
   b) $(x^2 + 2x) - (-x - 1)$
   c) $(x^2 + 3x - 2) - (-x^2 - x + 1)$

7. Explain how 0-pairs are used with algebra tiles to simplify two polynomials.

Practice

8. Simplify.
   a) $(6x + 2) + (3x + 4)$
   b) $(5a - 3) + (2a + 7)$
   c) $(8 - 4m) + (-3 - 2m)$
   d) $(-x + 4) + (7x - 2)$
   e) $(4n^2 - 3n - 1) + (2n^2 - 5n - 3)$
   f) $(3x^2 + 6x - 8) + (-5x^2 - x + 4)$
   g) $(2 - 3c + c^2) + (5 - 4c - 4c^2)$
   h) $(8 - 2n - n^2) + (-3 - n + 4n^2)$
   i) $(ab + 3b - 5) + (2ab - 4b - 6)$
   j) $(mn - 5m - 2) + (-6n + 3m + 7)$

9. State the opposite of each polynomial.
   a) $5x + 2$
   b) $2 - 3a$
   c) $7x^2 - 5x + 4$
   d) $5 - 2m - 4m^2$
   e) $6n^2 - 3n + 1$
   f) $-\frac{1}{2}x - 5$

10. Simplify.
    a) $(-2x + 3) - (3x + 2)$
    b) $(4 - 5n) - (-6n + 2)$
    c) $(8a^2 + 2a - 3) - (-6a^2 + 4a + 7)$
    d) $(-6x^2 + 5x + 1) - (4x^2 + 5 - 2x)$
    e) $(3 - 2m - n^2) - (7 - 6m + n^2)$
    f) $(2 + 6x^2) - (7 - 3x^2)$
    g) $(5 - 6t^2) - (3 - t^2)$
    h) $(5x^2 - 3x) - (-3x + 5x^2)$

11. Simplify.
    a) $(3x - 2) - (x - 1)$
    b) $(2a + 3) + (6a - 1)$
    c) $(5x^2 - 3x) - (x^2 + 2x)$
    d) $(5t - 4) + (3t - 1)$
    e) $(3 - 4x + x^2) - (2x - x^2)$
    f) $(3n^2 - 6n + 5) - (3n^2 - 2n - 1)$

Work together

12. Use algebra tiles to represent, then simplify, this expression. Explain how you did it.
    $(x^2 - 2x + 3) + (4x - 2)$

13. a) What polynomial sum do the tiles represent?

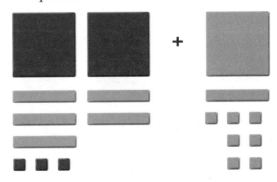

    b) Explain how to use the algebra tiles to simplify the sum of the polynomials in part a.

14. Take turns to explain why the two polynomials are not opposites.

a) $5x^2 - 3x - 2$
$5x^2 + 3x + 2$

b) $x^2 + 7x - 9$
$-x^3 - 7x + 9$

c) $-4y + y^2 + 11$
$4y - y^2 + 11$

d) $x^3 - 4x^2 + 9$
$-x^3 + 4x^2 - x$

15. a) Use algebra tiles to represent this difference of polynomials.
$(3x^2 - 2x + 5) - (x^2 - 3x - 1)$

b) Explain how you use the algebra tiles to simplify the expression in part a.

16. Simplify. Use algebra tiles if you wish.

a) $(3x^2 - 2x + 4) + (x^2 + 3)$

b) $(3x^2 - 2x + 4) - (x^2 + 3)$

c) $(5m - 2m^2) + (m^2 - 6)$

d) $(5m - 2m^2) - (m^2 - 6)$

17. Simplify. Find the value of the polynomial when: **i)** $x = 1$ **ii)** $x = -2$

a) $(1 - 2x^2 - x) + (2x - 3x^2 - 7)$

b) $(3 - 2x^2 - x) - (2x - 3x^2 - 7)$

18. Each rectangle is divided into squares and rectangles. Write one polynomial for the area of each piece and one polynomial for the area of the entire rectangle.

a)

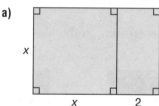

b)

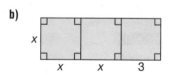

c)

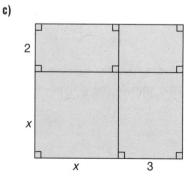

d)

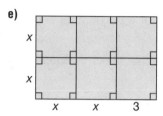

e)

On your own

19. Simplify.

a) $(3x^2 - 7x + 4) + (5x - 7x^2 + 6)$

b) $(6 - 3x + x^2) + (9 - x)$

c) $(1 - 7x^2 + 2x) + (x^3 - 3x^2 + 7)$

d) $(5x - x^2) + (3x + x^2 - 7)$

20. Simplify.

a) $(5x^2 + 7x + 9) - (3x^2 + 4x + 2)$

b) $(11m^2 - 5m + 8) - (7m^2 + m - 3)$

c) $(4a^2 - 3a^3 - 7) - (a^2 - 2a^3 - 13)$

d) $(-6x^2 + 17x - 4) - (3x^2 + 12x + 8)$

21. Simplify. Find the value of the polynomial when: **i)** $x = -2$ **ii)** $x = 3$

a) $(3x^2 - 8x + 6) - (-2x^2 + 7x + 3)$

b) $(x^2 - 4x + x^3) - (3x + 5 - x^3)$

22. a) Simplify.

i) $(5 - 2m - m^2) - (7m + 4 - 5m^2)$

ii) $(2m^2 - 5m + 3) - (4 - 3m)$

b) Find the value of each polynomial in part a when $m = 0$.

c) Find the value of each polynomial in part a when $m = -2$.

23. a) Simplify.

i) $(y^2 - 2y) - (5 - 2y)$

ii) $(8y - 5) - (y - 4) + (3y + 1)$

b) Find the value of each polynomial in part a when $y = 4$.

c) Find the value of each polynomial in part a when $y = 1$.

24. Choose any month on a calendar. Then choose a 3 by 3 square of 9 dates. Let x represent the date at the centre of the square.

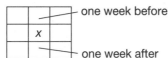

	x	

— one week before

— one week after

a) Write a polynomial for:
  i) the date one week before x
  ii) the date one week after x
  iii) the sum of the dates in each column
  iv) the sum of all 9 dates
b) If you knew the sum of all 9 dates, how could you determine the value of x?

Extend your thinking

25. When the terms of a polynomial in x are arranged from the lowest to the highest powers of x, the polynomial is in *ascending* powers of x.
  a) Simplify. Write the polynomial in ascending powers of x.

  $$7 - (3x^2 + 2x) - (5x + x^2 - 6) - (3x + 3x^2 - 12)$$

  b) Find the value of the polynomial in part a when $x = -0.5$.

COMMUNICATING

The Ideas

Look through this text. In your journal, record three formulas or expressions which cannot be represented with algebra tiles. Explain why they cannot be represented this way.

BOGGLE YOUR MIND

According to the *Guinness Book of Records*, Mrs. Shakuntala Devi is the fastest calculating prodigy in the world. In 1980, in a supervised test at the Computer Department of Imperial College, in London, England, she correctly multiplied 7 686 369 774 870 by 2 465 099 745 779 in 28 seconds without mechanical aid. How many digits are there in the product?

A Magic Birthday Card

Do you recognize the birthday card shown below?

It was a big seller in North America. People who were given the card were probably amused and mystified by the "magic" trick which appeared inside.

Using your birthday and the year of your birth, follow the procedure one step at a time. Why does it work?

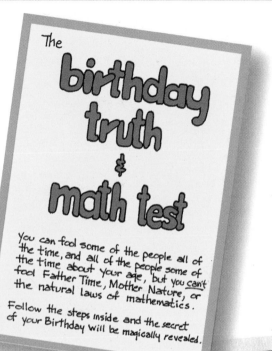

The **birthday truth & math test**

You can fool some of the people all of the time, and all of the people some of the time about your age, but you can't fool Father Time, Mother Nature, or the natural laws of mathematics.

Follow the steps inside and the secret of your Birthday will be magically revealed.

Tools: use a calculator, or scratch paper and pencil. Toes and fingers are permitted.

① Write the number of the <u>month</u> you were born here →☐

× 4

② Multiply that by four

+ 13

③ Now add unlucky "13" (that's both hands and 3 toes) →

× 25

④ Multiply this (number) by twenty five and write the answer here ↘ ☐

− 200

⑤ Subtract two hundred

⑥ Add your birthdate (day of the month) → + ___

× 2

⑦ Double that and write the answer in this box → ☐

⑧ Now transfer this number to ⑨

⑨ Subtract 40 from the number transferred from ⑧. − 40

⑩ Multiply by 50 and write the answer on the line right here → × 50
_____

⑪ Now (whew!), add the last 2 digits of your birth<u>year</u> (the <u>truth!</u>) → + ___

⑫ Think of a number between 10,499 and 10,501 and <u>subtract</u> it from #⑪ and write the answer in this box → − 10,500

☐ *
mo / day / year

Gottacha! Have a Happy Birthday!

Love Shelly

* (If the answer is wrong, two possibilities exist: ① You Lied ② You got thru school by cheating in math. Try it again.)

Understand the problem

- How many digits appear in the final answer in Step 12?
- What digits in this number tell you the year of your birth?
- What digits in this number tell you the month of your birth and the day?

Think of a strategy

- How many pieces of data are needed to specify your birth date?
- What variables might you use to specify an arbitrary birth date?

Carry out the strategy

- The first step in the procedure requires that you multiply the month of your birth by 4.
  Use the variable you chose to represent the number of the month.
  Write an expression for 4 times the number of the month.
- Add 13 to the expression you have written.
- Multiply this expression by 25 and expand.
- Then subtract 200.
- Add the variable that represents the day of your birthday.
- Multiply the expression you have by 2 and then subtract 40.
  Simplify your answer by collecting like terms.
- Multiply your answer by 50.
- Then add the variable representing the birth year and subtract 10 500.

Look back

- Look at your expression. Substitute a few different birth dates into your expression to see if it yields the appropriate numbers. Choose dates for which either or both the month and the day are single and double-digit numbers.
- Does the expression show the year of birth as the last two digits?
- When does it show the day of birth as:
  a) the third and fourth digits?
  b) the second and third digits?
- When does it show the month of birth as:
  a) the first digit?
  b) the first two digits?
- Explain why the trick works for everyone's birthday.

Communicating the Ideas

In your journal, write a description of this problem and your solution.

Developing the Ideas

▶ ▶ *Through Instruction*

In the previous section, we added and subtracted polynomials.

We will begin the multiplication of polynomials by investigating products of polynomials with one term. Recall that a polynomial with only one term is called a monomial.

How would we simplify the product $(3x^2)(5x^3)$?

We recall the meaning of the exponents.

$$
\begin{aligned}
(3x^2)(5x^3) &= (3 \cdot x \cdot x)(5 \cdot x \cdot x \cdot x) &&\triangleleft \text{Writing each term as a product of factors} \\
&= (3)(5)(x \cdot x \cdot x \cdot x \cdot x) &&\triangleleft \text{Rearranging the factors} \\
&= 15x^5 &&\triangleleft \text{Writing } x \cdot x \cdot x \cdot x \cdot x \text{ as } x^5
\end{aligned}
$$

This example and others like it illustrate the following rule for multiplying monomials.

. . . .

> To multiply two monomials, we multiply their coefficients and multiply their variables.

If the variables are the same, we add their exponents.
For example, to multiply $3x^2$ by $5x^3$:

Multiply the coefficients: $3 \times 5 = 15$

$$(3x^2)(5x^3) = 15x^5$$

Add the exponents: $2 + 3 = 5$

Similarly, to simplify the quotient, $\dfrac{7x^6}{3x^2}$, we recall the meaning of the exponents.

$$
\begin{aligned}
\frac{7x^6}{3x^2} &= \frac{7 \cdot x \cdot x \cdot x \cdot x \cdot x \cdot x}{3 \cdot x \cdot x} &&\triangleleft \text{Writing each term as a product of factors} \\
&= \frac{7}{3} \times \frac{x \cdot x \cdot x \cdot x \cdot \cancel{x} \cdot \cancel{x}}{\cancel{x} \cdot \cancel{x}_1} &&\triangleleft \text{Dividing common factors} \\
&= \frac{7}{3}x^4 &&\triangleleft \text{Writing } x \cdot x \cdot x \cdot x \text{ as } x^4
\end{aligned}
$$

This example and others like it illustrate the following rule for dividing monomials.

. . . .

> To divide two monomials, we divide their coefficients and divide their variables.

If the variables are the same, we subtract their exponents.

For example, to divide $7x^6$ by $3x^2$:

Subtract the exponents: $6 - 2 = 4$

$$\frac{7x^6}{3x^2} = \frac{7}{3}x^4$$

Divide the coefficients: $7 \div 3 = \frac{7}{3}$

Sometimes we multiply monomials which are powers.

For example, to simplify $(3x^2)^2(2x^3)^3$, we think of its meaning:

$(3x^2)(3x^2)(2x^3)(2x^3)(2x^3)$

This expression is the product of five monomials. To determine the product, we multiply the coefficients and multiply the variables.

The product of the coefficients is $(3)(3)(2)(2)(2) = 72$

The product of the variables is $(x^2)(x^2)(x^3)(x^3)(x^3) = x^{13}$

$(3x^2)^2(2x^3)^3 = 72x^{13}$

▶▶ *Through Guided Examples*

Example 1

Simplify.

a) $(3x^2)(-2x^3)$

b) $8x^4y \div 6x^2y$

Solution

a) $(3x^2)(-2x^3) = (3)(-2)(x^2)(x^3)$

$\qquad = -6x^{2+3}$

$\qquad = -6x^5$

b) $8x^4y \div 6x^2y = \dfrac{8x^4y}{6x^2y}$

$\qquad\qquad = \dfrac{8}{6} \cdot \dfrac{x^4}{x^2} \cdot \dfrac{y}{y}$

$\qquad\qquad = \dfrac{4}{3}x^{4-2}$

$\qquad\qquad = \dfrac{4}{3}x^2$

Example 2

Simplify. $(2a^2)^4(-5a^3)$

Solution

$(2a^2)^4(-5a^3) = (2a^2)(2a^2)(2a^2)(2a^2)(-5a^3)$

$\qquad\qquad\qquad = -80a^{11}$

Example 3

Simplify. $\dfrac{(2b^2)^4}{(-b)^2}$

Solution

$\dfrac{(2b^2)^4}{(-b)^2} = \dfrac{(2)^4(b^2)^4}{(-b)(-b)}$

$\qquad\qquad = \dfrac{16b^8}{b^2}$

$\qquad\qquad = 16b^{8-2}$

$\qquad\qquad = 16b^6$

Working with Mathematics

Something to talk about

1. Write as a product of factors.

   a) $3x^2$ **b)** $4x^3$

   c) $-x^2$ **d)** $2x^6$

   e) $-\dfrac{1}{2}a^4$ **f)** $9x^2y$

   g) $-6a^2b^2$ **h)** $5m^2n^3$

2. State each product.

   a) $(3x^2)(4x^3)$ **b)** $(-x^2)(2x^6)$

   c) $\left(-\dfrac{1}{2}a^2\right)\left(-\dfrac{1}{2}a^4\right)$ **d)** $(-5a)(6a^2)$

3. State each quotient.

   a) $\dfrac{5m^5}{2m^3}$ **b)** $\dfrac{-25x^5}{10x^2}$ **c)** $\dfrac{30x^6}{-6x^2}$

4. Name a pair of monomials that will satisfy each equation. Is there only one possible answer for each equation?

   a) $\boxed{} \times \boxed{} = 3x^6$ **b)** $\boxed{} \times \boxed{} = -5b^3$

   c) $\boxed{} \times \boxed{} = -6x$ **d)** $\boxed{} \div \boxed{} = 2x^2$

   e) $\boxed{} \div \boxed{} = \dfrac{3}{2}x^3$ **f)** $\boxed{} \div \boxed{} = \dfrac{1}{4}$

Practice

5. Find each product.

   a) $4(3b)$ **b)** $-7(2k)$ **c)** $5(4t)$ **d)** $-2(8p)$

   e) $a(5b)$ **f)** $p(-3q)$ **g)** $n(4m)$ **h)** $x(-2y)$

6. Find each product.

   a) $(3a)(2a)$ **b)** $(-2c)(5c)$ **c)** $(-2a)(-5a)$

   d) $(7x)(3x)$ **e)** $(5x)(2x)$ **f)** $(8y)(-7y)$

   g) $(-x)(-5x)$ **h)** $(3a)(-2a)$ **i)** $(-2a)(-3a)$

7. Simplify.

   a) $(12x)^2$ **b)** $(-3xy)^3$

   c) $-(5ab)^2$ **d)** $(2a)^2$

   e) $(9m^5n)^2$ **f)** $(-3x)^2$

   g) $(-5ab^2)^3$ **h)** $(3mn^4)^2$

8. Find each quotient.

   a) $\dfrac{12x^3}{3}$ **b)** $\dfrac{32y^4}{16}$

   c) $\dfrac{18y^4}{2y}$ **d)** $\dfrac{27m^3}{-9m}$

   e) $(-45y^6) \div (-5y^4)$ **f)** $3n^6 \div 5n^4$

   g) $25x^4 \div (-5x^4)$ **h)** $36c^5 \div 24c^2$

Work together

9. Find each product.

   a) $(x^3)(-x^2)$ **b)** $(2p^2)(3p^3)$

   c) $(6y^3)(-2y)$ **d)** $(3a^2b)(2ab^2)$

   e) $(3x^2)^2(2y)^2$ **f)** $(-2x)^2(-y^2)^3$

10. The base area and height of each solid are given. State the volume of each solid.

   a)   **b)**

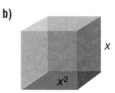

   c)   **d)**

11. Find each quotient.

   a) $15x^3 \div 3x$ **b)** $(-6y^2) \div 2y$

   c) $20a^3 \div (-4a^2)$ **d)** $\dfrac{6b^3n^2}{2b^2n}$

   e) $\dfrac{15m^5a^3}{3m^2a}$ **f)** $\dfrac{21y^6x^2}{7y^3x^2}$

12. The volume and base area of each solid are given. State the height of each solid.

   a)   **b)**

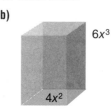

   c)   **d)**

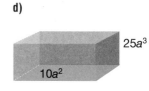

On your own

13. Find each product.

   a) $(3m^4)(7m^5)$ **b)** $(2x^2)(4x^3)$

   c) $(8a^3)(7a^{11})$ **d)** $(-5b^3)(2b^4)$

   e) $(6x^5)(-3x^3)$ **f)** $(-8p^4)(-6p^2)$

   g) $\left(\dfrac{2}{3}y^4\right)\left(\dfrac{3}{5}y^7\right)$ **h)** $\left(-\dfrac{5}{8}s^5\right)\left(-\dfrac{3}{10}s^3\right)$

14. Find each quotient.

a) $\dfrac{-28a^7}{4a^2}$ b) $\dfrac{20s^3}{-5s}$

c) $\dfrac{-32c^8}{-8c^2}$ d) $45x^9 \div 9x^3$

e) $18y^4 \div 3y^2$ f) $42m^{12} \div 6m^4$

g) $36k^4 \div 9k^3$ h) $\dfrac{49z^7}{7z^4}$

i) $\dfrac{56a^4b^4}{8a^3b^2}$ j) $\dfrac{60x^3y^5}{15x^3y^3}$

15. Simplify, then evaluate.

a) $\dfrac{36x^4y^2}{9xy}$ for $x = 2$ and $y = 1$

b) $\dfrac{54a^5b^2}{-9a^3b^2}$ for $a = 1$ and $b = 1$

c) $\dfrac{-28m^2n^2}{-4m^2n^2}$ for $m = n = 15$

d) $\dfrac{-18a^2b^5}{12a^2b^3}$ for $a = 3$ and $b = 4$

e) $\dfrac{42x^5y^5}{-14x^3y^3}$ for $x = y = -2$

f) $\dfrac{-25a^2b^3c^4}{-15ab^2c^3}$ for $a = 3$, $b = -2$, and $c = 2$

g) $\dfrac{2}{3}a^2b^4 \div \dfrac{1}{3}ab^3$ for $a = 5$ and $b = -3$

h) $\left(-\dfrac{1}{2}m^2n^5\right) \div \dfrac{2}{5}mn^3$ for $m = 6$ and $n = -2$

i) $27a^3b^4c \div 9ab^3c$, for $a = -1$, $b = 1$ and $c = 2$

j) $35x^5y^3 \div 10x^3y^2$, for $x = 2$ and $y = -1$

16. Multiply or divide as indicated.

a) $(2m^3)(5m^2)$ b) $(-x^4)(3x)$

c) $\dfrac{2x^5}{3x^3}$ d) $\dfrac{-9m^8}{12m^5}$

e) $(-x)^4(3x)$ f) $(3a^2b^3)(2ab^4)$

g) $\dfrac{15x^3y^4}{-5xy^3}$ h) $(3x^4)^2(-2x)^3$

i) $(5a^2)^3 \div 15a^5$ j) $\left(\dfrac{2}{5}a^2b^4\right)\left(\dfrac{10}{3}ab^3\right)$

17. Multiply or divide as indicated.

a) $(2d^3)(5d^4)$ b) $(-30m^2n^5) \div (-6mn^3)$

c) $(-x^2)(5x)$ d) $\dfrac{12x^3}{2x}$

e) $\dfrac{-25a^7}{15a^2}$ f) $\left(-\dfrac{3}{5}ab^2\right)\left(-\dfrac{10}{9}a^3\right)$

18. Simplify, then evaluate for $x = -2$.

a) $-x^2$ b) $(-x)^2$ c) $(2x^3)(-3x)$

d) $(5x^2)(4x^3)$ e) $\dfrac{12x^5}{3x^2}$ f) $\dfrac{-9x^7}{2x^3}$

19. Simplify, then evaluate for $a = 3$ and $b = 1$.

a) $(2a^2b^3)^2$ b) $(-3ab^3)(5a^2b)$

c) $(-4a^3b) \div 2ab$ d) $7a^5b^{10} \div (-3b^5)$

20. Simplify.

a) $(-2x^2)(6x)(-3x^3)$ b) $(-10m)(-8m)(-5m^2)$

c) $\dfrac{(3x^2y)(5xy^4)}{10x^3y^2}$ d) $\dfrac{(9ab^5)(2a^2c)}{6ab^2}$

e) $\dfrac{(3x^2)^2(-2x)^3}{10x^5}$ f) $\dfrac{(-5m^2)^3(3m^7)}{(15m^3)^2}$

Extend your thinking

21. **a)** Write the volume of the cube as a product of monomials.

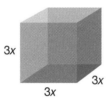

$3x$ $3x$ $3x$

b) Write the volume of the cube as a monomial.

c) Simplify. $(2x^2)(3x^3)(7x^4)$

The Ideas

In your journal, write a brief answer to each question.
Provide examples to support your answers.

a) When is the sum or difference of two monomials a monomial?

b) When is the product of two monomials a monomial?

c) When is the quotient of two monomials a monomial?

Developing the Ideas

▶ ▶ *Using Manipulatives*

In Chapter 2, you expanded a product such as $3(x + 4)$ using the
Distributive Law. You represented this product using algebra tiles by
combining 3 sets of tiles like this.

We can represent a product such as 3×5:

with a rectangle and...   with algebra tiles arranged in a rectangle

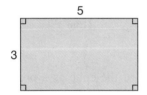

In each case, the area is $3 \times 5 = 15$

In a similar way, we can represent the product $2(x + 4)$
with algebra tiles to form a rectangle.

The area is $2(x + 4) = 2x + 8$

Instead of writing the length and width as algebraic terms,
we use algebra tiles.

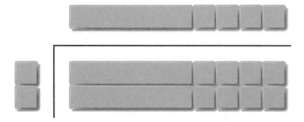

To represent the product $2x(x + 4)$ with algebra tiles, we make a rectangle that is $2x$ units wide and $(x + 4)$ units long. We place tiles to represent the length and the width.

We now fill in the rectangle with tiles. We need 2 x^2-tiles and 8 x-tiles. The area of the rectangle is $2x^2 + 8x$. We write: $2x(x + 4) = 2x^2 + 8x$

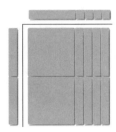

1. Illustrate each product with algebra tiles.

   a) $3(x + 2)$ **b)** $3x(x + 1)$ **c)** $4(2x + 3)$ **d)** $3x(2x + 1)$

This table compares the Distributive Law in arithmetic and in algebra.

· · · · · · · · · ·

To multiply in arithmetic, we use the Distributive Law.	To multiply in algebra, we use the Distributive Law.
$3 \times 27 = 3(20 + 7)$ $\quad\quad\;\; = 3(20) + 3(7)$ $\quad\quad\;\; = 60 + 21$ $\quad\quad\;\; = 81$	$2x(x + 4) = 2x(x) + 2x(4)$ $\quad\quad\quad\;\; = 2x^2 + 8x$

▶ ▶ *Through Guided Examples*

When we multiply a polynomial by a monomial using the Distributive Law, we say we are *expanding* the product. The following examples show how we expand the product of a monomial and a polynomial.

Example 1···

Expand. $8x(x - 3)$

Solution

$8x(x - 3) = 8x(x) + 8x(-3)$ ◁ Applying the Distributive Law
$\quad\quad\quad\; = 8x^2 - 24x$

We apply the same method when the polynomial has more than two terms. Since some polynomials cannot be represented with algebra tiles, sometimes we have to use the Distributive Law.

Example 2···

Expand. $(-5a)(a^2 - 4a - 7)$

Solution

$(-5a)(a^2 - 4a - 7) = (-5a)(a^2) + (-5a)(-4a) + (-5a)(-7)$ ◁ Applying the Distributive Law
$\quad\quad\quad\quad\quad\quad\;\; = -5a^3 + 20a^2 + 35a$

Working with Mathematics

Something to talk about

1. State the product that each diagram represents.

a)   b)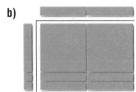

c)   d)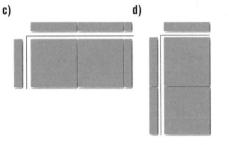

e)   f)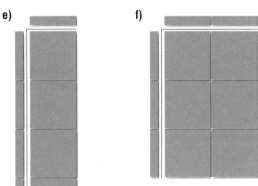

2. a) Explain the advantages of expanding by using algebra tiles.
   b) Explain the advantages of expanding by using the Distributive Law.
   c) Which method do you prefer? Why?

Practice

3. Expand.
   a) $5(x - 3)$ b) $7(a + 1)$
   c) $-3(2 + n)$ d) $-4(-x - 2)$
   e) $-1(2x - 5)$ f) $3(6x - 4)$
   g) $5(x^2 - 6x + 3)$ h) $-2(-3 + 5n - 3n^2)$

4. Match each product with the appropriate set of algebra tiles.
   a) $2x(x + 1)$ b) $2x(2x + 3)$ c) $2x(x + 5)$
   d) $3x(x + 1)$ e) $x(x + 3)$ f) $x(2x + 2)$

A 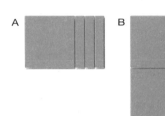 B

C

D

E

F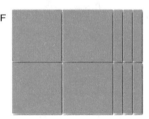

5. Expand.
   a) $x(3x + 2)$ b) $a(5a - 1)$
   c) $n(3 - 7n)$ d) $-x(x - 2)$
   e) $y(5 - y)$ f) $x(4x - 1)$
   g) $-x(7 - 2x + x^2)$ h) $n(5n^2 - n + 4)$

6. Expand.
   a) $x(x + 3)$ b) $-5(a - 3)$
   c) $b(2b^2 - 3b + 1)$ d) $p(4 - 3p - p^2)$
   e) $7(-6a^2 - 7)$ f) $-12(-3t^2 + 2t)$
   g) $-k(k^2 - 5k + 1)$ h) $-3(7 - 2m + 3m^2)$

Work together

7. Use algebra tiles to expand each expression. Take turns explaining what you are doing.

   a) $x(x + 1)$　　　　b) $x(3x + 2)$
   c) $2(x^2 + x + 3)$　　d) $2x(x + 2)$

8. Expand. Before you begin, decide for which expressions you can use algebra tiles.

   a) $x(5x^2 - 6)$　　　b) $2(x + 3x^2)$
   c) $(-3b)(b^3 - b^2)$　　d) $2a(3a + 1)$
   e) $(-4m)(m^2 - m)$　　f) $x^2(1 - x^3)$

9. Expand.

   a) $5x(2x + 3)$　　　　b) $2a(3a - 4)$
   c) $3c(5 - 2c)$　　　　d) $(-4n)(2n - 1)$
   e) $(-7y)(2y^2 - 5y + 2)$　f) $6k(3 - k + 2k^2)$
   g) $5s(3s^2 - 2s - 7)$　h) $(-3p^2)(2 - 3p - p^2)$

10. a) Use the Distributive Law to multiply 7×236.

    b) Use the Distributive Law to expand $7(2x^2 + 3x + 6)$. Evaluate this polynomial for $x = 10$.

    c) Compare your answers in parts a and b. Explain any relationship you discover.

11. Some algebra tile sets have two different variable tiles, of different lengths. We can call them x-tiles and y-tiles.

    Use grid paper, or cut out several paper strips and squares. Show how you can represent 1-tiles, x-tiles, y-tiles, x^2-tiles, y^2-tiles, and xy-tiles.

12. Use grid paper or the paper strips and squares you cut out in exercise 11.

    a) Complete this area model of the multiplication expression $2x(3y)$.

    b) Write the product as a monomial.

13. What product does each diagram represent?

    a)

    b)

    c)

    d)

    e)
    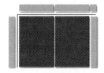

    f)

14. Use grid paper or the paper strips and squares you cut out in exercise 11. Complete an area model for each product. Record your results algebraically.

    a) $3x(2y + 1)$　　　b) $5(2x + y + 2)$
    c) $2y(y + 3x + 1)$　d) $3x(2x + y + 4)$

On your own

15. Expand.

    a) $5x(2x + 3)$　　　b) $3c(5 - 2c)$
    c) $(-4n)(2n - 1)$　　d) $(-7y)(2y^2 - 5y)$
    e) $4a(3a^2 - 2a)$　　f) $(-2x)(-3x - 5x^3)$
    g) $5s(3s^2 - 2s - 7)$　h) $3p(2 - 3p - p^2)$

16. Expand each expression.

a) $3x(2x - 1)$ b) $(-3x)(-2x - 1)$

c) $2x(-3x - 4)$ d) $4x^2(3x + 2)$

17. Expand.

a) $3x(2y + 5)$ b) $5y(2 - 7x)$

c) $(-2x)(x + 3y - 1)$ d) $2y(7 - 4x - 6y)$

e) $5a(2a - 3b + 4)$ f) $(-6m)(2 - 5m + n)$

g) $(-3s)(4 - 2t - s)$ h) $7p(9q - 3p + 1)$

18. Expand.

a) $2x^2(3x - 2y^2 - 5)$ b) $3a^2(ab - b^2)$

c) $(-2m^3)(mn^2 - m^2n)$ d) $(-3p)(pq^2 - 5pq)$

e) $2x^2y(xy - 3x^2)$ f) $(-3pqr)(2pq - 4qr)$

g) $7ab(2a^2b - 3ab^2)$ h) $(-4xy)(x^2 - y^2)$

19. Expand.

a) $3x(x^2y + y^2x + xy)$

b) $(-2x)(ab^2 - b + a^2b)$

c) $(-3m)(mn - m^2n - m)$

d) $4w(-3zw + w^2z - wz^2)$

e) $2xy^2(y - 2x^2y + 3xy)$

f) $-6xyz(-3xz^2 + 2xy^2 - yz^2 + 2xyz)$

Extend your thinking

20. The height of any television screen is about $\frac{3}{4}$ of its width.

a) Write an expression for the height of a television screen that is x units wide.

b) Write an expression for the height of a television screen that is 4 units wider than the screen in part a.

c) Write an expression for the area of the television screen in part b.

d) Write an expression for the difference in the areas of the screens in parts a and b.

e) Suppose the difference in areas of the screens in part a and part b is 120 square units. What is the area of each screen?

21. The dimensions of a cereal box, in centimetres, are $5x - 1$, $3x$, and x.

a) Determine an expression for each quantity.

  i) the volume V of the box

  ii) the surface area A of the box

b) Determine the volume and surface area of the box when $x = 7$.

COMMUNICATING

The Ideas

In your journal, draw a rectangle with a length of $2x$ units and a width of $(x + 3)$ units. Write the area as a product. Use the Distributive Law to write the area as a sum of the areas of two smaller rectangles. Divide the large rectangle into two smaller rectangles and show their lengths and widths.

Developing the Ideas

▷ ▷ *Using Manipulatives*

In the preceding section, we knew the length and width of a rectangle, and we had to decide which tiles completed the rectangle.

In this section, we'll reverse the procedure.

We'll begin with a set of tiles which we arrange as a rectangle, and then determine its length and width.

- Use 3 x-tiles and 6 1-tiles. What polynomial do they represent?
- Arrange these tiles to form a rectangle.
- Write the length of the rectangle as a polynomial.
- Write the width of the rectangle as a polynomial.
- Write the area of the rectangle as a product of the length and width.
- Check the rectangles of other students. Did you all arrange your tiles the same way?

Let's consider another example.

Suppose you have the tiles representing $4x + 8$.

They can be arranged in a rectangle in three ways.

The length is $4x + 8$. The width is 1. The area is $1(4x + 8)$.

The length is $2x + 4$. The width is 2. The area is $2(2x + 4)$.

The length is $x + 2$. The width is 4. The area is $4(x + 2)$.

We say that 1 and $4x + 8$ are *factors* of $4x + 8$.
Similarly, 2 and $2x + 4$ are factors of $4x + 8$,
and 4 and $x + 2$ are factors of $4x + 8$.

There are three ways to factor $4x + 8$, shown above.
The first two ways: 1, $4x + 8$ and 2, $2x + 4$ are incomplete because the
second factor in each case: $4x + 8$ and $2x + 4$, can be factored again. The
third way is complete. We say that $4x + 8$ is factored *fully* when we write
$4x + 8 = 4(x + 2)$.

The following chart compares factoring and expanding in arithmetic and
algebra.

. . . .

In Arithmetic	**In Algebra**
We *multiply* factors to form a product.	We *expand* an expression to form a product.
$(3)(5) = 15 \leftarrow$ product	$4(x + 2) = 4x + 8 \leftarrow$ product
factors	factors
We *factor* a number by expressing it as a product of factors.	We *factor* a polynomial by expressing it as a product of factors.
factors	factors
number $\rightarrow 15 = (3)(5)$	polynomial $\rightarrow 4x + 8 = 4(x + 2)$

The operations of expanding and factoring are inverses;
that is, each operation reverses the other.

BOGGLE YOUR MIND

According to the *Guinness Book of Records*,
the greatest distance a single car has been
driven is 2 180 279 km, by a Volkswagen
"Beetle." Ask a friend or relative the average
distance he or she drives in a week. How many
weeks would it take that person to drive as far
as the Beetle? How many years is this?

Example 1 ....

Factor fully. $2x^2 + 6x$

Solution

Use 2 x^2-tiles and 6 x-tiles to represent $2x^2 + 6x$.
Arrange the tiles to form a rectangle.

So we arrange the tiles in a different rectangle.

The width and length of this rectangle are x and $2x + 6$.
But $2x + 6$ can be factored again.

The length and width are $2x$ and $x + 3$.
From the diagram, $2x^2 + 6x = 2x(x + 3)$

As before, some polynomials cannot be represented with algebra tiles.
They have to be factored algebraically.

Example 2 ....

Factor fully. $2x^3 + 4x^2$

Solution ....

Factor each term of the polynomial.
$2x^3 = 2 \cdot x \cdot x \cdot x$
$4x^2 = 2 \cdot 2 \cdot x \cdot x$

We identify the factors that are common to each term.
Each term has the factors 2 and x and x in common.
We say that $2x^2$ is the *greatest common factor*.

We write each term as a product of the greatest common factor and another monomial.
$2x^3 + 4x^2 = 2x^2(x) + 2x^2(2)$
We use the Distributive Law to write the sum as a product.
$2x^3 + 4x^2 = 2x^2(x + 2)$

We use the same method to factor a polynomial with more than two terms.

Example 3 ....

Factor fully. $-6y + 3y^2 - 3y^3$

Solution ....

$6y = 2 \cdot 3 \cdot y$
$3y^2 = 3 \cdot y \cdot y$
$3y^3 = 3 \cdot y \cdot y \cdot y$

Each term has the factors 3 and y in common.
$3y$ is the greatest common factor.

$-6y + 3y^2 - 3y^3 = 3y(-2) + 3y(y) + 3y(-y^2)$
$\qquad\qquad\qquad\quad = 3y(-2 + y - y^2)$

Working with Mathematics

Something to talk about

1. Factor each set of monomials. State the greatest common factor.

   a) $3x,\ x^2$ **b)** $3b^3,\ 3b$

   c) $-5y,\ 25y^2$ **d)** $-3x,\ 6x^3,\ 9x^2$

   e) $2x^2,\ 6x^3,\ -8x$ **f)** $2y^2,\ 4xy,\ -8y^3$

2. State the greatest common factor of each pair of numbers. Each number is written in factored form.

   a) $9 = 3 \cdot 3$
   $15 = 3 \cdot 5$

   b) $18 = 2 \cdot 3 \cdot 3$
   $12 = 2 \cdot 2 \cdot 3$

   c) $50 = 2 \cdot 5 \cdot 5$
   $75 = 3 \cdot 5 \cdot 5$

   d) $16 = 2 \cdot 2 \cdot 2 \cdot 2$
   $28 = 2 \cdot 2 \cdot 7$

   e) $60 = 2 \cdot 2 \cdot 3 \cdot 5$
   $24 = 2 \cdot 2 \cdot 2 \cdot 3$

   f) $36 = 2 \cdot 2 \cdot 3 \cdot 3$
   $54 = 2 \cdot 3 \cdot 3 \cdot 3$

   g) $490 = 2 \cdot 5 \cdot 7 \cdot 7$
   $140 = 2 \cdot 2 \cdot 5 \cdot 7$

   h) $495 = 3 \cdot 3 \cdot 5 \cdot 11$
   $1650 = 2 \cdot 3 \cdot 5 \cdot 5 \cdot 11$

   i) $540 = 2^2 \cdot 3^3 \cdot 5$
   $450 = 2 \cdot 3^2 \cdot 5^2$

   j) $200 = 2^3 \cdot 5^2$
   $500 = 2^2 \cdot 5^3$

Practice

3. Find the greatest common factor.

   a) $xy,\ x^2y$

   b) $3x^2y^2,\ 6xy$

   c) $ab,\ -a^2b^2$

   d) $-4xy,\ 16$

   e) $-5xy^3,\ -10x^2y^2$

   f) $6p^2q,\ -12pq^3$

   g) $2m^2n,\ -4mn^4,\ 8$

   h) $3x^2y^4,\ 9x^2y^3,\ 12xy^2$

   i) $12ab^2,\ 18a^2bc^2,\ 24a^3bc$

4. Factor each binomial.

   a) $5y - 10$ **b)** $12a + 18$

   c) $3x^2 + 6x$ **d)** $2a^2 - 10a$

   e) $4w + 3w^2$ **f)** $8y^3 - 4y^2$

   g) $6s + 2s^2$ **h)** $7k^3 + 35k^4$

   i) $6m^2 - 36m^3$ **j)** $8y^4 - 2y^3$

5. Factor. Check by expanding.

   a) $14x^2 + 35x$ **b)** $25a + 30a^2$

   c) $20n^2 + 80$ **d)** $-5x + 10x^2$

   e) $9c^3 + 15c$ **f)** $-x^3 - x$

   g) $-6y^2 - 3y^3$ **h)** $4x + 12x^3$

   i) $16m^2 - 4m^3$ **j)** $-8d - 8d^3$

Work together

6. Use algebra tiles to factor each polynomial.

   a) $2x + 2$ **b)** $3x + 9$

   c) $4x + 10$ **d)** $3x + 15$

   e) $3k + 12$ **f)** $4m + 8$

   g) $4n + 6$ **h)** $5w + 15$

7. Use algebra tiles to factor each polynomial. Sketch the tiles.

   a) $x^2 + 2x$ **b)** $2x^2 + 4x$

   c) $3x^2 + 9$ **d)** $4x^2 + 8x$

   e) $4m^2 + 6$ **f)** $3k^2 + 18k$

   g) $k^2 + k$ **h)** $2z^2 + 4z$

   i) $4x^2 + 2x$ **j)** $2y^2 + 8$

8. Factor.

   a) $xy + x^2y$ **b)** $-3x^2y^2 + 6xy$

   c) $ab - a^2b^2$ **d)** $-4xy - 16$

   e) $5xy^2 + 10x^2y^2$ **f)** $6p^2q - 12pq^2$

   g) $2m^2n - 4mn$ **h)** $3x^2y^2 + 9x^2y^3$

   i) $-5x^6y - xy^6$ **j)** $12a^3bc^2 - 15a^2bc$

9. Simplify each expression by combining like terms, then factor.

   a) $5x^2 - 3x + 2 - x^2 + 11x + 10$

   b) $5x^2 - 2x + 2x^2 - 19x + 7$

   c) $4a^2 - 3 + 12a^2 - 13 - 24a$

   d) $6t^2 - 5t - 2 + 9t + 2$

   e) $m^2 - 2m + 3 - m^2 + 6m - 7$

   f) $k^3 - k^2 + 2k - 7k^3 - 5k^2 - 12k$

   g) $6x^2 + 2 - 3x + 4x^2 - 2x + 3$

   h) $9 - 5x + x^2 + 5 + 6x^2 + 12x$

On your own

10. Factor each polynomial. Make a diagram to illustrate each answer, where possible.
    a) $16x + 40$
    b) $15n - 24$
    c) $-2a^2 - 6a$
    d) $18n^2 - 12n$
    e) $a^3 + 9a^2 + 3a$
    f) $3x^2 + 9x$

11. Factor each polynomial. Show all steps.
    a) $10x + 15$
    b) $6x - 9$
    c) $15x + 25$
    d) $2x^2 - 4x$
    e) $4x^2 - 16x$
    f) $3y^3 + 9y^2$
    g) $2x^2 + 4x + 8$
    h) $12x^3 - 9x^2 + 6x$

12. Factor.
    a) $a^3 - 9a^2 + 3a$
    b) $-27x^2 - 9x + 3$
    c) $5x^3 + 3x^2 - x$
    d) $9a^3 + 7a^2 + 18a$
    e) $-8d - 24d^2 - 8d^3$
    f) $17k - 85k^2 - 51k^3$

13. Refer to *Start With What You Know* on page 318. The total surface area A of a cylinder of radius r and height h is given by this formula. $A = 2\pi rh + 2\pi r^2$ Factor this formula.

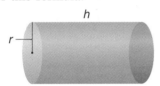

14. Factor. Expand to check your work.
    a) $3xy^2 + 6x^2y - 9xy$
    b) $-2a^2b + 6ab^2 - 4ab$
    c) $5m^2n^2 - 10m^3n^2 + 25m^2n$
    d) $-28x^2y^2 + 14x^3y^3 - 7x^2y^3$

Extend your thinking

15. Factor.
    a) $a(a + 6) + 7(a + 6)$
    b) $x(x - 9) - 2(x - 9)$
    c) $8(1 + y) + 2y(1 + y)$
    d) $5(2 - x) + x(2 - x)$
    e) $2x(x + 3) + 4(x + 3)$
    f) $-3a(2a - 1) + 6(2a - 1)$

16. Using algebra tiles, attempt to factor each polynomial. Interpret those that do factor in terms of area.
    a) $2x - 6$
    b) $2x^2 - 6x + 4$
    c) $2x^2 + 6$
    d) $2x^2 - 6$

17. Write the formula, for the total surface area in exercise 13, in terms of the circumference C and height h, instead of r and h.

18. Factor.
    a) $a^2 + 2a + ab + 2b$
    b) $3x - xy + 3y - y^2$
    c) $3a + 3b + ab + b^2$
    d) $4x - 4 + ax - a$
    e) $2p - 2q - p^2 + pq$
    f) $-4x - 4y + xy + y^2$
    g) $-3m + 3n - mn + n^2$
    h) $-5c - 5d - cd - d^2$

The Ideas

In your journal, explain how factoring and multiplying are related. Use examples to illustrate your explanation.

BOGGLE YOUR MIND

According to the *Guinness Book of Records*, the most popular surname in China is Zhang. It is estimated that between 10% and 12% of the approximately 1 160 000 000 people living in China have this surname. How many people is this? How does this number compare with the population of your province or territory?

Developing the Ideas

▶▶ *Through Guided Examples*

To divide a polynomial by a monomial, we divide each term of the polynomial by the monomial. In this way, we *simplify* the expression.

Example 1 ....

Simplify. $\dfrac{5x^2 - 10x}{5}$

Solution

$$\dfrac{5x^2 - 10x}{5} = \dfrac{5x^2}{5} - \dfrac{10x}{5}$$
$$= x^2 - 2x$$

Example 2 ....

Simplify. $\dfrac{3b^3 - 6b^2 + 9b}{6b}$

Solution

$$\dfrac{3b^3 - 6b^2 + 9b}{6b} = \dfrac{3b^3}{6b} - \dfrac{6b^2}{6b} + \dfrac{9b}{6b}$$
$$= \dfrac{1}{2}b^2 - b + \dfrac{3}{2}$$

There is another way to divide a polynomial by a monomial.

We factor the polynomial, and then divide the monomial into the common factor. If necessary, we factor the monomial before dividing.

For *Example 1*:

$$\dfrac{5x^2 - 10x}{5} = \dfrac{5(x^2 - 2x)}{5}$$
$$= \dfrac{\cancel{5}^1(x^2 - 2x)}{\cancel{5}_1}$$
$$= x^2 - 2x$$

For *Example 2*:

$$\dfrac{3b^3 - 6b^2 + 9b}{6b} = \dfrac{3b(b^2 - 2b + 3)}{6b}$$
$$= \dfrac{3b(b^2 - 2b + 3)}{(3b)(2)} \quad \text{◄ Factoring the monomial}$$
$$= \dfrac{b^2 - 2b + 3}{2}$$
$$= \dfrac{1}{2}b^2 - b + \dfrac{3}{2}$$

Working with Mathematics

Something to talk about

1. Simplify.

a) $\dfrac{5x^2}{2x^2}$ **b)** $\dfrac{3m^2n}{2m}$ **c)** $\dfrac{4y^3}{-2y}$

2. Simplify.

a) $\dfrac{3m^3 - 2m}{m}$ **b)** $\dfrac{5x^2 - 10}{2}$

c) $\dfrac{21y - 7y^3}{7y}$ **d)** $\dfrac{6a^2 - 2a}{-2a}$

3. a) Factor. $3x^2 - 12x + 6$

b) Simplify. $\dfrac{3x^2 - 12x + 6}{-3}$

4. a) Describe two different ways to simplify $\dfrac{3x^2 - 12x + 6}{-3}$.

b) Which is easier for you? Explain.

Practice

5. Simplify.

a) $\dfrac{8a + 4}{4}$ **b)** $\dfrac{12y - 3}{3}$

c) $\dfrac{18x^2 - 6}{6}$ **d)** $\dfrac{6a + 15}{3}$

e) $\dfrac{24x - 4}{4}$ **f)** $\dfrac{-10 + 4m}{-2}$

g) $\dfrac{15 - 5n}{-5}$ **h)** $\dfrac{18x^2 - 6x + 30}{6}$

i) $\dfrac{4a^2 + 12a - 16}{-4}$ **j)** $\dfrac{-6a^2 - 15a + 9}{3}$

k) $\dfrac{10 + 14m - 6m^2}{-2}$ **l)** $\dfrac{-14x - 21x^2 + 42}{-7}$

Work together

6. Simplify.

a) $\dfrac{3x^2 - 6x}{3x}$ **b)** $\dfrac{5x^2 - 10x}{5x}$

c) $\dfrac{18a - 21a^2}{3a}$ **d)** $\dfrac{-28n^2 - 7n}{7n}$

e) $\dfrac{36y^3 - 9y^2}{-9y}$ **f)** $\dfrac{32b^4 + 8b^3}{-4b^2}$

7. Simplify.

a) $\dfrac{-21 + 7x}{-7}$ **b)** $\dfrac{-5 - 15c + 10c^2}{-5}$

c) $\dfrac{4x^3 - 12x^2 + 8x}{4x}$ **d)** $\dfrac{8a + 2a^2 - 2a^3}{2a}$

e) $\dfrac{15x^4 - 30x^3 + 5x^2}{5x^2}$ **f)** $\dfrac{18a^4 + 6a^3 - 12a^2}{-6a^2}$

Extend your thinking

8. A closed rectangular box has length l. Its depth and width are both x units. Write a polynomial for the surface area A of the box. Write A as a product of two factors.

The Ideas

In your journal, explain how dividing a polynomial by a monomial is related to factoring. Illustrate with examples.

BOGGLE YOUR **MIND**

D.W. Friesen, one of Canada's largest printing companies, is located in Altona, Manitoba. Their largest order was to print 530 000 copies of one book. It took more than 4 months to print these books. The presses ran 18 h a day, 6 days a week. What if there had been a power failure and the presses stopped for 3 h? How many books would not be printed during this time?

Developing the Ideas

▶ ▶ *Using Manipulatives*

Recall that a binomial is a polynomial with two terms.
We can multiply two binomials by using algebra tiles. We follow the
same procedure we used to multiply a polynomial by a monomial.

To expand $(x + 2)(x + 4)$

- We make a rectangle that is $(x + 4)$ units long and $(x + 2)$ units wide.
  We place tiles to represent the length and the width. We then fill in the
  rectangle with tiles.

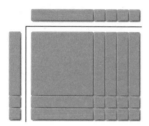

- We used 1 x^2-tile, 6 x-tiles, and 8 1-tiles.
  The area of the rectangle is $x^2 + 6x + 8$.
  We write: $(x + 2)(x + 4) = x^2 + 6x + 8$

1. Use algebra tiles to expand each product.

   a) $(x + 1)(x + 2)$ **b)** $(2x + 1)(x + 3)$

▶ ▶ *Through Instruction*

We can illustrate the product of two binomials with a diagram.

	x	7
x	x^2	$7x$
2	$2x$	14

The length of the large rectangle is $(x + 7)$ units and its width
is $(x + 2)$ units.

The area of the rectangle is
$(x + 7)(x + 2)$.

The area is also the sum of the areas of the
four small rectangles, $x^2 + 7x + 2x + 14$.

Therefore, $(x + 7)(x + 2) = x^2 + 7x + 2x + 14$
$$= x^2 + 9x + 14$$

This method shows that there are four terms in the product.

Example 1 ....

Expand. $(3x + 2)(x + 4)$

Solution

With algebra tiles, make a rectangle that is $(3x + 2)$ units long and $(x + 4)$ units wide. Fill in the rectangle with tiles.

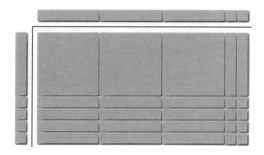

From the diagram, $(3x + 2)(x + 4) = 3x^2 + 14x + 8$

We can multiply two binomials without using algebra tiles.

Example 2 ....

Expand. $(3x + 2)(x + 4)$

Solution

$(3x + 2)(x + 4)$
Multiply each term of one binomial by each term of the other binomial. We draw lines to show which terms are multiplied.

$$(3x + 2)(x + 4) = 3x(x) + 3x(4) + 2(x) + 2(4)$$
$$= 3x^2 + 12x + 2x + 8$$
$$= 3x^2 + 14x + 8$$

The lines form a pattern. We can use this pattern to check that we have all the terms.

Example 3 ....

Expand. $(2x + 1)(7x - 3)$

Solution

$$(2x + 1)(7x - 3) = 14x^2 - 6x + 7x - 3$$
$$= 14x^2 + x - 3$$

Working with Mathematics

Something to talk about

1.

a) State the area of the tiles as the product of the length and width of the rectangle.

b) State the area as the sum of the areas of the tiles.

2.

a) State the area of the rectangle as the product of its length and width.

b) State the area of the rectangle as the sum of the smaller areas.

3. State the number that belongs in each square.

a) $(x + 3)(x - 2) = x^2 + \blacksquare x - 6$

b) $(a + 5)(a + 7) = a^2 + \blacksquare a + 35$

c) $(n - 4)(n - 6) = n^2 + \blacksquare n + 24$

d) $(x - 7)(x + 1) = x^2 + \blacksquare x - 7$

Practice

4. a) Write the area covered by each set of tiles as a product.

i)

ii)

iii)

iv)

b) Write each area in part a as a sum.

5. a) Write the area of each rectangle as a product.

i)

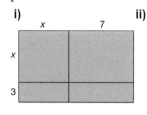

ii)

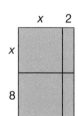

iii)

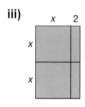

iv)

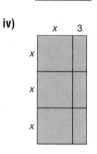

b) Write each area in part a as a sum.

6. Expand. Use algebra tiles.

a) $(x + 1)(x + 3)$ **b)** $(n + 2)(n + 5)$

c) $(a + 3)(a + 2)$ **d)** $(y + 1)(y + 5)$

7. Expand.

a) $(a + 1)(a - 2)$ **b)** $(b + 3)(b - 5)$

c) $(n - 3)(n - 2)$ **d)** $(y - 4)(y + 5)$

e) $(b - 6)(b + 3)$ **f)** $(a - 10)(a - 6)$

g) $(z - 5)(z - 6)$ **h)** $(b + 10)(b + 5)$

i) $(x - 9)(x - 1)$ **j)** $(a + 11)(a - 8)$

Work together

8. For each diagram of algebra tiles:
   i) Write the product of its length and width.
   ii) Write the area as a sum of the areas of
   the tiles.

a)

b)

c)

d)

e)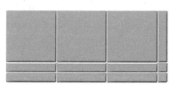

f)

g)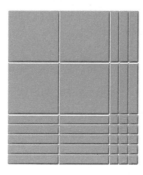

9. For each rectangle:
   i) Write the area as the product of its length
   and width.
   ii) Write the area as the sum of the smaller
   areas.

a)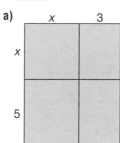

b)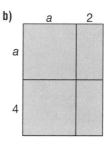

c)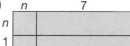

d)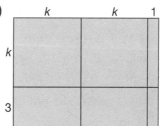

e)

10. Expand. Use algebra tiles. Check your answers with your partner.

   a) $(x + 3)(x + 4)$ b) $(n + 2)(n + 6)$
   c) $(a + 5)(a + 3)$ d) $(n + 1)(n + 9)$

11. Expand.

   a) $(t - 1)(t - 4)$ b) $(x - 2)(x + 5)$
   c) $(n + 3)(n - 4)$ d) $(a + 6)(a - 8)$
   e) $(x + 9)(x - 7)$ f) $(x + 12)(x - 5)$

12. Expand.

   a) $(2a + 1)(a - 2)$ b) $(3b + 1)(b + 5)$
   c) $(2x - 3)(x - 2)$ d) $(4x + 5)(x + 1)$
   e) $(2a - 3)(3a + 2)$ f) $(5x - 2)(3x + 4)$
   g) $(2z - 7)(3z - 2)$ h) $(5b + 1)(2b + 3)$
   i) $(7x - 2)(2x + 1)$ j) $(5a + 9)(2a - 3)$

13. Expand.

   a) $(x + 3)(x + 7)$ b) $(x - 3)(x - 7)$
   c) $(x - 3)(x + 7)$ d) $(x + 3)(x - 7)$

14. What patterns do you see in the products in exercise 13?

15. Expand.

   a) $(2a + 1)(3a + 2)$ b) $(2a - 1)(3a - 2)$
   c) $(2a - 1)(3a + 2)$ d) $(2a + 1)(3a - 2)$

16. What patterns do you see in the products in exercise 15? Compare these patterns with those in exercise 14.

17. Expand.

   a) $(2a + 1)(2a + 1)$ b) $(3n + 1)(3n + 1)$
   c) $(x - 6)(x - 6)$ d) $(a - 3)(a - 3)$
   e) $(2y - 5)(2y - 5)$ f) $(3b + 5)(3b + 5)$

18. What pattern do you see in the products in exercise 17?

19. Expand.

   a) $(x - 3)(x + 3)$ b) $(2a + 1)(2a - 1)$
   c) $(8n - 3)(8n + 3)$ d) $(4a + 3)(4a - 3)$
   e) $(3x - 2)(3x + 2)$ f) $(5x + 1)(5x - 1)$

20. What pattern do you see in the products in exercise 19?

21. Choose any month on a calendar. Then choose a 3 by 3 square of 9 dates. Let x represent the date at the centre of the square.

December

Sun	Mon	Tue	Wed	Thur	Fri	Sat
		1	2	3	4	5
6	7	8	9	10	11	12
13	14	15	16	17	18	19
20	21	22	23	24	25	26
27	28	29	30	31		

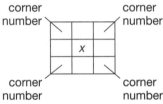

corner number   corner number

corner number   corner number

   a) Write a polynomial for:
      i) each corner number
      ii) the square of each corner number
      iii) the sum of the squares of the corner numbers
   b) If you knew the sum of the squares of the corner numbers, how could you determine the value of x?

On your own

22. Expand.

   a) $(a + 3)(a + 6)$ b) $(b + 2)(b - 7)$
   c) $(n - 6)(n + 5)$ d) $(y + 1)(y + 12)$
   e) $(b - 9)(b - 2)$ f) $(a + 3)(a - 10)$
   g) $(z + 8)(z - 10)$ h) $(b + 6)(b + 11)$
   i) $(x - 7)(x + 6)$ j) $(a - 15)(a - 3)$

23. Expand.

a) $(6x - 3)(2x - 5)$ b) $(3b + 2)(3b - 2)$

c) $(5a + 1)(4a - 7)$ d) $(a + 8)(8a + 1)$

e) $(2a - 3)(2a - 3)$ f) $(3a + 4)(2a - 3)$

24. Expand.

a) $(3x + 2)(x - 1)$ b) $(2a - 5)(a - 3)$

c) $(4n - 7)(n + 5)$ d) $(x + 3)(6x - 5)$

e) $(12x + 1)(3x - 1)$ f) $(5n - 1)(2n - 2)$

25. Expand.

a) $(7c - 5)(2c + 1)$ b) $(6x - 2)(3x + 1)$

c) $(3x - 1)(x + 2)$ d) $(3a + 1)(2a - 5)$

e) $(8y - 3)(5y - 1)$ f) $(2x - 3)(4x + 7)$

26. Expand.

a) $(2 - x)(3 - x)$ b) $(5 + a)(3 + a)$

c) $(4 - m)(3 + m)$ d) $(6 + t)(3 - t)$

e) $(7 - x)(7 - x)$ f) $(7 - x)(7 + x)$

g) $(3 + a)(4 - a)$ h) $(12 + b)(5 - b)$

27. Expand.

a) $(x + 2y)(x + 5y)$ b) $(a - 3b)(a + 2b)$

c) $(3m - n)(2m - n)$ d) $(5x + 3y)(4x - y)$

e) $(6r + s)(r - 3s)$ f) $(8a + 7b)(7a + 8b)$

g) $(p - 3q)(2p + 5q)$ h) $(3x - 8y)(2x + 5y)$

i) $(6a + 7b)(7a - 8b)$ j) $(2x - 3y)(2x + 5y)$

Extend your thinking

28. Expand.

a) $2(x + 2)(x + 5)$ b) $3(m - 1)(m + 4)$

c) $5(x + 6)(x - 2)$ d) $7(x - 5)(x - 5)$

e) $-3(x + 4)(x - 2)$ f) $-2(x + 6)(x - 10)$

g) $-(t - 2)(t + 2)$ h) $4(2 - x)(3 - x)$

29. Use algebra tiles to expand.

a) $(x - 2)(x + 1)$ b) $(2x + 1)(x - 3)$

c) $(2x - 3)(2x - 4)$ d) $(x + 3)(-2x - 1)$

e) $(-3x + 1)(-3x - 1)$ f) $(-x - 4)(-x - 4)$

30. Find the binomial to complete each equality.

a) $(n + 2)() = n^2 + 7n + 10$

b) $(x - 3)() = x^2 - 7x + 12$

c) $()(x + 6) = x^2 + 4x - 12$

d) $()(a - 5) = a^2 - 3a - 10$

e) $(x + 2)() = x^2 + 5x + 6$

f) $(t - 4)() = t^2 + t - 20$

g) $()() = x^2 + 9x + 20$

h) $()() = a^2 - 9a + 14$

31. Expand.

a) $(x + 5)(x^2 + 2x + 1)$

b) $(a + 3)(a^2 - 4a + 2)$

c) $(t - 4)(t^2 + 3t - 5)$

d) $(a - 2)(a^2 + 2a + 4)$

e) $(x + 1)(x + 2)(x + 3)$

f) $(n - 5)(n + 2)(n - 1)$

g) $(2x - 1)(2x + 1)(x - 2)$

h) $(m + 5)(3m - 1)(3m - 1)$

COMMUNICATING

The Ideas

Suppose you are talking with your friend about your homework. How would you explain, over the telephone, how to multiply two binomials? Write your answer in your journal.

A Student's Letter

This letter was received from a student, Amy Carter, who discovered an unusual way to add certain numbers. Explain why her method always works.

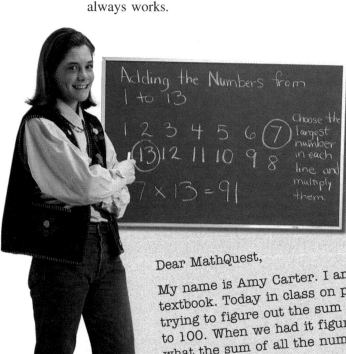

Adding the Numbers from 1 to 13

1 2 3 4 5 6 ⑦
⑬ 12 11 10 9 8

Choose the largest number in each line and multiply them.

7 × 13 = 91

Dear MathQuest,

My name is Amy Carter. I am working in your Grade 6 textbook. Today in class on pages 94 and 95 we were trying to figure out the sum of all the numbers from 1 to 100. When we had it figured out, we tried to find out what the sum of all the numbers from 1 to 13 was.

Our teacher rounded 13 to 14 and wrote:

We then multiplied:

$$\begin{array}{ccccccc} 1 & 2 & 3 & 4 & 5 & 6 & 7 \\ +\,14 & 13 & 12 & 11 & 10 & 9 & 8 \\ \hline 15 & 15 & 15 & 15 & 15 & 15 & 15 \end{array}$$

$$\begin{array}{r} 15 \\ \times\ 7 \\ \hline 105 \end{array}$$

Since we added the extra 14, we took 14 from 105 and ended up with a sum of 91. I then looked more closely at the question and thought of a faster way to do it. Although my idea only works with odd numbers, I wrote:

$$\begin{array}{ccccccc} 1 & 2 & 3 & 4 & 5 & 6 & 7 \\ & 13 & 12 & 11 & 10 & 9 & 8 \end{array}$$

You then find the greatest number in each line. In this case they are 7 and 13. If you multiply 7 times 13 you come up with 91. You automatically have the sum.

Please write to me with any comments.

Sincerely

Amy Carter

Understand the problem

- Read Amy's letter. What was her method?
- Try the teacher's method. How do you know how many numbers to write in the first line?
- Try Amy's method.
- What are you asked to do?

Think of a strategy

- Let $2n - 1$ represent an odd number, and try the two methods again.

Carry out the strategy

In the teacher's method:
- Write an expression for the first number in the second line.
- Above this expression, write the first number in the first line.
- How is the last number in the first line related to the first number in the second line?
- Write an expression for the last number in the first line.
- Below this expression, write an expression for the last number in the second line.
- Write an expression for the next to last number in the first line.
- Below this expression, write an expression for the next to last number in the second line.
- What is the sum of each pair of expressions?
- How many of these sums are there?
- Multiply this number by the sum of one pair of expressions.
- Subtract the extra number that was added at the beginning.
- What is the sum of the natural numbers from 1 to $2n - 1$?

In Amy's method:
- Write an expression for the greatest number in each line.
- What is the product of these expressions?
- Is this the same as the answer in the teacher's method?

Look back

- Why doesn't Amy's method work for even numbers?
- Try to modify her method so that it does work for even numbers. If you can do this, explain why your method works.

Communicating the Ideas

In your journal, write a letter to Amy Carter with your comments.

6.8 *FACTORING TRINOMIALS*

Developing the Ideas

Recall that a polynomial with three terms is a trinomial.

As we learned in the previous section, the product of two binomials is often a trinomial.

For example, $(x + 3)(x + 4) = x^2 + 7x + 12$

Factoring is the reverse process.

To factor a trinomial, such as $x^2 + 7x + 12$, is to write it as the product $(x + 3)(x + 4)$.

▶ ▶ *Using Manipulatives*

We'll begin with a set of tiles which we will try to arrange as a rectangle. Then we'll determine its length and width.

1. Use 1 x^2-tile, 7 x-tiles, and 10 1-tiles.
What polynomial do they represent?

2. a) Arrange these tiles to form a rectangle.
   b) Write the length of the rectangle as a binomial.
   c) Write the width of the rectangle as a binomial.
   d) Write the area of the rectangle as a product of the
      length and the width.

3. Check the rectangles of other students.
Did you all arrange your tiles the same way?

4. What are the factors of the polynomial?

Let's consider another example.
Suppose you have the tiles representing $x^2 + 5x + 6$.

They can be arranged like this.

The length is $x + 3$.
The width is $x + 2$.
The area is $x^2 + 5x + 6$.

We write: $x^2 + 5x + 6 = (x + 2)(x + 3)$

We say: The factors of $x^2 + 5x + 6$ are $x + 2$ and $x + 3$.

5. Use algebra tiles to factor each trinomial.
   a) $x^2 + 5x + 4$ **b)** $x^2 + 6x + 8$ **c)** $x^2 + 4x + 4$

Through Guided Examples

Consider this expansion.

$x^2 + 7x + 12 = (x + 3)(x + 4)$

7 is the sum of 3 and 4

12 is the product of 3 and 4

We use these relationships to factor a trinomial.

Example 1

Factor. $x^2 + 7x + 6$

Solution

$x^2 + 7x + 6$

We want to find two numbers whose sum is 7 and whose product is 6.
We list pairs of factors of 6. We add each pair of factors.
We look for the factors that have a sum of 7. They are 1 and 6.
We write these numbers as the second terms in the binomials.

$x^2 + 7x + 6 = (x + 1)(x + 6)$

Factors of 6	Sum
1, 6	$1 + 6 = 7$
–1, –6	$-1 - 6 = -7$
2, 3	$2 + 3 = 5$
–2, –3	$-2 - 3 = -5$

Example 2

Factor. $a^2 - 8a + 12$

Solution

$a^2 - 8a + 12$

We want two numbers whose sum is –8 and whose product is 12.
The factors that have a sum of –8 are –2 and –6.

$a^2 - 8a + 12 = (a - 6)(a - 2)$

Factors of 12	Sum
1, 12	$1 + 12 = 13$
–1, –12	$-1 - 12 = -13$
2, 6	$2 + 6 = 8$
–2, –6	$-2 - 6 = -8$
3, 4	$3 + 4 = 7$
–3, –4	$-3 - 4 = -7$

When you factor, you can check your work by expanding.

Example 3

Factor $m^2 - 5m - 14$, then check.

Solution

$m^2 - 5m - 14$

We want two numbers whose sum is –5 and whose product is –14.
The factors that have a sum of –5 are 2 and –7.

$m^2 - 5m - 14 = (m + 2)(m - 7)$

Factors of –14	Sum
–1, 14	$-1 + 14 = 13$
1, –14	$1 - 14 = -13$
–2, 7	$-2 + 7 = 5$
2, –7	$2 - 7 = -5$

Check: Expand $(m + 2)(m - 7)$.

$$\begin{aligned}(m + 2)(m - 7) &= m^2 - 7m + 2m - 14 \\ &= m^2 - 5m - 14\end{aligned}$$

Since this is the trinomial we started with, the factors are correct.

To factor some trinomials, you may need to simplify first. Check to see whether you can combine like terms. Look for common factors.

Example 4..

Simplify, then factor: $-5t - 3t^2 + 15 + 4t^2 - 3 - 3t$

Solution

$-5t - 3t^2 + 15 + 4t^2 - 3 - 3t$

This expression contains like terms such as $-5t$ and $-3t$, $-3t^2$ and $4t^2$. Combine like terms to simplify the expression.

$-5t - 3t^2 + 15 + 4t^2 - 3 - 3t = t^2 - 8t + 12$

The simplified expression, $t^2 - 8t + 12$, is similar to one factored in *Example 2*.

$t^2 - 8t + 12 = (t - 6)(t - 2)$

Example 5..

Factor completely. $7q^2 - 14q - 21$

Solution

$7q^2 - 14q - 21$

Look at the coefficients of the terms. There is a common factor of 7. Remove the common factor, then try to factor the remaining trinomial.

$\begin{aligned} 7q^2 - 14q - 21 &= 7(q^2 - 2q - 3) \\ &= 7(q + 1)(q - 3) \end{aligned}$

Factors of –3	Sum
–1, 3	2
1, –3	–2

Check by expanding $7(q + 1)(q - 3)$. Do this check on your own.

Example 6..

Factor. $3x^2 + 21x + 57$

Solution

$3x^2 + 21x + 57 = 3(x^2 + 7x + 19)$

Since 19 is a prime number, we know the only factors are 19 and 1. These do not add to 7. The expression $3(x^2 + 7x + 19)$ cannot be factored any further.

The solution to *Example 6* illustrates that not all trinomials are factorable into binomial pairs.

Working with Mathematics

Something to talk about

1. a) Name the pairs of numbers you would test to factor $x^2 - 9x + 14$.
   b) Which pair has a sum of -9 and a product of 14?
   c) What are the factors of $x^2 - 9x + 14$?

2. Is the product of two binomials always a trinomial? Explain.

3. Expand each expression.
   a) $(x + 3)(x + 5)$
   b) $(x - 3)(x - 5)$
   c) $(x - 3)(x + 5)$
   d) $(x + 3)(x - 5)$
   i) Why are the constant terms in the expansions in part a and part b positive?
   ii) Why are the constant terms in the expansions of part c and part d negative?
   iii) How can the coefficient of the x-term in an expansion be found?

Practice

4. Determine the numbers with each given sum and product.

	Product	Sum	Numbers
a)	12	8	
b)	12	−8	
c)	−12	4	
d)	−12	−4	

5. Factor.
   a) $x^2 + 7x + 12$
   b) $x^2 - 7x + 12$
   c) $x^2 + 10x + 25$
   d) $x^2 - 10x + 25$

6. For each product of two binomials in exercise 5, why are the signs in the binomials the same?

7. Factor.
   a) $x^2 + x - 20$
   b) $x^2 - x - 20$
   c) $x^2 + 2x - 24$
   d) $x^2 - 2x - 24$

8. For each product of two binomials in exercise 7, why are the signs in the binomials different?

9. Factor. Use algebra tiles or a diagram to model each solution.
   a) $x^2 + 7x + 10$
   b) $x^2 + 11x + 10$
   c) $x^2 + 5x + 6$
   d) $x^2 + 7x + 6$
   e) $n^2 + 6n + 8$
   f) $t^2 + 9t + 8$
   g) $x^2 + 13x + 30$
   h) $y^2 + 11y + 30$
   i) $t^2 + 31t + 30$
   j) $x^2 + 17x + 30$

10. Factor.
   a) $x^2 - 4x + 4$
   b) $x^2 - 5x + 4$
   c) $x^2 - 9x + 18$
   d) $x^2 - 11x + 18$
   e) $x^2 - 19x + 18$
   f) $x^2 - 14x + 45$
   g) $x^2 - 18x + 45$
   h) $x^2 - 46x + 45$
   i) $x^2 - 6x + 5$
   j) $x^2 - 4x + 3$

11. Factor. Check your answers by expanding.
   a) $x^2 + 19x - 20$
   b) $x^2 - 19x - 20$
   c) $y^2 + 8y - 20$
   d) $q^2 - 8q - 20$
   e) $x^2 + 23x - 24$
   f) $n^2 - 23n - 24$
   g) $a^2 + 10a - 24$
   h) $v^2 - 10v - 24$
   i) $x^2 + 5x - 24$
   j) $b^2 - 5b - 24$

Work together

12. For each diagram:
   i) Write the trinomial represented by the algebra tiles.
   ii) Rearrange the tiles into a rectangle.
   iii) Use the result to factor the trinomial.
   a)

   b)

   c)

   d)

13. Use algebra tiles to factor each trinomial.
   a) $x^2 + 2x + 1$ b) $x^2 + 3x + 2$
   c) $x^2 + 4x + 3$ d) $x^2 + 5x + 4$

14. a) Describe a pattern in the terms of the trinomials in exercise 13.
   b) Describe a pattern in the algebra-tile rectangles for the trinomials.
   c) Extend the pattern by writing three more trinomials.

15. Factor. Take turns with your partner to check each other's answers.
   a) $x^2 + 6x + 5$ b) $a^2 + 8a + 12$
   c) $m^2 + 6m + 9$ d) $x^2 - x - 2$
   e) $x^2 - 5x + 6$ f) $p^2 + 2p - 8$

16. Factor. Check your partner's answers.
   a) $x^2 - 6x + 8$ b) $x^2 + 9x + 18$
   c) $a^2 - 11a + 18$ d) $m^2 + 11m + 28$
   e) $n^2 - 10n + 25$ f) $n^2 - 13n + 30$
   g) $p^2 + 16p + 64$ h) $y^2 - 13y + 42$
   i) $x^2 + 15x + 56$ j) $x^2 - 10x - 56$

17. Factor completely. (You may need to remove common factors first.)
   a) $2x^2 + 12x + 10$ b) $5a^2 - 10a - 40$
   c) $10n^2 + 10n - 20$ d) $4a^2 - 16a - 20$
   e) $3x^2 + 15x - 18$ f) $7a^2 - 35a + 42$
   g) $x^3 - 2x^2 - 3x$ h) $a^3 - 2a^2 - 48a$
   i) $2y^3 + 14y^2 + 24y$ j) $3x^3 + 6x^2 - 24x$

18. Simplify, then factor.
   a) $5x^2 + 2x - 1 - 4x^2 - 4x - 14$
   b) $3m^2 - 5m + 6 - 2m^2 + 7m - 9$
   c) $5z^2 - 2z + 3 - 4z^2 + 6z - 15$
   d) $1 - 8a + a^2 + 4a - 22$
   e) $x^2 - 3x + 5 - x - 1$
   f) $8 - y + 4y^2 - 5y + 1 - 3y^2$
   g) $-6x - 8 - 2x^2 + 3x^2 - 2x - 12$
   h) $60 - 12y + y^2 - 5y + 12$
   i) $2(x - 5) + (x - 2)(x + 1)$
   j) $(a - 1)(a + 1) - 2a - 7$

On your own

19. Use algebra tiles to factor each trinomial.
   a) $x^2 + 12x + 11$ b) $a^2 + 13a + 12$
   c) $x^2 + 8x + 15$ d) $n^2 + 9n + 14$

20. Factor.
   a) $r^2 - 9r + 14$ b) $a^2 - 8a - 20$
   c) $n^2 - 8n + 16$ d) $m^2 - 9m + 20$
   e) $k^2 - 8k + 15$ f) $x^2 + 10x + 24$
   g) $a^2 - 2a - 15$ h) $m^2 + 9m + 20$
   i) $n^2 - 5n - 14$ j) $a^2 + 13a - 14$

21. Factor. Check your work by expanding.
   a) $r^2 - 5r - 36$ b) $a^2 - 4a - 45$
   c) $n^2 - 3n - 54$ d) $m^2 - 2m - 48$
   e) $k^2 - 2k - 63$ f) $x^2 - 7x - 30$
   g) $81 - 18a + a^2$ h) $121 + 22m + m^2$

22. Factor.
   a) $x^2 + 7x - 8$ b) $a^2 + 5a - 14$
   c) $t^2 - 2t - 3$ d) $n^2 + 13n + 42$
   e) $x^2 - 17x + 30$ f) $c^2 - 11c + 30$
   g) $m^2 + 6m - 55$ h) $a^2 + 10a + 9$

23. Factor completely.
   a) $2x^2 + 14x + 20$ b) $3a^2 + 15a + 18$
   c) $5m^2 - 10m - 120$ d) $3x^2 - 18x + 15$
   e) $p^3 - 2p^2 + p$ f) $2c^3 + 4c^2 - 70c$
   g) $3t^4 - 30t^3 + 75t^2$ h) $4x^2y - 32xy + 64y$

24. Consider the trinomial $x^2 - 2x - 15$.
   a) Find its value when $x = 17$.
   b) Factor the trinomial.
   c) Evaluate the factored expression when $x = 17$.
   d) Compare your work for parts a and c.

25. Consider the trinomial $x^2 - 13x + 36$.
   a) Find its value when $x = 59$.
   b) Factor the trinomial.
   c) Evaluate the factored expression when $x = 59$.
   d) Compare your work for parts a and c. Explain why it might be useful to factor an expression before you evaluate it.

Extend your thinking

26. Factor if possible.

a) $x^2 + 16x + 63$ **b)** $a^2 + 12a + 30$

c) $x^2 - 4x + 32$ **d)** $t^2 + 11t + 24$

e) $n^2 - 12n + 35$ **f)** $k^2 - 5k - 21$

27. Find an integer to replace each square so that each trinomial can be factored.

a) $x^2 + \blacksquare x + 12$ **b)** $x^2 - \blacksquare x + 20$

c) $x^2 + \blacksquare x - 18$ **d)** $x^2 + 5x + \blacksquare$

e) $x^2 + 4x + \blacksquare$ **f)** $x^2 - 2x + \blacksquare$

28. Use algebra tiles to factor each trinomial.

a) $x^2 - 2x + 1$ **b)** $x^2 - 3x - 4$

c) $x^2 + x - 6$ **d)** $x^2 - 6x + 9$

e) $x^2 - 6x - 7$ **f)** $x^2 - 10x + 16$

29. Follow these steps for each diagram below.

  i) Write the trinomial represented by the algebra tiles.

  ii) Rearrange the tiles into a rectangle.

  iii) Use the result to factor the trinomial.

a)

b)

c)

d)

e)

f)

g)

30. Use algebra tiles to factor each polynomial.

a) $2x^2 + 7x + 5$ **b)** $4x^2 + 13x + 3$

c) $3x^2 + 16x + 5$ **d)** $3x^2 + 10x + 8$

e) $5x^2 + 22x + 8$ **f)** $6x^2 + 7x + 2$

COMMUNICATING

The Ideas

In your journal, explain how you would factor a trinomial as a product of two binomials. Give an example of a trinomial that cannot be factored in this way. By looking at a trinomial, how can you tell whether or not it can be factored as a product of two binomials?

Review

1. Use algebra tiles to represent each polynomial.
   a) $2x^2 + 5x + 3$ b) $x^2 - 3x + 2$
   c) $4x^2 - 2x - 3$ d) $-3x^2 - 4x$

2. Write a polynomial that represents the perimeter and a polynomial that represents the area of each rectangle.

   a)
   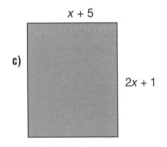
   $x + 4$
   x

   b)
   $2x + 3$
   $x + 1$

   c)
   $x + 5$
   $2x + 1$

3. Which of these expressions are polynomials?
   a) $x^2 + 4$ b) $5xy$
   c) $\dfrac{5x}{y}$ d) $7 - \dfrac{2y}{5} + 3x^2$

4. Classify each polynomial in exercise 3 as a monomial, a binomial, or a trinomial.

5. State the coefficient in each term.
   a) $5x$ b) $-2z^3$ c) y^2 d) $\dfrac{1}{3}x^2y^4$

6. State the constant term in each polynomial.
   a) $4 - 2x$ b) $a^2 + 2a + 3$
   c) $4y^2 - 1 + 3y$ d) $5x^2 + 2x$

7. Simplify.
   a) $(5x^2 - 3y^2) + (x^2 + 4y^2)$
   b) $(-2x - 7) - (-14x - 6)$
   c) $(8a^2 + 2a - 3) - (-6a^2 + 4a + 7)$
   d) $(3x - 2) - (x - 1) + (4x - 3)$
   e) $(4x^2 - 3x) - (x^2 + 2x) + (3x^2 - x)$
   f) $(3x^2 + 5x + 7) - (2x^2 - 4x + 9)$

8. Simplify. Find the value of the polynomial when: i) $x = 2$ ii) $x = -3$
   a) $(5 - 2x) - (3 - x) + (7x - 2)$
   b) $(5x^2 - 5x + 7) - (2x^2 - 3x - 5)$

9. Simplify.
   a) $(-25n^2)(8n^2)$ b) $(-35c^3)(-4c^2)$
   c) $(17x^2)(5x^3)$ d) $(-28n)(5n^3)$

10. Simplify.
   a) $\dfrac{-45y^6}{-5y^4}$ b) $\dfrac{3n^6}{5n^4}$
   c) $\dfrac{25x^4}{-5x^4}$ d) $\dfrac{36c^5}{24c^2}$
   e) $18x^4 \div 3x$ f) $(-52y^6) \div 13y^5$

11. Recall the x-tiles and y-tiles you cut out on page 341. What product does each diagram represent?

   a)
   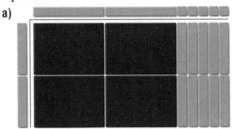

   b)

   c)

12. Expand.
   a) $4(y - 2)$ b) $8(a - 3)$
   c) $-4(x + 2)$ d) $3x(5 - x)$
   e) $2y(y - 6)$ f) $(-5x)(3 - x)$
   g) $5y(7 - 2y + 3y^2)$ h) $(-6x)(3x^2 + 5x - 12)$

13. Expand.

   a) $3c(5 - 2c)$ **b)** $(-4n)(2n - 1)$

   c) $(-7y)(2y^2 - 5)$ **d)** $6k(3 - k + k^2)$

   e) $5s(3s^2 - 2s - 7)$ **f)** $3p^2(2 - 3p - p^2)$

14. Factor each polynomial.

   a) $5y - 10$ **b)** $12a + 18$

   c) $-3x^2 + 6x - 12$ **d)** $2a^2 - 10a + 2$

   e) $4w + 3w^2 - 7w^3$ **f)** $8y^3 - 4y^2 + 2y$

15. Factor. Check by expanding.

   a) $6y + 18y^2$ **b)** $-3a + 12a^4$

   c) $5a^2 - 25a^3$ **d)** $3a^3 + 4a^2 + 7a$

   e) $3m - 9m^2 + 15m^3$ **f)** $12k^2 - 48k^4 - 18k^6$

   g) $6x^2y - 3xy + 9xy^2$ **h)** $8ab - 4a^2b^2 + 6ab^2$

16. Simplify.

   a) $\dfrac{3x^2 - 6x}{3x}$ **b)** $\dfrac{5x^2 - 10x}{5x}$

   c) $\dfrac{18a - 21a^2}{3a}$ **d)** $\dfrac{-28n^2 - 7n}{7n}$

   e) $\dfrac{36y - 9y^2}{-9y}$ **f)** $\dfrac{32b^4 + 8b^3}{-4b^2}$

17. Simplify.

   a) $\dfrac{12x^2 + 4x}{4x}$ **b)** $\dfrac{10a - 6a^2}{2a}$

   c) $\dfrac{3x^3 - 12x^2}{6x^2}$ **d)** $\dfrac{10a^3 - 5a^2}{-10a}$

   e) $\dfrac{18c^2 - 6c^3 + 12c^4}{-6c^2}$ **f)** $\dfrac{15x^5 + 20x^4 - 5x^3}{10x^3}$

   g) $\dfrac{-9m^3 + 12m^4 - 15m^2}{-9m^2}$ **h)** $\dfrac{12y^3 - 6y^2 + 18y^5}{12y^2}$

18. Expand.

   a) $(x - 3)(x - 4)$ **b)** $(y + 7)(y + 3)$

   c) $(a - 2)(a + 5)$ **d)** $(n - 6)(n + 7)$

   e) $(n + 4)(n - 7)$ **f)** $(x - 1)(x + 5)$

   g) $(2x + 3)(x - 4)$ **h)** $(3a + 1)(2a + 5)$

19. Expand.

   a) $(x - 3)(5x + 2)$ **b)** $(2a + 1)(2a + 3)$

   c) $(8n - 3)(2n - 1)$ **d)** $(4a + 3)(4a + 3)$

   e) $(3x - 2)(4x - 3)$ **f)** $(5x + 1)(6x - 4)$

20. Expand.

   a) $(x - 5)(x - 6)$ **b)** $(y + 1)(y + 5)$

   c) $(a - 2)(a + 9)$ **d)** $(n + 3)(n - 5)$

   e) $(a - 1)(a + 2)$ **f)** $(x - 4)(x - 2)$

21. Factor.

   a) $x^2 + 10x + 16$ **b)** $a^2 + 4a - 12$

   c) $x^2 - 10x + 25$ **d)** $c^2 - 2c - 35$

   e) $x^2 - x - 12$ **f)** $a^2 + a - 30$

22. Factor.

   a) $x^2 - 7x + 10$ **b)** $y^2 + 6y + 9$

   c) $x^2 + 6x + 5$ **d)** $15 + 2x - x^2$

   e) $8 + 7x - x^2$ **f)** $n^2 + 3n - 40$

23. Factor completely.

   a) $2x^2 - 12x - 72$

   b) $5m^2 + 10m - 40$

   c) $y^3 + 2y^2 - 3y$

   d) $a^3 - 3a^2 - 10a$

   e) $4m^3 - 40m^2 + 100m$

   f) $-2b^3 - 14b^2 - 24b$

24. Simplify, then factor completely.

   a) $4x^2 - 2x - 6 + 10x - 3x^2 - 3$

   b) $5x + 6 - 5x^2 + 4 - 12x + 6x^2$

   c) $30 - 2y - y^2 + 5 + 14y + 2y^2$

   d) $7a - 10 - 2a - 4 + a^2$

   e) $6m^2 - 2m - 1 - 4m^2 + 8m - 7$

   f) $2x - 12 - 8x^2 - 8x - 12 + 11x^2$

25. Factor if possible.

   a) $x^2 + 7x - 60$ **b)** $n^2 + 7n - 7$

   c) $x^2 - 6x + 24$ **d)** $a^2 - a - 45$

   e) $56 + t - t^2$ **f)** $6 - x + x^2$

26. Follow these steps for each diagram below.

   i) Write the trinomial represented by the algebra tiles.

   ii) Rearrange the tiles into a rectangle.

   iii) Use the result to factor the trinomial.

   a)

   b)

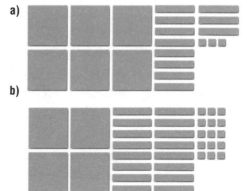

The SET Game

Have you ever played the game SET? It can be played alone or with two or more people. This game was invented by Marsha J. Falco, a mathematician and computer programmer.

Marsha Falco didn't start out to make a popular game of logic. In 1974, she was working as an applied mathematician at the University of Cambridge in England. She was trying to determine whether epilepsy in German Shepherd dogs was inherited. While compiling her research, she wrote information about each dog on file cards. Because blocks of information were the same on each file card, rather than writing the data, she drew a symbol to represent a piece of data. If the information was slightly different, she would make the symbol a different colour. The veterinarians she was working with would look over her shoulder at the cards spread out on the table. They tried to find patterns in the shapes and colours of the symbols on the different cards. This gave her the idea for the game SET. She invented the game for her co-workers. Her daughter and son enjoyed SET so much that they urged Marsha to sell the game.

Since 1991, SET has been a popular game enjoyed by young and old all over North America.

The game has 81 cards. Each card has 4 attributes.
- Number — each card has one, two, or three symbols
- Shape — each symbol is an oval, a squiggle, or a diamond
- Colour — each symbol is red, green, or purple
- Shading — each symbol is solid, striped, or unshaded

The purpose of the game is to find a set of three cards. In a set, each of the 4 attributes must be the *same* on every card or *different* on each card.

The three cards above right form a set.

Each card has a *different* number of symbols.
The symbols are the *same*.
The colours are the *same*.
The shadings are *different*.

Do the three cards on the right form a set? Explain.

The game is played by laying down 12 cards in a rectangle. The first person to see a set calls out "Set!". This person shows the set to the other players. If it is agreed that the cards form a set, this person is given 1 point. The three cards are removed and replaced by three cards from the deck. The game is over when all the cards have been used or no set can be made.

In this project, you will produce your own SET game, using mathematical expressions.

Each card should have a mathematical expression of the form $a \times b^c + d$. The four attributes are the values of a, b, c, and d. In the original game, each attribute has three possibilities. Let's use three different numbers for each of a, b, c, and d. It really does not matter which three numbers, so let's use 2, 3, and 5. There will be 81 cards altogether. Three examples are shown on the right. Do the three cards form a set?

Let's check. The values of $a\,(2, 2, 2)$ are all the *same*, the values of $b\,(3, 5, 2)$ are all *different*, the values of $c\,(5, 5, 5)$ are all the *same*, and the values of $d\,(5, 3, 2)$ are all *different*. These three cards *do* form a set.

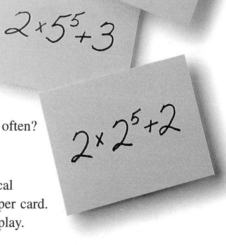

ACTIVITY 1

Make a complete set of these cards. Play the game on your own or with some friends.

ACTIVITY 2

How many cards would be in the set if each attribute had 4 different values? In such a version, would sets occur more often?

ACTIVITY 3

Design your own version of SET with or without mathematical expressions. You might try to use more than three attributes per card. Investigate whether this makes the game too complicated to play.

The Ideas

Prepare a report to illustrate your results. Include an explanation of your SET game.

Cumulative Review

1. For each of the following expressions:
   i) record the key strokes you use to evaluate it
   ii) evaluate the expression in a different way and record the key strokes
   iii) explain why one method uses fewer key strokes than the other
   a) $(23.8 - 32.5) \times (4.3 + 82.3)$
   b) $(9.2 - 4.8) \times (15.1 - 65.1)$
   c) $\dfrac{2.4}{9.6 - 12.4}$
   d) $\dfrac{4.8 - 3.6}{2.5 \times (3.7 - 2.5)}$

2. Draw a rectangle 8 cm by 10 cm. Suppose you increase each side by 20%. What is the percent increase in the area of the rectangle?

3. Students conducted an activity in which they attached different masses to the end of a spring. They recorded the length of the stretched spring for each mass. The table gives their results.

Mass (g)	100	200	300	400
Length of spring (cm)	45	58	66	74
Mass (g)	500	600	700	800
Length of spring (cm)	82	95	98	106

   a) Graph the results. Construct a line of best fit.
   b) Estimate the length of the spring for a 450-g mass; A 750-g mass.

4. As a teenage driver, you make a case for cheaper insurance rates for people under 25 based on these figures from Statistics Canada. How do you think the insurance company will respond?

PEOPLE KILLED IN CAR ACCIDENTS		
Age Group	Number	Percent
Under 25	1258	34.15
25 and over	2426	65.85

5. Maria has forgotten the six-digit code for her voice mail. She only remembers that the code is made up of 4s and 9s. She tries to select digits randomly to see if she can break her code. What is her probability of success? (She must select each digit at least once.)

6. Show how you solve each equation using algebra tiles. Record each solution using symbols.
   a) $4x + 1 = 9$
   b) $2x + 5 = x$
   c) $3x - 2 = 7$
   d) $3x + 6 = x$
   e) $5x - 8 = 7x$
   f) $3x - 7 = 2x + 4$

7. Solve and check.
   a) $4p - 3 = 2p + 7$
   b) $9k + 5 = 7 + 7k$
   c) $10 - x = 4x$
   d) $-2p = 2p + 12$
   e) $3(4 - y) = 2y + 1$
   f) $8s = 5s - 3$

8. Two consecutive numbers have a sum of 17. What are the numbers?

9. A vending machine accepts quarters and loonies. It contains 64 coins worth $32.50. How many of each type of coin are there?

10. A rectangle is 10 cm longer than it is wide. Its perimeter is 80 cm. What are the length and width of the rectangle?

11. Solve, graph, and check each inequality.
    a) $7 < 2x + 3$
    b) $9 - 3k > k + 1$
    c) $-5b > 15 - 2b$
    d) $-4j - 7 \le -j - 1$

12. Debra and Joel took these measurements to determine the height h metres of their school.

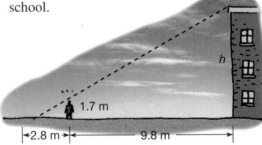

   a) Construct a scale diagram to estimate the height of the school.
   b) Use similar triangles to determine the height of the school.

13. Determine the measure of $\angle B$ to the nearest degree.
    a) $\tan B = 1.359$
    b) $\sin B = 0.455$
    c) $\cos B = 0.776$
    d) $\cos B = 0.122$

14. After a storm, a 10-m signpost is leaning over. It makes an angle of 81° with the ground. How far above the ground is the top of the post?

15. Two 10-m signposts are leaning over after a storm. The top of one post is 8.0 m above the ground. The top of the other post is 6.5 m above the ground. Determine the angle each signpost makes with the ground.

16. Evaluate.
    a) 5^{-3}
    b) $\left(\frac{1}{2}\right)^{-1}$
    c) 2^{-3}
    d) 4^{-1}
    e) 7^0
    f) $\left(\frac{2}{3}\right)^{-1}$
    g) $\left(\frac{1}{2}\right)^{-2}$
    h) 17^0
    i) 4^{-3}

17. Write each expression as a single power.
    a) $2^2 \times 2^5$
    b) $4^7 \div 4^5$
    c) $\left(3^4\right)^2$
    d) $(-2)^3 \div (-2)^2$
    e) $(-2^3)^5$
    f) $\frac{1}{5^3}$
    g) $(-3 \times 5)^3$
    h) $7^5 \times 7^{-8}$
    i) $6^{-2} \div 6^3$
    j) $\frac{1}{3^{-5}}$

18. Simplify each expression.
    a) $x^4 \times x^5$
    b) $k^{36} \div k^{12}$
    c) $m^{12} \times m^{-6}$
    d) $(b^2)^{-4}$
    e) $a^2 \times a^4$
    f) $p^9 \div p^4$
    g) $w^4 \times w^{-3}$
    h) $(-v)^{12} \div (-v)^4$
    i) $(5t)^3$
    j) $(-2c^2)^5$

19. Express in scientific notation, then simplify.
    a) $49\ 000\ 000 \times 730\ 000$
    b) $26\ 500\ 000 \times 7900 \times 0.0046$
    c) $\dfrac{320\ 000 \times 64\ 000\ 000}{12\ 800\ 000}$

20. It takes 1200 silkworm eggs to balance the mass of 1 g. What is the mass of one silkworm egg?

21. Determine the value of n in each case.
    a) $2^n = 32$
    b) $n^5 = 3125$
    c) $49 = n^2$
    d) $6^n = 1296$
    e) $1265 = 1.265 \times 10^n$
    f) $0.005 = 5.0 \times 10^n$

22. Given the area, determine the side length of each square. Give the answers to 1 decimal place where necessary.
    a) 64 mm^2
    b) 0.81 m^2
    c) 49 m^2
    d) 2.25 cm^2
    e) 0.25 m^2
    f) 1.44 m^2
    g) 50.0 cm^2
    h) 2.0 m^2
    i) 15.0 mm^2

23. Give examples of two rational numbers between the numbers in each pair.
    a) $25, 25.8$
    b) $18.1, 18.\overline{2}$
    c) $\sqrt{2}, \frac{1}{2}$
    d) $4, \sqrt{15}$

24. Multiply or divide.
    a) $(5x^2)(2x)$
    b) $(3a^2)(-a^3)$
    c) $12x^5 \div 3x^2$
    d) $\dfrac{-45b^7}{-3b^2}$
    e) $(2x^2)^3(-3x)^2$
    f) $(4a^3)^2 \div (-8a^6)$

25. Expand.
    a) $(x + 3)(x + 2)$
    b) $(a - 7)(a + 2)$
    c) $(n + 5)(n - 1)$
    d) $(y - 1)(y - 2)$
    e) $(k - 6)(k + 1)$
    f) $(5 - a)(3 + a)$
    g) $(t + 2)(t - 8)$
    h) $(m - 5)(m - 4)$

26. Factor. Check by expanding.
    a) $5m + 15m^2$
    b) $-4q + 20q^4$
    c) $7q^2 - 35q^3$
    d) $8q^3 + 4q^2 + 2q$
    e) $6m - 18m^2 + 15m^3$
    f) $-2k^2 - 8k^4 - 16k^6$
    g) $7b^2m - 21bm + 14bm^2$
    h) $64ab - 16a^2b^2 + 8ab^2$

27. Factor. Check by expanding.
    a) $x^2 + 5x + 4$
    b) $m^2 + 2m - 15$
    c) $a^2 - 2a - 15$
    d) $12 + 7y + y^2$
    e) $24 + 11k + k^2$
    f) $c^2 - c - 42$
    g) $n^2 - 6n + 5$
    h) $q^2 - 16q + 64$
    i) $49 + 14s + s^2$
    j) $w^2 + 9w + 14$

28. Simplify, then factor if possible.
    a) $5a^2 + 2a + 3a - 4a^2 - 4a - 6$
    b) $3k^2 + 7k - 2k + 2k^2 + 5$
    c) $-m^2 - 8m - 2 + 2m + m^2 + m^2 + 10$
    d) $1 + 5n - n^2 - 7n + 3$

29. Factor completely.
    a) $5n^2 + 10n - 15$
    b) $4x^2 + 16x - 84$
    c) $36 + 6m - 2m^2$
    d) $48 + 60b + 12b^2$
    e) $10n^2 - 25n$
    f) $3w^2 - 6w - 45$

TRANSFORMATIONS

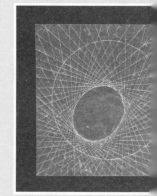

Mathematics Files

Quest

Minds on Math Project

Start With What You Know

For thousands of years, clans have worn coats of arms and nations have displayed flags. These flags display shields, icons, and geometric designs. Usually, the flags display line symmetry and sometimes rotational symmetry.

The flags of 20 nations are displayed on this page. Study the flags to find the flag with the greatest amount of symmetry.

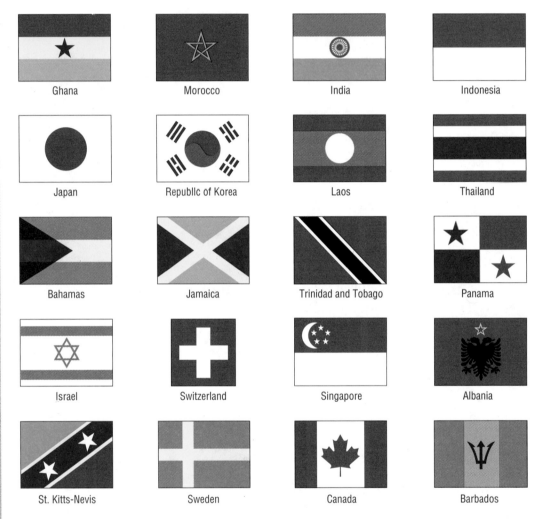

Ghana	Morocco	India	Indonesia
Japan	Republic of Korea	Laos	Thailand
Bahamas	Jamaica	Trinidad and Tobago	Panama
Israel	Switzerland	Singapore	Albania
St. Kitts-Nevis	Sweden	Canada	Barbados

1. Explain the meaning of the term *line symmetry*.

2. Which flags have a line of symmetry that is:
   a) horizontal?   b) vertical?

3. Which flags have more than one line of symmetry?

4. Explain the meaning of the term *rotational symmetry*.

5. Which flags have rotational symmetry? Describe the symmetry.

6. Which flag has the greatest amount of symmetry?

7. The pictures below are the images of the flags after transformations have been applied. These transformations are rotations (turns) and reflections (flips). In each case, identify the transformation that was applied to the flag to produce the image.

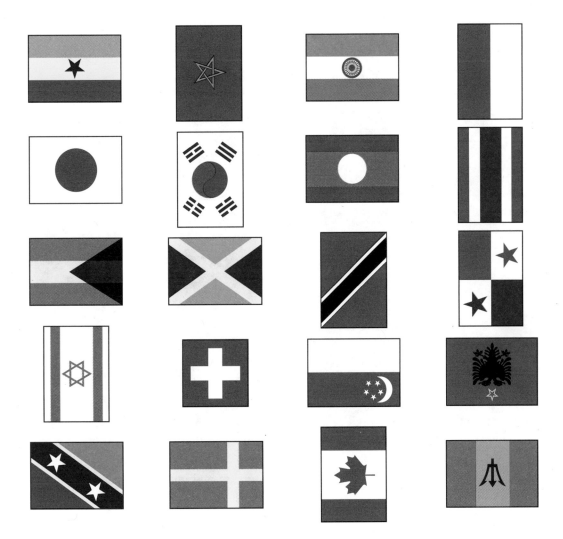

Wax Paper Designs

These designs were made by folding wax paper. You can create similar designs by following the steps below. You will need some wax paper, a circular template (such as a jar lid), and compasses or a pin.

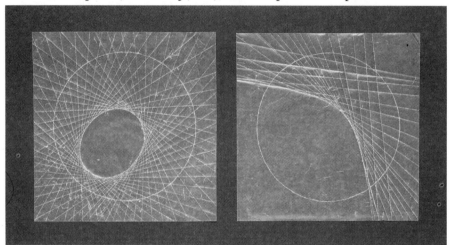

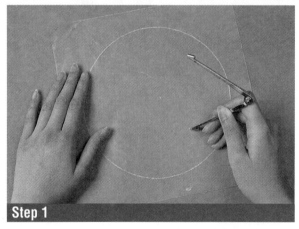

Step 1

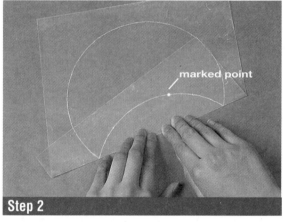

marked point

Step 2

Use a circular template and the point of your compasses or a pin to mark a circle on the wax paper. Mark a point inside the circle.

Carefully fold the wax paper so that a point on the circle falls on the marked point. Make a sharp crease and unfold. Repeat for many other fold lines.

1. How would your design change if the marked point were closer to the circle?

2. What happens if the marked point is on the circle? Is outside the circle?

3. Investigate what happens if a triangle, square, or straight line is used in place of the circle.

Make a display of the results of your investigations. Your display should include a description of how to make each design.

7.1 TRANSLATIONS

Developing the Ideas

▶▶ *Through Discussion*

When a ship is launched, it slides down
a specially constructed ramp to the water.
This motion provides a model for a translation.

1. What are some examples of translations
   in the world in which we live?

2. In what ways is a translation different
   from other kinds of motions?

3. Is the size or shape of a figure changed
   by a translation?

▶▶ *Through an Activity*

You will investigate translations on a grid to find out how a figure and
its translation image are related.

Work with a partner.

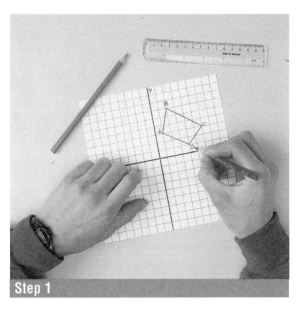

Step 1

Step 2

On grid paper, draw a set of *x-y* axes. Draw
a quadrilateral so its vertices lie on the
intersections of grid lines. Label the vertices
A, B, C, and D.

Choose a translation. For example, each vertex
could move 2 units left, 3 units down. You
choose the direction (right or left, and up or
down) and how many units. Translate each
vertex and draw the image quadrilateral in a
different colour. Label the vertices A′, B′, C′,
and D′.

1. Measure the sides of quadrilateral ABCD and the sides of quadrilateral A′B′C′D′. What do you notice?

2. Measure the angles of quadrilateral ABCD and the angles of quadrilateral A′B′C′D′. What do you notice?

3. How is quadrilateral A′B′C′D′ the same as quadrilateral ABCD?

4. How is quadrilateral A′B′C′D′ different from quadrilateral ABCD?

5. Compare your diagrams and results with those of other students. Did all of you have the same answers to the questions in exercises 1 to 4?

▶▶ *Through Guided Examples*

Example 1 ···

This trapezoid has vertices A(−1, −1), B(1, −1), C(1, 3), and D(−1, 1). The trapezoid is translated 5 units right, 2 units down.

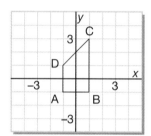

a) Draw a diagram to show the image of the trapezoid.

b) Join each vertex to its image. What do you notice about the lines you drew?

c) What do you notice about AD and A′D′, DC and D′C′, CB and C′B′, and AB and A′B′?

Solution

a) From each vertex, move 5 units right, then 2 units down. Mark a point. Join the points to form the image. Label the vertices of the image.

b) The line segments joining corresponding points and their images are parallel. That is, line segments AA′, BB′, CC′, and DD′ are parallel.

c) The line segments in each pair are equal and parallel. That is, corresponding sides of a figure and its translation image are equal and parallel.

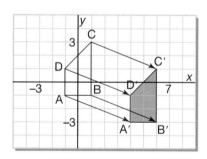

Example 2

In the diagram below, △A'B'C' is the image of △ABC after a translation. Identify the translation.

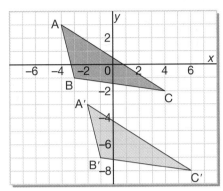

Solution

To go from A to A', move 2 units right and 6 units down. Similar movements are required to go from B to B' and from C to C'. The translation is 2 units right, 6 units down.

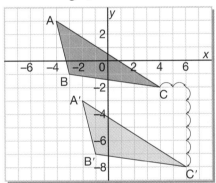

From the preceding activity and examples, you should have discovered these properties of a translation.

• • • • • • • • •

When a figure is translated:
- the lengths of its sides are unchanged
- the measures of its angles are unchanged
- the position of the figure is changed

After a translation:
- since the lengths of the side are unchanged, and the measures of the angles are unchanged, the translation image is congruent to the original figure
- the lines joining corresponding points and their images are parallel
- corresponding sides of the original figure and its image are parallel

Working with Mathematics

Something to talk about

1. For each translation described below:
   i) How is the image figure the same as the original figure?
   ii) How is the image figure different from the original figure?
   a) A triangle is translated 3 units right.
   b) A rectangle is translated 2 units down.
   c) A parallelogram is translated 5 units up.
   d) A square is translated 3 units left.

2. In each diagram below, △P′Q′R′ is the image of △PQR after a translation. Identify the translation in each case.

a)

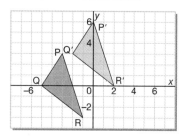

b)

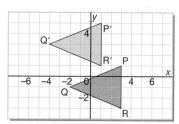

c)

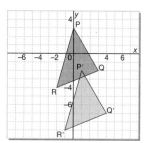

d)

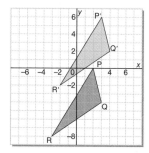

Practice

3. Find the coordinates of the image of each point after a translation of 4 units right.
   a) A(3, 0)   b) B(−2, 1)
   c) C(4, −5)   d) D(0, −10)
   e) E(7, 5)   f) F(−3, 0)
   g) G(0, 6)   h) H(−3, −7)

4. Find the coordinates of the image of each point after a translation of 6 units left.
   a) A(−1, −2)   b) B(2, 5)
   c) C(10, −3)   d) D(0, −4)
   e) O(0, 0)   f) F(−4, 9)
   g) G(−5, −3)   h) H(6, 0)

5. Find the coordinates of the image of each point after a translation of 5 units down.
   a) A(4, 4)   b) B(−3, −6)
   c) C(−7, 1)   d) D(2, −3)
   e) E(−7, 0)   f) F(5, −1)
   g) G(−3, 11)   h) H(0, 2)

6. Find the coordinates of the image of each point after a translation of 7 units up.
   a) A(0, −1)   b) B(3, −7)
   c) C(0, 6)   d) D(5, 8)
   e) E(−3, −9)   f) F(−7, −2)
   g) G(−5, 0)   h) O(0, 0)

7. Find the coordinates of the image of each point after a translation of 3 units right, 2 units down.
   a) A(−9, −2)   b) B(3, 3)
   c) C(−4, −5)   d) O(0, 0)
   e) E(0, 9)   f) F(5, 1)
   g) G(−3, 7)   h) H(8, −10)

8. Find the coordinates of the image of each point after a translation of 4 units left, 5 units up.
   a) A(0, −7)   b) B(6, −3)
   c) O(0, 0)   d) D(9, 0)
   e) E(−6, 2)   f) F(7, 7)
   g) G(−2, −5)   h) H(3, 1)

Work together

9. Draw the triangle with vertices P(3, 4), Q(−2, 7), and R(−4, 1). Draw the image triangle after a translation 2 units right, 4 units up. Label the image triangle P′Q′R′.
   a) Measure PP′, QQ′, and RR′. What do you notice?
   b) Measure the angle between each line segment in part a and a horizontal grid line. What do you notice? What does this tell you about PP′, QQ′, and RR′?

10. Draw the quadrilateral with vertices A(−3, 3), B(3, 5), C(3, 2), and D(−3, 0). Draw the image quadrilateral after a translation 3 units left, 5 units down. Label the image quadrilateral A′B′C′D′.
    a) What type of quadrilateral is ABCD?
    b) What type of quadrilateral is A′B′C′D′?
    c) How are quadrilateral ABCD and quadrilateral A′B′C′D′ the same? How are they different?

11. In each diagram below, △P′Q′R′ is the image of △PQR after the given translation. Find the coordinates of the vertices of △PQR in each case.
    a) 3 units right, 2 units down

    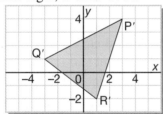

    b) 5 units left, 3 units down

    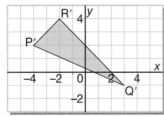

c) 4 units right, 1 unit up

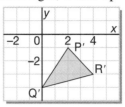

d) 6 units left, 2 units up

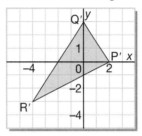

12. Draw a rectangle in the first quadrant. Translate the rectangle so that the image rectangle is completely in:
    a) the second quadrant
    b) the third quadrant
    c) the fourth quadrant

    For each image, write the coordinates of its vertices and describe the translation.

13. Triangle ABC has vertices A(−9, −2), B(3, 3), and C(−4, −5). A translation image of △ABC has vertices A′(−6, −4), B′(6, 1), and C′(−1, −7).
    a) Identify the translation.
    b) How can you check that △ABC is congruent to △A′B′C′?

14. a) Plot the points P(2, 2), Q(4, 3), R(6, 4), and S(8, 5). Draw the line through these points.
    b) Translate each point 4 units right, 3 units down. Label the image points P′, Q′, R′, and S′.
    c) Draw the line through the image points.
    d) How is line segment PS the same as line segment P′S′? How are these line segments different?

15. In the diagram, which of the images *a* to *h* are translation images of the shaded figure?

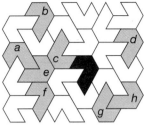

16. Given the translation 2 units left, 5 units up:
  a) Find the coordinates of the images of the points O(0, 0), A(3, 1), and B(2, −6).
  b) Find the coordinates of the points that have P′(0, 3), Q′(1, 7), and R′(−3, 1) as their images.
  c) Graph all the points and their images from parts a and b. Join matching points with line segments. What do you notice about these line segments?

17. Copy this parallelogram. Draw the image parallelogram A′B′C′D′ after each translation.

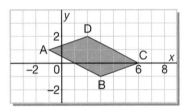

  a) 5 units right, 2 units up
  b) 8 units left, 1 unit down
  c) 2 units right, 4 units down
  d) 4 units left, 2 units up

On your own

18. Draw the quadrilateral with vertices A(−4, −2), B(−3, −5), C(−6, −6), and D(−7, −3). Draw the image quadrilateral A′B′C′D′ after a translation 6 units right, 8 units up.
  a) Measure AA′, BB′, CC′, and DD′. What do you notice?
  b) Measure the angle between each line segment in part a and a horizontal grid line. What do you notice?

c) Compare your answers to parts a and b with your answers to exercise 9. What statement can you make about the line segments that join matching points in a translation?

19. a) Plot the points M(−1, 1), N(−4, 2), P(−7, 3), and R(−10, 4). Draw a line through these points.
  b) Translate each point 3 units left, 1 unit up. Label the image points M′, N′, P′, and R′.
  c) Draw the line through the image points.
  d) How is line segment MR the same as line segment M′R′? How are these line segments different?
  e) How are MR and M′R′ different from PS and P′S′ in exercise 14? Explain.

20. A triangle has vertices A(−4, 2), B(2, 2), and C(−4, 5). Draw the triangle and its image after each translation.
  a) 5 units left, 1 unit down
  b) 3 units left, 4 units up
  c) 6 units right, 3 units up
  d) 2 units right, 1 unit down

21. Draw a square in the second quadrant. Translate the square so that the image square is partly in:
  a) the second quadrant and first quadrant
  b) the second quadrant and third quadrant
  c) the third quadrant and fourth quadrant
  d) the fourth quadrant and first quadrant

  For each image, write the coordinates of its vertices and describe the translation.

22. The image pentagon A′(−3, 3), B′(1, 4), C′(4, 0), D′(−2, −3), E′(−1, 0) was obtained by subtracting 4 from each *x*-coordinate of the vertices of ABCDE.
  a) Draw the image pentagon A′B′C′D′E′.
  b) Draw the original pentagon ABCDE.
  c) How can you check that A′B′C′D′E′ is a translation image of ABCDE?

23. A square has vertices A(1, 1), B(4, 2), C(3, 5), and D(0, 4). Draw the square and its image after the translation for which point B is the image of point A.

24. A square has vertices A(2, 0), B(5, 1), C(4, 4), and D(1, 3). A translation image of the square has the point (3, 2) as one vertex. How many different translations are possible? Explain.

Extend your thinking

25. You can use a *mapping rule* such as $(x, y) \rightarrow (x + 5, y - 2)$ to determine the image of any point with coordinates (x, y). A mapping rule tells you what to do to the coordinates of a point to determine the coordinates of its image. This mapping rule tells you to add 5 to the x-coordinate and to subtract 2 from the y-coordinate.

A triangle has vertices P(−3, 1), Q(3, 3), and R(−3, 4). Draw the triangle and its image after each translation.

a) $(x, y) \rightarrow (x + 4, y + 1)$

b) $(x, y) \rightarrow (x - 3, y - 2)$

c) $(x, y) \rightarrow (x + 2, y - 4)$

d) $(x, y) \rightarrow (x - 5, y + 3)$

26. The coordinates of the vertices of a triangle and its translation image are given. Identify the translation and write the mapping rule.

a) A(−4, 3), B(4, −2), C(−2, −1);
A′(−8, 5), B′(0, 0), C′(−6, 1)

b) D(−2, −3), E(3, 1), F(−4, 4);
D′(1, −5), E′(6, −1), F′(−1, 2)

c) G(2, 4), H(0, 1), I(7, 0);
G′(0, 1), H′(−2, −2), I′(5, −3)

d) J(4, −4), K(−1, −2), L(6, 1);
J′(9, −1), K′(4, 1), L′(11, 4)

COMMUNICATING The Ideas

In your journal, explain how you can tell if one figure is a translation image of another figure. Draw diagrams to illustrate.

BOGGLE YOUR **MIND**

In April 1992, it was reported in *Flight International* magazine that a McDonnell Douglas DC-9 (similar to the one shown) had completed 94 159 flights in 26 years and was still in operation. About how many flights would the plane have made each day during those 26 years?

Developing the Ideas

▶▶ *Through Discussion*

When we look in a mirror, we see a reflection.
The image in the mirror appears to have
the same shape and size as the object
being reflected.

1. In what ways are the object
and its image alike?

2. In what ways are the object
and its image different?

3. Are the size and shape of an object
and its image the same? Explain.

▶▶ *Through Activities*

ACTIVITY 1

You will investigate reflections on a grid to find out how a figure and its
reflection image are related.

Work with a partner.

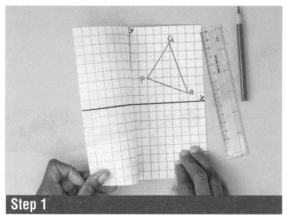

Step 1

On grid paper, draw a set of *x-y* axes. Draw
a triangle in the first quadrant so its vertices
lie on the intersections of grid lines. Label the
vertices P, Q, and R. Fold the paper along the
y-axis.

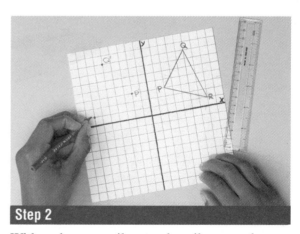

Step 2

With a sharp pencil, press heavily on each
point P, Q, and R. Unfold the paper. Mark
each indent with a dot. Label the points P′,
Q′, and R′, so that P′ is the reflection image of
P, Q′ is the reflection image of Q, and R′ is the
reflection image of R. Draw the image triangle
P′Q′R′ in a different colour.

1. Measure the sides of △PQR and the sides of △P′Q′R′. What do you notice?

2. Measure the angles of △PQR and △P′Q′R′. What do you notice?

3. Start at P. Do you move clockwise or counterclockwise when you move to Q, then to R?

4. Start at P′. Do you move clockwise or counterclockwise when you move to Q′, then to R′?

5. How is △P′Q′R′ the same as △PQR?

6. How is △P′Q′R′ different from △PQR?

7. Compare your diagram and results with those of other students. Did all of you have the same answers to the questions in exercises 1 to 6?

ACTIVITY 2

1. On grid paper, draw the same △PQR you drew in *Activity 1*.

2. Draw a vertical line 4 units to the right of the *y*-axis. Use this line as the reflection line. Fold the paper along this line. Repeat Step 2 of *Activity 1*. Complete exercises 1 to 7 in *Activity 1*.

3. Repeat step 1 above. Draw a horizontal line through the point H(0, 4). Use this line as the reflection line. Fold the paper along this line. Repeat Step 2 of *Activity 1*. Complete exercises 1 to 7 in *Activity 1*.

4. Repeat step 1 above. Draw a line through the points R(6, 5) and S(12, 11). Use this line as the reflection line. Fold the paper along this line. Repeat Step 2 of *Activity 1*. Complete exercises 1 to 7 in *Activity 1*.

As a result of *Activities 1* and *2*, you should have discovered these properties of a reflection.

· · · · · · · · · ·

When a figure is reflected:
- the lengths of its sides are unchanged
- the measures of its angles are unchanged
- the orientation of the figure reverses; that is, if △PQR is read clockwise, then △P′Q′R′ is read counterclockwise
- the reflection image is congruent to the original figure

Example 1 ··

A rectangle has vertices A(2, 0), B(6, 2), C(5, 4), and D(1, 2). On the same grid, draw the rectangle and its image after each reflection. Describe each rectangle and its image.

a) a reflection in the *x*-axis

b) a reflection in a vertical line 3 units to the left of the *y*-axis

Solution

Draw the rectangle on a grid.

a) For each vertex, mark the image point the same distance below the *x*-axis as the original vertex is above the *x*-axis. Label the image vertices. Draw the image rectangle A′B′C′D′.

b) Draw a vertical line 3 units to the left of the *y*-axis. For each vertex, mark the image point the same distance to the left of the reflection line as the original vertex is to the right of the line. Label the image vertices. Draw the image rectangle A″B″C″D″.

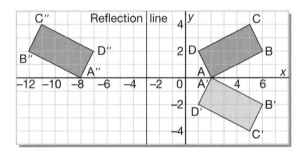

For each reflection, the rectangles are congruent, but their orientations are different.

Example 2 ···

Triangle ABC has vertices A(2, 1), B(−1, 2), and C(1, 5). After a reflection, the image of △ABC is △A′B′C′ with vertices A′(2, −3), B′(−1, −4), and C′(1, −7). Draw △ABC and △A′B′C′ on a grid. Describe the reflection.

Solution

Draw the two triangles. Look at A and A′. Fold the paper so that A coincides with A′. You should find that B coincides with B′, and C coincides with C′. The fold line is 1 unit below the *x*-axis. This is the reflection line.

△A′B′C′ is the image of △ABC after a reflection in a horizontal line 1 unit below the *x*-axis.

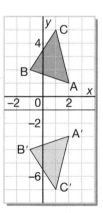

Working with Mathematics

Something to talk about

1. For each reflection described below:

  a) How is the image figure the same as the original figure?

  b) How is the image figure different from the original figure?

    i) A triangle entirely in the first quadrant is reflected in the *x*-axis.

    ii) A triangle in the first quadrant has one vertex on the *x*-axis. The triangle is reflected in the *x*-axis.

    iii) A triangle in the first quadrant has one vertex on the *y*-axis. The triangle is reflected in the *x*-axis.

    iv) A triangle entirely in the first quadrant is reflected in the *y*-axis.

    v) A triangle in the first quadrant has one vertex on the *x*-axis. The triangle is reflected in the *y*-axis.

    vi) A triangle in the first quadrant has one vertex on the *y*-axis. The triangle is reflected in the *y*-axis.

2. In each diagram below, △L′M′N′ is the image of △LMN after a reflection. Identify the reflection in each case.

a)

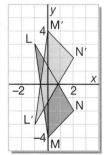

b)

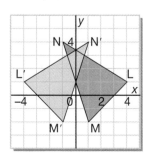

c)

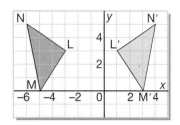

d)

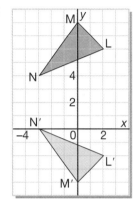

Practice

3. Find the coordinates of the image of each point after a reflection in the *y*-axis.

  a) A(3, 4)   **b)** B(−1, 7)   **c)** C(0, 5)

  d) D(−2, −8)   **e)** O(0, 0)   **f)** F(−10, 0)

4. Find the coordinates of the image of each point after a reflection in a vertical line 4 units to the right of the *y*-axis.

  a) G(0, −2)   **b)** H(7, −11)   **c)** I(−3, 1)

  d) J(7, 0)   **e)** K(9, 6)   **f)** L(−3, −1)

5. Find the coordinates of the image of each point after a reflection in the *x*-axis.

  a) A(0, 3)   **b)** B(−6, −1)   **c)** C(−8, 0)

  d) D(5, −2)   **e)** E(2, 0)   **f)** F(7, 2)

6. Find the coordinates of the image of each point after a reflection in a horizontal line 3 units below the *x*-axis.

  a) O(0, 0)   **b)** H(1, 5)   **c)** I(−2, 6)

  d) J(0, −4)   **e)** K(−2, 9)   **f)** L(−2, −2)

Work together

7. Draw the triangle with vertices D(3, 5), E(4, 9), and F(1, 1). Draw the image triangle after a reflection in the *x*-axis. Label the image triangle D′E′F′.

   a) Measure DD′, EE′, and FF′. What do you notice?

   b) Measure the distance of each of these points from the *x*-axis: D, D′, E, E′, F, and F′. What do you notice?

   c) Measure the angle each of these lines makes with the *x*-axis: DD′, EE′, and FF′. What do you notice?

8. Draw the quadrilateral with vertices G(3, 8), H(7, 4), J(8, 1), and K(1, 8). Draw the image quadrilateral after a reflection in a vertical line 2 units to the left of the *y*-axis. Label the image quadrilateral G′H′J′K′.

   a) What type of quadrilateral is GHJK?

   b) What type of quadrilateral is G′H′J′K′?

   c) How are quadrilateral GHJK and quadrilateral G′H′J′K′ the same? How are they different? What do you notice?

9. In each diagram below, △B′C′D′ is the image of △BCD after a reflection in the *x*-axis. Find the coordinates of the vertices of △BCD in each case.

   a)
   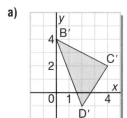

   b)
   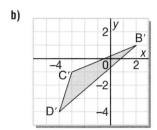

c)
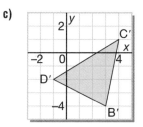

d)
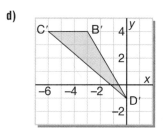

10. Draw any quadrilateral so that its image, after a reflection in the *y*-axis, is:

    a) partly in the first quadrant and partly in the second quadrant

    b) partly in the first quadrant and partly in the fourth quadrant

    How can you check that each image is congruent to the original quadrilateral?

11. Given the reflection line is a horizontal line 2 units above the *x*-axis:

    a) Find the reflection images of the points A(1, 3), B(4, −2), and C(−1, 5).

    b) Find the points that have P′(2, −3), Q′(−1, 2), and R′(3, 0) as their images.

    c) Graph all points and their images from parts a and b.

12. a) Plot the points P(2, 2), Q(4, 3), R(6, 4), and S(8, 5). Draw the line through these points.

    b) Plot the points A(3, 10) and B(8, 0). Join AB. Use AB as the reflection line.

    c) Reflect each point in part a, in the line AB. Label the image points P′, Q′, R′, and S′.

    d) Draw the line through the image points.

    e) How is line segment PS the same as line segment P′S′? How are these line segments different?

13. A triangle has vertices A(−3, 1), B(7, 1), and C(7, −3). Graph the triangle and its image after each reflection.

   a) the reflection line joins P(2, 1) to Q(−6, 9)

   b) the reflection line joins S(−4, −3) to T(8, 9)

14. The image △B′C′D′ has vertices B′(−3, 2), C′(2, 5), and D′(−1, −3). This image was obtained after a reflection in the *x*-axis.

   a) Draw △B′C′D′.

   b) Draw the original triangle, △BCD.

   c) How can you check that △B′C′D′ is a reflection image of △BCD?

On your own

15. Draw the triangle with vertices S(−1, 3), T(−6, −1), and U(1, −3). Draw the image triangle after a reflection in the *y*-axis. Label the image triangle S′T′U′.

   a) Measure SS′, TT′, and UU′. What do you notice?

   b) Measure the distance of each of these points from the *y*-axis: S, S′, T, T′, U, and U′. What do you notice?

   c) Measure the angle each of these lines makes with the *y*-axis: SS′, TT′, and UU′. What do you notice?

   d) Use the results of parts a, b, and c above and of exercise 7. What general statement can you make about a line of reflection, and the lines joining corresponding points on a figure and its reflection image?

16. In each diagram below, quadrilateral S′T′U′V′ is the image of quadrilateral STUV after a reflection in the *y*-axis. Find the coordinates of the vertices of quadrilateral STUV in each case.

   a)

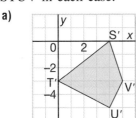

   b)

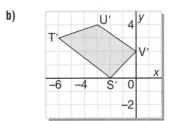

   c)

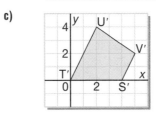

   d)

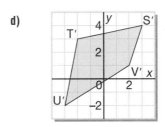

17. Draw △STU with vertices S(1, 1), T(7, 1), and U(4, 6).

   a) Draw the image of △STU after a reflection in a vertical line 4 units to the right of the *y*-axis. Label the image triangle S′T′U′.

   b) Describe △STU and △S′T′U′.

18. Draw a scalene triangle so that its image, after a reflection in the *x*-axis, is:

   a) partly in the second quadrant and partly in the third quadrant

   b) partly in the second quadrant and partly in the first quadrant

How can you check that you have completed each reflection correctly?

19. Draw the quadrilateral with vertices C(1, 4), D(−2, 2), E(1, −5), and F(4, 2).

   a) What type of quadrilateral is CDEF?

   b) Draw quadrilateral C′D′E′F′ after reflecting quadrilateral CDEF in line DF.

   c) Draw quadrilateral C″D″E″F″ after reflecting quadrilateral CDEF in line CE.

   d) How are quadrilaterals C′D′E′F′ and C″D″E″F″ the same? How are they different?

20. A square has vertices A(0, 2), B(−5, 0), C(−3, −5), and D(2, −3). Graph the square and its image after a reflection in the *x*-axis.

21. a) Plot the points M(−1, 1), N(−4, 2), P(−7, 3), and R(−10, 4). Draw a line through these points.

   b) Reflect each point in a horizontal line 3 units above the *x*-axis. Label the image points M′, N′, P′, and R′.

   c) Draw the line through the image points.

   d) How is line segment MR the same as line segment M′R′? How are these line segments different?

   e) How are MR and M′R′ different from PS and P′S′ in exercise 12?

Extend your thinking

22. Draw △CDE with vertices C(2, −4), D(−4, −2), and E(1, 2).

   a) Reflect △CDE in the *x*-axis. Label the image triangle, △C′D′E′.

   b) Reflect △C′D′E′ in the *y*-axis. Label the image triangle, △C″D″E″.

   c) Is △C″D″E″ a reflection image of △CDE? Explain.

23. Look at the points and their reflection images in the previous exercises. Write a mapping rule for each reflection line.

   a) the *x*-axis

   b) the *y*-axis

   c) the line through (0, 0) inclined at 45° to the *x*-axis

d) the vertical line 4 units to the right of the *y*-axis

e) the horizontal line 3 units below the *x*-axis

24. In previous grades, you studied how a plane of symmetry divides a three-dimensional object into two congruent parts. The diagram below shows a plane of symmetry for a cube.

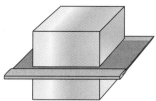

a) Make a model of a cube. Describe at least four other planes of symmetry for the cube.

b) Use interlocking cubes. Make a model of the object represented below. Describe at least four planes of symmetry for this object.

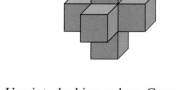

c) Use interlocking cubes. Construct an object that has at least one plane of symmetry. How many planes of symmetry can you find in your object?

The Ideas

In your journal, explain what is meant by this statement.

Orientation is reversed after a reflection.

Use your explanation to describe how you can tell if one figure is a reflection image of another figure.

7.3 ROTATIONS

Developing the Ideas

▶ ▶ *Through Discussion*

When a Ferris wheel turns, the path of a point on the rim of the wheel illustrates a *rotation*. The centre of rotation is the centre of the Ferris wheel.

1. What are some other examples of rotations we see in our world?

2. What is the rotation centre in each case?

3. How is a rotation different from a translation?

4. How is a rotation different from a reflection?

▶ ▶ *Through Activities*

You will investigate rotations on a grid, to find out how a figure and its rotation image are related.

ACTIVITY 1

Work with a partner. You will need tracing paper.

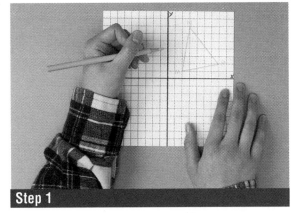

Step 1

On grid paper, draw a set of *x-y* axes. Draw a triangle in the first quadrant so its vertices lie on the intersections of grid lines. Label the vertices M, N, and P.

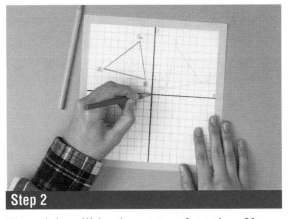

Step 2

The origin will be the centre of rotation. You will rotate △MNP about the origin, through an angle of 90° counterclockwise. Trace △MNP and the axes on tracing paper. Place a pencil point at the origin. Rotate the tracing paper 90° counterclockwise. The positive *x*-axis should lie on the positive *y*-axis.

Step 3

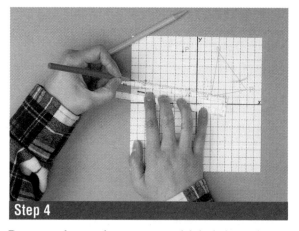

Step 4

Mark the new positions of M, N, and P, with a sharp pencil through the tracing paper.

Remove the tracing paper and label the points M′, N′, and P′. Draw the image △M′N′P′ in a different colour.

1. Measure the sides of △MNP and △M′N′P′. What do you notice?

2. Measure the angles of △MNP and △M′N′P′. What do you notice?

3. Compare the orientations of △MNP and △M′N′P′. What do you notice?

4. How is △M′N′P′ the same as △MNP?

5. How is △M′N′P′ different from △MNP?

6. Compare your diagrams and results with those of other students. Did all of you have the same answers to exercises 1 to 5?

ACTIVITY 2

Work with a partner. You will need tracing paper.

1. On grid paper, draw △VWX with vertices V(−3, 4), W(2, 2), and X(6, 12).

2. Rotate △VWX 90° counterclockwise about V. That is, rotate a tracing of △VWX and the axes until the y-axis coincides with a horizontal grid line. Draw the image triangle a different colour. Label △V′W′X′.

3. Rotate △VWX 90° clockwise about T(−8, 6). That is, rotate a tracing of △VWX and the axes until the y-axis coincides with a horizontal grid line. Draw the image triangle a different colour. Label △V′W′X′.

4. Rotate △VWX 90° counterclockwise about S(−1, −1). Draw the image triangle a different colour. Label the image △V′W′X′.

5. Measure the sides of △VWX and each △V′W′X′. What do you notice?

6. Measure the angles of △VWX and each △V′W′X′. What do you notice?

7. Compare the orientations of △VWX and each △V′W′X. What do you notice?

8. How are these rotation images the same as the rotation image in *Activity 1*? How are they different?

9. Compare your answers to exercises 5 to 8 with those of other students. Did all of you have the same answers?

▶▶ *Through a Guided Example*

Example ⋯⋯⋯⋯⋯⋯⋯⋯⋯⋯⋯⋯⋯⋯⋯⋯⋯⋯⋯⋯⋯⋯⋯⋯⋯⋯⋯⋯

Triangle ABC has vertices A(−2, 3), B(−4, 6), and C(−1, 5). After a rotation about O, the image △A′B′C′ has vertices A′(3, 2), B′(6, 4), and C′(5, 1).

a) Draw △ABC and △A′B′C′ on a grid. Describe the rotation.

b) Measure the distance of each of these points from O: A, B, C, A′, B′, and C′. What do you notice?

Solution

a) Trace △ABC and the axes. Rotate △ABC about O until it coincides with △A′B′C′. This can be done two ways: a 90° clockwise rotation or a 270° counterclockwise rotation.

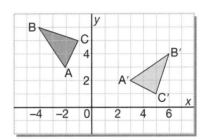

b) Measure OA, OB, OC, OA′, OB′, and OC′.
We see that   OA = OA′
                    OB = OB′
and   OC = OC′
Each vertex and its image are the same distance from the centre of rotation.

As a result of *Activities 1* and *2* and the *Example*, you should have discovered these properties of a rotation.

• • • • • • • • • •

When a figure is rotated:
• the lengths of its sides are unchanged
• the measures of its angles are unchanged
• the orientation is unchanged
• the rotation image is congruent to the original figure
• each point and its rotation image are the same distance from the centre of rotation

Working with Mathematics

Something to talk about

1. One complete rotation is 360°.
   a) Which clockwise rotation is the same as a 90° counterclockwise rotation?
   b) Which clockwise rotation is the same as a 270° counterclockwise rotation?
   c) Which clockwise rotation is the same as a 180° counterclockwise rotation?
   d) Why do we not need to include "clockwise" or "counterclockwise" when describing a 180° rotation?

Practice

2. Find the coordinates of the image of each point after a counterclockwise rotation of 90° about the point P(3, −2).
   a) O(0, 0)   b) B(5, 4)
   c) C(−7, 2)   d) D(−5, 0)
   e) E(0, −2)   f) F(0, 3)
   g) G(−1, −2)   h) H(3, −2)

3. Find the coordinates of the image of each point after a rotation of 180° about the origin.
   a) J(0, 5)   b) K(−3, −1)
   c) L(5, −1)   d) M(0, −3)
   e) N(3, 5)   f) O(0, 0)
   g) Q(−3, 5)   h) R(−3, 0)

4. Find the coordinates of the image of each point after a clockwise rotation of 90° about the point Q(−2, 4).
   a) S(−1, 8)   b) T(7, 1)
   c) U(0, 7)   d) V(1, −6)
   e) O(0, 0)   f) X(−4, −6)
   g) Y(−2, 0)   h) Z(0, −5)

5. Find the coordinates of the image of each point after a counterclockwise rotation of 270° about the origin.
   a) A(0, 6)   b) B(−8, 0)
   c) C(3, −5)   d) D(0, −4)
   e) E(−3, −7)   f) F(−6, 4)
   g) O(0, 0)   h) H(8, 3)

6. Find the coordinates of the image of each point after a clockwise rotation of 270° about the point R(1, 6).
   a) J(2, 5)   b) K(0, 9)
   c) O(0, 0)   d) M(0, −10)
   e) N(−3, 8)   f) P(−3, −5)
   g) Q(8, −2)   h) S(−1, 0)

Work together

7. In each diagram below, △F′G′H′ is the image of △FGH after a rotation about the origin. Identify the rotation in each case.
   a)
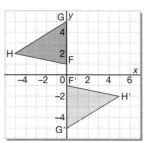
   b)
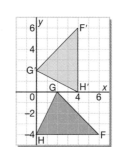
   c)
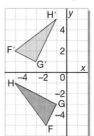
   d)
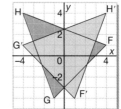

8. What do you know about the coordinates of the image of the rotation centre after any rotation?

9. Draw the triangle with vertices B(3, 7), C(9, 4), and D(6, 9). Draw the image triangle after a clockwise rotation of 90° about the point M(−4, 3). Label the image triangle B′C′D′.
  a) Join MB and MB′. Measure ∠BMB′.
  b) Join MC and MC′. Measure ∠CMC′.
  c) Join MD and MD′. Measure ∠DMD′.
  d) What do you notice about the answers to parts a to c?

10. Draw the quadrilateral with vertices C(3, 4), D(−2, 4), E(−2, −2), and F(3, −2). Draw the image quadrilateral after a rotation of 180° about the point N(2, −5). Label the image quadrilateral C′D′E′F′.
  a) What type of quadrilateral is CDEF?
  b) What type of quadrilateral is C′D′E′F′?
  c) How are quadrilateral CDEF and quadrilateral C′D′E′F′ the same? How are they different?

11. In each diagram below, △J′K′L′ is the image of △JKL after the given rotation. Find the coordinates of the vertices of △JKL in each case.
  a) 90° counterclockwise about O

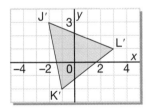

  b) 180° about O

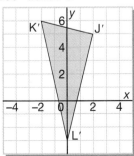

  c) 90° clockwise about O

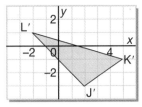

  d) 270° clockwise about O

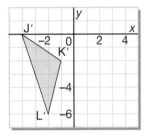

12. Draw a rectangle in the first quadrant. Rotate the rectangle so that the image rectangle is completely in:
  a) the fourth quadrant
  b) the second quadrant
  c) the third quadrant
  d) the first quadrant
  For each image, write the coordinates of its vertices, and describe the rotation.

13. a) Plot the points P(2, 2), Q(4, 3), R(6, 4), and S(8, 5). Draw a line through these points.
  b) Rotate each point 90° counterclockwise about the point A(2, −2). Label the image points P′, Q′, R′, and S′.
  c) Draw the line through the image points.
  d) How is line segment PS the same as line segment P′S′? How are these line segments different?

14. Draw the triangle with vertices C(3, 1), D(6, 1), and E(5, 3). Draw the image triangle after a clockwise rotation of 90° about the point C.

15. Rectangle ABCD has vertices A(−1, 5), B(2, 5), C(2, −4), and D(−1, −4). The rectangle is rotated so that its image coincides with ABCD. That is, the coordinates of the vertices of the image rectangle are A′(−1, 5), B′(2, 5), C′(2, −4), and D′(−1, −4).

a) Suppose the rotation centre was point A. What was the angle of rotation?

b) The diagonals of rectangle ABCD meet at P. Suppose the rotation centre was P. What was the angle of rotation?

c) Suppose the rectangle was rotated about P, and the image rectangle was not labelled. How many different angles of rotation would have the image coinciding with the original rectangle?

On your own

16. Draw the triangle with vertices P(4, −3), Q(9, −4), and R(2, −9). Draw the image triangle after a counterclockwise rotation of 90° about O. Label the image triangle P′Q′R′.

a) Join OP and OP′. Measure ∠POP′.

b) Join OQ and OQ′. Measure ∠QOQ′.

c) Join OR and OR′. Measure ∠ROR′.

d) What do you notice about the answers to parts a to c?

e) Use your answer to part d above and your results from exercise 9. Suggest a way to draw a rotation image without using tracing paper.

f) Use your method from part e. Draw △ABC with vertices A(1, −1), B(3, 2), and C(5, −3). Find the coordinates of the image of each vertex after a counterclockwise rotation of 90° about the origin.

17. Draw the quadrilateral with vertices A(−3, 1), B(−2, −2), C(1, −1), and D(3, 3). Draw the image quadrilateral after a clockwise rotation of 270° about the point D. Label the image quadrilateral A′B′C′D′.

a) What type of quadrilateral is ABCD?

b) What type of quadrilateral is A′B′C′D′?

c) How are quadrilateral ABCD and quadrilateral A′B′C′D′ the same? How are they different?

18. The coordinates of a figure and the coordinates of its rotation image, after a rotation about the origin, are given. Describe the rotation in each case.

a) P(4, 3), Q(6, −4), R(−2, −5); P′(−4, −3), Q′(−6, 4), R′(2, 5)

b) A(−2, 1), B(3, 4), C(6, 0), D(0, −3); A′(1, 2), B′(4, −3), C′(0, −6), D′(−3, 0)

c) M(−3, −2), N(−5, −4), P(−1, 6); M′(2, −3), N′(4, −5), P′(6, −1)

d) P(6, −2), Q(9, −1), R(9, 3), S(2, 0); P′(−6, 2), Q′(−9, 1), R′(−9, −3), S′(−2, 0)

e) P(2, 1), Q(−1, 3), R(2, 7), S(4, 3); P′(−2, −1), Q′(1, −3), R′(−2, −7), S′(−4, −3)

19. Draw the triangle with vertices M(−3, 2), N(2, 6), and P(0, −4). Draw the image triangle after a counterclockwise rotation of 270° about the point M. Label the image triangle M′N′P′. How are △MNP and △M′N′P′ the same? How are they different?

20. a) Plot the points M(−1, 1), N(−4, 2), P(−7, 3), and R(−10, 4). Draw the line through these points.

b) Rotate each point 180° about the point B(5, −1). Label the image points M′, N′, P′, and R′.

c) Draw the line through the image points.

d) How is line segment MR the same as line segment M′R′? How are these line segments different?

e) How are MR and M′R′ different from PS and P′S′ in exercise 13?

21. Square WXYZ has vertices W(−3, −1), X(1, −1), Y(1, −5), and Z(−3, −5). The square is rotated so that its image coincides with WXYZ. That is, the coordinates of the vertices of the image square are W′(−3, −1), X′(1, −1), Y′(1, −5), and Z′(−3, −5).
  a) Suppose the rotation centre was point W. What was the angle of rotation?
  b) Suppose the rotation centre was point X. What was the angle of rotation?
  c) Suppose the square was rotated about the point where its diagonals intersect, and the image square was not labelled. How many different angles of rotation would have the image coinciding with the original square?

22. Draw a scalene triangle so that its image, after a clockwise rotation of 90° about one vertex, is:
  a) partly in the second quadrant and partly in the first quadrant
  b) partly in the third quadrant and partly in the fourth quadrant
  In each case, write the coordinates of the vertices of the original triangle, and the image triangle.

Extend your thinking

23. Triangle CDE has vertices C(3, 2), D(2, 6), and E(9, 5). It is rotated about a point P. The coordinates of the vertices of the image triangle are (8, −5), (4, −6), and (5, 1).
  a) Match each vertex of the image triangle with its coordinates.
  b) What are the coordinates of point P?

24. Write a mapping rule for each rotation.
  a) a 90° counterclockwise rotation about the origin
  b) a 180° rotation about the origin
  c) a 270° counterclockwise rotation about the origin

25. a) Explain what you think it means for a three-dimensional object to have rotational symmetry. Use the cube below as an example.

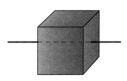

  b) The line segment in the diagram above shows one axis of symmetry for the cube. Describe at least three other axes of symmetry for the cube.
  c) Refer to the object in exercise 24b on page 388. How many different axes of symmetry can you find?
  d) For each axis of symmetry you found in part c, what is the smallest angle of rotation through which the object turns and coincides with itself?
  e) Use interlocking cubes. Construct an object that has at least one axis of symmetry. How many different axes of symmetry can you find in your object?
  f) Exchange your work with that of another student. Did either of you locate an axis of symmetry that the other did not? Discuss any differences and similarities in your results.

The Ideas

In your journal, explain how the rotation image of a figure is different from a translation image and a reflection image of the same figure.

Transformations and Grids

This diagram shows a grid made from squares, an original figure, and some images of that figure. The original figure is red. Each image can be obtained by applying one or more transformations to the original figure.

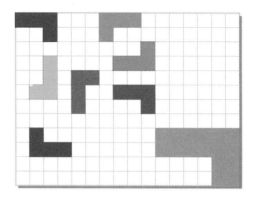

1. Identify a transformation or a sequence of transformations that relate the original figure to each image.

   The grid does not have to be square. Here is a grid made from isosceles triangles. You can create some interesting patterns when you transform a figure on a grid like this.

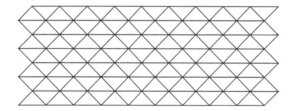

2. Use a Draw program for this activity. Construct a figure you can Duplicate and drag into position many times to create a grid. Experiment with different figures until you find one that will tessellate; that is, form a grid with no gaps.

   Draw an original figure in the upper left corner of your grid by filling parts of the grid with colours or patterns. Create a variety of images of your figure by applying different transformations to it.

   Print your diagram and exchange it with a friend. Challenge your friend to identify the transformations you used.

Mathematics & Technology

Linking Ideas

Developing the Ideas

In this section, we will investigate the images produced when two transformations are applied to a figure. The photograph illustrates reflections of an object in two mirrors.

▶ ▶ *Through Activities*

We can use a grid to discover what happens to a figure when successive translations, reflections, or combinations of these are applied.

ACTIVITY 1

You will translate a figure, then reflect it in an axis.

Work with a partner.

1. On grid paper, draw a set of *x-y* axes. Draw a triangle with its vertices on the intersections of grid lines. Each vertex should lie in a different quadrant. Label the vertices P, Q, and R.

2. Choose a translation. Translate each vertex. Label the image vertices P′, Q′, and R′. Draw the image △P′Q′R′ in a different colour.

3. Choose a reflection in either the *x*- or *y*-axis. Reflect △P′Q′R′. Label the image vertices P″, Q″, and R″. Draw the image △P″Q″R″ in a different colour.

4. Measure the angles of the three triangles. What do you notice?

5. Measure the sides of the three triangles. What do you notice?

6. How is the final image △P″Q″R″ the same as the original △PQR?

7. How is △P″Q″R″ different from △PQR?

8. Compare your diagrams and results with those of other students. Did all of you have the same answers to the questions in exercises 4 to 7?

You will reflect a figure first in one line, then in a parallel line.

Work with a partner.

1. On grid paper, draw a set of *x-y* axes. Draw a triangle with its vertices on the intersections of grid lines. Label the vertices D, E, and F.

2. Draw the first vertical reflection line 2 units to the left of the *y*-axis. Draw the second vertical reflection line 4 units to the right of the *y*-axis.

3. Draw the image of △DEF after a reflection in the first reflection line. Label the image △D'E'F'.

4. Draw the image of △D'E'F' after a reflection in the second reflection line. Label the image △D"E"F".

5. Compare the orientations of △DEF, △D'E'F', and △D"E"F". What do you notice?

6. How is △D"E"F the same as △DEF?

7. How is △D"E"F" different from △DEF?

8. Which single transformation is equivalent to the two reflections? That is, for which single transformation is △D"E"F the image of △DEF?

9. Compare your answers to the questions in exercises 5 to 8 with those of other students. Did all of you have the same answers?

In *Working with Mathematics*, you will investigate whether the order in which you reflect a figure in two parallel lines affects the final image.

BOGGLE YOUR MIND

Moniika Vega was the first woman to travel all the way around the world alone on a motorcycle. She left Milan, Italy, on March 7, 1990, and returned to Italy on May 24, 1991. During this time, she travelled 83 500 km. How many days did her trip last? What was the mean distance she travelled each day?

Example 1 ....

The vertices of △ABC are A(4, 1), B(1, 2), and C(3, 5).

a) Draw △ABC. Translate △ABC 2 units right, 5 units down. Label the image △A′B′C′.

b) Translate △A′B′C′ 1 unit right, 3 units up. Label the image △A″B″C″.

c) What single translation moves △ABC to △A″B″C″?

Solution

a) The original △ABC is shown below in red. The image △A′B′C′ is shown in blue.

b) The image △A″B″C″ is shown below in yellow.

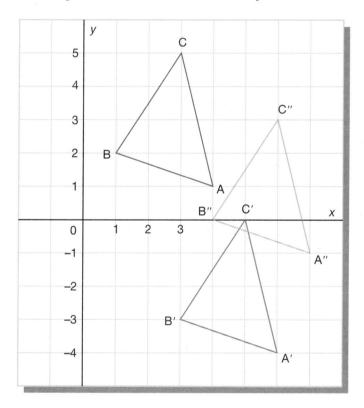

c) From the diagram above, to go from △ABC to △A″B″C″ in a single transformation, we move 3 units right and 2 units down.

Notice that the combined translation is obtained by adding the horizontal moves and the vertical moves of the two translations. That is,

2 units right + 1 unit right = 3 units right, and
5 units down + 3 units up = 2 units down

Example 2 ....

Triangle P″Q″R″ has vertices P″(3, 6), Q″(0, 4), and R″(4, 1). It is the final image after a translation 4 units left, 5 units down; and a reflection in the y-axis. Find the coordinates of the vertices of the original △PQR.

Solution

Draw △P″Q″R″. To get to this position, a triangle was reflected in the y-axis. We will label this △P′Q′R′. Reflect △P″Q″R″ in the y-axis to get the position of △P′Q′R′.

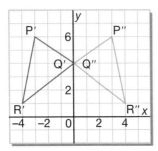

To get △P′Q′R′, a triangle was translated 4 units left, 5 units down. We will label this △PQR. Reverse the translation to get the position of △PQR. That is, translate △P′Q′R′ 4 units right, 5 units up.

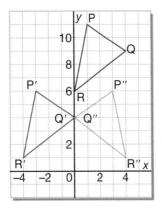

△PQR is the original triangle. The coordinates of the vertices are P(1, 11), Q(4, 9), and R(0, 6).

In the exercises that follow, you will be investigating these combined transformations.
- reflections in parallel lines
- reflections in perpendicular intersecting lines
- reflections in non-perpendicular intersecting lines
- translation and reflection, where the translation is perpendicular to the reflection line
- translation and reflection, where the translation is parallel to the reflection line

Working with Mathematics

Something to talk about

1. In *Activity 2*, what single transformation was equivalent to the two successive reflections? Explain.

2. When would two successive translations result in the final image figure coinciding with the original figure?

Practice

3. **a)** Write the coordinates of the image of each point after a translation 5 units left, 5 units up, followed by a translation 3 units right, 4 units down.

   i) A(5, 3) **ii)** B(4, −4) **iii)** C(−5, 0)
   iv) D(2, −1) **v)** E(−3, −5) **vi)** F(0, 2)

   b) Write the coordinates of the image of each point in part a after a translation 3 units right, 4 units down, followed by a translation 5 units left, 5 units up.

   c) Does the order in which two translations are applied to a point affect the final image? Explain.

4. **a)** Write the coordinates of the image of each point after a reflection in the *x*-axis followed by a reflection in the *y*-axis.

   i) E(−3, 2) **ii)** F(−5, −2) **iii)** G(−6, −6)
   iv) H(−3, 0) **v)** J(0, 8) **vi)** K(5, 7)

   b) Write the coordinates of the image of each point in part a after a reflection in the *y*-axis followed by a reflection in the *x*-axis.

   c) Does the order in which reflections in the axes are applied to a point affect the final image? Explain.

5. **a)** Write the coordinates of the image of each point after a reflection in the *x*-axis followed by a translation 3 units right, 4 units down.

   i) J(5, 6) **ii)** K(4, −2) **iii)** L(−7, 2)
   iv) M(−3, 0) **v)** P(3, 0) **vi)** Q(−7, −8)

   b) Write the coordinates of the image of each point in part a after a translation 3 units right, 4 units down, followed by a reflection in the *x*-axis.

   c) Does the order in which a reflection and a translation are applied to a point affect the final image? Explain.

Work together

6. The point P″(3, −5) is the image of a point P after the translations and reflections below. Find the coordinates of P in each case.

   a) a translation 1 unit left, 2 units down, followed by a reflection in the *x*-axis

   b) a reflection in the *y*-axis followed by a translation 2 units right, 3 units down

   c) a reflection in a horizontal line 2 units above the *x*-axis followed by a translation 5 units left, 3 units up

   d) a translation 4 units right, 7 units up, followed by a translation 3 units right, 2 units down

7. In each diagram below, △P″Q″R″ is the image of △PQR after a translation, then a reflection. Identify the translation and the reflection in each case.

   a)

   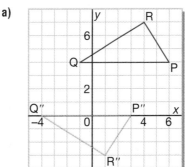

   b)

   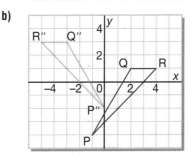

8. Draw the triangle with vertices A(3, −2), B(2, 2), and C(−3, −4). Draw the image triangle after a translation 3 units left, 4 units up, followed by a reflection in the x-axis. Label the image △A″B″C″.

 a) Measure the sides of △ABC and △A″B″C″. What do you notice?

 b) Measure the angles of △ABC and △A″B″C″. What do you notice?

 c) Based on your answers to parts a and b, describe how △ABC is related to △A″B″C″. Explain why this relationship must follow from the properties of translations and reflections.

 d) Does the orientation of a figure change after a translation followed by a reflection? Explain.

9. Quadrilateral C″D″E″F″ is the image of quadrilateral CDEF after two translations.

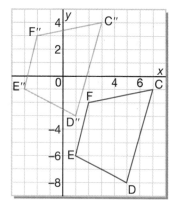

 a) Write two translations that could have been applied to quadrilateral CDEF to produce quadrilateral C″D″E″F″.

 b) Compare your translations in part a with those of other students. Did all of you write the same translations?

 c) If your answer to part b is no, does this mean that only one student is correct? Explain.

 d) If your answer to part b is yes, can you think of other pairs of translations that could produce the same image quadrilateral? Explain.

10. Each triangle below is the image after the two combined transformations. Draw each image triangle. Find the coordinates of the vertices of the original △ABC.

 a) A″(1, 3), B″(8, 5), C″(6, 4), after a reflection in the x-axis followed by a translation 3 units right, 2 units up

 b) D″(2, 7), E″(−7, 6), F″(−3, −2), after a reflection in a vertical line 3 units to the left of the y-axis followed by a translation 2 units left, 5 units down

 c) G″(3, −6), H″(−1, −2), J″(4, 2), after a reflection in the x-axis followed by a translation 1 unit right, 3 units down

 d) K″(−2, 6), L″(3, 1), M″(5, −3), after a reflection in the y-axis followed by a translation 4 units left, 2 units up

11. Draw the quadrilateral with vertices M(−7, 1), N(2, 6), P(4, −3), and Q(−3, −7).

 a) Draw the image of MNPQ after a translation 3 units left, 5 units down, followed by a reflection in a vertical line 5 units to the left of the y-axis.

 b) Draw the image of quadrilateral MNPQ after a reflection in a vertical line 5 units to the left of the y-axis, followed by a translation 3 units left, 5 units down.

 c) Write the coordinates of the vertices of the final image in each of parts a and b.

12. Quadrilateral W″X″Y″Z″ has vertices W″(2, −3), X″(5, 7), Y″(−3, 1), and Z″(−3, −3). It is the final image after a translation 4 units right, 3 units up, followed by a reflection in the x-axis. Find the coordinates of the vertices of the original quadrilateral WXYZ.

13. Draw the triangle and the reflection lines you used for *Activity 2*, page 398.

 a) Reflect the triangle first in the reflection line 4 units to the right of the y-axis. Label the image △D′E′F′.

 b) Reflect △D′E′F′ in the reflection line 2 units to the left of the y-axis. Label the image △D″E″F″.

c) Write the single translation for which △D″E″F″ is the image of △DEF.

d) Compare this △D″E″F″ with the image triangle △D″E″F″ in *Activity 2*. How are these triangles the same? How are they different?

14. a) Draw the line through S(−10, −10) and T(10, 10). This line is a reflection line. Another reflection line is the y-axis.

b) Draw △JKL with vertices J(6, 3), K(9, 5), and L(11, 2). Reflect △JKL in the line ST. Label the image △J′K′L′.

c) Reflect △J′K′L′ in the y-axis. Label the image △J″K″L″.

d) For which single transformation is △J″K″L″ the image of △JKL?

e) Repeat parts b, c, and d, but reverse the order of the reflections. That is, reflect △JKL in the y-axis first, then reflect the image △J′K′L′ in the line ST.

f) How are the final image triangles the same? How are they different?

On your own

15. Draw the quadrilateral with vertices B(2, 6), C(6, 1), D(1, −3), and E(−3, 2). Draw the image quadrilateral after a reflection in the y-axis followed by a translation 4 units right, 1 unit up. Label the image B″C″D″E″.

a) What type of quadrilateral is BCDE?

b) What type of quadrilateral is B″C″D″E″?

c) Measure the sides of quadrilaterals BCDE and B″C″D″E″. What do you notice?

d) Measure the angles of quadrilaterals BCDE and B″C″D″E″. What do you notice?

e) Does the orientation of a figure change after a reflection followed by a translation?

f) Use the results of parts c to e above and those of exercise 8. What can you say about a figure and its image after a translation and a reflection in either order?

16. In each diagram below, quadrilateral M″N″P″Q″ is the image of quadrilateral MNPQ after a reflection, then a translation. Identify the reflection and the translation in each case.

a)

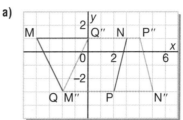

b)

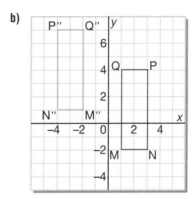

c)

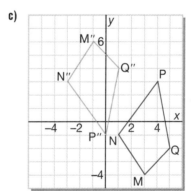

d)

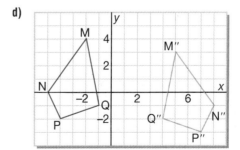

17. Triangle DEF has vertices D(−1, −7), E(7, −2), and F(4, 5).

a) Draw △DEF and its final image after a reflection in the *x*-axis followed by a reflection in the *y*-axis. Label the final image △D″E″F″.

b) Draw △DEF and its image after a reflection in the *y*-axis followed by a reflection in the *x*-axis. Label the final image △D″E″F″.

c) What do you notice about the images in parts a and b?

d) In each case, for which single transformation is △D″E″F″ the image of △DEF?

18. Draw the triangle with vertices E(−3, −5), F(−7, −1), and G(−4, 2).

a) Draw the image of △EFG after a reflection in a horizontal line 4 units above the *x*-axis followed by a translation 2 units right, 3 units up.

b) Draw the image of △EFG after a translation 2 units right, 3 units up, followed by a reflection in a horizontal line 4 units above the *x*-axis.

c) What are the coordinates of the vertices of the final image in each of parts a and b?

d) Look at the results of parts a to c above and those of exercise 11. What can you say about the final image and the order in which a translation and a reflection are applied to a figure?

19. Draw a horizontal reflection line 3 units above the *x*-axis. Draw another horizontal reflection line 5 units below the *x*-axis. Draw △GHJ with vertices G(2, 3), H(−3, 1), and J(4, −1).

a) Reflect △GHJ in the reflection line above the *x*-axis. Label the image △G′H′J′.

b) Reflect △G′H′J′ in the reflection line below the *x*-axis. Label the image △G″H″J″.

c) For which single transformation is △G″H″J″ the image of △GHJ?

d) Repeat parts a to c, but reverse the order of the reflections.

e) How are the final image triangles the same? How are they different?

20. Draw the line through A(−10, 10) and B(10, −10). This line is a reflection line. Another reflection line is the *x*-axis.

a) Draw quadrilateral MNPQ with vertices M(−6, 3), N(−8, 5), P(−10, 1), and Q(−6, 0).

b) Reflect quadrilateral MNPQ in the *x*-axis. Label the image quadrilateral M′N′P′Q′.

c) Reflect quadrilateral M′N′P′Q′ in the line AB. Label the image quadrilateral M″N″P″Q″.

d) For which single transformation is quadrilateral M″N″P″Q″ the image of quadrilateral MNPQ?

e) Repeat parts b to d, but reverse the order of the reflections. That is, reflect quadrilateral MNPQ in the line AB first; then reflect the image quadrilateral M′N′P′Q′ in the *x*-axis.

f) How are the final image quadrilaterals the same? How are they different?

21. Triangle M″N″P″ has vertices M″(0, 6), N″(5, 0), and P″(−4, −4). It is the final image after a reflection in the *y*-axis followed by a translation 3 units left, 1 unit down. Find the coordinates of the original △MNP.

22. Draw a triangle entirely in the second quadrant. Apply a reflection and a translation, in any order, so the final image lies entirely in:

a) the second quadrant

b) the first quadrant

c) the fourth quadrant

d) the third quadrant

Describe the transformations you applied in each case.

23. Draw any quadrilateral ABCD on a grid so each vertex is in a different quadrant.

a) Draw the final image of quadrilateral ABCD after a reflection in the *y*-axis followed by a reflection in the *x*-axis.

b) Draw the final image of quadrilateral ABCD after a reflection in the *x*-axis followed by a reflection in the *y*-axis.

c) Compare your final images in parts a and b. What do you notice?

d) Compare your answer to part c with those of other students. What can you say about the final image and the order in which two reflections are applied to a figure, when the reflection lines are perpendicular?

24. Draw a vertical line 6 units to the right of the *y*-axis. This is the reflection line.

a) Draw △STU with vertices S(8, −3), T(4, 0), and U(10, 4). Reflect △STU in the reflection line. Label the image △S′T′U′.

b) Translate △S′T′U′ 4 units left. Label the image △S″T″U″.

c) For which single transformation is △S″T″U″ the image of △STU?

d) Repeat parts a to c, but reverse the order of the transformations. That is, translate △STU 4 units left, then reflect the image triangle in the reflection line.

e) These transformations are a reflection, and a translation perpendicular to the reflection line. Does the order in which these transformations are applied affect the final image? Explain.

25. Draw a horizontal line 4 units above the *x*-axis. This is the reflection line.

a) Draw quadrilateral ABCD with vertices A(−5, 2), B(1, 3), C(−1, −2), and D(−7, −3). Translate quadrilateral ABCD 5 units right. Label the image quadrilateral A′B′C′D′.

b) Reflect quadrilateral A′B′C′D′ in the reflection line. Label the image quadrilateral A″B″C″D″.

c) Is there a single transformation for which A″B″C″D″ is the image of quadrilateral ABCD? If your answer is yes, describe the transformation. If your answer is no, explain why not.

d) Repeat parts a to c, but reverse the order of the transformations. That is, reflect quadrilateral ABCD first, then translate the image quadrilateral 5 units right.

e) These transformations are a reflection, and a translation parallel to the reflection line. Does the order in which the transformations are applied affect the final image? Explain.

Extend your thinking

26. Use the results of exercise 23 to write a single mapping rule for a reflection in the *y*-axis followed by a reflection in the *x*-axis.

COMMUNICATING

The Ideas

In your journal, explain how you can tell whether the image of a figure is the result of:

- two translations
- two reflections
- a translation and a reflection

Developing the Ideas

▶▶ *Through Discussion*

Sanda's school pictures came in different sizes.

1. In what ways are the photographs alike?

2. In what ways are the photographs different?

3. Are the size and shape of an object in the photographs the same?

When a photograph is increased in size, it is *enlarged*.

When a photograph is decreased in size, it is *reduced*.

Enlargements and reductions are examples of a transformation called a *dilatation*.

▶ ▶ *Through an Activity*

You will investigate dilatations on a grid, to find out how a figure and its dilatation image are related.

Work with a partner.

Step 1

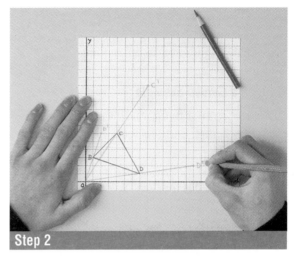

Step 2

On grid paper, draw a set of *x-y* axes so that the first quadrant fills the entire page. Draw a triangle so its vertices lie on the intersections of grid lines, close to the origin. Label the vertices B, C, and D.

Join OB. Extend OB until the line is double the length of OB. Mark a point at this length and label it B′. Repeat the same process to locate C′, the image of point C, and D′, the image of point D. Draw the image △B′C′D′ a different colour.

1. Measure the sides of △BCD and the sides of △B′C′D′. What do you notice?

2. Measure the angles of △BCD and △B′C′D′. What do you notice?

3. How is △B′C′D′ the same as △BCD?

4. How is △B′C′D′ different from △BCD?

5. Compare your diagrams and results with those of other students. Did all of you have the same answers to exercises 1 to 4?

You have drawn the dilatation image of △BCD, with dilatation centre O. The dilatation centre is the point from which measurements are made to draw the dilatation image.

In the *Activity*, you should have discovered that OB′ = 2OB; OC′ = 2OC; and OD′ = 2OD.

Since each side of △B′C′D′ is twice the length of the corresponding side of △BCD, we say the *scale factor* of the dilatation is 2. You should also have discovered that ∠B′ = ∠B; ∠C′ = ∠C; and ∠D′ = ∠D.

From Chapter 3, you know that if two triangles have corresponding angles equal, then the triangles are similar.

We can list these properties of a dilatation.

• • • • • • • • •

After a dilatation with scale factor 2:
- the measures of the angles of the image figure equal the measures of the corresponding angles of the original figure
- the lengths of the sides of the image figure are 2 times the lengths of the corresponding sides of the original figure
- the figure and its image are similar

▶ ▶ *Through a Guided Example*

If we are given a figure and its dilatation image, we can find the dilatation centre, and the scale factor for the dilatation.

Example

Triangle ABC has vertices A(4, 6), B(8, 2), and C(2, 2). Triangle A′B′C′ has vertices A′(2, 3), B′(4, 1), and C′(1, 1). Triangle A′B′C′ is a dilatation image of △ABC.

a) Find the dilatation centre.

b) Find the scale factor for the dilatation.

Solution

Draw △ABC and △A′B′C′ on a grid.
Join corresponding vertices with broken lines.
Extend the lines until they meet.

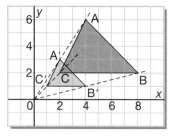

a) The broken lines meet at the origin O.
This is the dilatation centre.

b) Measure OA and OA′. Measure OB and OB′.
Measure OC and OC′. In each case, the distance from O to an image vertex is one-half the distance from O to the original vertex. That is:

$$OA' = \tfrac{1}{2}OA$$

$$OB' = \tfrac{1}{2}OB$$

$$OC' = \tfrac{1}{2}OC$$

The scale factor for the dilatation is $\tfrac{1}{2}$.

Look at the coordinates of the vertices of each triangle. In each case, for corresponding vertices, the x-coordinate of the image vertex is one-half the x-coordinate of the original vertex. The y-coordinates are similarly related.

Working with Mathematics

Something to talk about

1. How can you tell whether two triangles are similar?

2. △ABC is similar to △A′B′C′. The dilatation that relates △ABC and △A′B′C′ has scale factor 3. Make as many statements as you can about the relationships between these triangles and their parts.

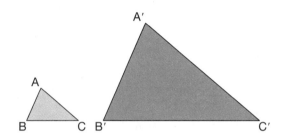

3. **a)** How do you find the scale factor of the dilatation relating two similar figures?
   b) How do you locate the dilatation centre?

Practice

4. Each point is transformed by a dilatation, centre the origin, and scale factor 2. Find the coordinates of the dilatation image of each point.
   a) A(−5, 7)   **b)** B(0, 3)
   c) C(8, 3)   **d)** D(−2, −5)
   e) E(−4, 0)   **f)** F(10, −3)
   g) G(7, 0)   **h)** O(0, 0)

5. Each point is transformed by a dilatation, centre the origin, and scale factor $\frac{1}{2}$. Find the coordinates of the dilatation image of each point.
   a) J(0, 2)   **b)** K(−4, −6)
   c) L(−4, 0)   **d)** O(0, 0)
   e) N(10, 3)   **f)** P(−7, 6)
   g) Q(11, 0)   **h)** R(5, −8)

6. Each point is transformed by a dilatation, centre the origin, and scale factor 3. Find the coordinates of the dilatation image of each point.
   a) S(3, 7)   **b)** O(0, 0)
   c) U(−5, 8)   **d)** V(1, −2)
   e) W(0, 12)   **f)** X(5, 1)
   g) Y(−2, −4)   **h)** Z(−2, 0)

Work together

7. What do you know about the coordinates of the image of the dilatation centre after any dilatation?

8. Each set of points represents a figure and its dilatation image. State the centre of dilatation and the scale factor.
   a) A(3, 5), B(7, 10), C(−2, 8);
   A′(1.5, 2.5), B′(3.5, 5), C′(−1, 4)
   b) A(3, 5), B(7, 10), C(−2, 8);
   A′(6, 10), B′(14, 20), C′(−4, 16)
   c) P(6, −3), Q(9, −6), R(6, −9), S(0, −6);
   P′(12, −6), Q′(18, −12), R′(12, −18),
   S′(0, −12)
   d) P(6, −3), Q(9, −6), R(6, −9), S(0, −6);
   P′(2, −1), Q′(3, −2), R′(2, −3),
   S′(0, −2)
   e) P(2, 1), Q(−1, 3), R(2, 7), S(4, 3);
   P′(5, −5), Q′(11, −9), R′(5, −17), S′(1, −9)

9. Draw a triangle with vertices P(−2, −3), Q(−4, −6), and R(−5, −4). Draw the image of △PQR after a dilatation, centre P, and scale factor 3. How do you know the triangle and its image are similar?

10. A square has vertices D(−6, −1), E(−3, −1), F(−3, −4), and G(−6, −4). Draw the image square after a dilatation of scale factor 2, with dilatation centre D. Label the image square D′E′F′G′.
    a) How are square DEFG and square D′E′F′G′ the same?
    b) How are the squares different?

On your own

11. Draw a quadrilateral with vertices R(−4, 2), S(−4, −2), T(4, 0), and U(0, 4). Draw the image quadrilateral after a dilatation of scale factor $\frac{1}{2}$, with dilatation centre the origin. Label the image quadrilateral R′S′T′U′.

a) Measure the angles of quadrilateral RSTU and quadrilateral R′S′T′U′. What do you notice?

b) Measure the sides of quadrilateral RSTU and quadrilateral R′S′T′U′. What do you notice?

c) Is the dilatation a reduction or an enlargement? How do you know?

12. Draw a triangle with vertices A(−1, 1), B(−3, 1), and C(−2, 3). Draw the image triangle after a dilatation of scale factor 4, with dilatation centre C. Label the image triangle A′B′C′.

a) What type of triangle is △ABC?

b) What type of triangle is △A′B′C′?

c) How are △ABC and △A′B′C′ the same? How are they different?

d) Is the dilatation a reduction or an enlargement? How do you know?

e) Use your results to this and previous exercises. Are there any examples of dilatations in which the orientation of the original figure is the reverse of that of the image figure? Find examples of dilatations in which the orientation of the original figure and its image are the same. Determine whether you can predict the orientation of a dilatation image.

Extend your thinking

13. Draw a triangle with vertices P(2, 2), Q(6, 2), and R(5, 6). Draw the image triangle after a dilatation of scale factor 2, with dilatation centre the origin. Label the image triangle P′Q′R′.

a) What is the area of △PQR?

b) What is the area of △P′Q′R′?

c) How are the areas related?

14. Use the original triangle in exercise 13. Draw the image triangle after a dilatation of scale factor 3, with dilatation centre the origin. Label the image triangle P″Q″R″.

a) What is the area of △P″Q″R″?

b) How is the area of △PQR related to the area of △P″Q″R″?

c) Suppose you know the scale factor of a dilatation for a triangle. How can you calculate how many times as large as the original triangle the image triangle is?

15. a) Write a mapping rule for the dilatation you drew in the *Activity*, page 407.

b) Write a mapping rule for the dilatation in the *Example*, page 408.

c) Write a mapping rule for a dilatation of scale factor 4, with dilatation centre the origin. Apply your mapping rule to △ABC with vertices A(3, 1), B(1, 3), and C(3, 2). Use measurement to check your mapping rule.

d) Write a mapping rule for a dilatation of scale factor k, with dilatation centre the origin.

The Ideas

In your journal, explain how the dilatation image of a triangle is the same as and different from the image after each transformation.

a) translation

b) reflection

c) rotation

Scott Kim's Inversions

Scott Kim is known for his unusual designs made of words which are meant to be seen as well as read. Here are five examples of his work. If you study these examples closely, you will see how he has created each desired effect.

1. Find examples of reflections, translations, rotations, and dilatations in these designs.

2. How many times does the word "infinity" appear in the design at the lower right?

3. **a)** Which designs have rotational symmetry?
   b) Which designs have line symmetry?

4. **a)** Which designs would look the same in a mirror?
   b) Which designs look the same when you turn them upside down?

5. Scott Kim calls these designs *inversions*. Look up this word in the dictionary. Why do you think he chose this word for his designs?

How Far Is It across the Street?

Without crossing a street, how can you determine the distance across it? Work with a partner. You will need a piece of cardboard, scissors, and a tape measure.

Understand the problem

- What are you asked to do?

Think of a strategy

- Visualize a view from above the street. Imagine that one person is at A and the other person is at B. There is a traffic light at T across the street very close to the street.
- The person at A is directly across the street from the traffic light.
- The person at A is the same distance from B and from the traffic light.

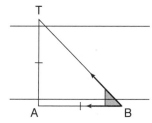

Carry out the strategy

- Get a rectangular piece of cardboard such as the cardboard backing from a pad of paper. Measure and mark an isosceles right triangle. Cut off the triangle.

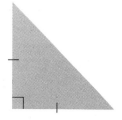

- Go out to the street to make the measurement. One person stands at A, across the street from an object such as a traffic light. The other person moves to a location where it is possible to hold the triangle horizontally at eye level, and sight along one side to see the traffic light at T and along another side to see the person at A.
- Use the tape measure to measure the distance AB.

Look back

- Why does the distance across the street equal the distance between you and your partner?
- Do you think that you could use this method to determine the distance across a river or a lake?
- What other distances could you determine using this method?

Communicating the Ideas

In your journal, describe how you can measure the distance across a street without crossing the street. Someone reading your explanation should be able to understand what you did and why the method works.

Developing the Ideas

▶▶ *Through Discussion*

In the previous sections, you discovered these properties of transformations.

Translations

Corresponding sides of the figure and its image are parallel.

Rotations

Each vertex of a figure and its image are the same distance from the centre of rotation.

Reflections

The orientations of a figure and its image are reversed.

Dilatations

The figure and its image are similar.

We can use these properties, along with the congruence of the figure with its image after a translation, reflection, or rotation, to identify a transformation.

▶▶ *Through a Guided Example*

Example ....

The vertices of △ABC are A(4, −4), B(7, −3), and C(7, −8). Triangle A′B′C′ is a transformation image of △ABC. Triangle A′B′C′ has vertices A′(4, 4), B′(3, 7), and C′(8, 7). Identify the transformation that relates △ABC and △A′B′C′.

Solution

Draw both triangles on a grid.

For a translation, corresponding sides of the figure and its image are parallel. Since B′C′ is not parallel to BC, the transformation is not a translation.

For a reflection, the orientations of the figure and its image are reversed. Since △A′B′C′ and △ABC have the same orientation, the transformation is not a reflection.

For a dilatation, the figure and its image are similar. Since △A′B′C′ and △ABC are congruent, the transformation is not a dilatation.

It appears as though the triangles are related by a rotation.

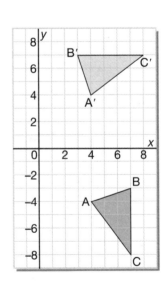

Working with Mathematics

Something to talk about

1. How do we know that the image of any triangle after a translation, reflection, or rotation is congruent to the original triangle?

2. How do you find the translation given a polygon on a grid and its translation image?

3. How do you find the reflection line given a polygon and its reflection image?

Practice

4. Name the transformation that relates each figure with the other.

a)

b)

5. In each diagram, state the transformation that relates each coloured figure with its white image.

a)

b)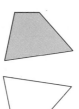

c)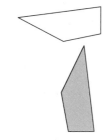

6. The vertices of △MNP are M(4, 2), N(6, −4), and P(2, −8). Triangle M′N′P′ has vertices M′(10, 5), N′(15, −10), and P′(5, −20). Draw each triangle. Identify the transformation that relates △MNP and △M′N′P′.

Work together

7. Identify the transformation that relates each figure with its image.

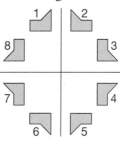

a) Figure 1 → figure 2
b) Figure 1 → figure 5
c) Figure 6 → figure 3
d) Figure 8 → figure 3
e) Figure 1 → figure 3
f) Figure 7 → figure 6
g) Figure 8 → figure 6
h) Figure 7 → figure 8
i) Figure 5 → figure 3
j) Figure 1 → figure 6

8. In each diagram, identify the transformation that relates each figure with its image.
   i) Figure I → figure II
   ii) Figure II → figure III
   iii) Figure I → figure III

a)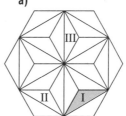

b)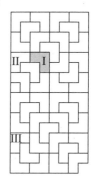

9. In each diagram below, △C′D′E′ is the image of △CDE after a transformation. Identify the transformation in each case.

a)

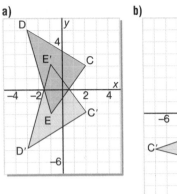

b)

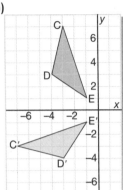

c)

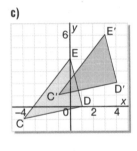

d)

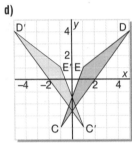

10. The vertices of PQRS are P(−3, −4), Q(4, −1), R(3, 4), and S(−2, 1). Quadrilateral P′Q′R′S′ has vertices P′(0, −8), Q′(7, −5), R′(6, 0), and S′(1, −3). Draw each quadrilateral. Identify the transformation that relates PQRS and P′Q′R′S′.

11. Triangle MNP has vertices M(−5, 1), N(−3, −7), and P(6, 2). Triangle M′N′P′ has vertices M′(−1, −5), N′(7, −3), and P′(−2, 6).
a) Identify the transformation that relates △MNP and △M′N′P′.
b) How can you check that △MNP is congruent to △M′N′P′?

12. Name the transformation that relates each shaded triangle to its congruent image.

a)
b)

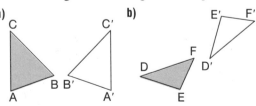

c)

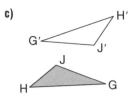

13. Copy each figure and divide it into two congruent parts. State the transformation that relates one part with the other.

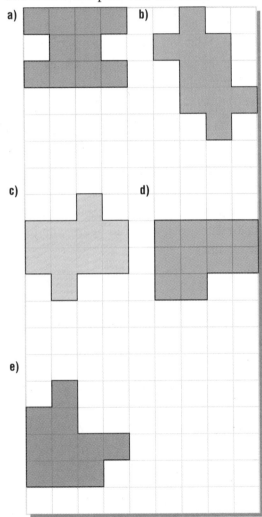

14. By drawing two straight lines through a square, divide it into four congruent:
a) squares **b)** triangles **c)** quadrilaterals
For each division of the square, explain how one part is a transformation image of another part.

15. Trace each figure below. Divide each figure into the number of congruent parts indicated. Identify the transformation that relates one congruent part to another.

a) i) 2 congruent parts
   ii) 3 congruent parts

b) 2 congruent parts

c) i) 2 congruent parts ii) 4 congruent parts

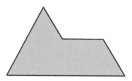

16. The puzzle below consists of five pairs of congruent figures which, when assembled, fit into a rectangular array. Copy this figure onto grid paper.

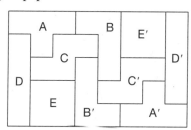

a) Identify a transformation that relates each figure with its image figure.

b) Are there sometimes two or more different answers to part a?

On your own

17. Triangle A′B′C′ has vertices A′(4, −3), B′(8, −7), and C′(−3, −5). It is the transformation image of △ABC, with vertices A(−4, −3), B(−8, −7), and C(3, −5).

   a) Identify the transformation that relates △ABC and △A′B′C′.

   b) How can you check that △ABC is congruent to △A′B′C′?

18. Quadrilateral MNPQ has vertices M(−6, 2), N(−2, 6), P(2, 6), and Q(6, −2). It is transformed and its image has vertices M′(−9, −3), N′(−5, 1), P′(−1, 1), and Q′(3, −7). Identify the transformation that relates MNPQ and M′N′P′Q′.

Extend your thinking

19. Trace this polygon onto stiff paper. Cut out the polygon.

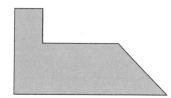

Place the cutout polygon on a piece of paper. Trace around the polygon.

Flip your cutout, move it somewhere else on the page, and trace around it to draw a congruent copy. Find a transformation that relates one polygon with its congruent copy.

20. Repeat the procedure in exercise 19 without flipping the polygon before drawing it on the page. Draw the congruent copies. Locate the centre of a rotation that relates one polygon with the other.

The Ideas

In your journal, explain how you identify a transformation given a figure and its transformation image.

Distortions

A simple way to make an enlargement of a figure is to use square grids. You draw the figure on one grid and then "follow the squares" to make the enlargement on another grid with larger squares.

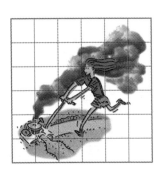

This principle was used to draw the following diagrams, which illustrate other kinds of transformations. These are called *distortions*.

The grid lines do not have to be the same distance apart.

The grid lines do not have to be perpendicular.

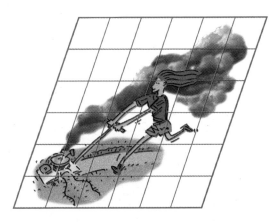

The grid lines do not have to be straight.

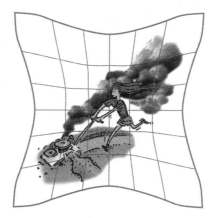

The transformation does not have to be one-to-one.

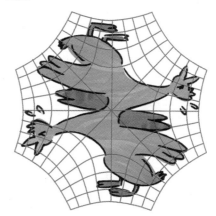

Graphic designers and artists often use distortions in their work. Look for examples in newspapers, magazines, and on television.

1. Make a distortion of your own drawing. You can trace one of the grids on these pages, or create your own grid. The examples on these pages may give you some ideas.

2. Look at the diagram on the right in the last transformation above.
  a) There is something unusual about this diagram that makes it different from the others. What do you think this is?
  b) What do you think "one-to-one" means? Explain why the transformation in the last diagram is not one-to-one.

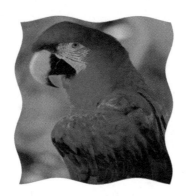

Review

1. The original figure, shown in black, was transformed to produce the images shown in colour. Identify the transformation that produced each coloured image.

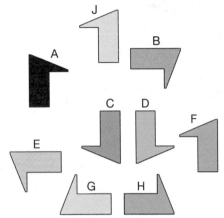

2. Find the coordinates of the image of each point after a translation of 5 units left, 3 units down.
   a) M(6, 9)
   b) N(7, −2)
   c) O(0, 0)
   d) P(−15, 6)
   e) Q(−7, −8)
   f) R(0, −11)
   g) S(−3, 2)
   h) T(13, −4)

3. Repeat exercise 2 for the translation 3 units right, 4 units up.

4. Is it possible to translate a triangle so that the image is a rectangle? Explain.

5. Quadrilateral K′L′M′N′ is a translation image of quadrilateral KLMN. One of the vertices of KLMN is (−3, −1). Determine as many different translations as you can that satisfy these conditions. For each translation, draw a diagram showing KLMN and K′L′M′N′. Describe the translation.

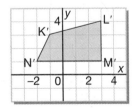

6. Find the coordinates of the image of each point after a reflection in the x-axis.
   a) A(3, 2)
   b) B(−4, 5)
   c) C(0, −7)
   d) D(−3, −9)
   e) E(11, −1)
   f) F(6, 0)
   g) G(0, 5)
   h) H(−4, −8)

7. Find the coordinates of the image of each point in exercise 6 after a reflection in a vertical line that is 2 units to the left of the y-axis.

8. Quadrilateral WXYZ is shown below.

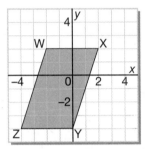

   a) Graph the image of quadrilateral WXYZ after a translation 2 units right, 3 units up. Label it W′X′Y′Z′.
   b) Graph the image of quadrilateral W′X′Y′Z′ reflected in the x-axis. Label it W″X″Y″Z″.
   c) What are the coordinates of the vertices of quadrilateral W″X″Y″Z″?
   d) Is there a single transformation for which quadrilateral W″X″Y″Z″ is the image of quadrilateral WXYZ? Explain.

9. Triangle A″B″C″ has vertices A″(−1, 1), B″(−7, −1), and C″(−1, −2). It is the final image after a translation 3 units right, 2 units down; and a reflection in the y-axis. Find the coordinates of the vertices of the original △ABC.

10. Find the coordinates of the image of each point after a clockwise rotation of 90° about the origin.
    a) G(4, −5)
    b) H(2, 7)
    c) I(−8, −3)
    d) J(0, −9)
    e) K(−7, 6)
    f) L(5, 0)
    g) M(0, 8)
    h) N(−12, −9)

11. Repeat exercise 10 for these rotations.
    a) 180° about the origin
    b) 90° counterclockwise about the origin
    c) 270° clockwise about the point B(2, 3)

12. The figure below is divided into eight congruent parts.

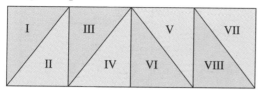

    a) Name six pairs of parts related by a rotation.
    b) Name four pairs of parts related by a translation.
    c) Name two pairs of parts related by a reflection.

13. A triangle has vertices G(−4, 2), H(0, 3), and I(1, −4). Graph △GHI and its image after each transformation.
    a) a translation 6 units right, 2 units down
    b) a rotation of 180° about the origin
    c) a counterclockwise rotation of 90° about I
    d) a clockwise rotation of 90° about H
    e) a dilatation of scale factor 2, and dilatation centre G
    f) a clockwise rotation of 90° about the origin
    g) a rotation of 180° about G
    h) a translation 4 units left, 3 units up

14. A figure undergoes a dilatation with the given scale factor. Is the image larger or smaller than the original figure?
    a) 3   b) 6   c) $\frac{1}{2}$
    d) $\frac{4}{3}$ e) $\frac{1}{4}$ f) $\frac{9}{10}$

15. Each point is transformed by a dilatation, centre the origin, and scale factor 4. Find the coordinates of the dilatation image of each point.
    a) Z(−3, 1)   b) Y(2, −5)
    c) X(0, 6)   d) W(−4, −1)
    e) V(10, −5)   f) U(8, 0)
    g) T(0, −3)   h) S(−2, −6)

16. The vertices of a figure and its dilatation image are given. Draw the figure and its image. Mark the dilatation centre.
    a) A(3, 6), B(9, 0), C(3, 3);
       A′(1, 2), B′(3, 0), C′(1, 1)
    b) D(−1, −1), E(−4, −2), F(−1, −2);
       D′(−2, −2), E′(−8, −4), F′(−2, −4),
    c) G(−2, 1), H(2, 2), J(2, −1), K(−2, −2);
       G′(−3, 1.5), H′(3, 3), J′(3, −1.5),
       K′(−3, −3)

17. What is the scale factor of each dilatation in exercise 16?

18. a) How many triangles in the diagram below are dilatations of △AOC?
    b) What are the scale factors for the dilatations in part a?
    c) How many triangles in the diagram are dilatations of △LOD?
    d) What are the scale factors for the dilatations in part c?

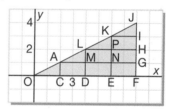

19. Draw a vertical line 2 units to the left of the y-axis. Draw another vertical line 3 units to the right of the y-axis. Draw △JKL with vertices J(−1, 4), K(−3, −1), and L(0, −2).
    a) Reflect △JKL in the reflection line to the left of the y-axis. Label the image △J′K′L′.
    b) Reflect △J′K′L′ in the reflection line to the right of the y-axis. Label the image △J″K″L″.
    c) For which single transformation is △J″K″L″ the image of △JKL?
    d) Repeat parts a to c, but reverse the order of the reflections. How does your answer to part c change?

20. Draw the line that joins A(−10, 10) and B(10, −10). This line is a reflection line. Another reflection line is the *x*-axis.

  a) Draw △RST with vertices R(−3, 5), S(1, 6), and T(−1, 4).

  b) Reflect △RST in AB. Label the image △R′S′T′.

  c) Reflect △R′S′T′ in the *x*-axis. Label the image △R″S″T″.

  d) For which single transformation is △R″S″T″ the image of △RST?

  e) Repeat parts a to d, but reverse the order of the reflections. How does your answer to part d change?

21. The design below comprises four congruent figures. Which parts are related by each transformation?

  a) a translation

  b) a reflection

  c) a rotation

  d) a dilatation

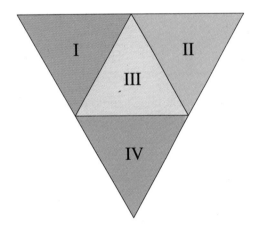

22. For each image of △ABC below, identify the transformation.

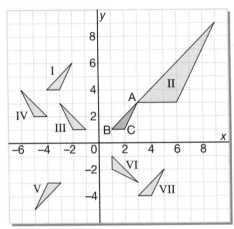

23. The coordinates of the vertices of a figure and its image are given. Describe the transformation in each case.

  a) A(5, 2), B(5, −3), C(−4, 1);
     A′(−5, 2), B′(−5, −3), C′(4, 1)

  b) E(−2, 3), F(3, 1), G(4, −4), H(−1, −5);
     E′(−7, 6), F′(−2, 4), G′(−1, −1), H′(−6, −2)

  c) P(0, −1), Q(3, −1), R(−3, −6);
     P′(−1, 0), Q′(−1, −3), R′(−6, 3)

  d) H(−2, 5), I(2, 4), J(6, −3), K(−1, −8);
     H′(2, −5), I′(−2, −4), J′(−6, 3), K′(1, 8)

  e) L(−3, 2), M(3, −2), N(−2, −4);
     L′(−3, −2), M′(3, 2), N′(−2, 4)

  f) S(−3, 9), T(3, 9), U(3, −9), V(−3, −9);
     S′(−1, 3), T′(1, 3), U′(1, −3), V′(−1, −3)

Suppose you have only a 5-L container and an 8-L container. How can you use them to obtain exactly 4 L of sand?

Investigating Transformations with *The Geometer's Sketchpad*

In this project, you will use *The Geometer's Sketchpad* to investigate some properties of translations, reflections, and rotations. *Activity 1* will help you become familiar with some of the tools and commands of *The Geometer's Sketchpad.*

ACTIVITY 1

Constructing, Labelling, and Changing Polygons

1. Use the Point tool to construct several points. Choose the Selection tool. Hold down the shift key. Click on the points you created until they have all been selected. From the Construct menu, choose Segment. The computer will join the points to draw a polygon. To de-select the polygon, click on a blank area of the screen.

2. To label the vertices of the polygon, choose the Text tool. Click on each vertex. To change a label, double-click on it with the Text tool. In the dialog box that appears, enter the label you want.

3. Practise changing the appearance of the polygon. Drag one of its sides or vertices with the Selection tool.

Before you begin any other activities, clear the screen by choosing Select All from the Edit menu; press Delete.

	Selection Tools
•	Point Tool
⊕	Circle Tool
/	Straight Object Tools
🖐	Text Tool

ACTIVITY 2

Properties of Translations

1. Construct a triangle and label its vertices. If necessary, change the labels to A, B, and C.

2. **a)** Use the Selection tool to drag a rectangle around the triangle. This is called a *marquee*, and it selects everything inside it. From the Transform menu, choose Translate…. In the dialog box that appears, choose By Fixed Cartesian. Enter the horizontal and vertical distances you want, and click OK. Label the vertices of the image.

   b) Construct a line segment joining a pair of matching points. Use the Selection tool to shift-click a pair of matching points, such as A and A′. From the Construct menu, choose Segment.

   c) Use the Selection tool to click on the segment you just created. From the Measure menu, choose Length.

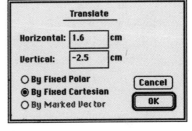

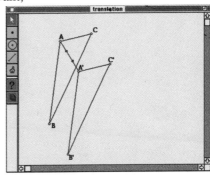

d) Repeat parts b and c, using the other pairs of matching points. What do you notice about the lengths of the line segments joining matching points? What do you notice about the slopes of the line segments?

e) Change the appearance of the original triangle. What happens to the image triangle? Do your observations from part d still hold?

ACTIVITY 3

Properties of Reflections

1. Construct a triangle and label its vertices. If necessary, change the labels to A, B, and C.

2. Click on the Straightedge tool and drag to the right to choose the Line tool. Use the Line tool to construct a line that will be the mirror line for your reflection. From the Transform menu, choose Mark Mirror.

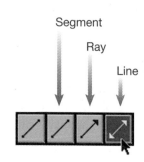

Segment

Ray

Line

3. a) Use the Selection tool to draw a marquee around the triangle. From the Transform menu, choose Reflect. Label the vertices of the image.

b) Construct a line segment joining a pair of matching points. First make sure the Line Segment tool is chosen, not the Line tool. Use the Selection tool to shift-click a pair of matching points, such as A and A′. From the Construct menu, choose Segment.

c) Use the Point tool to mark the point where AA′ intersects the mirror line. Label this point F.

d) Measure the angle at which AA′ intersects the mirror line. Use the Selection tool to shift-click A, F, and another point on the mirror line. From the Measure menu, select Angle. What do you notice?

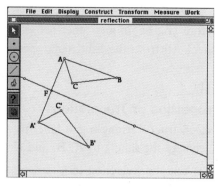

e) Measure the distance from A to the mirror line. Use the Selection tool to shift-click the points A and F. From the Measure menu, choose Distance. Measure the distance from A′ to the mirror line. What do you notice?

f) Repeat parts b through e using the other pairs of matching points.

g) Change the appearance of the original triangle. What happens to the image triangle? Do your observations from parts d and e still hold?

ACTIVITY 4

Properties of Rotations

1. Construct a triangle and label its vertices. If necessary, change the labels to A, B, and C.

2. Use the Point tool to draw a point that will be the rotation centre. With the point selected, choose Mark Centre from the Transform menu.

3. a) Use the Selection tool to draw a marquee around the triangle. From the Transform menu, choose Rotate…. In the dialog box that appears, choose By Fixed Angle. Enter the number of degrees you want, and click OK. Label the vertices of the image.

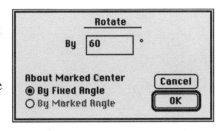

   b) Construct a line segment joining a pair of matching points. Use the Selection tool to shift-click a pair of matching points, such as A and A′. From the Construct menu, choose Segment.

   c) With the segment still selected, choose Point at Midpoint from the Construct menu. Label this point M.

   d) Use the Selection tool to shift-click the segment AA′ and the point M. From the Construct menu, choose Perpendicular Line. The computer draws a line through M perpendicular to AA′. What other point does the line pass through?

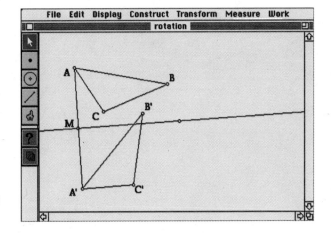

   e) Repeat parts b, c, and d using the other pairs of matching points. What do you notice about the perpendicular bisectors of the line segments joining matching points?

   f) Change the appearance of the original triangle. What happens to the image triangle? Does your observation from part e still hold?

ACTIVITY 5

Do you think the results of *Activities 2, 3,* and *4* would be true if you started with a polygon other than a triangle? Repeat exercises 2 and 3 for each *Activity*, using a quadrilateral.

The Ideas

For each transformation you investigated, create a poster explaining what you did and describing the properties you discovered. If your computer has a printer, include printouts of your constructions.

GEOMETRY

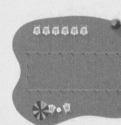

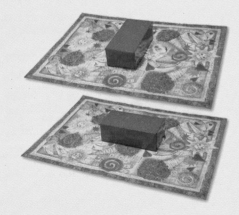

Start With What You Know

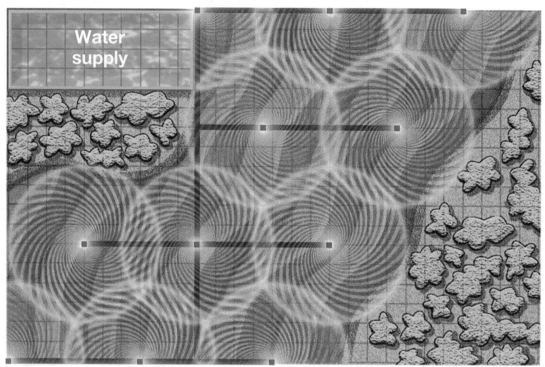

Scale: The side of 1 square = 0.25 m

The planning and use of an underground sprinkler system for a lawn involve measurement in different ways.

Four questions related to the sprinkler system are given below.
For each question:

- Discuss whether it involves length, area, or volume.
- Decide how you would answer the question.
- Answer the question.

1. How many square metres of lawn must be watered?

2. Approximately how many square metres of lawn are watered by each sprinkler?

3. Approximately how much water would be needed to cover the entire lawn with 2 cm of water?

4. Suppose you were installing this sprinkler system. How much pipe would you need to connect the sprinklers to each other and to the water supply?

5. **a)** What does *length* mean?

   b) Without using any formulas, explain what *area* means.

   c) Without using any formulas, explain what *volume* means.

6. In previous grades, you learned several measurement formulas.
   Some of these are listed below.

   a) Explain what each formula represents. Match each formula with one
   of the figures above.

   b) In your journal, summarize the formulas in a systematic way.
   Use diagrams to illustrate what the formulas represent.

$A = lw$	$A = s^2$	$V = lwh$
$C = 2\pi r$	$V = \pi r^2 h$	$P = 4s$
$A = \pi r^2$	$V = x^3$	$C = \pi d$
$A = \frac{1}{2}bh$	$A = 2\pi rh + 2\pi r^2$	$P = 2(l + w)$

Representing 3-Dimensional Objects in 2 Dimensions

Hundreds of years ago, artists did not give depth to their pictures. Objects and figures often looked distorted, and those in the background were frequently too large.

Geometry was used to achieve a 3-dimensional effect. Artists then achieved the appearance of reality in their paintings. We say that these paintings have *perspective*. A painting has perspective if you can see lines that appear to meet at one or more distant points.

1. Which of the two paintings on this page has perspective? In this painting, find some examples of lines that would meet if they were extended.

The National Gallery, London

The Annunciation

Paradise Garden

This painting was painted around 1410 by someone called Master of the Upper Rhine. The artist has such an unusual name because many artists from that time never signed their work. So if a group of paintings looked like they were painted by the same person, art historians would name the artist "Master of...". An artist could be named after the region in which he painted or after the painting itself. So this artist is known as either Master of the Upper Rhine or Master of the Paradise Garden.

Artists sometimes intentionally violate the laws of perspective to create amusing scenes or objects that cannot exist. Here are two examples.

2. Examine the engraving *Satire on False Perspective*. Find as many examples as you can of things that are wrong with this picture.

3. What is wrong with *Waterfall*? To find out, follow the path of the water as it goes over the waterfall and through the channels back to the top of the waterfall.

4. Look up the word *perspective* in the dictionary. Are any meanings that are listed different from the meaning given here?

Satire on False Perspective

Waterfall © 1995 M.C. Escher / Cordon Art - Baarn - Holland. All rights reserved.

Maurits Cornelis Escher was born in Holland in 1898. He first studied architecture then changed to graphic arts. Much of his early work was with woodcuts. After 1930, Escher also produced lithographs. *Waterfall* was completed in 1961 as a lithograph. The waterfall feeds itself, and will only cease to exist if the water evaporates.

The waterfall is surrounded by Italian landscapes. The fantasy garden is based on a drawing that Escher did in 1942.

Mathematics & Art

Linking Ideas

Developing the Ideas

Computer-assisted drawing (CAD) programs can show different views of an object. The monitor below shows a portable cassette player.

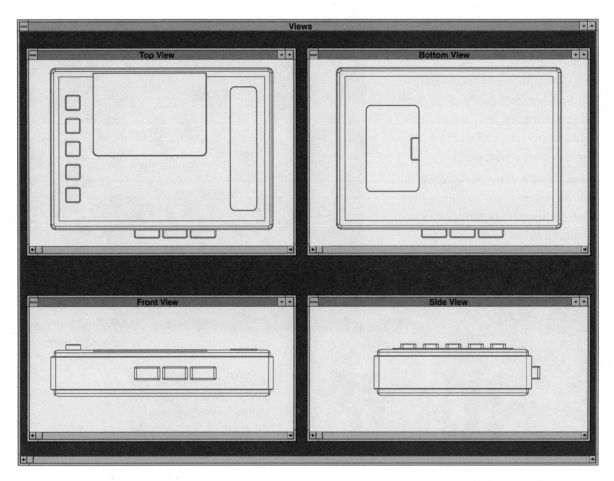

▶ ▶ *Through an Activity*

Work with a partner. You will need some three-dimensional solids.

1. **a)** Place a triangular prism on your desk. Look at it from directly above. Sketch its top view. This is sometimes called the *plan*.

   b) Sketch the front and side views, sometimes called the *elevations*. Decide which direction will represent the front, and which will represent the side.

   i) Look at it from the front, and sketch its front view.

   ii) Look at it from the side, and sketch its side view.

   c) Place the triangular prism on your desk in a different way. Then sketch three more top, front, and side views. How do these compare with the views you drew in parts a and b?

2. Sketch top, front, and side views of some other polyhedra.

Computer-assisted drawing programs can also show an object as it would appear in three dimensions. They can rotate the object to show it from different positions. Views like these are called *isometric views*. In this example, different views of a yoyo are shown.

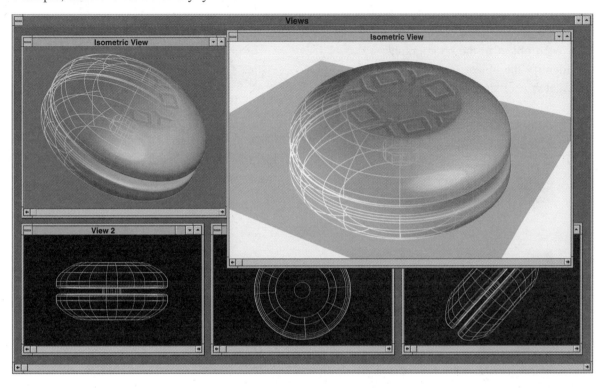

Example

Sketch an isometric view of a cube.

Solution

Use isometric dot paper and a cube. Hold the cube so you can see three faces.

Find edges on the cube that look parallel. Draw these edges so they are parallel on the dot paper.

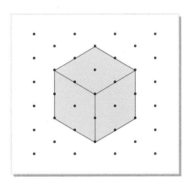

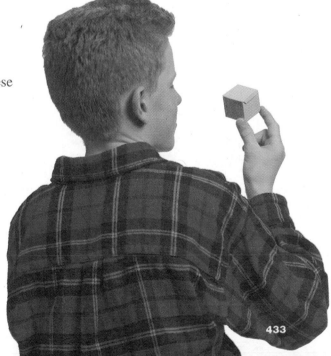

Working with Mathematics

Something to talk about

1. Can an object have more than one set of top, front, and side views?

2. What are the "three dimensions" in three-dimensional geometry?

3. For each object in the photographs:
   a) Identify the object.
   b) Sketch another view of the object.

A

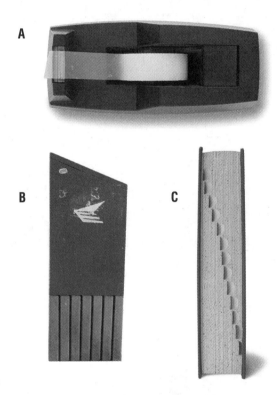

B   **C**

D

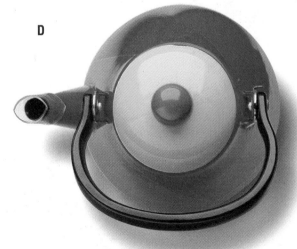

4. Which polyhedron has each set of views?

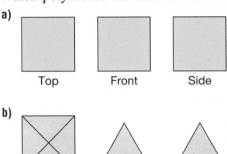

a)

Top   Front   Side

b)

Top   Front   Side

Practice

5. Identify each polyhedron and sketch its front, side, and top views.

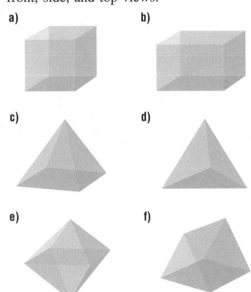

a)   b)

c)   d)

e)   f)

6. Sketch front, top, and side views of each object.

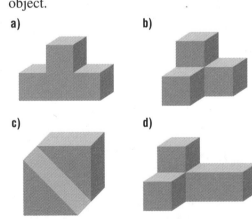

a)   b)

c)   d)

Work together

7. a) Make a structure using cubes. Sketch the six different views suggested by the diagram below.

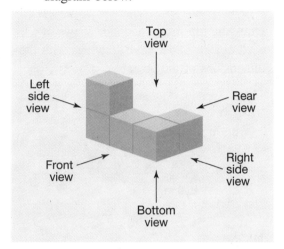

b) Sketch the six views of the structure in the diagram above.

8. Identify as many polyhedra as you can that can have each view.

a)

b)

On your own

9. Identify as many polyhedra as you can that can have each view.

a)

b)

c)

10. This temple was built in Mexico about 1000 years ago. Sketch the temple as it would appear from above.

11. Each object contains 8 cubes. Build each object. Sketch the object on isometric dot paper.

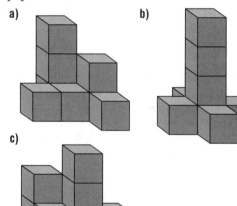

a)   b)   c)

12. Use the diagram to build the object below. Draw six different views of the object.

13. Sketch an isometric view of the object formed by placing cube 4 on top of each cube.

a) cube 1   **b)** cube 2   **c)** cube 3

i)

ii)

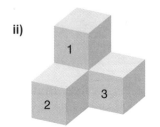

iii)

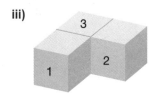

14. a) Build the object represented by each set of views.

i)

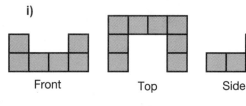

Front   Top   Side

ii)

Front   Top   Side

b) Use isometric dot paper to sketch each object.

15. Compare your results for exercise 14 with those of other students. Did all of you sketch the same object? What additional views would you have to create to represent only one object?

16. Draw the top, front, and side views of each object. Label your drawings with the dimensions of the objects.

a)

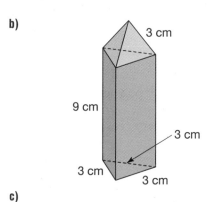

b)

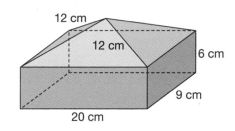

c)

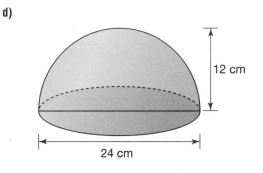

d)

Extend your thinking

17. The first figure shows a skeleton of a box. The second figure shows the box with five faces covered and one left open. Sketch other ways of covering five faces, with the opening in different positions.

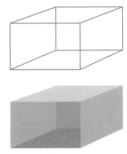

18. Use a square pyramid. Imagine that the centres of all the faces are vertices of a polyhedron. Sketch this polyhedron.

19. An object has the front, top, and side views shown below.

a) Is the object a polyhedron?
b) Describe the object.
c) Find a common household object that can have views that are almost like these. Here are some hints:
  • The three views don't look exactly like these.
  • The object doesn't always look like this.
  • You have all used this object.
  • It is in your bathroom.
What changes in these views would be necessary to represent this object more accurately?

COMMUNICATING

The Ideas

Choose a polyhedron. In your journal, sketch its front, top, side, and isometric views.

Most people would probably think that when you have three views of an object you can always tell what it is. But this is not true, as these two polyhedra show.

octahedron

octahedron with part removed

Sketch front, top, and side views of each polyhedron. Your views should be the same. There are 33 other polyhedra that also have these three views!

Developing the Ideas

▶ ▶ *Through Activities*

Some situations can be represented with a two-dimensional diagram or a model. In these activities, you will use diagrams to solve problems related to landscaping and gardening. You will need heavy paper, scissors, a paper clip, compasses, and 1-cm grid paper.

ACTIVITY 1

Investigate the geometry involved when you mow a lawn.

1. When you turn over a rotary lawnmower to clean or repair it, you can see the single blade that cuts the grass.

   a) Suppose the lawnmower is standing with the motor running. Predict the shape of the lawn that is cut under the mower.

   b) To model the situation, cut a strip of paper about 20 cm long and 1 cm wide. Place the paper strip on your notebook. Hold it firmly at the centre using a pencil point or compasses point. Turn the paper strip around the point. Describe the shape of the region covered by the rotating strip.

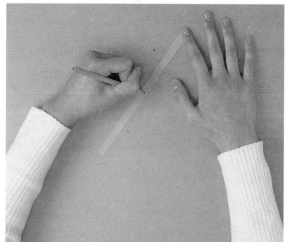

2. In step 1, you should have found that the lawnmower blade cuts a circular region. However, when you push a lawnmower in a straight line, you cut a long strip of lawn. Model the situation. Use heavy paper to cut a circle about 20 cm in diameter. This circle represents the rotating lawnmower blade. Slide the circle along a straight line.

3. Sketch the region covered by the rotating lawnmower blade when it travels along a straight line path. Discuss your results with a partner.

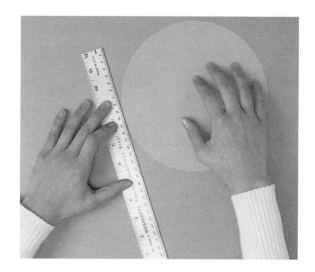

ACTIVITY 2

What do you think is the best way to cut a lawn?
Is it more efficient to trace a path back and forth, up and down,
or around the perimeter?

Follow these steps to investigate this problem.

1. Suppose the lawn is 9 m by 6 m, and the lawnmower cuts a path 1 m wide.

2. On 1-cm grid paper, draw three rectangles 9 cm long and 6 cm wide. What does each square represent?

3. On one rectangle, draw the path if you cut the lawn moving back and forth across the width of the lawn. Determine the total distance you would walk.

4. On a second rectangle, draw the path if you cut the lawn moving up and down the length of the lawn. Determine the total distance you would walk.

5. On a third rectangle, draw the path if you cut the lawn by walking around its perimeter. Determine the total distance you would walk.

6. What assumptions did you make in steps 3, 4, and 5? How might these assumptions affect your results?

7. Are there any differences in the distances you walk in steps 3, 4, and 5? Which method of cutting the lawn do you prefer? What other factors might determine your preference?

8. Is there a more efficient way to cut the lawn? Explain.

ACTIVITY 3

You are installing a sprinkler system for a 12-m square lawn. Each sprinkler will water an area within a specific distance. How can the sprinklers be arranged so the whole lawn is watered?

1. Determine the region covered by one sprinkler.
   a) A sprinkler waters all points within 2 m of the sprinkler. Predict the shape of the region that will be covered.
   b) To visualize the situation, place a paper clip on a sheet of paper. The length of the paper clip represents 2 m. Use a pencil point to hold one end of the paper clip. Spin the paper clip. Describe the shape of the region covered by the rotating paper clip.

2. Plan to position many sprinklers in the 12-m square lawn.

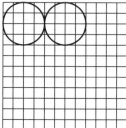

   a) Make a grid 12 squares by 12 squares to represent the 12-m square lawn. What area of the lawn is represented by each square on the grid?
   b) Draw several circles to represent sprinklers with diameter 4 m. Position the circles as shown.
   c) How many circles are needed to fill the grid?

3. a) What is the area of a 4 by 4 square?
   b) What is the area of a circle that just fits inside a 4 by 4 square?
   c) What area of a 4 by 4 square is not covered by the circle? Give your answer to three decimal places.
   d) What area of the whole grid is not covered by the arrangement of circles you drew in step 2?
   e) What fraction of the whole grid is not covered by circles? Write this fraction as a percent.
   f) Is any part of the grid from step 2 covered by more than one circle?

4. Repeat steps 2 and 3 using larger circles on a new grid. The larger circles represent more powerful sprinklers.

5. Design an efficient arrangement of sprinklers to water the whole lawn. An efficient arrangement has the least possible amount of double coverage (two sprinklers covering the same area), or coverage outside the lawn area. Show how your plan uses water efficiently.

Working with Mathematics

Use materials to help you complete these exercises. You could use paper strips, paper circles, string, grid paper, and any other materials you think might help.

Something to talk about

1. Refer to your results for *Activity 2*. Suppose the lawnmower cut a path 0.75 m wide. How would this assumption affect the distances travelled to cut the lawn?

2. Refer to *Activity 3*. The sprinklers spin around a fixed point and cover a circular area. Describe other types of sprinklers you have seen. What shape of lawn would be covered by each?

3. A dog is leashed to a lamppost. The leash is 1.8 m long. Describe the region within reach of the dog. Assume there are no other objects within 2 m of the lamppost.

4. A diver jumped off a diving board. Describe the path of the tip of the diving board after the diver jumps off.

5. Esmé made a radio transmitter for a science fair project. She determined that she could transmit messages up to 30 km away. Draw a scale diagram to show the region covered by Esmé's transmissions.

Work together

6. Kittens are kept in a cage. Their paws can reach 4 cm outside their cage. Draw the region within the kittens' reach. Make your diagram to scale.

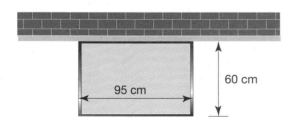

7. A dog is tied by a 2-m leash to a corner of its doghouse. Draw a diagram to show the region within the dog's reach.

8. A goat is tethered to a post in a square fenced-in field. The tether is 6 m long.
   a) Suppose the post is in the middle of the field. Draw a scale diagram to show the region in which the goat could move.
   b) What is the smallest square field that can contain the region in part a?
   c) Suppose the post is at a corner of the field. How would the region in part a change? How would your answer to part b change?

9. A ladder leans against a wall. A painter's cap hangs from a point part way up the ladder. The ladder starts to slip down the wall.

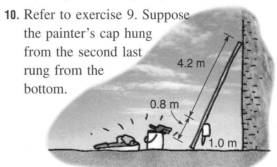

   Make a diagram to show the path followed by the painter's cap.

10. Refer to exercise 9. Suppose the painter's cap hung from the second last rung from the bottom.
   a) Make a diagram to show the path followed by the painter's cap.
   b) How is this path similar to the path in exercise 9? How are the paths different?

11. When you ride a bicycle along a flat surface, the wheel follows a straight line path. What path is traced by the valve on the wheel? Model the situation. From heavy paper, cut a circle about 10 cm in diameter. Punch a hole about 1 cm from the edge of the circle, to represent the bicycle valve. Place a pencil tip in the hole to trace a path, while rolling the circle along a ruler.

12. Cut out two circles, one with radius 5 cm and one with radius 8 cm. Mark a point P on the smaller circle.

Determine the path traced by P when you roll the small circle around the large circle.

13. Use your circles from exercise 12. Mark a point Q on the larger circle.

Determine the path traced by Q when you roll the large circle around the small circle.

14. **a)** How are the paths in exercises 12 and 13 similar?
    b) How are they different?

On your own

15. A dog is sometimes tied to a leash that moves freely along a wire. This allows the dog more running space.

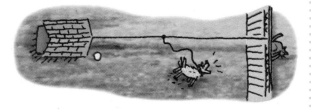

Suppose a dog is tied to a 6-m wire by a 1.5-m leash. The wire joins the doghouse and the fence. Draw a diagram to show the region the dog can reach.

16. A bird in a cage scatters seeds around the edges of the cage. Suppose 12 cm is the farthest distance from the dish the bird seed will be scattered. For each situation below, draw a diagram to show the region in which the bird seed might fall. The dish is circular with radius 2 cm.

a)

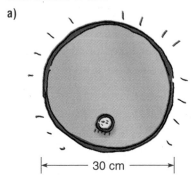

|← 30 cm →|

b)

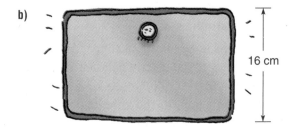

16 cm

17. A detective is following two suspects when they walk behind a wall 2 m high. Trace the diagram below.

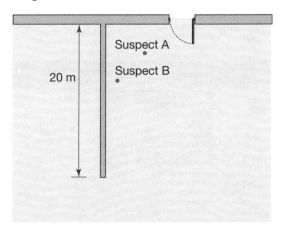

Suspect A

Suspect B

20 m

On your diagram, colour in each region as indicated.

a) **Blue:** the region in which the detective would stand and not see the suspects
b) **Green:** the region from which the detective would see only one suspect
c) **Yellow:** the region from which the detective would see both suspects

Extend your thinking

18. Make a drawing to show the position of Earth, the moon, and the sun during a solar eclipse.

19. The game *Spirograph* contains circles and rings that work like gears. Players make geometric designs by tracing the path of a point within one circle, as it rolls around or inside another circle. *Spirograph* also contains bars, which are shaped like rectangles with semicircular ends.

If you have *Spirograph*, experiment with making different geometric designs. Otherwise, make paper cutouts of circles, rings, and bars to try some of these exercises.

a) A small circle rolls around a larger circle. What path is traced by the centre of the small circle?
b) A small circle rolls within a larger circle. What path is traced by the centre of the small circle?
c) A small circle rolls within a larger circle. What path is traced by a point in the small circle that is not the centre?

d) A small circle rolls around a bar. What path is traced by the centre of the circle?
e) A small circle rolls around a bar. What path is traced by a point in the small circle that is not the centre?

COMMUNICATING
The Ideas
Select one of the exercises you completed for this section. In your journal, describe the problem and your solution. Explain why your solution provides a valid model of the problem.

Developing the Ideas

triangular
pyramid

rectangular
pyramid

pentagonal
pyramid

hexagonal
pyramid

In ancient times people built large pyramids as burial chambers for their leaders. Pyramids have also been built in modern times to serve as art galleries and conservatories.

A *pyramid* is a solid with a base that is a polygon. The other faces are triangles with a common vertex.

Here is a net for a pyramid. Identify the base and the triangular faces. Predict the type of pyramid you would form if you fold the net.

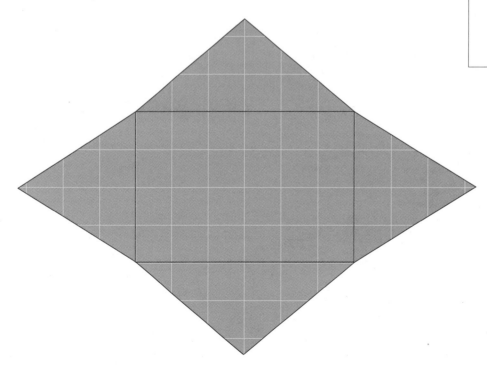

Work with a partner or in a group. You will need 1-cm grid paper, scissors, and a millimetre ruler.

1. Draw the net on page 444 on 1-cm grid paper. Cut out the net.

2. Fold the net to make the pyramid. Identify the type of pyramid.

3. Explain what surface area means. Explain how you could determine the surface area of the pyramid you have just constructed.
   a) How many faces does the pyramid have?
   b) Are any faces congruent?
   c) Determine the area of each face.
   d) Determine the surface area of the pyramid.

4. How could you find the surface area of a square pyramid?

5. How could you find the surface area of a triangular pyramid?

▷ ▷ *Through a Guided Example*

To calculate the surface area of a pyramid, calculate the total area of its faces.

Example ···

The Great Pyramid in Egypt was originally constructed with a smooth limestone surface. Over the ages, this limestone was removed and used on other buildings. Each face of the Great Pyramid is a triangle with base 229 m and height 185 m. Calculate the total area of the four triangular faces of the pyramid.

Solution

There are four triangular faces, each with base 229 m and height 185 m.
The area of each face is
$$\frac{\text{base} \times \text{height}}{2} = \frac{229 \text{ m} \times 185 \text{ m}}{2}$$
$$= 21\ 182.5 \text{ m}^2$$

The total area of all four faces is $4 \times 21\ 182.5 \text{ m}^2 = 84\ 730 \text{ m}^2$

To the nearest 1000 m², the surface area is 85 000 m².

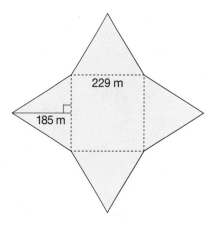

229 m

185 m

Working with Mathematics

Something to talk about

1. In the *Example* we did not include the areas of all the faces of the pyramid. How can you tell whether to include the areas of all the faces or just some of them?

2. **a)** How does the area of the faces in the pyramid in the *Example* compare with the area of the walls in your classroom?
   b) How many classrooms like yours would you need to have walls with the same total area as the walls in the pyramid?

3. In the *Example*, the square pyramid has four congruent triangular faces.
   a) How many congruent faces are there in a triangular pyramid? Explain.
   b) How many congruent faces are there in a hexagonal pyramid? Explain.

4. Which net folds to make a pyramid? Explain how you know.

   a)   **b)**

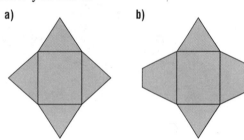

Practice

5. Determine the surface area of each pyramid. Give the answer to one decimal place.

   a)   3.0 cm   **b)**   6.0 cm
   4.0 cm   5.0 cm
   4.0 cm   5.0 cm

   c)   8.0 cm   **d)**   8.4 cm
   10.0 cm   12.5 cm
   10.0 cm   12.5 cm

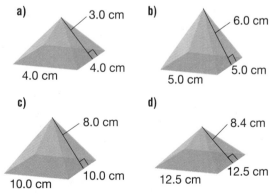

6. Determine the surface area of each tetrahedron to one decimal place.

   a)   **b)**
   2.6 cm   3.0 cm   3.9 cm   4.5 cm
            3.0 cm   4.5 cm
   3.0 cm   4.5 cm

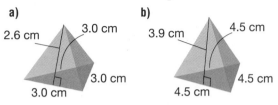

Work together

7. Draw a net for each pyramid. Determine its surface area to one decimal place.
   a) a square base with side length 5.5 cm, triangular faces with height 8.4 cm
   b) a rectangular base 12.00 cm by 7.50 cm, the triangular face on the longer side has height 14.25 cm, the triangular face on the shorter side has height 15.00 cm
   c) each face an equilateral triangle with side lengths 4.1 cm

8. Set up a spreadsheet document.
   a) Design a spreadsheet that will calculate the area of the four faces of a square pyramid. Use the solution to the *Example*, page 445 to help you. Use the dimensions in the *Example* to check your spreadsheet.
   b) Change the spreadsheet so that it will calculate the total surface area of a pyramid. Use the pyramids in exercise 9 to check your spreadsheet.

On your own

9. Determine the surface area of each pyramid.

   a)   **b)**
   12 cm   33 cm   34 cm
        18 cm
                               25 cm   18 cm

   c)   **d)**
            3.4 m   54 mm   47 mm
                                           75 mm
   2.1 m   54 mm

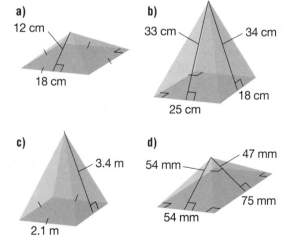

10. The Louvre is a famous art gallery in Paris, France. It is housed in a historic palace and was opened in 1793. In 1989, it was expanded. One addition is a large glass square pyramid that covers the main entrance. Each wall of this pyramid is a triangle with base 35.4 m and height 27.9 m.

Calculate the surface area of the glass in the pyramid.

11. A carpenter is building two playhouses for a day-care centre. The roof of each playhouse is a pyramid. One roof has a square base with length 3.8 m. The height of each triangular face is 4.2 m. The other roof has a rectangular base 1.9 m by 2.6 m. The heights of the triangular faces are 2.4 m and 2.2 m respectively. For each playhouse, the roof sits on walls 1 m high.
   a) How much wood is needed for each playhouse?
   b) Which playhouse needs more wood?
   c) Suppose wood costs $15.25/m². How much would it cost to build each playhouse?

12. The square base of a pyramid has side lengths of 6 cm. Each triangular face has a height of 10 cm.
   a) Find the surface area of the pyramid.

b) Find the surface area of the pyramid if the side lengths and height are doubled.
c) Find the surface area of the pyramid if the side lengths and height are tripled.
d) Compare your answers for parts a, b, and c. What do you notice?

Extend your thinking

13. A large triangular pyramid is cut to produce a smaller pyramid. The vertical height of the large pyramid is 10 cm. The vertical height of the small pyramid is 4 cm.

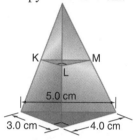

   a) The base of the small pyramid is △KLM. What are the lengths of the sides of △KLM?
   b) What is the area of the base of each pyramid?

14. A tray has the shape shown. It is like a rectangular pyramid with a top portion removed. The heights of the triangular faces are: 22.9 cm on base 15.4 cm; 23.7 cm on base 9.3 cm; 15.3 cm on base 10.3 cm; and 15.9 cm on base 6.2 cm.

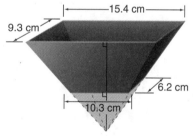

Determine the amount of wood needed to construct the tray.

The Ideas

In your journal, describe how you calculate the surface area of a pyramid if you know its dimensions. Illustrate your description with some examples.

Which Cylinder Has the Greater Volume?

You can roll a rectangular piece of paper into a cylinder in two different ways. If there is no overlap, do the cylinders have the same volume? If not, then which has the greater volume—the one with the long side of the rectangle as its height or the one with the short side of the rectangle as its height?

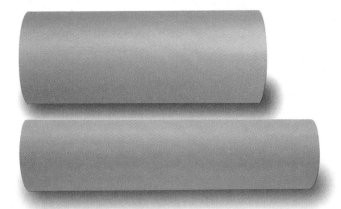

Understand the problem

- Do the two cylinders have the same height? Do they have the same radius?
- What are you asked to do?

Think of a strategy

- You could take two sheets of paper and make the two cylinders.
- What information would you need to calculate the volumes of the cylinders?

Carry out the strategy

- Before making the cylinders, measure the length and the width of the paper.
- When you roll the paper to form a cylinder, how does the circumference and the height of the cylinder compare with the dimensions of the paper?
- Determine the height and the base radius for each cylinder.
- Calculate the volumes of the cylinders.
- Are the volumes the same? If not, which cylinder has the greater volume?

Look back

- What shape would the paper have to be for the volumes to be equal?
- Suppose another piece of paper had the same width, but was twice as long. How would the volumes of the two cylinders compare?
- Suppose another piece of paper had the same length, but was half as wide. How would the volumes of the two cylinders compare?
- Determine the dimensions of a sheet of paper for which the volume of one cylinder is two times the volume of the other cylinder.

Communicating the Ideas

In your journal, write a description of this problem and your solution. Include drawings of the cylinders.

Developing the Ideas

▶▶ *Through an Activity*

Workers at a resort set up a rectangular area to store outdoor equipment
and furniture. They use metal stands. They have 26 stands, each 3 m
long. The storage enclosure they set up could have different shapes.

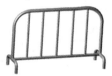

The length could be much longer
than the width.

The length and width could be
almost equal.

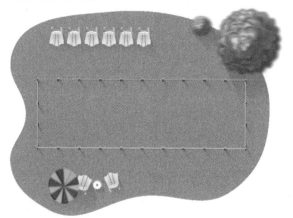

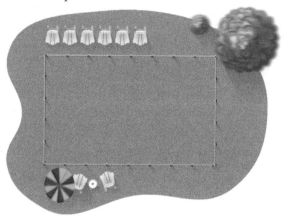

1. Suppose 3 metal stands are used for the width.
   a) How many stands could be used for the length?
   b) What are the dimensions of this enclosure, in metres?
   c) What is the area enclosed?

2. Repeat step 1 for each condition given.
   a) The workers use 4 stands for the width.
   b) They use 5 stands for the width.

3. a) Record your results from steps 1 and 2 in a table.

Number of stands along the width	Number of stands along the length	Width of enclosure (m)	Length of enclosure (m)	Area enclosed (m²)
3				
4				
5				

   b) Extend your table to show the results for greater widths.
   c) How many stands should be used for the width and the length to
      make the largest possible enclosure? What are the dimensions of
      this enclosure?

Working with Mathematics

Something to talk about

1. In the *Activity*, suppose the workers found two more metal stands. What would be the dimensions of the largest enclosure they could make using 28 stands? What is its area?

Practice

2. A city zoo rents strollers and wagons. Zoo workers are building a rectangular enclosure to contain the strollers and wagons. They have 30 metal stands, identical to the ones described in the *Activity*.
   a) What are the dimensions of the largest rectangular area of the enclosure?
   b) Can they make an enclosure with an area of 50 m²? If so, what are its dimensions?

3. Melanie has 36 patio tiles, each 0.6 m square.
   a) Suppose she wants to use the patio tiles to form a path. What are the dimensions of the narrowest rectangular path she can make?
   b) Suppose she wants to use the patio tiles to form a square patio. What are the dimensions of the patio?

4. Campbell has 10 railroad ties, each 1.8 m long. He wants to use the ties to enclose a rectangular garden.
   a) What are the possible dimensions of the different rectangles he could form?
   b) What is the area of each rectangle in part a?

Work together

5. Steve wants to fence a rectangular garden. The fencing material comes in 1-m long units that cannot be cut. Suppose Steve has 20 m of fencing. What are the dimensions of the largest garden he can make? Explain your answer.

6. If a spreadsheet program is available, use it to complete this exercise. A lifeguard has 400 m of rope to enclose a rectangular swimming area at a beach. The diagrams show different ways she can do this.

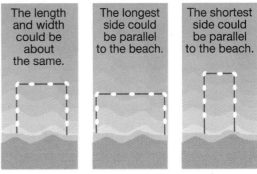

| The length and width could be about the same. | The longest side could be parallel to the beach. | The shortest side could be parallel to the beach. |

   a) Do you think the area of the enclosed region depends on the way the rope is arranged? Explain.
   b) Suppose the side parallel to the beach measures 300 m. How long is the other side of the rectangle? Calculate the area of water enclosed by the rope.
   c) Repeat part b if the side parallel to the beach measures:
   i) 250 m ii) 200 m iii) 150 m iv) 100 m
   d) Record your results in a table.

Length of side parallel to beach (m)	Length of side perpendicular to beach (m)	Total length of rope (m)	Area enclosed (m²)
300			
250			

   e) What are the dimensions of the largest possible rectangular swimming area? How are these dimensions related?

On your own

7. A store owner wants to create a rectangular area for a store display. He has 6 m of rope. What are the dimensions of the largest area he can enclose in each situation? Explain your answers.
   a) The rope encloses the entire area.
   b) There is a wall on one side.
   c) There are walls on 2 sides.

8. Refer to the *Activity*. Determine the dimensions of the largest enclosure the resort workers can make for each situation.

   a) Use metal stands for 3 sides of the enclosure, with a wall on the remaining side.

   b) Use metal stands for 2 sides of the enclosure, with walls on two adjacent sides.

9. The resort workers in the *Activity* decide to separate the outdoor equipment from the furniture. They set up two storage enclosures of equal area, with a common side. The diagram shows one way to do this, using 26 metal stands.

   a) Calculate the combined area of the two storage enclosures.

   b) Find some other ways to arrange the metal stands to make the two storage areas. Calculate the combined area for each. Record your results in a table.

Number of stands along each of the 3 sides	Number of stands along each of the other 2 sides	Overall width (m)	Overall length (m)	Combined area (m²)
6 .	4			

   c) How should the stands be arranged to make the largest possible enclosure? What are the dimensions and the area of this enclosure?

10. You will need some string and a sheet of 1-cm grid paper. Cut a piece of string and tie the ends together to form a loop.

    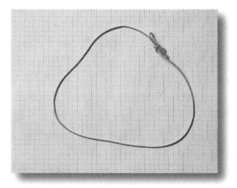

    a) Describe the shape of the largest region on the graph paper you can enclose with the string. Experiment, using different shapes.

    b) What is the area of the largest region?

    c) Suppose the string is 42.5 cm long. What are the dimensions of the largest region?

Extend your thinking

11. The opposite corners of a checkerboard are removed, as shown. Suppose you have a supply of dominoes, each of which covers two squares of the checkerboard. What is the maximum number of dominoes you can place on the checkerboard, without overlapping?

    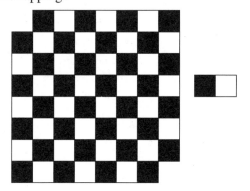

The Ideas

Suppose you have several rectangles that have the same area. In your journal, explain how you could tell, just by looking, which one has the least perimeter. Illustrate your answer with some examples.

Developing the Ideas

▶ ▶ *Through an Activity*

The Acme Box Company designs and manufactures boxes, cans, and other containers. It has been hired to design a box to hold 1000 cm^3 of popcorn kernels. The box could have different shapes.

The length, width, and height of the box could be different.

The length, width, and height could be about the same.

1. Suppose the base is 20 cm long and 5 cm wide.
  a) What is the area of the base?
  b) What height is needed so that the volume is 1000 cm^3?
  c) Calculate the surface area of this box.

2. Repeat step 1 for each base described below.
  a) 25 cm long and 4 cm wide
  b) 25 cm long and 8 cm wide

3. a) Record your results from steps 1 and 2 in a table.

Length (cm)	Width (cm)	Height (cm)	Volume (cm^3)	Surface area (cm^2)
20	5			
25	4			
25	8			

  b) Which of these three sizes requires the least amount of cardboard to make?
  c) Find another size of box that requires less cardboard than the one in part b. Include it in your table.
  d) Describe the shape of the box that requires the minimum amount of cardboard.

Working with Mathematics

Something to talk about

1. For the *Activity*, suppose Acme needs to design a larger box to hold 2000 cm³ of popcorn kernels. It is to be made with the minimum amount of cardboard. Would the dimensions of this box be double the dimensions of the box in step 3c of the *Activity*? Explain your answer.

Practice

2. **a)** List the possible dimensions of a rectangular prism with volume 24 cm³. Each dimension should be a whole number.
   b) Which prism has the least surface area?

3. **a)** List the possible whole-number dimensions of a rectangular prism with volume 32 cm³.
   b) Which prism has the least surface area?

4. **a)** List the possible whole-number dimensions of a rectangular prism with volume 100 cm³.
   b) Which prism has the least surface area?

Work together

5. If a spreadsheet program is available, use it to complete this exercise. The Acme Box Company has been hired to design boxes to hold 4000 cm³ of popcorn for movie theatres. The boxes have an open top and a square base.

   a) Suppose the base is 10 cm long and 10 cm wide. What is the height for a volume of 4000 cm³? Calculate the surface area of this box.
   b) Repeat part a for each base described below.
       i) 12 cm by 12 cm   **ii)** 14 cm by 14 cm

c) Record your results from parts a and b in a table.

Length (cm)	Width (cm)	Height (cm)	Volume (cm³)	Surface area (cm²)
10	10			
12	12			
14	14			

d) Determine the dimensions of the box that requires the minimum amount of cardboard. Describe the box. Do you think it would be a good idea for movie theatres to use this shape? Explain.

6. Suppose you have an 8-cm cube.

Step 1   1 8-cm cube
V = 512 cm³

The 8-cm cube can be divided into 4-cm cubes.

Step 2   8 4-cm cubes
V = 512 cm³

These 4-cm cubes can be divided further into 2-cm cubes.

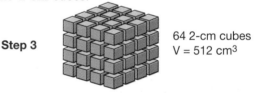

Step 3   64 2-cm cubes
V = 512 cm³

a) Calculate the total surface area of the cubes in each step above.
b) Suppose you divided the 2-cm cubes in a fourth step. Determine the total surface area of the 1-cm cubes.
c) Look for a pattern in the total surface area from step to step. Suppose you know the surface area of the cubes in a step. How could you find the surface area of the cubes in the next step?
d) What is the surface area of the cubes in the tenth step?

On your own

7. Sugar cubes come in boxes of 144 cubes. There are 2 layers of cubes. Each layer forms a 12 by 6 rectangle. The company wants to design a box that uses less cardboard and still holds 144 sugar cubes.

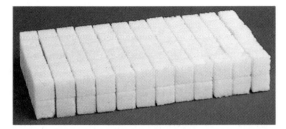

   a) Calculate the surface area of the box, in square units, that would enclose the cubes shown.
   b) Determine three other ways to arrange 144 sugar cubes in a box. Calculate the surface area of each box.
   c) How would you arrange 144 sugar cubes to use the least amount of cardboard?
   d) Do you think it would be a good idea for sugar cube boxes to be redesigned? Why?

8. Mary bought some caramels at the bulk food store. She wants to pack them in a box. The caramels are 2 cm by 2 cm by 1 cm.
   a) Mary found a box measuring 8 cm by 5 cm by 4 cm. What is the maximum number of caramels she can pack in this box? Explain your answers.
   b) Mary found another box whose dimensions are double the dimensions of the box in part a. What is the maximum number of caramels she can pack in it?

9. If a spreadsheet program is available, you may wish to use it to complete this exercise.
   a) Measure a juice box. Calculate its total surface area.
   b) Determine some dimensions of boxes that contain the same volume of juice, but have a smaller surface area.
   c) Do you think it would be a good idea for juice box manufacturers to change the dimensions of their boxes? Why?

10. If a spreadsheet program is available, you may wish to use it to complete this exercise. The Acme Box Company makes boxes from pieces of cardboard 28.0 cm long and 21.6 cm wide. Equal squares are cut from each corner and the sides are folded up. Plain copy paper measures approximately 28.0 cm by 21.6 cm. On a piece of paper like this, draw lines 6 cm from each side. Cut a 6-cm square from each corner. Fold up the sides to make an open box.

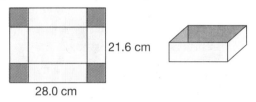

21.6 cm

28.0 cm

   a) Calculate the volume of the box.
   b) Suppose you change the size of the cutout square. Predict what will happen to the volume. Will it be the same, greater, or smaller?
   c) To check your prediction, copy and complete the table below.
      i) Suppose the length of the cutout square increases from 1 cm to 9 cm. What happens to the volume of the box?
      ii) Suppose the length of the cutout square increases beyond 9 cm. What would happen to the volume of the box? What would happen if this length were less than 1 cm?

Length of the cut out square (cm)	Length of the box (cm)	Width of the box (cm)	Height of the box (cm)	Volume of the box (cm³)
1				
2				
3				
4				
5				
6				
7				
8				
9				

d) Draw a graph of the volume of the open box against the length of the cutout square. Use the graph to answer these questions.

  i) What is the volume of the largest box that could be made from this size of cardboard? What size of square should be cut from the corners to make this box?

  ii) Suppose the Acme Box Company wanted to use the cardboard to make a box with a volume of 900 cm³. What size of square should be cut from the corners to make this box?

11. Here are two designs for a building.

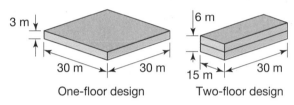

One-floor design   Two-floor design

a) Check that each building has 900 m² of floor space and a volume of 2700 m³.

b) For each design, calculate the total area of the roof and the four outside walls. Which building do you think is cheaper to heat in the winter? Explain.

c) Three other designs for a building are shown below. Check that each has 900 m² of floor space and a volume of 2700 m³.

  i) two-floor design

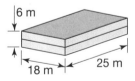

  ii) three-floor design

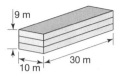

  iii) four-floor design

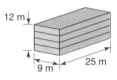

d) For each design, calculate the total area of the roof and the four outside walls. Are any of these likely to be cheaper to heat in the winter than those above?

e) For each design, calculate the ratio of surface area to volume. Record your results in a table. Is it better to have a high ratio of surface area to volume or a low ratio of surface area to volume? Explain.

Length (cm)	Width (cm)	Height (cm)	Volume (cm³)	Outside surface area (cm²)	Ratio of surface area to volume

Extend your thinking

12. Refer to exercise 7. Sugar cubes measure 1.5 cm along each edge.

  a) Calculate the surface area of the box for exercise 7a, in square centimetres.

  b) Calculate the surface area of the box that uses the minimum amount of cardboard.

13. Refer to exercise 8.

  a) Mary found a smaller box measuring 5 cm by 5 cm by 3 cm. What is the maximum number of caramels she can pack in this box? Explain your answer.

  b) Mary found another box whose dimensions are double the dimensions of the box in part a. What is the maximum number of caramels she can pack in it?

The Ideas

Suppose you have several rectangular prisms, all with the same volume. In your journal explain how you could tell, just by looking, which one has the least surface area. Illustrate your answer with some examples.

Total Surface Areas and Volumes of Cylinders with the Same Radius

Some cylinders have the same radius but different heights. How might their total surface areas be related? How might their volumes be related?

To answer these questions you will need as many different cans as you can find that have the same radius and different heights.

Work in a group.

1. Why do you think manufacturers would make cans with the same radius but different heights?

2. Without measuring, how can you be certain that all the cans have the same radius?

3. Measure the diameter and the height of each can. Then calculate its radius and total surface area. Record the height and the total surface area of each can in a table. Recall that the total surface area of a cylinder is given by the formula $A = 2\pi rh + 2\pi r^2$.

Height (cm)	Surface area (cm²)

4. a) Graph the data on a grid like that at the right. Draw a straight line or smooth curve through the plotted points.

b) Use your graph. Estimate the total surface areas of cans with the same radius as the others and with heights of 1 cm, 2 cm, 3 cm, and 10 cm.

c) Discuss your results with other groups. Did everyone get similar results?

5. a) All the cans have the same radius r. Substitute your value of r into the formula in exercise 3. You obtain an equation expressing the total surface area of a can in terms of its height h.

b) Use your equation to verify your estimates from exercise 4b.

6. Conduct a similar investigation to determine how the volumes of the cans are related. Follow the same steps: create a table; graph your results; from your graph, estimate volumes of cans with different heights; and obtain an equation expressing the volume of a can in terms of its height h. Recall that the volume of a cylinder is given by $V = \pi r^2 h$.

7. Conduct similar investigations using cylinders that have the same height, but different radii. How are their total surface areas and their radii related? How are their volumes and their radii related?

Surface area of cans with the same radius

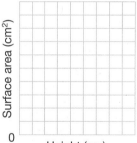

Surface area (cm²)

0

Height (cm)

MEASUREMENT & GRAPHING

Linking Ideas

Designing Package Sizes

Suppose you are asked to design a cylindrical can to have a specific volume. You could try many different combinations of height and base diameter for your can and still have the same volume. How can you decide which dimensions to use? Which dimensions would require the least amount of material?

You can answer this question using a spreadsheet. You will need a can which has the capacity in millilitres marked on the label. You will use the spreadsheet to determine the dimensions of a can which has the same capacity as yours, and which can be made from the least amount of material.

Start your spreadsheet program and enter the information shown below. You can use the numbers shown in cells C3 and C4 (which represent a pasta sauce can), or you can use the volume and diameter of your own can.

1. Look at the formulas in cells C6 to C10.
   What does each formula tell the computer to do?

TEMPLATE DISK

	A	B	C
1	Minimizing the surface area of a can		
2			
3	Enter :	Volume	725
4		Base diameter	8.2
5			
6	Calculate :	Radius	=C4/2
7		Height	=C3/(Pi()*C6*C6)
8		Area of base	=Pi()*C6*C6
9		Area of label	=2*Pi()*C6*C7
10		Total area	=2*C8+C9

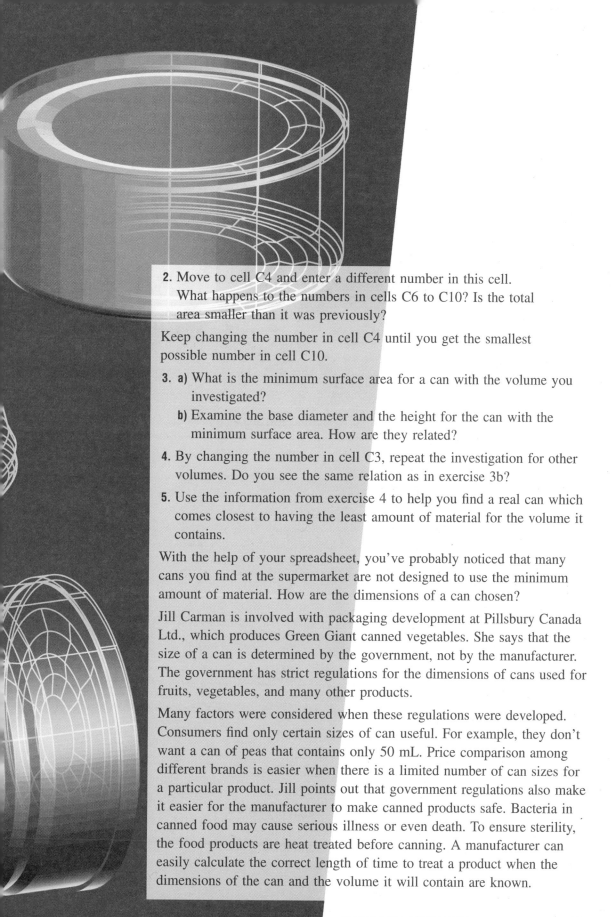

2. Move to cell C4 and enter a different number in this cell. What happens to the numbers in cells C6 to C10? Is the total area smaller than it was previously?

Keep changing the number in cell C4 until you get the smallest possible number in cell C10.

3. a) What is the minimum surface area for a can with the volume you investigated?

   b) Examine the base diameter and the height for the can with the minimum surface area. How are they related?

4. By changing the number in cell C3, repeat the investigation for other volumes. Do you see the same relation as in exercise 3b?

5. Use the information from exercise 4 to help you find a real can which comes closest to having the least amount of material for the volume it contains.

With the help of your spreadsheet, you've probably noticed that many cans you find at the supermarket are not designed to use the minimum amount of material. How are the dimensions of a can chosen?

Jill Carman is involved with packaging development at Pillsbury Canada Ltd., which produces Green Giant canned vegetables. She says that the size of a can is determined by the government, not by the manufacturer. The government has strict regulations for the dimensions of cans used for fruits, vegetables, and many other products.

Many factors were considered when these regulations were developed. Consumers find only certain sizes of can useful. For example, they don't want a can of peas that contains only 50 mL. Price comparison among different brands is easier when there is a limited number of can sizes for a particular product. Jill points out that government regulations also make it easier for the manufacturer to make canned products safe. Bacteria in canned food may cause serious illness or even death. To ensure sterility, the food products are heat treated before canning. A manufacturer can easily calculate the correct length of time to treat a product when the dimensions of the can and the volume it will contain are known.

8.6 VOLUME OF A CONE

Developing the Ideas

▷ ▶ *Through an Activity*

Work in a group.

You will need an empty tin can, scissors, paper, tape, some clean
sand or water, and an overflow container.

1. Use scissors, paper, and tape to make a paper cone that just fits
   inside the can.

2. **a)** Suppose you fill the cone with water or sand, and then empty
   it into the can. How many times do you think you could do
   this until the can is full?
   b) Check using water or sand.

3. Suppose you have a cone that just fits inside a cylinder.
   a) Based on your observations, if you know the volume of the
   cylinder, how could you determine the volume of the cone?
   b) A cylinder and a cone have base radius *r* and height *h*. Write a
   formula for the volume of the cylinder.
   c) Use your answers to parts a and b. Write a formula for the volume
   of the cone with base radius *r* and height *h*.
   d) Compare your formulas with those of other groups.

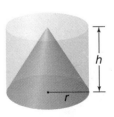

▶ ▶ *Through Instruction*

If a cone just fits inside a cylindrical can, you can fill the cone three times and pour its contents into the can. Then the can will be full.

These three volumes taken together …

… are equal to this volume.

This is because the volume of a cylinder is exactly three times the volume of a cone with the same height and the same base radius. That is, the volume of the cone is one-third the volume of the cylinder.

The volume of a cone with radius r and height h is given by the formula:

$$V = \frac{1}{3} \times \text{base area} \times \text{height}$$

or $\quad V = \frac{1}{3}\pi r^2 h$

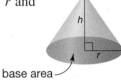

base area

▶ ▶ *Through a Guided Example*

Example ···

Coke is one by-product of Suncor's crude oil plant in Fort McMurray, Alberta. This fuel is used to produce electricity and steam for other parts of Suncor's operations. Because such vast quantities of coke are produced, it is stored in large, conical piles. When Suncor's engineers have to assess how much coke is in a pile, they survey it to measure the height and the diameter of the base. Suppose a coke pile has a base diameter of 20 m and a height of 8 m. Calculate the volume of coke in the pile.

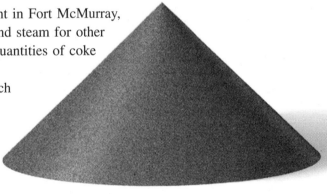

Solution

The base radius is 10 m. Substitute 10 for r and 8 for h in the formula for the volume of a cone. Use the π key on your scientific calculator.

$$V = \frac{1}{3}\pi r^2 h$$
$$= \frac{1}{3} \times \pi \times 10^2 \times 8$$
$$\doteq 838$$

The volume of the pile is about 840 m³. Allowing for air spaces, the volume of coke in the pile is less than this. We cannot be certain, but the volume of coke is probably between 600 m³ and 800 m³.

Working with Mathematics

Something to talk about

1. One litre is often represented by a cube measuring 10 cm along each edge.
   a) Calculate the volumes of a cylinder and a cone that fit inside the cube.
   b) What percent of the space in the cube is occupied by the cylinder? By the cone? Give the answers to one decimal place.

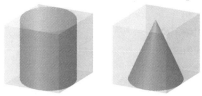

2. How would you determine the height of the cone below?

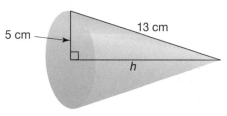

Practice

3. A cylinder has volume 96 cm³. What is the volume of a cone that just fits inside the cylinder?

4. A cone has a volume of 54 cm³. What is the volume of a cylinder that just holds the cone?

5. Find the volume of each cone.

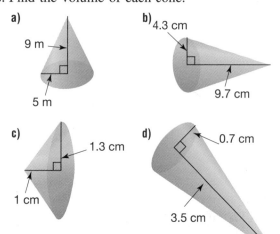

a) 9 m, 5 m
b) 4.3 cm, 9.7 cm
c) 1.3 cm, 1 cm
d) 0.7 cm, 3.5 cm

6. Determine the volume of each cone, to two decimal places.
   a) base radius 1.6 cm, height 3.5 cm
   b) base radius 0.35 m, height 1.8 m
   c) height 27 cm, base radius 8 cm
   d) height 57 cm, base radius 42 cm

Work together

7. A cone-shaped funnel has radius 5.7 cm and height 4.3 cm. How much can the funnel hold? Express your answer to one decimal place.

8. A farmer stores feed in a cone-shaped storage unit. The storage unit has base diameter 14.3 m and height 27.4 m. How much feed can this unit store?

9. An engineer is designing a cone-shaped storage unit to hold 5000 m³ of sand. The unit has a base radius of 15 m. What is its height, to one decimal place?

10. Cone A has base radius 25 cm and height 10 m. Cone B has height 25 cm and base radius 10 m. Which cone has the greater volume?

11. Construct the three figures shown. Make a cone from each figure by joining the straight edges and securing them with tape.

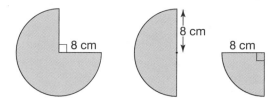

Without measuring, determine the base radius, the height, and the volume of each cone to the nearest tenth of a unit.

On your own

12. Sand is discharged from a conveyor and forms a conical heap with a base diameter of 5.4 m and a height of 2.7 m. What is the volume of the sand in the heap?

13. Grain is stored in a cone-shaped pile. The dimensions of the cone are shown. How much grain is in the pile?

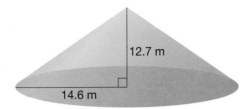
12.7 m

14.6 m

14. A cone has volume 47 cm³. It has a height of 5 cm. Determine the length of the radius of the base, to one decimal place.

15. A cone has volume 376 m³. The diameter of its base is 12 m. Determine the height of the cone, to one decimal place.

16. Find the volume of each cone with the given dimensions. Give each answer to the nearest cubic centimetre.
a) base radius 5.00 cm; height 3.18 cm
b) base radius 7.50 cm, height 1.42 cm
c) base radius 3.99 cm; height 5.00 cm
d) base radius 3.26 cm; height 7.50 cm
What do you notice about the volumes?

Extend your thinking

17. Calculate the volume of the cone formed if right △ABC is rotated about:

a) side AB   b) side BC

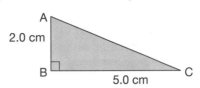
A
2.0 cm
B   5.0 cm   C

COMMUNICATING

The Ideas

In your journal, describe how you calculate the volumes of a cylinder and a cone if you know their dimensions. Include in your account:
- an explanation of how the volume of a cone is related to the volume of a cylinder with the same base radius and the same height
- formulas for the volumes in terms of the radius r and the height h
- formulas for the volumes in terms of the diameter d and the height h

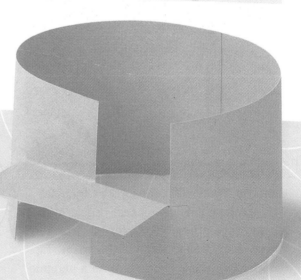

BOGGLE YOUR MIND

Can you figure out how to make this object? You need one strip of paper, scissors, and tape. Tape is used only where you can see it in the photograph. After you make the object, show it to someone and challenge her or him to make one like it!

Developing the Ideas

▶ ▶ *Through an Activity*

You will need an open rectangular box, some pieces of cardboard, scissors, a millimetre ruler, some popcorn or clean sand, and tape. Work with a partner to make a pyramid with its height equal to the height of the box.

Step 1

Measure the length, width, and height of the box. Recall that this is a rectangular prism. Record the results.

Step 2

Imagine one face of the pyramid. One edge of this face coincides with the length of the prism. The other two edges meet at the vertex at the centre of the top of the prism. Use the Pythagorean Theorem to find the height of the triangle. This is the *slant height* of the face.

Step 3

Construct two cardboard isosceles triangles with this height, and with bases equal to the length of the prism. Repeat for two triangles whose bases are the width of the prism. Tape the four triangles together to form a pyramid with no base. Use tape on both the inside and the outside, to make it as rigid as possible.

Step 4

Suppose the pyramid were filled with popcorn or sand, and then emptied into the prism. Estimate how many times you could do this until the prism is full. Check your estimate.

1. What probable conclusion can you make about the volume of the pyramid compared with the volume of the prism?

▶ ▶ *Through Instruction*

When a rectangular pyramid just fits inside a rectangular prism, you can fill the pyramid three times and pour its contents into the prism. Then the prism will be full.

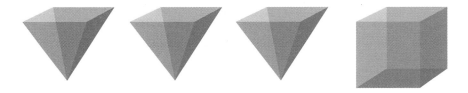

This is because the volume of a prism is exactly three times the volume of a rectangular pyramid with the same base and the same height. That is, the volume of the pyramid is one-third the volume of the prism.

The volume of a rectangular pyramid with base dimensions l and w, and height h is given by the formula:

$$V = \tfrac{1}{3} \times \text{base area} \times \text{height}$$

or $\quad V = \tfrac{1}{3}lwh$

Working with Mathematics

Something to talk about

1. How does the formula for the volume of a rectangular pyramid compare with the formula for the volume of a cone?

2. a) Suppose the base of a pyramid has 3 sides. How many faces, vertices, and edges does the pyramid have?

   b) Repeat part a for a pyramid whose base has 4 sides.

   c) Repeat part a for a pyramid whose base has 5 sides.

   d) Repeat part a for a pyramid whose base has 6 sides.

3. Suppose you know the number of sides in the base of a pyramid. How could you determine the numbers of its faces, edges, and vertices?

4. The diagrams show three views of the same rectangular prism. How do the volumes of the three pyramids compare? Explain your answer.

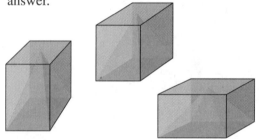

Practice

5. Determine the volume of each pyramid.

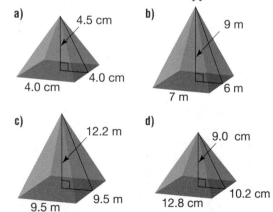

a) 4.5 cm, 4.0 cm, 4.0 cm

b) 9 m, 7 m, 6 m

c) 12.2 m, 9.5 m, 9.5 m

d) 9.0 cm, 10.2 cm, 12.8 cm

6. Determine the volume of each pyramid.
   a) base 12 m by 12 m, height 4 m
   b) base 24 m by 12 m, height 4 m
   c) base 12 m by 12 m, height 8 m
   d) base 12 m by 12 m, height 16 m
   e) base 12 m by 12 m, height 24 m
   f) base 12 m by 24 m, height 8 m
   g) base 12 m by 32 m, height 8 m

Work together

7. A cube is divided into six congruent pyramids. The base of each pyramid is a face of the cube. The edges of the cube are 30 cm long. What is the volume of each pyramid?

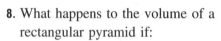

8. What happens to the volume of a rectangular pyramid if:
   a) its base is not changed, but its height is doubled? Tripled?
   b) its height and base width are not changed, but its base length is doubled? Tripled?
   c) its height is not changed, but both its base length and width are doubled? Tripled?
   d) all three of its dimensions are doubled? Tripled?

On your own

9. The Louvre is a famous art gallery in Paris, France. See exercise 10 on page 447 for information about the Louvre. Calculate the volume of the pyramid over the main entrance to the Louvre.

10. The Great Pyramid in Egypt has a square base of 229 m. Its original height was 147 m.
    a) Calculate the volume of stone that was used to build the pyramid.
    b) About 2.3×10^6 blocks of stone were used to build the pyramid. Calculate the average volume of one block.

c) The average mass of one block is about 2760 kg. Calculate the total mass of stone in the pyramid.

d) Why do we use the word "original" in the second sentence?

11. The Muttart Conservatory in Edmonton consists of two large and two small pyramids. Each small pyramid has a square base of side length 19.5 m and a height of 18.0 m. The dimensions of each large pyramid are about 1.3 times as great as these.

a) How many times as great as the volume of a small pyramid is the volume of a large pyramid?

b) Compare the method you used to solve part a with the method used by other students. Did everyone use the same method to solve this problem?

Extend your thinking

12. Suppose you were to trace this net, cut it out, and fold it to form a rectangular pyramid. By taking measurements from this diagram, determine the volume of the pyramid.

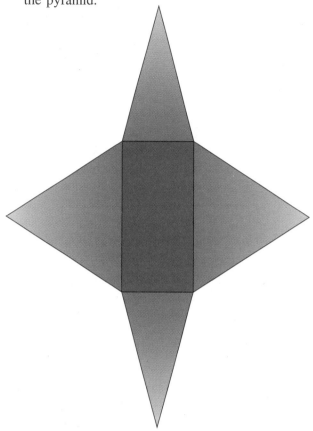

COMMUNICATING

The Ideas

In your journal, describe how you calculate the volume of a rectangular pyramid if you know its dimensions. Include in your account:

- an explanation of how the volume of a rectangular pyramid is related to the volume of a rectangular prism with the same base and the same height
- formulas for the volumes in terms of l, w, and h

Review

1. Draw the front, top, and side views of each object.

a) **b)**

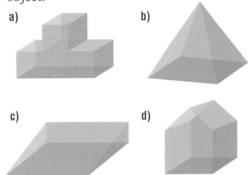

c) **d)**

2. Name an object that could have each set of views.

a)

Front Top Side

b)

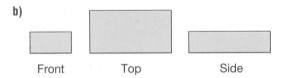

Front Top Side

3. Name an object that could have these front, side, and top views.

Front Top Side

4. Each object contains 6 cubes. Build each object. Sketch it on isometric dot paper.

a) **b)**

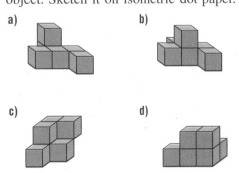

c) **d)**

5. A dog is tied to a 1.5-m leash. The leash is attached to one end of a park bench. Make a scale diagram to show the region within the dog's reach.

0.6 m

3.5 m

6. Imagine rolling this circle along a straight path. Determine the path traced by point Q.

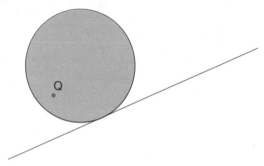

Q

7. Suppose a rectangular prism and a rectangular pyramid have the same base area and height. Also, a cylinder and a cone have the same base area and height. How do the volumes of the rectangular prism and the cylinder compare with the volumes of the rectangular pyramid and the cone?

8. Determine the surface area of each pyramid.

a)

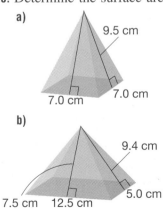

9.5 cm

7.0 cm

7.0 cm

b)

9.4 cm

5.0 cm

7.5 cm   12.5 cm

9. The design for the top of a bell tower is in the shape of a pyramid.

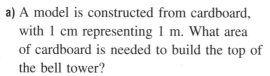

2.4 m
3.1 m
3.1 m

a) A model is constructed from cardboard, with 1 cm representing 1 m. What area of cardboard is needed to build the top of the bell tower?

b) Is the base of the pyramid included in part a? Explain.

10. Use the information in exercise 11 on page 467. The dimensions of the large pyramids of the Muttart Conservatory are 1.3 times as great as the dimensions of the small pyramids. Determine the area of the glass in one of the large pyramids.

11. a) List the possible whole-number dimensions of a rectangle with area 64 cm².

b) Which rectangle with area 64 cm² has the greatest perimeter?

c) Which rectangle has the least perimeter?

12. Ginny has 16 lengths of beam. She wants to enclose a rectangular garden using all 16 pieces. What is the greatest area she can enclose?

13. a) List the possible dimensions of a rectangular prism with volume 64 cm³.

b) Which prism has the greatest surface area?

c) Which prism has the least surface area?

14. Design a rectangular prism to hold 125 cm³ of a product. You have to use the least amount of material. What will the dimensions of the package be?

15. Calculate the volume of each cone to the nearest cubic unit.

a)

22 cm
11 cm

b)

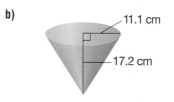

11.1 cm
17.2 cm

c)

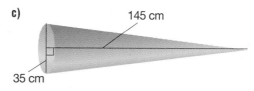

145 cm
35 cm

16. What is the volume of sawdust in a conical pile that is 3.2 m in diameter and 2.8 m in height?

17. Calculate the volume of each pyramid to the nearest cubic unit.

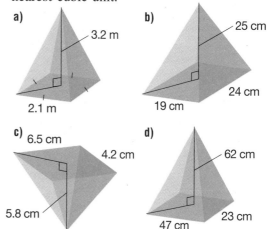

a)
3.2 m
2.1 m

b)
25 cm
24 cm
19 cm

c)
6.5 cm
4.2 cm
5.8 cm

d)
62 cm
23 cm
47 cm

18. A square pyramid is 24 cm wide and 52 cm high. It is cut, as shown, to create a pyramid 39 cm high with base 18 cm square. The other piece is discarded. What is the volume of the discarded portion, to the nearest unit?

Wrapping Presents without Wasting Paper

When you wrap a present you have to decide which way to put it on the paper. Which way is best, or does it matter? What are the dimensions of the largest present you could wrap with a piece of gift wrap? In this project you will determine answers to questions like these.

You will need a box to represent a present that you want to wrap, 2 sheets of gift wrap, and a ruler or tape measure.

ACTIVITY 1

Measure and record the dimensions of the box and the dimensions of the gift wrap. Decide how much to allow for overlapping.

Two ways to put the box on the paper are shown below. For each one, determine the length and width of the smallest piece of gift wrap you need. Also determine the length and width of each piece of gift wrap left over.

Allowing for the overlap, are the dimensions of the gift wrap you need the same in each method? If your answer is no, then which uses less paper? If your answer is yes, then are the pieces left over the same size? If not, does one method leave pieces that are more useful?

ACTIVITY 2

Suppose you decide to allow twice as much for overlapping as before. How would the results in *Activity 1* change?

 ACTIVITY 3

Determine some possible dimensions of boxes you can wrap without having any pieces of gift wrap left over. Think about the following questions as you do this:

- How much will you allow for overlapping?

- Does it matter which way you put the box on the paper? Investigate some of the possibilities. Are the volumes the same in each case?

ACTIVITY 4

Suppose you decide to allow twice as much as before for overlapping. How would the results in *Activity 3* change?

ACTIVITY 5

Sometimes a box is too large to wrap with one sheet of paper. Then you have to tape two pieces of paper together to make a larger sheet. Determine some possible dimensions of boxes you can wrap with two sheets of gift wrap, without having anything left over.

Think about these questions as you do this:

- How much overlap will you need for taping the two sheets together?

- Is there more than one way to combine the sheets? If there is, do the combined sheets have the same dimensions or different dimensions? How will this affect the results?

The Ideas

Write a report summarizing the results of your investigations. Include examples and diagrams in your report.

Cumulative Review

1. For each of the following:
   i) record the key strokes you use to evaluate the expression
   ii) evaluate the expression in a different way and record the key strokes
   iii) explain why one method uses fewer key strokes than the other
   a) $(33.3 + 4.5) \div (39.7 - 30)$
   b) $(6.4 - 2.25) \times (9.36 - 15)$
   c) $\dfrac{10}{10.8 - 13.6}$
   d) $\dfrac{4.5 + 8.7}{12.0 \times (4.2 - 5.6)}$

2. Priyanka is earning $42 000 a year. She receives a 3.5% increase at her annual review. What will her new salary be?

3. Suppose one of Priyanka's colleagues also received a 3.5% salary increase. His new salary is $42 000 a year. What was his salary before the increase?

4. Students placed a container outdoors on a snowy day. Every half hour they measured the depth of snow in the container. The table gives their results.

Elapsed time (h)	0.5	1.0	1.5	2.0
Depth of snow (mm)	4	7	12	15
Elapsed time (h)	2.5	3.0	3.5	4.0
Depth of snow (mm)	20	24	28	31

   a) Graph the results and construct a line of best fit.
   b) Estimate the depth of snow after 75 min.
   c) Can you predict the depth of snow after 8.0 h? Explain.

5. A used-car lot contains two Chevrolets, two Hondas, and two Dodges. Two customers enter the lot. Each customer decides to test-drive one of the six cars.
   a) What is the probability that each customer test drives a Honda?
   b) What assumptions did you make to answer part a?

6. Read this article. Answer the questions.

WOMEN OUTLIVE MEN

Dr. Thelma Gleason, famous gerontologist, says "Old age is a woman's world." Using her own study statistics, Dr. Gleason told her audience that more than 50% of women over 65 years of age are widows - clear evidence that women live longer than men.

   a) Is it possible that more than 50% of men over 65 years of age are widowers *and* over 50% of women over 65 years of age are widows? Explain.
   b) Do Dr. Gleason's data indicate anything about the relative life spans of men and women? Explain.
   c) What additional information might Dr. Gleason need to prove that women live longer than men?

7. Solve and check each equation.
   a) $4b - 7 = 2b + 5$
   b) $3k + 4 = 4$
   c) $9(1 - 2a) = 81$
   d) $2.5t + 7.5 = 1.5t$
   e) $\frac{1}{4}x - \frac{3}{4} = 1$
   f) $\frac{1}{2} - \frac{5}{2}w = \frac{2}{3} + w$

8. Find two consecutive numbers in which the lesser one, plus double the greater one, is equal to 62.

9. A rectangle is 5 cm longer than it is wide. Its perimeter is 34 cm. Determine the length and width of the rectangle.

10. Tammy has 25 bills. They are all $2 and $5 bills, worth $71. How many of each type of bill does she have?

11. An airplane left Banff heading northwest. After 30 min, it was 220 km from Banff. Another airplane left Banff at the same time, heading due north. After 30 min, it was 250 km from Banff. Construct a scale diagram to determine the distance between the two planes 30 min after take-off.

12. How many different triangles can you construct with the given measures? Explain how you know.

  a) side lengths of 5 cm, 3 cm, and 7 cm

  b) an angle of 55°, contained by sides of length 8 cm and 9 cm

  c) an angle of 90° contained by sides of 10.5 cm and 10.5 cm

  d) angles of 90°, 30°, and 60°

  e) an angle of 30° and side lengths of 15.2 cm and 12.8 cm

  f) side lengths of 18.5 cm, 3.0 cm, and 8.2 cm

13. Name the similar triangles in each diagram. Determine the values of x and y.

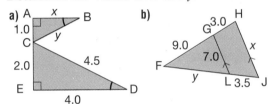

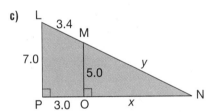

14. In $\triangle$VWX, for each given length, find the measures of $\angle$W and $\angle$X to the nearest degree.

  a) VW = 18.0 cm   **b)** VX = 24.0 cm

  c) VX = 20.6 cm   **d)** VW = 7.5 cm

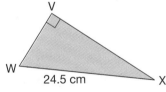

15. Calculate the measures of all unmarked angles and sides of these triangles.

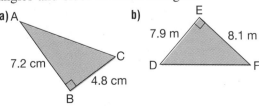

16. Fatima is 1.7 m tall. She worked with a partner one morning to determine that her shadow was 3.6 m long. What was the angle of elevation of the sun when the measurement was taken?

17. To determine the height of a building, Clay measures the length of its shadow. It is 74.6 m. Clay measures the angle the sun makes with the ground. It is 61°. Determine the height of the building.

18. Evaluate.

  a) 3^{-2} **b)** $\left(\frac{2}{3}\right)^{-3}$ **c)** 2^{-5}

  d) 10^{-2} **e)** 25^{0} **f)** $\left(\frac{1}{5}\right)^{-1}$

  g) $\left(\frac{1}{3}\right)^{-4}$ **h)** 5^{-3} **i)** 14^{0}

19. Simplify each expression.

  a) $y^3 \times y^2$ **b)** $k^{25} \div k^{15}$

  c) $m^4 \times m^{-4}$ **d)** $(m^3)^{-5}$

  e) $n^3 \times n$ **f)** $n^4 \div n^7$

  g) $s^3 \times s^{-5}$ **h)** $(-v)^8 \div (-v)^5$

  i) $(3t)^4$ **j)** $(-5c^2)^2$

  k) $\left(\frac{1}{8y}\right)^2$ **l)** $\frac{1}{(8y)^2}$

20. The volume of water in Earth's oceans is estimated to be 1.35×10^{18} m^3. The density of sea water is 1025 kg/m^3. What is the mass of the water in the oceans?

21. A leaking faucet drips water at the rate of 0.1 cm^3/s.

  a) About how long will it take to fill a rectangular basin 30 cm by 20 cm by 20 cm?

  b) About how much water will be lost in one year?

22. Determine the length of one side of each square with the given area. Give your answer to one decimal place.

  a) 45 cm^2 **b)** 3 m^2 **c)** 72 mm^2

23. Give examples of two rational numbers between the numbers in each pair.

  a) $100, 99.8$ **b)** $3.5, 3.\overline{5}$

  c) $\sqrt{5}, 2\frac{1}{2}$ **d)** $7, \sqrt{50}$

24. Simplify. Evaluate for $m = 3$ and $n = -2$.

a) $(3m^2)(2m)$

b) $(2n)\left(-\frac{1}{2}n^2\right)$

c) $14m^3 \div 2m^2$

d) $\frac{48mn}{m^2n^2}$

e) $(4n^3)(2n)$

f) $\frac{12m^5}{6m^3}$

25. Factor. Check by expanding.

a) $18m^2 + 6m^3$

b) $-8w + 16w^3$

c) $5q - 25q^3$

d) $7c^4 + 14c^3 + 42c^2$

e) $6 - 18m^2 + 24m^3$

f) $-3k^2 - 24k^3 - 12k^4$

g) $27ab - 21a^2b + 9ab^2$

h) $ab - 4a^2b^2 + 8ab^2$

26. Factor. Check by expanding.

a) $x^2 + 2x + 1$

b) $x^2 - 2x - 15$

c) $x^2 - 6x - 7$

d) $x^2 - x - 56$

e) $x^2 + 13x + 42$

f) $x^2 - 13x + 42$

g) $x^2 - 5x - 50$

h) $x^2 + 15x + 36$

i) $x^2 - 10x + 24$

j) $x^2 - 10x + 16$

27. Factor completely.

a) $-84 - 7y + 7y^2$

b) $3m^2 + 18m + 27$

c) $3c^2 + 18c + 24$

d) $8d^2 - 48d + 64$

e) $-4m^2 - 32m + 36$

f) $-5w^2 - 15w + 120$

g) $4ab^2 - 8ab - 60a$

h) $2km^2 - 18km + 28k$

i) $-3xy^2 + 9xy + 12x$

j) $2pqr^2 - 10pqr - 12pq$

28. Find the coordinates of the image of each vertex after a translation of 3 units right, 4 units down.

a) $\triangle OBC$: O(0, 0), B(2, 9), C(4, 5)

b) $\triangle PQR$: P(1, 2), Q(5, 3), R(1, 6)

c) WXYZ: W(3, 4), X(0, 1), Y(−1, −3), Z(2, −2)

29. Refer to your results for exercise 28. Compare each original figure with its translation image. Explain how each figure is related to its image.

30. Refer to the figures in exercise 28. Find the coordinates of the image of each vertex after a reflection in the y-axis.

31. Repeat exercise 30 for these reflections.

a) a reflection in the x-axis

b) a reflection in the vertical line passing through (3, 0)

c) a reflection in the horizontal line passing through (0, −4)

32. Refer to the original figures in exercise 28. Find the coordinates of the image of each vertex after a rotation of 180° about the origin.

33. Repeat exercise 32 for these rotations.

a) 90° counterclockwise about the origin

b) 90° clockwise about the origin

c) 270° clockwise about the point (5, 5)

34. A square has vertices with coordinates (2, 1), (7, 3), (5, 8), and (0, 6). Draw the square and its image after each dilatation.

a) centre (0, 0), scale factor 3

b) centre (0, 0), scale factor 0.5

c) centre (8, 8), scale factor 2

d) centre (0, −2), scale factor 0.5

35. Identify similar figures in your results for exercise 34. How are the sides of the original square and each image square related? How are the areas related in each case?

36. The coordinates of the vertices of a figure and its image are given. Describe the transformation in each case.

a) A(3, 5), B(2, 0), C(−1, 3); A′(5, 8), B′(4, 3), C′(1, 6)

b) P(−3, 5), O(0, 0), R(−5, −1); P′(3, 5), O′(0, 0), R′(5, −1)

c) D(−3, 5), E(5, 3), F(0, −2); D′(−6, 10), E′(10, 6), F′(0, −4)

37. Draw the front, top, and side views of each object.

a)

b)

38. Identify two polyhedra that can have a view like this.

39. A guinea pig might scatter its food pellets up to 16 cm from its dish. Make a scale diagram of each cage below. Sketch the region that might be covered by food pellets. In each case, the dish measures 10 cm by 6 cm.

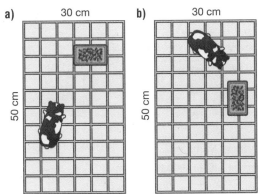

40. The managers of a mall are planning to add 6 skylights shaped like pyramids. Each skylight has a square base with side 6.7 m. The height of each triangular face is 6.7 m. The height of the pyramid is 5.8 m. The top half of each skylight will be glass. The bottom half will be metal.

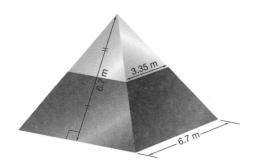

a) How much glass is needed for all six skylights?

b) How much metal is needed?

41. The roofs of a house and the adjoining square garage are shaped like pyramids. The owner wants to shingle both roofs. One shingle covers 0.09 m². This includes overlap.

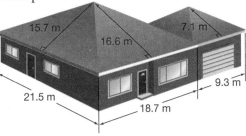

a) What area needs to be shingled?

b) About how many shingles are needed?

c) Suppose the shingles come in bundles of 25. Each bundle costs $15.75. How much will the shingles cost?

42. a) List the possible dimensions of a rectangle with area 200 cm².

b) Which rectangle with area 200 cm² has the greatest perimeter?

c) Which rectangle has the least perimeter?

43. Design an efficient package to hold 560 cm³ of a product. What are the dimensions of your package? Explain why your design is efficient.

44. Repeat exercise 43 for a carton that will hold 1000 mL of fluid. (One millilitre of water has a volume of 1 cm³.)

45. Calculate the volume of each pyramid.

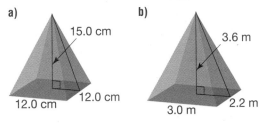

46. Calculate the volume of each cone.

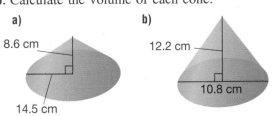

ANSWERS

INTRODUCTION: CHANGE

Start With What You Know, page 24

Answers may vary.

Integers

Developing the Ideas, page 26

1. a) Wind-chill equivalent temperature every hour: 4°C, −2°C, −7°C, −12°C, −18°C, −23°C, −28°C, −33°C, −39°C, −44°C

b) It did drop about 5°C every hour; but some hours it dropped 6°C.

Working with Mathematics, page 29

1. a) −3; the product of a positive number and a negative number is a negative number.

b) −2, −1, 0, 1

c) The product of two negative numbers is a positive number.

2. The quotient of two integers with opposite signs is negative. The quotient of two integers with the same sign is positive.

3. −15°C; "Five times colder" implies a positive multiplier, and the result is negative.

4. a) 19   **b)** 2   **c)** 8   **d)** −11   **e)** −18
   f) −4   **g)** 33   **h)** 13   **i)** −25   **j)** 21

5. a) −11   **b)** −14   **c)** −9   **d)** 11   **e)** 14
   f) 9   **g)** −5   **h)** −4   **i)** −5   **j)** 5

6. a) −20   **b)** −16   **c)** −12   **d)** −8
   e) −4   **f)** 0   **g)** 4   **h)** 8
   i) 12   **j)** 16   **k)** 20   **l)** 24
   m) −8   **n)** 12

7. a) 3   **b)** −3   **c)** −3   **d)** 3
   e) −5   **f)** −3   **g)** 6   **h)** −6
   i) −8   **j)** 8   **k)** −8   **l)** 8

8. a) −36   **b)** 0   **c)** −14   **d)** 14
   e) −7   **f)** 4   **g)** 6   **h)** 48

9. a) 1   **b)** 1   **c)** −1   **d)** −1   **e)** 1

10. a) Negative   **b)** Positive   **c)** Negative
   d) Positive   **e)** Negative   **f)** Positive

11. a) −1   **b)** 11   **c)** 1   **d)** −1   **e)** −5   **f)** −12

12. From left to right, the diagonals show consecutive integers. This is because $(+4) + (−3) = +1$. From right to left, the numbers in each diagonal decrease by 7. This is because $(−3) − (+4) = −7$.

−10	−6	−2	2	6
−7	−3	1	5	9
−4	0	4	8	12
−1	3	7	11	15

13. , 14. Answers may vary.

15. a) −9   **b)** 0   **c)** 12   **d)** −6   **e)** 2

16. a) June   **b)** −6   **c)** 209

17. From left to right, the numbers in the diagonals increase by a factor of 6, alternating signs. This is because $(+3) \times (−2) = −6$.

8	24	72	216
−4	−12	−36	−108
2	6	18	54
−1	−3	−9	−27

18. a) The wind-chill equivalent temperature changed by −8°C or −7°C per hour.

b) After the first hour, the wind-chill equivalent temperature changed by −18°C every 2 h.

19. Answers may vary.

20. a) Answers may vary. For example:

Wind speed (km/h)	50	27	18	12	8
Temperature (°C)	−10	−15	−20	−25	−30

Rational Numbers

Working with Mathematics, page 34

1. A, 1.7; B, 1.0; C, −0.2; D, −1.6; E, −2.9; F, −3.5

2. a) , b) Answers may vary. It is possible but unlikely.

3. The average number of boxes is the number in the set multiplied by the sum of all the fractions with a numerator of 1, and a denominator from 1 to the number in the set.

4. a) $-\frac{1}{2}$ **b)** $-\frac{2}{3}$ **c)** $\frac{2}{5}$ **d)** $-\frac{2}{5}$
   e) $\frac{6}{11}$ **f)** $\frac{1}{3}$ **g)** $\frac{2}{7}$ **h)** $-\frac{14}{25}$
   i) $-\frac{3}{7}$ **j)** $-\frac{1}{3}$ **k)** $-\frac{3}{2}$ **l)** $\frac{2}{3}$

5. a) −4   **b)** −5   **c)** −7   **d)** 0
   e) 0   **f)** −1   **g)** −1   **h)** 0
   i) −8   **j)** −4   **k)** −17   **l)** −7

6. a) 0.6 **b)** $-0.\overline{6}$ **c)** $0.\overline{4}$ **d)** -0.375
   e) $0.\overline{3}$ **f)** $-0.1\overline{36}$ **g)** $2.\overline{142\ 857}$ **h)** $-0.1\overline{6}$
   i) 0.3125 **j)** $-0.\overline{629}$ **k)** $0.91\overline{6}$ **l)** $1.\overline{18}$

7. a) >   **b)** >   **c)** >   **d)** <   **e)** <   **f)** <   **g)** >   **h)** <

8. a) 2.536   **b)** 98.13   **c)** −51.2   **d)** −19.329
   e) −3.49   **f)** 281.8   **g)** 567.37   **h)** 47.83

9. a) 3598.608   **b)** 3.1   **c)** 169.36   **d)** −29.79   **e)** 0.06   **f)** −0.0412

10. a) True; −8 can be written as $\frac{-8}{1}$.

b) False; whole numbers cannot be negative.

c) True; −9 can be written as $\frac{-9}{1}$; whole numbers cannot be negative.

d) False; integers cannot contain fraction or decimal parts.

e) False; −18 is an integer as well as a rational.

f) False; $-5\frac{2}{3}$ is not an integer because it has a fractional part.

11. a) Maral, 0.217; Ari, 0.202; Kim, 0.192; Ange, 0.181; Nicki, 0.198

b) Maral, Ari, Nicki, Kim, Ange

c) Explanations may vary. Maral is most reliable because she has the highest success rate of the 5 players shown.

12. a) 1.5   **b)** $1.4\overline{9}$

  c) i) 1.15   **ii)** 0.375   **iii)** $-0.3\overline{8}$

    iv) $-0.\overline{23}$ **v)** $0.854\ 1\overline{6}$ **vi)** $0.\overline{486}$

13. Parts b, c, d, g, and i are positive.

14. Key sequences may vary. Final calculator displays are shown.

  a) 983.62   **b)** 916.37   **c)** −88.32

  d) 1068.36   **e)** 19.826 153 85   **f)** 2.900 318 134

  g) 0.348 214 285   **h)** −0.248 185 637   **i)** 6.513 157 895

  j) −98.638 845 15   **k)** 20 025   **l)** 154.175

15. $1; 2 \times (1 + \frac{1}{2}); 5 \times (1 + \frac{1}{2} + \frac{1}{3} + \frac{1}{4} + \frac{1}{5});$

  $6 \times (1 + \frac{1}{2} + \frac{1}{3} + \frac{1}{4} + \frac{1}{5} + \frac{1}{6});$

  $8 \times (1 + \frac{1}{2} + \frac{1}{3} + \frac{1}{4} + \frac{1}{5} + \frac{1}{6} + \frac{1}{7} + \frac{1}{8});$

  $9 \times (1 + \frac{1}{2} + \frac{1}{3} + \frac{1}{4} + \frac{1}{5} + \frac{1}{6} + \frac{1}{7} + \frac{1}{8} + \frac{1}{9});$

  $10 \times (1 + \frac{1}{2} + \frac{1}{3} + \frac{1}{4} + \frac{1}{5} + \frac{1}{6} + \frac{1}{7} + \frac{1}{8} + \frac{1}{9} + \frac{1}{10})$

a)

Number of items in the set	Average number of boxes needed
1	1
2	3
3	6
4	8
5	11
6	15
7	18
8	22
9	25
10	29

c) The average number of boxes needed increases as the number in the set increases. Up to 5 items, the average number of boxes is approximately double the number of items. But for 10 items, the average number of boxes is approximately 3 times the number of items.

16. Key sequences may vary. Final calculator displays are shown.

  i) 613.36   **ii)** −339.3

  iii) 0.518 248 175   **iv)** 0.078 307 62

17. $175.22   **18.** About 5.5 h

19. a) The fraction increases.   **b)** The fraction decreases.

  c) The fraction increases.

20. a) The fraction increases.   **b)** The fraction decreases.

  c) The fraction decreases.

21. It appears that when the numerator is larger than the denominator, and each is increased by 1, the fraction decreases. When the numerator is smaller than the denominator, and each is increased by 1, the fraction increases.

22. a) To get each denominator, add the numerator and denominator of the preceding fraction. To get each numerator, add the denominator to the preceding denominator.

  b) Answers may vary.

  c) Answers may vary. The values appear to approach 1.414 214…

23. a) To get each denominator, add the numerator and denominator of the preceding fraction. To get each numerator, add the denominator to twice the preceding denominator.

b) Answers may vary.

c) Answers may vary. The values appear to approach 1.732 051…

24. b, c, d, g, h, j

Linking Ideas: Mathematics and Technology
How Many Cereal Boxes?, page 37

Answers may vary.

Quest: A Ring around Earth, page 38

For a circle, the distance is always 2π m, or approximately 6.3 m.

Percents
Developing the Ideas, page 40

1. a) Increase   **b)** 17 425   **c)** $\frac{17\ 425}{20\ 830}$ **d)** About 84%

2. a) Increase   **b)** 108 960   **c)** $\frac{108\ 960}{1\ 043\ 015}$ **d)** About 10%

3. English

4. Punjabi

Working with Mathematics, page 41

1. Student: +$1000; +83%

  Other person: +$1000; +0.22%

2. a) 80%   **b)** 25%   **c)** 12.5%   **d)** $33\frac{1}{3}$%

  e) $83\frac{1}{3}$%   **f)** $55\frac{5}{9}$%   **g)** 250%   **h)** $266\frac{2}{3}$%

  i) 160%   **j)** 240%   **k)** 68%   **l)** 57.5%

3. a) 0.24   **b)** 0.39   **c)** 0.574   **d)** 0.03   **e)** 0.058

  f) 0.115   **g)** 0.016   **h)** 0.009   **i)** 1.37   **j)** 2.64

  k) 3.75   **l)** 3.758   **m)** 0.001   **n)** 0.0203   **o)** 0.0025

4. a) $\frac{27}{100}$ **b)** $\frac{9}{25}$ **c)** $\frac{3}{5}$ **d)** $\frac{7}{25}$ **e)** $\frac{3}{4}$ **f)** $\frac{9}{20}$

  g) $\frac{12}{25}$ **h)** $\frac{4}{25}$ **i)** $\frac{17}{20}$ **j)** $\frac{19}{100}$ **k)** $\frac{5}{4}$ **l)** $2\frac{3}{20}$

5. a) 10   **b)** 8   **c)** 0.9   **d)** 1.75

  e) 81.75   **f)** 6   **g)** 0.665   **h)** 11.7

  i) 103.04   **j)** 1.25   **k)** 864.8   **l)** 125

6. a) 20   **b)** 15   **c)** 25   **d)** 40   **e)** 70

  f) 100   **g)** 27   **h)** 80   **i)** 25   **j)** 70

7. a) 20%   **b)** About 11%   **c)** About 167%   **d)** 90%

  e) 12.5%   **f)** About 333%   **g)** 0.1%   **h)** 0.05%

8. Price decreases by about $34.12. Sale price is $193.38.

9. $99

10. About $9380

11. $13.31

12. a) 7.6%   **b)** 20.0%

13. a) i) Compact disc/digital tape equipment

    ii) Compact disc/digital tape equipment

  b) i) Colour televisions

    ii) Colour televisions

  c), d) Answers may vary.

14. $400 000 000

15. 1280

16. Answers may vary.

17. a) For each 10% decrease in exam mark, the final mark decreases by 2%.

Term mark	Examination mark	Final mark
84%	100%	87%
84%	90%	85%
84%	80%	83%
84%	70%	81%
84%	60%	79%
84%	50%	77%
84%	40%	75%
84%	30%	73%
84%	20%	71%
84%	10%	69%
84%	0%	67%

c) For each 10% decrease in exam mark, the final mark decreases by 4%.

Term mark	Examination mark	Final mark
84%	100%	90%
84%	90%	86%
84%	80%	82%
84%	70%	78%
84%	60%	74%
84%	50%	70%
84%	40%	66%
84%	30%	62%
84%	20%	58%
84%	10%	54%
84%	0%	50%

d) 100%, 90%, 80%, 70%, 60%, 50%, 40%, 30%, 20%, 10%, 0%
e) 105%   **f)** Answers may vary.

18. Answers may vary.

19. a) Answers may vary.   **b)** Answers may vary.
c) We need to know the total number of players in 1991–92. There are now more teams so the total number of Canadians may be greater but their percent may be less.

Linking Ideas: Mathematics and the Consumer
The Cost of Natural Gas, page 45
1. a) $181.02   **b)** $176.46   **c)** Zone 1, zone 11
2. a) $201.34   **b)** $17 673.45

Measurement
Developing the Ideas, page 46
1. Each dimension of the Post decreased by 50%, one-half. For the Star, its width decreased by 2 cm and its length decreased by 3 cm.

2. The Post decreased by 75%. The Star decreased by approximately 11%.
3. 963 000 m^2 **4.** Answers may vary.

Page 47
1. The length and width have each been reduced by 50%.
2. The area has been reduced by 75%.
3. The mass has been reduced by 75%.

Working with Mathematics, page 48
1. a) Answers may vary. Probably not, since 1 mL is very small.
b) Answers may vary.
2. a) 240 cm, 3375 cm^2 **b)** 160 cm, 1543.75 cm^2
c) 22 m, 11.76 m^2 **d)** 24.2 m, 34.2 m^2
3. Answers may vary: 15 m^2, 16 m^2, 12 m^2, or 7 m^2
4. a) 160 cm^3 **b)** 2137.5 cm^3 **c)** 387.872 m^3 **d)** 10 451.7 cm^3
5. a) 4 m, 0.96 m^2 **b)** 20%   **c)** 20%   **d)** 44%
6. a) 3024 cm^3
b) i) 3240 cm^3 **ii)** 3360 cm^3 **iii)** 4032 cm^3
c) No; the package usually states that contents settle during shipping.
7. Answers may vary for parts a, c, and d.   **b)** 81%
8. a) Both changes save the same amount.   **b)** Answers may vary.
9. Answers may vary.
10. b) 21%   **c)** 19%
d) The amounts are different, because the percent calculations are based on different areas.

Review, page 50
1. −45°C
2. a) 0   **b)** 0   **c)** −1   **d)** −2   **e)** 1   **f)** 9
g) 2   **h)** −9   **i)** −2   **j)** −8   **k)** −3   **l)** −8
3. a) −56   **b)** 54   **c)** −4   **d)** −35   **e)** 2
f) −3   **g)** 144   **h)** −27   **i)** −60   **j)** 8
4. a) −8   **b)** −3   **c)** 11   **d)** −6   **e)** −5
f) 12   **g)** 3   **h)** −16   **i)** −12   **j)** −4
5. a) $-\frac{3}{4}$ **b)** $\frac{4}{5}$ **c)** $-\frac{5}{6}$ **d)** $\frac{7}{8}$ **e)** −3   **f)** $\frac{5}{8}$
6. a) $-0.8\overline{3}$ **b)** $-0.\overline{3}$ **c)** 5.375
d) $-7.\overline{1}$ **e)** 3.4   **f)** $0.\overline{4}$
g) −3.5   **h)** −6.125   **i)** −0.56
7. About 5 h 8 min
8. a) −5.0652   **b)** −0.6   **c)** −29 717.16
d) −32.8   **e)** 0.086   **f)** 0.967 73
9. a) 0.2, $\frac{1}{5}$ **b)** 0.04, $\frac{1}{25}$ **c)** 0.15, $\frac{3}{20}$
d) 0.75, $\frac{3}{4}$ **e)** 1.1, $1\frac{1}{10}$ **f)** 1.5, $1\frac{1}{2}$
g) 0.015, $\frac{3}{200}$ **h)** 0.035, $\frac{7}{200}$ **i)** 0.005, $\frac{1}{200}$
10. a) $700   **b)** $707.25   **c)** $879.75   **d)** About 29%
11. a) $7649.15   **b)** $8261.08
12. Answers may vary.
a) (−6) + (−5)   **b)** (+5) + (+6) + (+7)
c) (−5) + (−4) + (−3) + (−2)   **d)** (−9) + (−8)
e) (+6) + (+7) + (+8)
f) (+2) + (+3) + (+4) + (+5) + (+6)
13. a) $2.80; $1.72   **b)** $4.71; $1.88

14. 17 by 1, 17 square units; 16 by 2, 32 square units; 15 by 3, 45 square units; 14 by 4, 56 square units; 13 by 5, 65 square units; 12 by 6, 72 square units; 11 by 7, 77 square units; 10 by 8, 80 square units; 9 by 9, 81 square units

15. $33\frac{1}{3}\%$

16. a) 120 cm by 45 cm by 40 cm, 60 cm by 90 cm by 40 cm, 60 cm by 45 cm by 80 cm **b)** 60 cm

CHAPTER 1 DATA ANALYSIS

Start With What You Know, page 56

1. 43% **2.** 486 **3.** By using a bar graph
4. 17% **5.** 70–79 **6.** 14%
7. 2 **8.** April to October **9.** March
10. Answers may vary.
  a) In a pictograph, a symbol represents a certain number of items. In a bar graph, the length of a bar is proportional to the number of items in a set of data.
  b) In a broken-line graph, line segments join adjacent points. In a continuous-line graph, the points are joined by one straight line or a smooth curve.
11. Your friend is more likely to pay for the movie.
12. Bag A **13.** $\frac{2}{5}$

1.1 Investigating Relationships in Data
Developing the Ideas, page 58

Experimental results may vary.

Working with Mathematics, page 60

1. Answers may vary.
  a) The more hours you work, the more you earn.
  b) Bacteria increase more and more rapidly as time goes by.
  c) For each additional ticket you buy, you pay more in total.
  d) Water is draining out of a container until there is almost none left.
2. Answers may vary.
  a) Age and height
  b) Income and spending
  c) Income and debt
  d) Time spent studying, time spent watching TV
  e) Time spent reading and number of pets
3. a) The heavier the mass, the greater extension of the spring.
  b) In general, the closer you are to the basket, the higher the percent of baskets sunk.
  c) The closer to noon, the higher the temperature
4. b) Join the points with a straight line: although it is not possible to have parts of coins, the straight line helps us to see possible values between points.
  c) 25 g
  d) 450 g
5. b) Join the points with a smooth curve: it is possible to have squares with fractional side lengths.
  c) About 12 cm² **d)** About 4.5 cm
6. b) Join the points with line segments in order to see possible values between points.
  c) About 114; about 87 **d)** About 12; about 22

7. Answers may vary. **a)** About 0.68 kg
b)

Number of textbooks	Mass (kg)
1	0.68
2	1.36
3	2.04
4	2.72
5	3.4
6	4.08
7	4.76
8	5.44
9	6.12
10	6.8

  d) No; it does not make sense to have parts of books.
  e) As the number of books increases, their mass increases steadily.
8. , 9. , 10. Experimental results may vary.
11. When the side length doubles, the area of the square quadruples.
12. Heart rate changes more rapidly near the beginning of the climb. Heart rate cannot increase indefinitely; it will level off when the person reaches maximum heart rate.
13. Experimental results may vary.
14. Descriptions should match those suggested for exercise 3.
15. b) About 1954 **c)** About 8 000 000
16. b) Answers may vary. The new graph would show two quantities increasing at the same time, since the percent forgotten increases as time increases.
17. a) The distance covered by the car before the driver reacts to a situation by braking
  b) The distance covered by the car after the driver applies the brakes
  c) Answers may vary. Join the points using line segments.
  d) i) 35 m **ii)** 72 m
  e) Since a wet road is slippery, stopping distances increase.
18. a) i) 13.5 cm **ii)** 1 cm **iii)** 13.5 cm
  b) i) 0.3 s, 1.5 s, 2.3 s, 3.7 s, 4.4 s
  ii) 0.5 s, 1.3 s, 2.5 s, 3.4 s, 4.6 s
  c) 2 s
  d) i) Height increases. **ii)** Height decreases.
  iii) Height increases again.
  e), f) Answers may vary.

Quest: Predicting Long Jump Records, page 64

Answers may vary: about 1995.

1.2 Graphing Scatterplots
Developing the Ideas, page 66

Through an Activity

1. The graph is a series of points. As you move to the right, the points get higher.
2. a) Yes **b)** Yes **c)** Answers may vary.

Through Discussion

1. a) As you move to the right, the points get lower. The more time a person spends each week doing homework, the less time the person spends watching television.

b) As you move to the right, the points get higher. The more people there are in a household, the more telephone calls are made in the household.

c) The points are not arranged in a pattern. The number of people in a family does not affect the number of pets the family has.

Working with Mathematics, page 67

1. Graph b shows the more money a person earns, the more the person is likely to spend.

2. Graph a shows the more frequently a teenager brushes her or his teeth, the fewer cavities the teenager should get.

3. **a)** It seems reasonable that the taller the mother is, the taller the child is likely to be compared to children of the same age. As you move to the right, the points should get higher.
   b) You would expect the same pattern as described in part a.
   c) Yes; generally, the older a child is, the taller she or he will be. So, if you graph data for children of many different ages on one graph, you would not expect to find a pattern in the results.

4. Answers may vary. As length increases, width decreases. Length and width add to 30 m in all cases.

5. Answers may vary. There is no clear relationship. The heights of the buildings seem to be independent of their ages.

6. Answers may vary. The scatterplot seems to indicate that taller plants have had a longer growing period.

7. Experimental results may vary.

8. Results may vary.

9. **a)** As you move to the right, the points should get higher. The taller a person is, the greater is that person's mass.
   b) As you move to the right, the points should get higher. The more chin-ups a person can do, the more push-ups the person can do.

10. As you move to the right, the points get higher. In general, the taller a person is, the greater is that person's mass.

11. **c)** The two scatterplots should be quite similar.

12. **c)** European countries with small land areas appear to have lower populations. However, for European countries with greater land areas, there is no pattern in the points. The areas of countries do not always seem to affect their populations.

13. **a)** Answers may vary.
    b) As you move to the right, the points get higher. The taller a woman is, the larger her shoe size.
    c) Men's and women's shoe sizes are different. A women's size 8 is similar to a men's size 6. So, it would not make sense to graph the data on the same grid.

14. **a)** As you move to the right, the points get higher. In general, the higher the hourly wage, the higher the cost of food.
    b) In Lagos, food is much more expensive relative to people's salaries than in other cities.

15. Answers may vary. You would expect that the greater the population, the more pets there would be.

16. **b)** As you move to the right, the points get higher. The older a red pine, the greater its diameter.

17. Answers may vary. You would expect that people who were tall at age 16 compared to other 16-year-olds will also be tall adults. The scatterplot would be similar to the one in exercise 1b.

18. No, the data for people with larger shoe sizes probably represent older students rather than people with larger than average feet. You would expect older students to have higher reading levels than younger students.

1.3 Line of Best Fit

Developing the Ideas, page 71

5. Answers may vary. One possible estimate is 75.5 m.

Page 72

1. About 86 m

2. Answers may vary. It might not be realistic to expect the same increase in performance at every Olympic Games event.

3. It is possible, but probably not likely. Women discus throwers have consistently exceeded 60 m since 1972.

4. Answers may vary.

5. Answers may vary. A line of best fit helps to make approximate predictions; it cannot provide an exact solution for events not yet held.

Working with Mathematics, page 73

1. **a)** Yes, all but one of the points lie on a line.
   b) No, the line of best fit crosses the y-axis at about 10.
   c) No, we need to consider all points. Try to have as many points above the line as below.

2. No, the pattern of points does not suggest a line. A smooth curve through the points would be more appropriate.

3. Graph b would give the most reliable predictions because the line fits the data more closely than the lines in parts a and c, where the points are more widely scattered.

4. Answers may vary.

5. **b)** Answers may vary. Extending a line of best fit suggests a mass of about 300 kg.

6. **a)** Answers may vary. More experienced players probably have a faster slap shot.

7. **a)** Answers may vary. For the men, 71.5 m; for the women, 73 m.
   b) Answers for graphs may vary. From the actual results: 1972.

8. Predictions may vary.
   a) 101 s, 108 s   **b)** 2076

9. **c)** Answers may vary. Since the points are all within about 1 s of the line, it does provide a good representation of the data.
   d) Estimates may vary; about 48 s. The actual 1992 winning time was 49.02 s.

10. Answers may vary depending on calculator model.

11. **b)** Estimates may vary. White pine: 27 cm, black spruce: 16 cm
    c) Estimates may vary. White pine: 55 years; black spruce: 105 years
    d) White pine: 0.47 cm/year; black spruce: 0.28 cm/year. The white pine grew about 1.7 times as fast as the black spruce.

12. **a)** Answers may vary. Some birds are much larger than others, so they need larger entrances to their houses. Small entrances help to keep out predators.
    d) Estimates may vary; 10.8 cm. The red-headed woodpecker needs a house with an inside length and width of 11 cm.

13. **, 14.** Answers may vary.

1.4 Reliable Sampling Methods
Developing the Ideas, page 76

1. Gallup interviews random samples of Canadians. Nielsen monitors TV sets in randomly selected Canadian households. SOCAN analyzes samples of radio broadcasts.

2. Gallup, $\frac{1}{18\ 000}$; Nielsen, $\frac{1}{7000}$; SOCAN, $\frac{1}{26}$

3. Possible reasons include cost, time, and volume of data.

Working with Mathematics, page 78

1. Answers may vary.
   a) We have to consider students from all classes, and not only from our class.
   b) The choice of music varies with people of different age groups. A survey of the senior citizens will not include students, children, and middle-aged people.
   c) The people working in the Assembly Plant will be encouraged to buy the cars they produce. This sample will not cover students, senior citizens, and many other groups.
   d) My close friends are likely to have tastes similar to mine, and they would not be a random sample.
   e) There will be many people of different groups not listening to the talk show, so the sample will not be random.

2. Answers may vary.
   a) A survey of a certain number of students in each class in school will give valid information on the average age of the students.
   b) A random sample covering all age groups in different provinces
   c) A survey at a parking lot in a mall or at a busy intersection
   d) A random sample of teenagers from different schools
   e) A random sample covering people of all age groups

3. Answers may vary.

4. Answers may vary. Many voters may be swayed to follow what they think is the "popular vote."

5. Answers may vary.
   a) When a bulb has been checked, it cannot be sold or used.
   b) It would be impossible to survey the entire population of Canada.
   c) Food, when cooked in bulk, has the same ingredients; so for its purity, a small sample is sufficient.
   d) Testing all ladders until they break will not leave any ladders to be sold.
   e) It is not possible to ask every shop manager how much he or she charges.
   f) It is not possible to check the blood sample of every person.

6. Answers may vary.
   a) i) CD   ii) Listening to one song   iii) No; the title song can be quite different from all the others.
   b) i) Wheat and canola farmers   ii) Names are selected at random from farm mailing lists.   iii) Yes
   c) i) Alberta's residents   ii) Names are selected at random from Edmonton directory.   iii) No; the sample would not include rural residents.
   d) i) Canadian teenagers   ii) Interviewing teens at a mall   iii) No; the sampling would not include teens from various communities or teens who shop by catalogue or by modem.
   e) i) Canadian voters   ii) Names are selected from each political riding.   iii) Yes, provided the names are selected randomly.

7. , 8. Answers may vary.

9. Answers may vary.   a) There are so many new drivers, it might be impractical to obtain data for everyone.   b) Each test destroys the light bulb, so only a sample should be tested.   c) It may be too time-consuming and wasteful to measure every bag.

10. Answers may vary.
    a) i) Canadians   ii) Names are selected randomly from the Calgary directory.   iii) No; nobody living outside Calgary has a chance to be selected.
    b) i) Canadians   ii) Phone in response.   iii) No
    c) i) Canadians   ii) People are selected randomly on city streets.   iii) No, Canadians living and working in the countryside do not have a chance to be selected.
    d) i) Canadian teenagers   ii) Students' names are selected Canada wide.   iii) Yes, provided we can assume the vast majority of teens are in high school.

11. Answers may vary.

Linking Ideas: Mathematics and the Media
Sampling and TV Ratings, page 81

1. Because we cannot be sure exactly how many households watched the program

2. Approximately 0.015%

3. 20 668 200, 17 968 300, 17 409 700, 15 733 900, 15 082 200

4. 9.8 million   5. 3 000 000

6. All the measurements were not taken at the same time.

7. , 8. Answers may vary.

1.5 Assessing Reported Data
Working with Mathematics, page 84

1. Answers may vary.
   a) The graph suggests an increase but, for 6 out of the past 7 years, the numbers have been decreasing.
   b) The bars are not aligned horizontally and the unemployment rate appears to be greater than it is.

2. Answers may vary.
   a) It does not say what percent of people who ski do not take lessons. There could be many more people who don't take lessons who have accidents, but the percent would be smaller.
   b) This is not misleading.
   c) We need to know what percent of drivers 1775 is, and what percent of cyclists 102 is, before we can say which is the safer mode of transport.

3. Graphs may vary.

4. to 7. Answers may vary.

8. Answers may vary. There are few accidents because there is little traffic on the road at this time, drivers reduce their speeds in fog, and very few drivers travel at 150 km/h.

9. , 10. , 11. Answers may vary.

1.6 Making Predictions
Working with Mathematics, page 89

1. a) .400   b) .389   c) .382   d) .382
   e) Answers may vary. It is better to use his average at the end of the season because that is more current.

2. a) 24   **b)** 33   **c)** 120   **d)** 300

3. a) 0.375   **b)** 0.375   **c)** 0.625   **d)** $0.9\overline{4}$

4. a) 0.13   **b)** 0.1275   **c)** 1.36   **d)** 0.0035

5. 1, 0.138; 2, 0.169; 3, 0.177; 4, 0.185; 5, 0.169; 6, 0.162

6. 0.03

7. 0.0714

8. a) Two heads, 0.24; two tails, 0.28; head and tail, 0.48
  b) 0.72

9. a) Two red, 0.253; two green, 0.267; red and green, 0.48
  b) 0.52

10. a) 0.475   **b)** 0.118

11. a) 0.3   **b)** 0.671

12. a: 48; e: 65; n: 33; s: 25

13. a) 1: 0.163; 2: 0.170; 3: 0.159; 4: 0.162; 5: 0.177; 6: 0.169
  b) Answers may vary. It does seem to represent a fair die.
Each number turns up approximately the same number of
times.

14. 0.026   **15.** 621 students

16. O: 889; A: 700; B: 166; AB: 95

17. , 18. Answers may vary.

19. Answers may vary.
  c) The shortest cylinder is most likely to land on its end.

20. Answers may vary.

21. a) Education prepares us for tomorrow, but am I ready
for today?
  b) With statistics you can fool most of the people most of the
time, but not all of the people all of the time.

22. Answers may vary.

1.7 Probability

Working with Mathematics, page 94

1. a) $\frac{1}{50}$ **b)** $\frac{3}{25}$ **c)** $\frac{1}{25}$

2. a) $\frac{3}{8}$ **b)** $\frac{1}{4}$ **c)** $\frac{3}{8}$ **d)** $\frac{5}{8}$ **e)** $\frac{3}{4}$ **f)** $\frac{1}{4}$

3. a) i) Pink ball, yellow ball, orange ball   **ii)** Equally likely
  b) i) HH, HT, TH, TT   **ii)** Equally likely
  c) i) Purple marble, green marble, red marble
  ii) Not equally likely
  d) i) A, B, C, D, E, F, G, H   **ii)** Equally likely

4. a) $\frac{1}{6}$ **b)** $\frac{1}{4}$ **c)** $\frac{1}{13}$ **d)** $\frac{3}{13}$ **e)** $\frac{1}{52}$ **f)** $\frac{8}{13}$

5. a) $\frac{1}{3}$ **b)** $\frac{1}{5}$ **c)** $\frac{1}{3}$ **d)** $\frac{1}{5}$

6. a) Spades and hearts, spades and clubs, spades and diamonds,
hearts and clubs, hearts and diamonds, clubs and diamonds
  b) $\frac{1}{6}$

7. a) $\frac{1}{4}$ **b)** $\frac{1}{2}$ **c)** 0

8. a) $\frac{15}{77}$ **b)** $\frac{3}{77}$ **c)** $\frac{3}{11}$ **d)** $\frac{17}{77}$

9. a) $\frac{9}{22}$ **b)** $\frac{13}{22}$ **c)** $\frac{4}{11}$

10. a) $\frac{6}{25}$ **b)** $\frac{12}{25}$ **c)** 0   **d)** $\frac{2}{25}$

11. a) $\frac{688}{4800}$ **b)** Greater   **c)** $\frac{688}{4800}$

12. a) i) 0.834 43   **ii)** 0.467 74   **iii)** 0.366 69
  b) $\frac{2220}{95\ 144}$ **c)** Answers may vary. Older people pay premiums
for a shorter time.

Quest: What if a Coin Shows Heads on 10 Tosses?, page 96

Indira reasoned correctly. Heads and tails are equally likely on
any toss of a fair coin.

1.8 Independent Events

Developing the Ideas, page 98

Activity 3

2. a) $\frac{1}{8}$ **b)** $\frac{1}{8}$ **c)** $\frac{3}{8}$ **d)** $\frac{3}{8}$

Working with Mathematics, page 100

1. When two or more events occur together, but do not influence
each other, they are said to be independent events.

2. a) Two heads, two tails, a head and a tail
  b) Three heads, three tails, two heads and a tail, two tails and
a head
  c) 1 and H, 1 and T, 2 and H, 2 and T, 3 and H, 3 and T,
4 and H, 4 and T, 5 and H, 5 and T, 6 and H, 6 and T

3. a) 1,1; 1,2; 1,3; 1,4; 1,5; 1,6; 2,2; 2,3; 2,4; 2,5; 2,6; 3,3; 3,4;
3,5; 3,6; 4,4; 4,5; 4,6; 5,5; 5,6; 6,6
  b) No, some numbers can be rolled in two ways, for example:
3, 1 and 1, 3. This makes these outcomes more likely
than doubles.

4. a) Two red, two green, red and green
  b) $\frac{1}{4}$, $\frac{1}{4}$, $\frac{1}{2}$

5. a) $\frac{1}{3}$ **b)** $\frac{1}{3}$ **c)** $\frac{1}{9}$ **d)** $\frac{1}{9}$ **e)** $\frac{1}{9}$ **f)** $\frac{4}{9}$

6.

	A	A	B	B	C	C
A	A,A	A,A	A,B	A,B	A,C	A,C
A	A,A	A,A	A,B	A,B	A,C	A,C
B	B,A	B,A	B,B	B,B	B,C	B,C
B	B,A	B,A	B,B	B,B	B,C	B,C
C	C,A	C,A	C,B	C,B	C,C	C,C
C	C,A	C,A	C,B	C,B	C,C	C,C

7. a)

	1	2	3	4	5	6
1	1,1	1,2	1,3	1,4	1,5	1,6
2	2,1	2,2	2,3	2,4	2,5	2,6
3	3,1	3,2	3,3	3,4	3,5	3,6
4	4,1	4,2	4,3	4,4	4,5	4,6
5	5,1	5,2	5,3	5,4	5,5	5,6
6	6,1	6,2	6,3	6,4	6,5	6,6

  b) $\frac{1}{36}$ **c)** $\frac{1}{6}$
  d) P(two 6s) = P(two 2s) = $\frac{1}{36}$,
so P(two 6s and two 2s) = $\frac{1}{36} \times \frac{1}{36}$

8. $\frac{1}{6}$

9. a) $\frac{1}{1296}$
  b) Results are the same, because P(two 2s) = P(two 6s)

10. All numbers have an equal chance of being selected in each
draw, since all lottery selections are independent events.

11. Answers may vary.

12. $\frac{1}{1000}$ **13.** $\frac{1}{1\ 000\ 000}$

14. a) $\frac{1}{216\ 000}$ **b)** $\frac{1}{1000}$

15. Assuming she does not return the queen of spades,
P(queen of hearts) = $\frac{1}{3}$

16. a) $\frac{3}{8}$

 b) The head could come up on any of the three coins, penny, dime, or quarter. In each case, the probability is $\frac{1}{8}$.

P (HHT or HTH or THH) = $\frac{1}{8} + \frac{1}{8} + \frac{1}{8}$

17. a) $\frac{1}{28\ 561}$ **b)** $\frac{1}{2197}$

18. Answers may vary.

Mathematics File: Games of Chance, page 102

Answers may vary.

Review, page 103

1. b) The graph shows that Lee makes better tips closer to the weekend. It would not make sense to join the points.

2. b) It is appropriate to join the points, since population is constantly changing over time.

 c) Population growth is increasing more and more rapidly with time.

3. b) 325 min or 5 h 25 min **c)** 500 min or 8 h 20 min

 d) No; for example, compare the cooking times given for 4 kg and 8 kg — 400 is not double 300.

 e) 25 min

4. , 5. , 6. Answers may vary.

7. Answers may vary.
 a) Training should improve speed.
 d) No, eventually Kirsty's speed will start to level off as she reaches her own personal best condition.

8. b) Miguel saves different amounts each week. This shifts the points away from the diagonal line through the origin.

9. b) About 7 cm
 c) No, the rainfall could have changed at any time after the students took their last measurement.

10. , 11. Answers may vary.

12. Answers may vary. It could be that many more teenagers ski than any other age group. Similarly, it could be that very few people over the age of 50 ski.

13. Graphs may vary.

14. a) 0.08 **b)** 0.163 **c)** 0.5

15. a) 0.121, 0.363, 0.388, 0.129
 b) i) About 36 times
 ii) Answers may vary. One hundred tosses are insufficient to draw a conclusion.

16. a) $\frac{1}{6}$ **b)** $\frac{1}{2}$ **c)** $\frac{1}{2}$ **d)** 0 **e)** 1 **f)** 0

17. a) $\frac{1}{15}$ **b)** 6 **c)** 4

18. b) $\frac{1}{9}$ **c)** $\frac{2}{9}$

19. $\frac{1}{64}$

20. a) Boris and Andre, Boris and Teresa, Martina and Andre, Martina and Teresa
 b) $\frac{1}{4}$

21. $\frac{1}{10\ 000}$ **22.** $\frac{1}{32}$ **23. b)** $\frac{1}{32}$

CHAPTER 2 ALGEBRAIC OPERATIONS AND EQUATIONS

Start With What You Know, page 110
Activity 1

1. a) Multiply the number of wins by 2 and add the number of ties.
 b) Variables may differ. $P = 2w + t$

2. a) 62 **b)** 9 **c)** 34

Activity 2

1. 163.0 cm, 166.0 cm **2.** Tables and graphs may vary.

3. a) The formula in cell B4 multiplies the number in cell A4 by 3.34 and then adds 81.2. The formula in cell C4 multiplies the number in cell A4 by 3.27 and then adds 85.9. The formula in cell B5 multiplies the number in cell A5 by 3.34 and then adds 81.2. The formula in cell C5 multiplies the number in cell A5 by 3.27 and then adds 85.9.

Activity 3

1. Answers may vary.

2.1 The Concept of a Variable
Developing the Ideas, page 112
Activity 1

Number of green squares	Number of blue squares
2	6
4	8
6	10
8	12
10	14

1. a) 24 **b)** 104

2. Add 4 to the number of green squares.

3. $s + 4$; an even number **4.** 78

5. 96 **6.** See page 114.

Activity 2

1. 14 m, 17 m

2. Widths and perimeters may vary.

Width (m)	Perimeter (m)
2	14
2.5	15
3	16
3.5	17
4	18
4.5	19

3. a) Add 10 m to twice the width. **b)** $2w + 10$
 c) $2(w + 5)$ **d)** A positive rational number
4. 14.8 m **5.** 1.5 m

6. a) See page 114.
 b) Find the width along the horizontal axis. From this point, move vertically until you meet the graph. Move horizontally until you meet the vertical axis. The point will be the perimeter.

c) Find the perimeter along the vertical axis. From this point, move horizontally until you meet the graph. Move down until you meet the horizontal axis. This point will be the width.

Working with Mathematics, page 115

1. a) A symbol that represents numbers that can vary
   b) , **c)** Answers may vary.

2. a) Because we do not have an odd number of green squares
   b) Because it represents the width, a measurable distance

3. a) i) For the square — P: perimeter, s: side length, A: area
   ii) For the circle — C: circumference, r: radius, A: area
   iii) For the right triangle, the Pythagorean Theorem —
      c: hypotenuse, a, b: shorter sides
   b) π is not a variable; explanations may vary.

4. a) Yes   **b)** Yes; examples may vary.

5. b)

Number of cubes	Number of faces
1	5
2	8
3	11
4	14
5	17

   c) 14, 17   **d)** 32, 92
   e) Multiply the number of cubes by 3, then add 2.
   f) $3n + 2$ **g)** 50
   h) No; there are only whole numbers of cubes and faces in any step in the pattern.
   i) Answers may vary.

6. a) 10 m^2, 17.5 m^2
   b)

Width (m)	Area (m²)
2	10
2.5	12.5
3	15
3.5	17.5
4	20
4.5	22.5

   c) Multiply the width by 5.
   d) $5w$; positive rational number; between 0 and 5
   e) 6 m^2 **f)** 3 m
   g) i) Yes, join the points since widths and areas do not need to be whole numbers only.
   ii) Find the width along the horizontal axis. From this point, move vertically until you meet the graph. Move horizontally until you meet the vertical axis. This point will be the area.
   iii) Find the area along the vertical axis. From this point, move horizontally until you meet the graph. Move down until you meet the horizontal axis. This point will be the width.
   h), **i)** Answers may vary.

7. b) Tables may vary.

Number in the UL corner	Sum of the numbers in the UR and LL corners
1	10
2	12
3	14
15	38
20	48
23	54

   c) Double the number and add 8.
   d) i) $2n + 8$ **ii)** Natural numbers between 1 and 23

8. Descriptions of patterns may vary.
   a) 1:   **i)** 4 cm   **ii)** 4 cm   **iii)** 0 cm
       2:          **i)** 8 cm   **ii)** 8 cm   **iii)** 4 cm
       3:          **i)** 12 cm   **ii)** 12 cm   **iii)** 8 cm
       4:          **i)** 16 cm   **ii)** 16 cm   **iii)** 12 cm
   b) i) 20 cm   **ii)** 20 cm   **iii)** 16 cm
   c) 10th: **i)** 40 cm   **ii)** 40 cm   **iii)** 36 cm
       100th: **i)** 400 cm   **ii)** 400 cm   **iii)** 396 cm
   d) i) Multiply the number by 4.   **ii)** Multiply the number by 4.
   iii) Multiply 4 by 1 less than the number.
   e) i) $4n$ **ii)** $4n$ **iii)** $4(n - 1)$
   f) 15 cm   **g)** 12 cm   **h)** No; explanations may vary.

9. a) $2s + 4$ **b)** $s + 10$

10. $1.50(2w + 10)$

11. a) $F = 2C + 30$ **b)** Answers may vary.

12. 10°C, 50°F

Quest: What If You Saved 1¢, Then 2¢, Then 3¢, Then 4¢, …?, page 118

1. $4.65; $50.50; $667.95   **2.** $\dfrac{n(n + 1)}{2}$

Linking Ideas: Arithmetic and Algebra
The Distributive Law, page 120

1. a) 50 m^2 **b)** Answers may vary.

2. Yes; rational numbers

3. Answers may vary.

2.2 Representing Variables and Expressions
Developing the Ideas, page 121

1. Variables may differ.
   a) $3x - 4$ **b)** $-2x + 5$

3. a) $2x + 8$ **b)** $6x - 3$ **c)** $12 - 6a$ **d)** $-4m + 6$

4. Answers may vary.

Working with Mathematics, page 124

1. a) Sometimes true   **b)** Sometimes true   **c)** Sometimes true

2. Yes; yes; explanations may vary.

3. Any pair of opposite tiles, such as a 1-tile and a flipped 1-tile

4. Part b, $6y - 15$, is equivalent, by application of the Distributive Law.

5. Yes; explanations may vary.

6. Variables may differ.

a) $4x + 6$ b) $-3x + 4$ c) $3x - 7$ d) $-2x - 3$

7. a) $-4x - 6$ b) $3x - 4$ c) $-3x + 7$ d) $2x + 3$

8. a) $22, -6$ b) $-8, 13$ c) $5, -16$ d) $-11, 3$

9. a) $-22, 6$ b) $8, -13$ c) $-5, 16$ d) $11, -3$

The answers to exercise 9 are the opposites of those for exercise 8.

10. a) $-4x + 3$ b) $2x - 7$ c) $-5x - 6$ d) $2x - 4$

11. a) $4x - 3$ b) $-2x + 7$ c) $5x + 6$ d) $-2x + 4$

12. a) $15 + 24$ b) $30 - 20$ c) $55 - 77$ d) $-48 + 24$
e) $60 - 72$ f) $-28 + 36$ g) $13 + 13h$ h) $88 - 8d$
i) $4k + 20$ j) $-72 + 9x$ k) $18 + 3m$ l) $-5f - 45$

13. a) $20 + 50 + 10$ b) $44 - 20 - 8$
c) $36 + 45 - 72$ d) $-72 + 16 - 64$

14. a) $17, -10$ b) $4, -14$ c) $-18, 9$ d) $0, -9$
e) $18, -18$ f) $-16, 2$ g) $-14, 31$ h) $13, -23$

15. a) $24, -31$ b) $-18, 26$ c) $20, -13$ d) $14, -19$
e) $-16, 6$ f) $-22, 11$

16. a) $5k + 5$ b) $6 - 4w$ c) $8m + 4$ d) $-4 - 5y$
e) $-6 + 3p$ f) $3 - 9b$ g) $-8t + 10$ h) $-8s - 8$

17. a) -35 b) 38 c) -60 d) 36
e) -30 f) 75 g) 74 h) 56

18. a) $3x + 2, 2 + 3x$ b) $-5g + 4, 4 - 5g$
c) $7 - 2j, -2j + 7$ d) $-3 - 5b, -5b - 3$

19. a) $6 - 4x$ b) $-3z - 4$ c) $10 - 5a$ d) $6s - 3$
e) $8y + 6$ f) $-8 + 8p$ g) $-5 - 5b$ h) $6t + 9$

20. a) $-3(2 + y)$, $-6 - 3y$ b) $8x - 4$, $4(2x - 1)$

21. a) $15x + 21$ b) $-40 + 24y$ c) $33y - 77$ d) $30a + 6$
e) $6vy + 18v$ f) $4a - 4ac$ g) $35mn - 10m$ h) $-ps + 7p$

22. a) $77 + 21 - 56$ b) $-32 + 8 - 12$ c) $20a + 5b - 15$
d) $-72 + 16f + 64s$ e) $44b - 20a + 8a$ f) $36c + 45d - 27$

23. a) $15y - 55.8$ b) $2.8x + 10.5$
c) $3 + 4z$ d) $61.2x - 27.9$
e) $-7 - 10.5m$ f) $\frac{4}{3} - 2z$

24. Part b; explanations may vary.

25. a) $5m + 28$ b) $21a - 37$ c) $-14x + 14$
d) $-18k + 8$ e) $c + 27 + 3d$ f) $p - 18$

26. a) 14 b) -18 c) -2 d) -19
e) 19 f) -15 g) 1 h) 12

27. a) -10 b) -5 c) 8 d) -6
e) 2 f) -3 g) -5 h) -3

28. a) $7, -14$ b) $15, -13$ c) $-13, 22$ d) $-10, 11$
e) $15, -34$ f) $-9, 5$ g) $-17, 11$ h) $-3, 18$

29. a) $6a + 3$ b) $6 - 2x$ c) $4 - 8t$ d) $-8 - 6x$
e) $-6v - 3$ f) $4u - 6$ g) $6 - 12t$ h) $6 + 12s$

30. a) $24x + 54$ b) $-15c - 9$ c) $33 - 88z$ d) $20 - 70y$
e) $30z + 10$ f) $-3y + 6$ g) $-22x + 6$ h) $-48w - 12$

31. Part a; explanations may vary.

32. Part b; explanations may vary.

33. Part c; explanations may vary.

34. a) $3x + 6y - 21$ b) $-2a + 10b - 4$
c) $-6m + 7n$ d) $36p + 4q - 36r$
e) $5x + 30y - 20$ f) $21c - 27 + 3d$

35. a) $2.5n + 5$ b) $6.4 - 4.8r$ c) $2x - 4$ d) $2\pi R - 2\pi r$
e) $-2.2c + 9.9$ f) $9 + 3b$ g) $13\pi - 26y$ h) $10d - 2.5$

36. Answers may vary.

37. a) $2xy - 4x^2 + y$ b) $3x - 5xy + 6y^2$ c) $4pq - 5p^2 + q^2$

d) $6bc - 22ac$ e) $6a^2 + 3ab + 3b^2$ f) $9x^3 - 8x^2 + 12x - 5x^4$

2.3 Combining Like Terms

Developing the Ideas, page 128

1. a) $5x$ b) $-2n$ c) $-3a$

2. a) $6x + 4$ b) $2y - 1$ c) $-4a + 5$

3. a) $5x - 3$ b) $m + 5$ c) $2k - 3$

Working with Mathematics, page 130

1. Answers may vary.   **2.** a, d, f, g

3. $2x, 5x$; $2x, -x$; $2x, 4x$; $5x, -x$; $5x, 4x$; $-x, 4x$; $-3y, -y$; $3, 5$; $3, -1$; $5, -1$

4. Parts a, e, f

5. Variables may vary.
a) $2x + 5$ b) $-x + 4$ c) $3x - 3$

6. a) $9s$ b) $2v$ c) b d) $9p$
e) $-9c$ f) $8t + 5$ g) $5 - 5a$ h) $-n + 6$
i) $9 - d$ j) $5u - 3$ k) $2k$ l) $-7q - 7$

7. a) $3x - 2$; -8; -2 b) $5x - 3$; -13; -3
c) $1 + x$; -1; 1 d) $5x + 3$; -7; 3
e) $3x + 1$; -5; 1 f) $-x - 9$; -7; -9
g) $-5x + 3$; 13; 3 h) $10x + 12$; -8; 12

8. a) $4x$ b) $-2a$ c) $-8 + 2c$
d) $2k + 4$ e) $13b + 5$ f) $-7u + 6$

9. a) $-9x + 12$; 3; 21 b) $-3x - 4$; -7; -1
c) $17x - 52$; -35; 69 d) $-5x + 21$; 16; 26
e) $17x - 18$; -1; -35

10. a) $6x - 2$; 22; -20 b) $-x - 2$; -6; 1
c) $4x - 9$; 7; -21 d) $-5x + 21$; 1; 36
e) $14x - 6$; 50; -48 f) $10x - 31$; 9; -61

11. a) $10a - 3b$ b) $m - 5n$
c) $40s + 10t - 7$ d) $3x - 2y$
e) $30p - 16p - 6r$ f) $-47g + 4h + 7$
g) $-22 - 3c + 2d$ h) $4 - x$

12. a) $6x + 2$ b) $3x + 2$ c) $-4x - 2$ d) $3a + 8$
e) $-x$ f) $8a - 8$ g) $-20a - 6$ h) $15a - 9$

13. a) $11a - 3$; 30 b) $4m + 21$; -7
c) $14s + 30$; 30 d) $14x - 3$; 32
e) $5p - 16$; -66 f) $-14g$; 56
g) $-10c - 30$; -31 h) $-3 + 2d$; -25

14. a) $x - 1$; 6; -6; -1 b) $2x - 8$; 6; -18; -8
c) $-5x + 6$; -29; 31; 6 d) $2x + 12$; 26; 2; 12
e) $-5x + 14$; -21; 39; 14 f) $11 - 13x$; -80; 76; 11
g) $x - 3.2$; 3.8; -8.2; -3.2 h) $1.7x - 3.6$; 8.3; -12.1; -3.6

15. a) $6m - 3n$ b) $-a + 2b + 4c$
c) $2x + 5y$ d) $9s - 13r + 4$
e) $-21d - 27e + 20$ f) $28q - 36m - 11n$
g) $-a - 6b + 6c$ h) $13x - 47y$

16. a) 27 b) -96

17. a) $P = 6x$, $A = 2x^2$ b) $P = 12z$, $A = 6z^2$

18. Answers may vary.

Mathematics File: Number Tricks, page 132

3. Change the last instruction to "Subtract the number you started with." Everyone will end up with 2 as an answer.

4. The steps can be written as follows: n; $n + 2$; $3n + 6$; $2n + 6$; $n + 3$; 3. You will always end up with 3.

2.4 Solving Equations Using Algebra Tiles

Developing the Ideas, page 134

1. -2 **2.** 2 **3.** 2 **4.** -5 **5.** 3 **6.** 2

Working with Mathematics, page 137

1. No; explanations may vary.   **2.** Answers may vary.

3. Answers may vary.

4. Explanations may vary.
   a) Yes   **b)** Yes   **c)** Yes   **d)** Yes   **e)** Yes

5. a) i) $3x = -6$ **ii)** $-2x - 3 = 3$
   iii) $3x + 2 = 2x - 3$ **iv)** $4x + 5 = 2x + 3$
   b) i) -2 **ii)** -3 **iii)** -5 **iv)** -1

6. a) 3 **b)** -2 **c)** -5 **d)** 5 **e)** 2 **f)** 1 **g)** 2
   h) 3 **i)** 2 **j)** 2 **k)** 1 **l)** 1 **m)** -1 **n)** 2

7. Explanations may vary. Symbolic record follows.
$$3x - 4 = 5x + 6$$
$$-4 = 2x + 6$$
$$-10 = 2x$$
$$-5 = x$$

8. a) -3 **b)** 5 **c)** -1 **d)** 3
   e) 1 **f)** 1 **g)** -1 **h)** 3

9. a) 2 **b)** -4 **c)** -2 **d)** 1
   e) 1 **f)** -2 **g)** -3 **h)** 1

10. Explanations and examples may vary. The Opposites Principle states that two equal sets remain equal when you multiply each part of each set by -1. The Sharing Principle states that two equal sets remain equal when you divide them into the same number of groups.

11. a) $3x - 4 = 5$; $x = 3$ **b)** $-2x + 3 = 7$; $x = -2$
   c) $-3x + 5 = -2x$; $x = 5$ **d)** $2x - 2 = -x + 7$; $x = 3$

12. a) 5 **b)** -2 **c)** -3 **d)** 2 **e)** -5 **f)** 3

13. a) -6 **b)** -2 **c)** 2 **d)** -2 **e)** 3 **f)** 1

14. a) $9 = 6x - 3$ **b)** $x = 2$

15. a) $12 = 5x$ **b)** $x = 2.4$

16. Answers may vary.

2.5 Solving Equations Algebraically

Working with Mathematics, page 141

1. Answers may vary.

2. a) 3 **b)** -5 **c)** 4 **d)** 3
   e) 3 **f)** 2 **g)** 4 **h)** 7
   i) 9 **j)** 7 **k)** -2 **l)** -3

3. a) 3 **b)** 3 **c)** 4 **d)** 7
   e) 4 **f)** -9 **g)** $-\frac{3}{5}$ or -0.6 **h)** 42

4. a) 21 **b)** 7 **c)** -5 **d)** -4
   e) 7 **f)** $-2\frac{1}{3}$ or $-2.\overline{3}$ **g)** -8 **h)** 4
   i) $\frac{1}{6}$ or $0.1\overline{6}$ **j)** 3 **k)** $\frac{4}{3}$ or $1.\overline{3}$ **l)** 3

5. a) $\$3353.66$ **b)** $\$2916.16$ **c)** 37

6. a) $\$101$ **b)** 7 weeks

7. a) Nasmin, $S = 15 + 4.25n$; Mayumi, $S = 20 + 3.5n$
   b) Nasmin, $\$36.25$; Mayumi, $\$37.50$
   c) Nasmin

8. Answers will vary.

9. a) 2; 44 L   **b)** 5.5; 16 L   **c)** 750 km

10. a) $\$58.50$ **b)** 310 km   **c)** Answers may vary.

11. a) 4.9 **b)** 3.3 **c)** -11.4 **d)** 4.5
   e) 2.7 **f)** -1.8 **g)** 3 **h)** 1.7

12. a) 7 **b)** 8 **c)** -13 **d)** $\frac{3}{2}$ or 1.5
   e) -4 **f)** 9 **g)** $\frac{3}{5}$ or 0.6 **h)** 0
   i) $\frac{26}{6}$ or $4.\overline{3}$ **j)** -10 **k)** -6 **l)** $-\frac{9}{4}$ or -2.25

13. a) 4 **b)** $\frac{20}{3}$ **c)** 0.6 **d)** -4.5 **e)** $-\frac{1}{2}$ **f)** 3
   g) 7.2 **h)** $\frac{4}{3}$ **i)** $\frac{1}{3}$ **j)** -1.2 **k)** $\frac{5}{9}$ **l)** 0

14. a) The fixed cost; the cost that depends on the number of books printed
   b) 222 **c)** 1333

15. a) The temperature that varies with depth; the temperature at Earth's surface
   b) 3 km   **c)** 8 km

16. a) 90 m   **b)** 145 m

17. a) $d = \frac{1}{3}t$ **b)** 1.2 km   **c)** 24 s

18. , 19. Explanations and equations may vary.

2.6 Simplifying Equations before Solving

Developing the Ideas, page 144

1. a) 5 **b)** 7 **c)** $-\frac{7}{3}$

2. Answers may vary.

3. a) 4 **b)** $\frac{19}{6}$ **c)** 2

4. Answers may vary.

5. a) 2 **b)** -6 **c)** 10

6. Answers may vary.

Working with Mathematics, page 146

1. , 2. , 3. Answers may vary.

4. a) -6 **b)** 10 **c)** $-\frac{1}{5}$ or -0.2 **d)** -2
   e) -3 **f)** 9 **g)** $-\frac{4}{5}$ or -0.8 **h)** 1
   i) 8 **j)** $-\frac{24}{5}$ or -4.8 **k)** 6 **l)** -36

5. a) 2.0 **b)** 1.5 **c)** 1 **d)** -16 **e)** -0.5 **f)** -4.9

6. a) 0.5 **b)** -1 **c)** 5 **d)** -2.2
   e) 7 **f)** -3 **g)** 9 **h)** $\frac{7}{6}$ or $1.1\overline{6}$
   i) -15 **j)** $\frac{12}{5}$ or 2.4

7. Explanations may vary.
   a) $15x + 18 = 120$ **b)** $60 = 27 - 4r$

8. a) About 7 min   **b)** About 15 min

9. a) -2 **b)** 4 **c)** -6 **d)** 7 **e)** -4
   f) 4 **g)** $-\frac{4}{3}$ **h)** 1.5 **i)** 40

10. a) 9 **b)** 3 **c)** $-\frac{5}{6}$ **d)** -6 **e)** 0.5 **f)** -3

11. a) $-\frac{5}{3}$ or $-1.\overline{6}$ **b)** $\frac{1}{5}$ or 0.2 **c)** 0 **d)** $\frac{7}{2}$ or 3.5
   e) $-\frac{1}{2}$ or -0.5 **f)** 5 **g)** $\frac{19}{2}$ or 9.5 **h)** $-\frac{1}{2}$ or -0.5

12. a) -56 **b)** $-\frac{4}{13}$ **c)** -10 **d)** $\frac{12}{7}$
   e) 10 **f)** 24 **g)** $\frac{32}{3}$ **h)** 11.5
   i) -24 **j)** 6

13. a) 39 words/min   **b)** 5 **c)** 180

14. a) $3, -3$ **b)** $5, -5$ **c)** $10, -10$
   d) $\sqrt{2}, -\sqrt{2}$ **e)** 0 **f)** No solution

15. a) Subtract 30 and divide by 2. $C = \frac{F - 30}{2}$
   b) $C = \frac{F - 32}{1.8}$ **c)** $50°F$, $10°C$

Quest: How Can You Design a Trundle Wheel?, page 148

Radius is approximately 15.9 cm.

2.7 Solving Problems in Different Ways
Developing the Ideas, page 150

15 dimes, 8 quarters

Working with Mathematics, page 152

1. Answers may vary.
2. 15 kg peanuts; 8 kg pecans
3. 15 h running; 8 h cycling
4. Answers may vary.
5. 54 nickels, 18 dimes
6. 482 g
7. 12.5 km
8. $10.90

Linking Ideas: Mathematics and Science
Keeping Ships Afloat, page 153

1. a) 135 922 330 L   b) 136 585 366 L
2. a) 153 005 465 L   b) 157 977 883 L

2.8 Solving Problems Using Equations
Working with Mathematics, page 157

1. Answers may vary.
2. 5¢
3. a) $a + 8$ b) $2a + 8$
   c) $2a + 8 = 42$; they are 17 and 25.
4. a) $27 - y$ b) $2y$
   c) $27 - y + 2y = 43$; they are 16 and 11.
5. a) $54 - x$ b) $2x$
   c) $2x = (54 - x) + 9$; the numbers are 21 and 33.
6. a) $28 - m$ b) $3m$
   c) $28 - m = 3m$; they are 7 kg and 21 kg.
7. a) $s - 7.5$ b) $2s - 7.5$
   c) $2s - 7.5 = 116.5$; they are 62 kg and 54.5 kg.
8. a) $2n$ b) $n - 3, 2n - 3$
   c) $n - 3 + 2n - 3 = 48$; they are now 18 and 36.
9. 136 and 137
10. 16 and 32 bars
11. 3.5 km and 6 km
12. 11.8 kg and 47.2 kg
13. 26.5 m by 33.5 m
14. 3.5 and 3.75
15. $250
16. $142.50
17. 24 cm, 48 cm
18. 228 cm
19. $13 000
20. 9 of each
21. 20 cm, 38 cm, and 60 cm
22. There is one such pair of numbers, 12 and 108.
23. 60 km/h, 480 km/h
24. a) $63 - k$ b) $3k$
   c) $3k - 14 = 2(63 - k)$; the numbers are 28 and 35.
25. a) $12 - p$ b) $\frac{1}{3}(12 - p)$
   c) $p = \frac{1}{3}(12 - p)$; the pieces are 3 m and 9 m.
26. 16 years
27. 13
28. $17
29. 10
30. a) 54   b) 104
31. Answers may vary.
32. $2.30
33. 30 m
34. 16, 11, and 64 bars
35. Yes: 57, 58, 59, and 60
36. 31 km
37. No; 93 to 97 add to 475
38. 20 cm, 12 cm, 12 cm
39. 25 cm, 25 cm, 75 cm, 75 cm
40. 48, 49
41. Rob
42. Both will be able to buy the bicycle after 10 weeks. Rob will be able to buy the jacket first.
43. a) Between 230 cm and 215 cm
   b) The length decreases by 1 cm.

Linking Ideas: Mathematics and Technology
Solving Problems with a Spreadsheet, page 161

1. a) Explanations may vary.   c) 15 dimes, 8 quarters
2. 21.5 m by 50.0 m
3. a) $10 625   b) $15 000
4. 43, 44, 45, 46

2.9 Solving Inequalities
Working with Mathematics, page 165

1. Explanations may vary.
2. a) $x > 1$ b) $x \leq 2$ c) $x < -10$ d) $x \geq 8$
3. a) $x > 0$; No, because -1 is not part of the graph.
   b) $x \leq 3$; Yes, the graph continues to the left of 0.
   c) $x > -7$; Yes, the graph continues to the right indefinitely.
   d) $x \leq 14$; Yes, the graph continues to the left.
   e) $x < -2$; No, because -1 is not part of the graph.
   f) $x \geq -7$; Yes, the graph continues to the right.
4. a) Only 7 is a solution.   b) Only -7 is a solution.
   c) Only 7 is a solution.   d) Both 7 and -7 are solutions.
   e) Only -7 is a solution.   f) Both -7 and 7 are solutions.
6. Explanations may vary.
   a) Neither 3 nor -3 b) Both 3 and -3
   c) Only 3   d) Both 3 and -3
   e) Both   f) Both
7. a) $s \geq 5$ b) $a < -3$ c) $d \leq -4$ d) $x \geq -12$
   e) $y > -16$ f) $p \leq -27$ g) $t \leq -10$ h) $k \leq 8$
   i) $j > 10$ j) $x \geq -9$
8. a) Only 10   b) Only -10 c) Only -10 d) Both
   e) Both   f) Neither   g) Only -10 h) Only -10
   i) Neither   j) Only -10
9. a) $d \leq -6$ b) $h > 4$ c) $v > -2$ d) $a > -4$
   e) $-5 > p$ f) $t \leq -5$ g) $q \geq 2$ h) $\frac{3}{2} \geq y$
   i) $-36 \geq j$ j) $-10 < b$
10. a) $x > -1$ b) $x \leq 3$ c) $y \geq -5$ d) $x < -4$
   e) $a > -5$ f) $x \geq 2$ g) $t < 4$ h) $p \geq 7$
   i) $r < 3$ j) $z \geq -\frac{19}{12}$
11. a) 8   b) $\frac{1}{2}$ c) $-5, -3$ d) 9
   e) $-5, 5, 10$ f) 3   g) $-5, 0$ h) -6
   i) $1, -4$ j) $-3, 2$
12. 73% or higher
13. a) $\frac{2}{3}x$
   b) $\frac{2}{3}x \leq 100$; Shaulin can afford a jacket priced at $150 or less.
   c) Afshar can afford a ski suit regularly priced at $262.50 or less.

d) Rosie can afford a set regularly priced at $25.50 or less.

14. a) $x \geq 3$ **b)** $y \geq 5$
c) $x < -2$ **d)** $c < \frac{11}{4}$ or $c < 2.75$
e) $x < -\frac{9}{2}$ or $x < -4.5$ **f)** $z < -1$
g) $a \leq 4$ **h)** $4.5 > s$
i) $m \leq 2.5$ **j)** $g < 3$
k) $1 \geq d$ **l)** $y < 2.5$

15. a) 3 and -3 **b)** Neither   **c)** -3 **d)** -3
e) Neither   **f)** -3 **g)** 3 and -3 **h)** 3 and -3
i) -3 **j)** -3 **k)** -3 **l)** -3

16. a) $x > -5$ **b)** $x < -3$ **c)** $k \leq -15$ **d)** $t \leq -1.5$
e) $x \geq 16$ **f)** $a \leq -3$ **g)** $a \leq -1.75$ **h)** $w \geq -2.6$
i) $x > -16$ **j)** $3 < h$

17. a) $\frac{3}{4}x$ **b)** $\frac{3}{4}x \leq 50$; $x \leq 66.\overline{6}$; Yes   **c)** No

18. Answers may vary.

Review, page 167

1. a)

Number of squares	Number of toothpicks
1	4
2	7
3	10

b) 13, 16, 31, 151, 301   **c)** Multiply by 3 and add 1.
d) $3s + 1$; a natural number   **e)** 106   **f)** 33

2. a) The sum is 4 times the number in the middle.
b) Multiply by 4.   **c)** $4n$; from 9 to 23

3. a) 50 m, 60 m   **b)** Tables may vary.

Length (m)	Perimeter (m)
15	50
20	60
25	70
30	80
35	90
40	100

c) Add the length to 10 m, and double the answer.
d) $2(10 + l)$; l is any rational number greater than 10.
e) 27 m

4. a) $4 - 3x$ **b)** $2x - 9$ **c)** $-2x + 6$

5. a) 15, -5 **b)** -3, 27   **c)** 38, -22 **d)** -4, 36
e) -15, 5   **f)** -25, 25   **g)** -10, 20   **h)** -42, 18
i) 0, -20 **j)** -12, 2

6. a) $6x + 21$ **b)** $-20 - 15n$ **c)** $48s - 60$ **d)** $-8b + 6$
e) $-6p - 10$ **f)** $2 - t$ **g)** $18c + 30$ **h)** $-22 + 4.4k$
i) $-2a + 4$ **j)** $12 - 4d$

7. a) $5x + 2$ **b)** $-4m - 10$ **c)** $13a - 7b$ **d)** $-5y + 5$
e) $-13t$ **f)** $-5m - 25n$ **g)** $2q + 6$ **h)** $-9k - 1$
i) $6v - 0.3$ **j)** $39g - 35h$

8. a) $7x$; 28, -21, -7 **b)** $12x + 6$; 54, -30, -6
c) $-4x - 4$; -20, 8, 0   **d)** $7x - 22$; 6, -43, -29
e) $-5x + 2$; -18, 17, 7   **f)** $-10x - 17$; -57, 13, -7
g) $7x - 5$; 23, -26, -12 **h)** $13x - 14$; 38, -53, -27
i) $20x - 36$; 44, -96, -56 **j)** $-22x + 23$; -65, 89, 45

9. a) 2   **b)** 2   **c)** 3   **d)** -7 **e)** -3
f) 4   **g)** 4   **h)** 3   **i)** -3 **j)** -1

10. a) 5   **b)** -6 **c)** -9 **d)** -5 **e)** $\frac{1}{6}$
f) 2   **g)** 3   **h)** 3   **i)** -1 **j)** 16

11. a) i) 19.6 m/s   **ii)** 49 m/s   **iii)** 78.4 m/s

b) i) 3 s   **ii)** 9 s   **iii)** 14 s
c) 3.3 m/s, 8.2 m/s, 13.0 m/s; 18.0 s, 54.1 s, 84.2 s

12. a) 2.5   **b)** -2 **c)** 4   **d)** 9   **e)** 60
f) 20   **g)** -27 **h)** -15 **i)** 12   **j)** 180

13. 14 quarters, 17 dollars

14. 12, 13   **15.** Mercedes: 120 km/h; Jaguar: 144 km/h

16. 11 cm by 16 cm

17. 17 Delicious, 136 Macintosh

18. 12   **19.** 11 and 8

20. a) $x > -2$ **b)** $x \leq -5$ **c)** $x > -5$
d) $x < 33$ **e)** $x \leq 1$

21. a) Only 5   **b)** Neither   **c)** Both
d) Both   **e)** Only -3

22. a) $x > -4.5$ **b)** $y < 3$ **c)** $x \leq 2$ **d)** $a \geq 5$
e) $m > 4.\overline{3}$ **f)** $x < -0.75$ **g)** $5 \geq h$ **h)** $r > 3$
i) $f \geq 7$ **j)** $b < 6$

Cumulative Review, page 172

1. a) 11   **b)** -3 **c)** 3   **d)** -11
e) 5   **f)** 6   **g)** -6 **h)** -14

2. a) -3 **b)** 11   **c)** -11 **d)** 3
e) 9   **f)** 14   **g)** 10   **h)** 4

3. a) -12 **b)** 5   **c)** 48   **d)** -16 **e)** -2 **f)** 3

4. a) Negative   **b)** Positive   **c)** Negative
d) Positive   **e)** Positive

5. a) -3989.25 **b)** 35 189.945 6   **c)** -2.49
d) 0.452   **e)** 0.3

6. About 20%

7. a) 120 cm   **b)** 44%

8. a) 80 cm   **b)** 36%
c) Explanations may vary.

9. a) 5 m   **b)** 5 m
c) D; the points all show the car 10 m away from the measuring device, which indicates the car is stationary.
d) A, B; the points are rising steadily in each case.
e) C; the points are moving higher at an increasing rate.

10. Answers may vary.

11. b) It does make sense because the graph shows accumulated totals over time.

12. Explanations may vary.
a) Most people recover from a cold after 5 days even if they don't take any medication for it.
b) The unemployed people may not be qualified for the advertised jobs. Also, even several pages of classified ads would not contain more than 1000 ads, yet the number of unemployed is over one million.

13. a) Blue, yellow   **b)** No; there are more yellow marbles.
c) P(Blue) $= \frac{5}{13}$, P(Yellow) $= \frac{8}{13}$

14. a) 3 blue; 2 blue and 1 yellow; 1 blue and 2 yellow; 3 yellow
b) No; there are several ways to pick 2 blue and 1 yellow, depending on order. Also, there are more yellow marbles and this affects the probability in each draw.
c) P(3 blue) $= \frac{125}{2197}$ or about 0.06

P(2 blue, 1 yellow) $= \frac{600}{2197}$ or about 0.27

P(1 blue, 2 yellow) $= \frac{960}{2197}$ or about 0.44

$$P(3 \text{ yellow}) = \frac{512}{2197} \text{ or about } 0.23$$

15. a) $\frac{1}{1296}$ **b)** $\frac{1}{1296}$ **c)** $\frac{1}{216}$

16. a) $4a + 20$ **b)** $3a - 6$ **c)** $5a^2 + 35a$
    d) $18a - 6a^2$ **e)** $-10 + 4a$ **f)** $-3a^2 + 5a$

17. a) 12   **b)** -12 **c)** -50 **d)** -60 **e)** -18 **f)** -22

18. a) $9p + 4q$; 19   **b)** $5q + 4p$; 2   **c)** $4r - 4p - 2q$; -12
    d) $2r - 3q$; 4   **e)** $3r + 2p$; 3   **f)** $-q - 2p$; -4

19. a) -4 **b)** -6 **c)** 2   **d)** 10   **e)** -8 **f)** 2

20. a) $b < -5$ **b)** $k > 11$ **c)** $g < 3$ **d)** $g < 5$

CHAPTER 3 CONGRUENCE AND SIMILARITY

Start With What You Know, page 176

Answers may vary.

3.1 Constructing Triangles Using Compasses and Ruler

Developing the Ideas, page 178

Activity 1

1. a) 4 cm; all points on the circle are 4 cm from the centre.
   b) 4 cm; see part a for an explanation.
   c) No; all points that are 4 cm from P are on the circle.

Activity 2

1. Yes, all the triangles look the same.

Working with Mathematics, page 181

1. No; all points inside the circle are less than 4 cm from A.

2. No; suppose you draw side AB 21 cm long. When you draw arcs with radius 5 cm and 8 cm from A and B, the arcs will not intersect.

3. In a triangle, none of the sides is longer than the sum of the lengths of the other two sides.

4. a) Scalene   **b)** Equilateral   **c)** Scalene
    d) Isosceles   **e)** Scalene   **f)** Equilateral

5. a) Equilateral   **b)** Isosceles   **c)** Scalene
    d) Scalene   **e)** Scalene   **f)** Scalene

6. For a typical sheet of copy paper, the largest equilateral triangle you can draw has side length 25 cm. The width of the sheet of paper is the height of the triangle.

7. For a typical sheet of copy paper, you can draw two large isosceles triangles that have different shapes but the same area. One has the length of the paper as its base, and the width as its height. The other has the width as its base and the length as its height.

8. All triangles with these side lengths have the same shape.

10. Yes; an isosceles triangle has at least 2 sides of equal length. Since an equilateral triangle has 3 sides of equal length, it is also an isosceles triangle.

Linking Ideas: Mathematics and Technology
Investigating the Medians of a Triangle, page 182

For any triangle, the medians intersect at a point inside the triangle.

3.2 Constructing Triangles Using Ruler and Protractor
Developing the Ideas, page 184

Activity 1

1. All the triangles look the same.

Activity 2

1. All the triangles look the same.

Activity 3

2. For each set of measurements, all the triangles look the same.

Working with Mathematics, page 187

1. a) Acute   **b)** Right   **c)** Straight
    d) Acute   **e)** Obtuse   **f)** Right

2. a) Obtuse   **b)** Acute   **c)** Right
    d) Right   **e)** Obtuse   **f)** Acute

3. $\angle ABE$, $\angle FBC$, $\angle BFC$, $\angle HFG$

4. a) Equilateral   **b)** Obtuse scalene   **c)** Acute isosceles
    d) Acute isosceles   **e)** Acute isosceles   **f)** Right scalene

5. a) e   **b)** b   **c)** c   **d)** a   **e)** f   **f)** d

6. b) You can draw 2 acute isosceles triangles, 3 right isosceles triangles, 1 right scalene triangle, and 2 obtuse scalene triangles.

7. a) i) Yes   **ii)** Yes   **iii)** No   **iv)** No

8. a) i) 5 cm   **ii)** 7 cm   **c)** 10.7 cm   **d)** 1070 m

9. a) Answers may vary in parts i and iii.
    i) $\angle ABD$, $\angle EBC$; $\angle ABE$, $\angle DBC$
    ii) $\angle JKM$; $\angle MKL$
    iii) $\angle PQU$, $\angle UQT$, $\angle TQS$, $\angle SQR$; $\angle PQS$, $\angle UQR$
   b) Answers may vary.

10. b) Right, scalene

11. Acute

12. The triangle in part d is acute, the triangle in part e is obtuse.

13. b) Each triangle has 2 sides of equal length. Triangles drawn for parts i and ii may vary in size and shape. The right isosceles triangles may vary in size, but will all have the same shape.

14. b) All the triangles may vary in size and shape. The side lengths in each triangle are all different.

15. It is not possible to draw either triangle.

16. 700 m   **17.** All the angles measure 60°.

18. For each triangle, the angles opposite the equal sides are equal.

19. a) 3   **b)** Equilateral   **c)** Isosceles
    d) No; in an obtuse triangle, two of the altitudes are outside the triangle.
    e) Yes; in a right triangle, the sides adjacent to the right angle are altitudes of the triangle.

20. a) 3   **b)** Equilateral   **c)** Isosceles
    d) Yes; because the midpoint of a side must be on the side.
    e) No; a side joins two vertices, not a vertex and the midpoint of a side.

3.3 Congruent Line Segments, Angles, and Figures

Developing the Ideas, page 190

Activity 1

1. Each figure is symmetrical about the fold line.
2. 4

Activity 2

1. GH   2. ∠PQR   3. △DFE

5. a) Measure the lengths of the line segments.
   b) They have the same length.
6. a) Use a protractor to measure the angles in degrees.
   b) They have the same measures.
7. a) Measure the lengths of the sides.
   b) The sides and angles have the same lengths and measures.

Activity 3

2. $a = c$ and $b = d$
6. When two lines intersect, the angles across from each other have equal measure.

Working with Mathematics, page 193

1. a) AB and CD have the same length.
   b) ∠ABC and ∠DEF have the same measure.
   c) △ABC and △XYZ have the same side lengths and angle measures.
2. a) When the size of the photocopied figure is the same as the size of the original figure
   b) When the size of the photocopied figure is smaller or larger than the size of the original figure
3. Yes, you can place one segment on top of the other so they coincide.
4. Measure the radii. If the radii are equal, the circles are congruent.
5. a) So they can be used in and counted by machines
   b) So it fits the lock
   c) So they can be filled and packed by machine
   d) So they all travel the same distance when hit with the same force
6. a) Yes, since one completely covers the other when they are placed on top of one another, they must have the same area.
   b) No; for example, triangles with base 4 cm and height 3 cm and with base 6 cm and height 2 cm both have an area of 6 cm^2 but are not congruent.
7. a) Yes; since the side lengths are equal, the perimeters will be equal.
   b) No; for example triangles with side lengths 12 cm, 6 cm, 8 cm, and 10 cm, 9 cm, 7 cm both have perimeter 26 cm, but are not congruent.
8. a) Yes; the two angles have the same measure.
   b) No; they only have 1 pair of equal sides.
9. ∠PQR and ∠STU are congruent.
10. a) ∠BAC = ∠QPR, ∠ACB = ∠PRQ, ∠CAB = ∠RQP, AB = PQ, AC = PR, BC = QR
    b) ∠JKL = ∠XYZ, ∠KLJ = ∠YZX, ∠LJK = ∠ZXY, JK = XY, KL = YZ, JL = XZ
11. CD = LM
12. a) 52°   b) 121°   c) 53°   d) 53°
13. a) Yes, the triangles have the same side lengths and angles.
    b) Yes, the triangles have the same side lengths and angles.

c) No
d) Yes, the triangles have the same side lengths and angles.
14. A and D are congruent.
15. b) The angles across from each other are equal.
    d) Use the fact that when two lines intersect, the opposite angles are equal.
16. a) 116°   b) 23°   c) 90°   d) 52°   e) 81°   f) 49°
17. b) The angles at the centre are equal and each has measure 90°.
    d) In exercise 13, there are two pairs of equal angles. The measures of the angles in each pair depend on the length and width of the rectangle.
18. a) A and C, B and E, D and F   b) D and F
19. △MNP and △QSR: ∠MPN = ∠QRS, ∠PMN = ∠RSP, ∠MNP = ∠QSR, MN = QS, PM = RQ, PN = RS; △DEF and △JKL: ∠FDE = ∠LJK, ∠DEF = ∠JKL, ∠EFD = ∠KLJ, DE = JK, EF = KL, DF = JL; △ABC = △YWX: ∠ABC = ∠YWX, ∠ACB = ∠YXW, ∠ACB = ∠YXW, AB = YW, AC = YX, BC = WX
20. By joining the dots with horizontal or vertical lines, you can draw 4 other pairs of congruent figures different from the figures shown here.
21. a) The angles opposite the congruent sides have equal measures.
    b) The two figures are congruent. Each figure is a right triangle.
    c) The two figures formed by the line of symmetry are congruent, so corresponding angles in these figures have the same measure. This shows that the third angle of the isosceles triangle is bisected by the line of symmetry.
22. a) △ABC and △AFE, △ACD and △AED, △ABD and △AFD, △AEB and △ACF
    b) △QUR and △TUS, △PTR and △PQS, △RQS and △STR

Linking Ideas: Mathematics and Science

Fingerprints, page 196

Answers may vary.

3.4 Conditions for Congruence

Developing the Ideas, page 199

Activity 1

1. 6.2 km, 24.8 km   2. △MBX   3. 6.2 km
4. The angle from the balloon to the tornado

Activity 2

1. No; △ABC must be congruent to △DEF.
2. Yes; you can draw △GHI so that it is an enlargement or reduction of △JKM.
3. No; △NPQ must be congruent to △RST.
4. Yes; you can draw two triangles with these conditions that are not congruent.
5. No; △ABC must be congruent to △DEF.
6. Only one triangle can be drawn if you are given any of the following pieces of information:
   • the lengths of the three sides
   • the lengths of two sides and the measure of the angle between them

- the measures of two angles and the length of the side between them

Working with Mathematics, page 202

1. One

2. a) Yes   b) No
   c) No, one may be an enlargement or reduction of the other.

3. a) 4 cm, 5 cm, 2 cm   b) 5 cm, 6 cm, 4 cm

4. a) 6.2 cm   b) 130°   c) 3 cm

5. a) 6.7 cm   b) 84°   c) 57°   d) 57°

6. a) 5   b) 1   c) 4   d) 3

7. Yes, the triangles have the same side lengths.

8. a) Yes; AB = DE, BC = EF, AC = DF, ∠BAC = ∠EDF, ∠BCA = ∠EFD, ∠ABC = ∠DEF
   b) No   c) No

10. △CDE and △UVW (3 equal sides); △ABC and △SRT (3 equal sides); △PQR and △LKJ (2 equal sides and the angle between them); △EFG and △MNL (2 equal angles and the side between them)

11. a) 5 cm, 110°   b) 60°, 70°

12. Yes; since two pairs of angles in the triangles have equal measure and the angles in a triangle have a sum of 180°, you know that ∠R = ∠U. So, since the measure of two angles and the length of the side between them are equal, the two triangles are congruent.

13. Answers may vary.
    a) Cut out one triangle. Place it over the other triangle to see whether you can find matching sides and angles.
    b) Measure all sides in each triangle. Look for 3 pairs of equal sides.

14. a) Not necessarily; not necessarily
    b) Yes; not necessarily
    c) The length of a corresponding side of each triangle

3.5 Similar Figures

Developing the Ideas, page 204

1. 1.5 cm, 2.6 cm, 0.6; 1.5 cm, 5.2 cm, 0.3; 3.0 cm, 5.2 cm, 0.6

2. The first and third logos have the same height-to-width ratio.

3., 4.

Rectangle	Length (cm)	Width (cm)	Length/Width
A	4.5	1.0	4.5
B	3.0	1.0	3.0
C	2.5	2.5	1.0
D	2.0	1.5	1.$\overline{3}$
E	4.5	1.5	3.0
F	5.0	2.0	2.5

5. B, E   6. B, E

Working with Mathematics, page 206

1. Answers may vary. Measure their lengths and widths. If the length-to-width ratios are equal, the rectangles are similar.

2. Answers may vary. Two figures are similar if they have the same shape.

3. No; explanations may vary; for example, they do not have the same shape.

4. Yes; explanations may vary; for example, corresponding sides are in the same ratio.

5. EFGH and KLMN: corresponding sides EF and KL, FG and LM, GH and MN, EH and KN
   ABCD and QRST: corresponding sides AB and QR, BC and RS, CD and ST, DA and TQ
   HIJK and VWXY: corresponding sides HI and VW, IJ and WX, JK and XY, KH and YV
   PQRS and STUV: corresponding sides PQ and ST, QR and TU, RS and UV, SP and VS

6. a) 4 : 2; 6 : 3   b) Yes   c) 1.5
   d) Yes; explanations may vary; all circles are similar to each other.

7. c) Yes; ratios of corresponding sides are equal.

8. c) No; the two rectangles have a different ratio of length to width.

9. a) 3.6 m   b) 143 cm

10. C; it has the same length-to-width ratio.

11. a) 2 : 1   b) 2 : 1   c) 3.7 cm   d) 1.8 cm
    e) 11.5 cm², 6.8 cm²   f) 59%

12. a) kp b) k^2A

3.6 Similar Triangles

Developing the Ideas, page 208

Activity 1

Answers may vary due to measures taken.

1. △ABC: 117.0 mm, 104.0 mm, 39.0 mm
   △DEF: 70.0 mm, 40.0 mm, 90.0 mm
   △GHJ: 30.0 mm, 67.5 mm, 45.0 mm
   △KLM: 30.0 mm, 67.5 mm, 52.5 mm

2. △ABC: 177.0 mm, 104.0 mm, 39.0 mm
   △DEF: 90.0 mm, 70.0 mm, 40.0 mm
   △GHJ: 67.5 mm, 45.0 m, 30.0 mm
   △KLM: 67.5 mm, 52.5 mm, 30.0 mm

3. △ABC, 117.0 : 104.0 : 39.0 or 9 : 8 : 3
   △DEF, 90.0 : 70.0 : 40.0 or 9 : 7 : 4
   △GHJ, 67.5 : 45.0 : 30.0 or 9 : 6 : 4
   △KLM, 67.5 : 52.5 : 30.0 or 9 : 7 : 4

4. △ABC, 3 : 2.$\overline{6}$: 1
   △DEF, 2.25 : 1.75 : 1
   △GHJ, 2.25 : 1.5 : 1
   △KLM, 2.25 : 1.75 : 1

5. △DEF, △KLM

6. △DEF, △KLM

Activity 2

1. to 6. Answers may vary.

7. Yes, the two triangles should be similar.

8. Corresponding angles should be equal.

Working with Mathematics, page 213

1. Determine whether the triangles have 3 pairs of equal angles, or whether all sides are proportional.

2. a) Similar triangles are not necessarily congruent. For example, the triangles constructed in Activity 2 were similar but not congruent. Corresponding sides were not the same length.
   b) Congruent triangles are always similar, since all congruent triangles have 3 pairs of equal angles.

3. R; by measuring, all angles are equal.

4. a) ∠A = ∠F, ∠B = ∠D, ∠C = ∠E; AB = FD, BC = DE, CA = EF

b) ∠P = ∠Z, ∠Q = ∠X, ∠R = ∠Y; PQ = ZX, QR = XY, RP = YZ

5. a) ∠A = 34°, ∠P = 56°, ∠Q = 90°
  b) ∠D = ∠G = ∠J = 70°, ∠F = 40°
  c) All angles equal 60°.

6. a) Since ∠B = ∠S and ∠C = ∠T, and the angles in any triangle add to 180°, we know that ∠A = ∠R, $x = 7.2$, $y = 7.8$.
  b) Since ∠J = ∠V and ∠Q = ∠R, and the angles in any triangle add to 180°, we know that ∠C = ∠A; $x = 6$, $y = 7.5$.

7. Trace one triangle, then check for pairs of equal angles by placing the tracing over the other angles. Alternatively, measure all the angles in each triangle and compare.

8. a) $\frac{11.0}{6.0} = \frac{x}{4.0}$, $x = 7.3$ **b)** $\frac{12.0}{7.0} = \frac{x}{10.0}$, $x = 17.1$

9. a) △XYZ and △PQR; $x = 4.8$, $y = 6.7$
  b) △PQR and △PST; $x = 15$, $y = 2$

10. a) △CAB and △CED; CE = 5
  b) △ABD and △ACE; CE = 12

11. Since the ironing board is parallel to the floor, ∠CAE = ∠DBE and ∠ACE = ∠EDB. Since opposite angles are equal, ∠AEC = ∠BED.

12. a) $x = 10$, $y = 9$ **b)** $x = 9$, $y = 10$

13. a) △QPR and △QTS   **b)** △UXY and △UVW

14. a) No
  b) All the known measures are from the same triangle. You need at least one measure from the second triangle to determine unknown lengths.

15. a) $x = 10$, $y = 18$ **b)** $x = 4.8$, $y = 1.2$
  c) $x = 4.88$, $y = 15.00$

16. a) $\frac{FD}{DE}$ **b)** $\frac{DE}{EF}$ **c)** $\frac{ED}{DF}$

17. a) 7   **b)** 4.2   **c)** 7.5

18. 1.2 cm, 2.4 cm, 1.9 cm, 3.8 cm; yes

19. △DGE is similar to △FDE. Both have a right angle, and ∠E is common to both triangles. Also, △DGF is similar to △EDF, for the same reasons. Finally, △DGE is similar to △FGD, because both have a right angle and ∠P is common to both.

20. a) △ADC ~ △ABC; $x = 7.2$, $y = 7$
  b) △GFI ~ △GHF ~ △FHI; $x = 7.0$, $y = 3.8$
  c) △BDE ~ △BAC; $x = 10.5$, $y = 5.5$
  d) △RQS ~ △RPQ; $x = 1.6$, $y = 3.2$

Quest: Is a Laser Gun Better for Catching Speeders than a Radar Gun?, page 216

At 200 m, the radar beam is about 21 m wide while the laser beam is 60 cm wide. The laser gun is better because it has only one car in its field of vision at this range.

3.7 Solving Problems Using Similar Triangles
Working with Mathematics, page 221

1. The angles in any triangle add to 180°. If we know the measures of two angles, we can find the measure of the third angle.

2. a) Side lengths of similar triangles are proportional.
  b) Corresponding angles of similar triangles are equal.

3. a) If we know AB||CD, we can show ∠A = ∠D and ∠C = ∠B
  b) If we know PQ||RS, we can show ∠TPQ = ∠TRS and ∠TQP = ∠TSR

4. a) △WXY is similar to △VTU; $x = 9$, $y = 7.5$
  b) △CDE is similar to △BZA; $x = 26.7$, $y = 24$
  c) △FGH is similar to △KIJ; $x = 14.4$, $y = 10$

5. a) △CED is similar to △CBA; $x = 9$
  b) △MKL is similar to △MPN; $x = 15$
  c) △XYZ is similar to △XWV; $x = 10$
  d) △ABE is similar to △ACD; $x = 6$

6. 26.5 m   **7.** 22.4 m   **8.** 18.7 m

9. $x = 4.3$ m, $y = 9.6$ m   **10.** 38.4 m

11. 30 m

12. a) △PMY is similar to △PNX; $x = 5.3$, $y = 5$
  b) △ACE is similar to △BCD; $x = 9$, $y = 5$

13. 34.9 m   **14.** 32 m   **15.** 14.0 m   **16.** 225 m

17. 22.8 m   **18.** 9.9 cm   **19.** 7.1 m

20. a) 75, 90, 105, 120, 135   **b)** 2535

Review, page 224

3. a) Scalene; no equal sides are indicated.
  b) Isosceles; two equal sides are indicated.
  c) Isosceles; two equal sides are indicated
  d) Equilateral; three equal sides are indicated.

4. There are two possible triangles ABC, on either side of segment AB. The two triangles are congruent.

5. Yes

6. Each triangle has three medians.

8. a) Right   **b)** Obtuse   **c)** Acute   **d)** Right

9. Answers may vary.

10. a) 9 cm   **b)** 19 cm
  d) About 11.5 cm   **e)** About 115 m

11. There are three sets of conditions: three sets of corresponding sides are equal; two sets of corresponding sides and the angles between them are equal; two sets of corresponding angles and the side between them are equal.

12. Triangle Z is congruent to △ABC. By measuring, determine that three pairs of corresponding sides are equal.

13. a) ∠A = ∠D, ∠B = ∠E, ∠C = ∠F; AB = DE, BC = EF, CA = FD
  b) ∠P = ∠X, ∠Q = ∠Z, ∠R = ∠Y; PQ = XZ, QR = ZY, RP = YX

14. a) 87°   **b)** 64°   **c)** 90°   **d)** 48°

15. △ABC is congruent to △XYZ. Since two pairs of angles are known to be congruent, the third pair of angles must also be congruent. This gives us two pairs of equal angles and the sides between them.

16. a) 3.6   **b)** 15.7

17. Triangle C is similar to △DEF. Measure to confirm that corresponding angles are equal.

18. a) 10.85   **b)** 2.3

19. The crosspiece ST is parallel to QR. The properties of parallel lines indicate that ∠PST = ∠PQR, and ∠PTS = ∠PRQ. The third angle, P, is common to both triangles. So △PST and △PQR have three pairs of equal angles and are therefore similar triangles.

20. 70 m

CHAPTER 4 RIGHT TRIANGLE CALCULATIONS

Start With What You Know, page 230

1. a) 72° **b)** 10.4 m

2. a) 48 m **b)** 49 m

3. a) 2.5 cm **b)** 2.9 cm

4. a) 4.2 cm **b)** 7.3 cm

5. a) 45 **b)** 1.5 **c)** 0.375 **d)** 14.786

6. a) 3 cm **b)** 10 cm **c)** AB and BC

4.1 The Tangent Ratio in Right Triangles
Developing the Ideas, page 232

3. In each case, the other two angles are about 53° and 37°.

5. The triangles are similar.

Working with Mathematics, page 237

1. a) Since all the triangles have a common angle, and a right angle, the third angle in each triangle must be equal. Triangles with all corresponding angles equal are similar.

2. Parts a and d are true.

3. Because the tangent of 45° is 1

4. a) 63°

b) Calculate tan B $\doteq$ 1.9626; multiply by 5 to obtain 9.813.

c) Answers may vary.

5. Parts a, b, c, and d are all true.

6. a) PQ, MN **b)** PA, MA

7. a) $\frac{PQ}{PA}, \frac{MN}{MA}$ **b)** $\frac{PA}{PQ}, \frac{MA}{MN}$

8. Answers may vary. Possible side lengths for AB and BC are given.

a) BC = 5, AB = 9 **b)** BC = 3, AB = 7

c) BC = 4, AB = 11 **d)** BC = 12, AB = 5

9. a) $\frac{9}{5}$ **b)** $\frac{7}{3}$ **c)** $\frac{11}{4}$ **d)** $\frac{5}{12}$

10. a) 0.700 **b)** 1.150 **c)** 2.145 **d)** 5.671

11. a) tan A $\doteq$ 0.6, tan B $\doteq$ 1.667

b) tan A $\doteq$ 1.5, tan B $\doteq$ 0.667

c) tan A $\doteq$ 0.864, tan B $\doteq$ 1.158

12. a) i) 0.364 **ii)** 0.754 **iii)** 1.428 **iv)** 2.904

b) Answers may vary. For part iii, the diagram should show that the side opposite the 55° angle is about 1.4 times the length of the adjacent side.

13. All statements are true.

14. a) 3.9 cm **b)** 8.7 cm **c)** 18.5 cm **d)** 75.8 cm

15. a) 23.9 cm **b)** 3.0 cm **c)** 17.6 cm **d)** 6.4 cm

16. a) 5.2 m **b)** 5.3 m

17. a) 6435 m **b)** 3202 m

18. a) i) 0.3 **ii)** 0.6 **iii)** 1 **iv)** 1.7 **v)** 3.7

b) In this diagram, tan A represents the length of BC, since AC = 1.

c) Answers may vary. The tangent of an acute angle in a right triangle gives the length of the side opposite that acute angle, relative to the adjacent side.

19. a) i) 0.577 **ii)** 0.966 **iii)** 1.963 **iv)** 14.031

b) Answers may vary. For part ii, the diagram should show that the side opposite the 44° angle is almost equal to the adjacent side.

20. a) 32 cm **b)** 269 cm **c)** 60 cm **d)** 178 cm

21. a) 10.4 m **b)** 3.3 **c)** 10.4 m **d)** 3.3 m

22. a) 1176 m **b)** 2858 m

23. a) 179 m **b)** 369 m

24. a) 6.5 cm **b)** 15.5 cm **c)** 37.3 m **d)** 4.1 m

e) 3.5 cm **f)** 1.7 m **g)** 7.7 m **h)** 2.0 cm

25. $A \doteq 11$ cm², $P \doteq 15.8$ cm

26. a) i) 32.00000198 **ii)** 56.99889586

b) The TAN⁻¹ key gives the angle for a tangent entered.

c) Since tan 45° = 1, the calculator should display 45.

4.2 Calculating the Angles in a Right Triangle: Part I
Developing the Ideas, page 240

1. a) $\frac{3}{4}$ **b)** tangent of ∠A

2. About 37°; using a protractor

3. 37° is the angle whose tangent is $\frac{3}{4}$.

Working with Mathematics, page 243

1. a) They are complementary angles, since they are the two acute angles in a right triangle.

b) Tan A and tan C are reciprocals of each other.

c) Yes

2. a) 14° **b)** 35° **c)** 54° **d)** 73°

e) 29° **f)** 43° **g)** 64° **h)** 78°

3. a) 27° **b)** 22° **c)** 53° **d)** 51°

e) 37° **f)** 31° **g)** 68° **h)** 55°

4. a) i) 59° **ii)** 15° **b) i)** 31° **ii)** 75°

5. a) 63° **b)** 56° **c)** 37°

6. a) 58° **b)** 67° **c)** 70° **d)** 77°

7. a) 76° **b)** About 10.3 m

8. a) 27°, 63° **b)** 126°, 54°

9. 2.6°

10. a) ∠A $\doteq$ 28°, ∠B $\doteq$ 62° **b)** ∠A $\doteq$ 53°, ∠B $\doteq$ 37°

c) ∠A $\doteq$ 44°, ∠B $\doteq$ 46°

11. a) 14° **b)** 27° **c)** 37°

12. About 71°

13. Answers may vary.

14. 39°, 39°, 102°

15. a) From least to greatest angle: 11°, 14°, 18°, 27°, 45°, 63°, 72°, 76°, 79°

b) i) 6 **ii)** 12 **iii)** 29 **iv)** 58

c) i) 6 **ii)** 12 **iii)** 29 **iv)** 58

Quest: What Is Wrong with These Diagrams?, page 245

Area of square is 64 square units. Area of rectangle is 63 square units. Explanations may vary. We can determine, from the diagram of the rectangle, that
∠AOD $\doteq$ 21.0°, ∠BOE $\doteq$ 20.6°, and ∠COF $\doteq$ 21.8°

This tells us that the pieces, when rearranged, do not lie along the true diagonal of the rectangle. The angles are, however, close enough in measure to trick the eye.

4.3 The Sine and Cosine Ratios in Right Triangles

Developing the Ideas, page 246

2. From least to greatest: 5.0 cm, 10.0 cm, 15.0 cm, 20.0 cm

3. For each triangle, $\frac{BC}{AB} = 0.6$

4. For each triangle, $\frac{AC}{AB} = 0.8$

6. The same ratios result from the similarity of the four triangles, all of which have proportional sides.

Working with Mathematics, page 250

1. Explanations may vary.

2. Parts b and c are true.

3. a) Pythagorean Theorem

4. a) RG, LQ   **b)** AR, AL   **c)** AG, AQ

5. a) $\frac{RG}{AG}, \frac{LQ}{AQ}$ **b)** $\frac{AR}{AG}, \frac{AL}{AQ}$

6. a) $\frac{AR}{AG}$ **b)** $\frac{RG}{AG}$ **c)** $\frac{AL}{AQ}$ **d)** $\frac{LQ}{AQ}$

7. a) 0.9703, 0.2419   **b)** 0.6820, 0.7314   **c)** 0.3256, 0.9455
   d) 0.9877, 0.1564   **e)** 0.8829, 0.4695   **f)** 0.2419, 0.9703
   g) 0.7314, 0.6820   **h)** 0.9455, 0.3256   **i)** 0.1564, 0.9877
   j) 0.4695, 0.8829

8. a) 5.3 cm   **b)** 14.1 cm   **c)** 3.5 cm   **d)** 13.4 cm

9. a) AB $\doteq$ 24.1 m, BC $\doteq$ 6.5 m   **b)** AB $\doteq$ 10.6 m, BC $\doteq$ 22.7 m

10. a) PR $\doteq$ 19.6 cm, QR $\doteq$ 12.6 cm
   b) PR $\doteq$ 17.2 cm, QR $\doteq$ 8.3 cm

11. a) i) 0.5   **ii)** 0.927   **iii)** 0.978   **iv)** 0.326
   b) Answers may vary. For part i, the diagram should show that the side opposite the 30° angle is half the length of the hypotenuse.

12. a) If $b = 1$, then $a = 0.4226$
   b) True   **c)** True
   d) The length of b is 2.3662 times the length of a.

13. a) AB $\doteq$ 21.4 m, BC $\doteq$ 12.9 m   **b)** AB $\doteq$ 24.5 m, BC $\doteq$ 5.2 m

14. a) 9.6 m   **b)** 2.9 m

15. a) i) AC = 0.966, BC = 0.259   **ii)** AC = 0.866, BC = 0.5
   iii) AC = 0.707, BC = 0.707   **iv)** AC = 0.5, BC = 0.866
   v) AC = 0.259, BC = 0.966
   b) Cos A represents the length of AC, relative to AB. Sin A represents the length of BC, relative to AB.
   c) Answers may vary.

16. a) True
   b) If $b = 10\ 000$, then $c = 9063$.
   c) The length of c is 0.9063 times the length of b.
   d) True

17. a) i) 0.848   **ii)** 0.766   **iii)** 0.5   **iv)** 0.309
   b) Answers may vary. For part i, the diagram should show that the side opposite the 58° angle is 0.848 times the length of the hypotenuse. For part ii, the diagram should show that the side adjacent to the 40° angle is 0.766 times the length of the hypotenuse.

18. a) PR $\doteq$ 28.3 cm, QR $\doteq$ 24.0 cm
   b) PR $\doteq$ 22.4 cm, QR $\doteq$ 16.7 cm

19. 118 m   **20.** 2.9 m   **21.** 13.3 m   **22.** 16.9 cm

23. a) In the right triangle with angle 60°, the shorter leg is half the length of the hypotenuse (since the height of the equilateral triangle bisects the base).
   b) sin 30°

24. a) The $\boxed{\text{SIN}^{-1}}$ and $\boxed{\text{COS}^{-1}}$ keys provide the angles that have a given sine or cosine.
   b) 30

4.4 Calculating the Angles in a Right Triangle: Part II

Developing the Ideas, page 253

1. a) $\frac{3}{5}$ or 0.6   **b)** The sine of $\angle A$

2. About 37°

3. 37° is the angle whose sine is $\frac{3}{5}$.

4. a) $\frac{4}{5}$, or 0.8   **b)** The cosine of $\angle A$

5. 37° is the angle whose cosine is $\frac{4}{5}$.

Working with Mathematics, page 256

1. a) sin C $\doteq$ 0.923, cos C $\doteq$ 0.385, $\angle C \doteq 67°$
   b) They are complementary angles.
   c) Explanations may vary.
     i) Sin C = cos A, since the side adjacent to $\angle C$ is opposite $\angle A$.
     ii) cos C = sin A
   d) Yes

2. a) 37°   **b)** 39°   **c)** 73°   **d)** 77°
   e) 12°   **f)** 74°   **g)** 29°   **h)** 68°

3. a) 42°   **b)** 76°   **c)** 51°   **d)** 25°
   e) 37°   **f)** 13°

4. a) 71°   **b)** 14°   **c)** 30°   **d)** 41°   **e)** 53°
   f) 65°   **g)** 39°   **h)** 27°   **i)** 34°

5. a) 65°   **b)** 22°   **c)** 31°   **d)** 38°   **e)** 66°   **f)** 52°

6. a) $\angle A \doteq 23°$, $\angle C \doteq 67°$ **b)** $\angle A \doteq 53°$, $\angle C \doteq 37°$
   c) $\angle A \doteq 59°$, $\angle C \doteq 31°$ **d)** $\angle A \doteq 64°$, $\angle C \doteq 26°$

7. a) i) 56°   **ii)** 34°
   b) They are complementary.
   c) They are equal.
   d) They are equal.

8. a) 24°   **b)** 25°   **c)** 27°   **d)** 51°

9. a) $\angle A \doteq 24°$, $\angle C \doteq 66°$ **b)** $\angle A \doteq 47°$, $\angle C \doteq 43°$

10. $\angle P \doteq 49°$, $\angle R \doteq 41°$, PQ $\doteq$ 2.6 cm

11. a) 50°   **b)** 11.5 m

12. Explanations may vary. Both the sine and cosine ratios have the length of the hypotenuse as the second term. Since the hypotenuse is always the longest side in a right triangle, all sine and cosine ratios have a second term greater than the first term. This results in a value between 0 and 1.

13. a) 48°   **b)** 33°   **c)** 42°   **d)** 49°

14. a) 34.8°   **b)** 41.8°

15. a) 55.2°   **b)** 48.2°

16. a) 52.3°   **b)** 36.9°

17. a) 37.7°   **b)** 53.1°

18. a) $\angle P \doteq 58°$, $\angle R \doteq 32°$ **b)** $\angle P \doteq 59°$, $\angle R \doteq 31°$

19. a) 72.5°   **b)** 5.7 m

20. 53°

21. a) 41°, 41°, 98°   **b)** 71°, 71°, 38°

22. 7.3 m

Mathematics File: Gondola Lifts, page 258

Banff Sulphur Mountain, 26.8°
Lake Louise, 8.6°
Jasper, 33.1°

4.5 Working with Right Triangles

Working with Mathematics, page 262

1. Answers may vary.

2. a) sine   **b)** tangent   **c)** cosine

3. a) tangent   **b)** cosine

4. $BC \doteq 13.5$ cm, $AC \doteq 22.0$ cm

5. a) $\angle D = 60°$, $\angle F = 30°$ **b)** $\angle P \doteq 52°$, $\angle Q \doteq 38°$

6. a) $BC \doteq 10.9$, $CR \doteq 8.3$ **b)** $DS \doteq 10.3$, $DW \doteq 14.7$

7. a) $JL \doteq 21.0$ m, $\angle K \doteq 51°$, $\angle J \doteq 39°$
  b) $GH \doteq 20.6$ km, $\angle G \doteq 51°$, $\angle H \doteq 39°$

8. a) $NE \doteq 34.2$ cm, $PN \doteq 14.5$ cm, $\angle N \doteq 65°$
  b) $\angle Q \doteq 68°$, $QM \doteq 8.2$ m, $FM \doteq 20.4$ m

9. 62 m   **10.** 432 m   **11.** About 10 cm

12. Solutions may vary. Problem 1, 8.7 cm; Problem 2, 11.5 cm

13. $\angle X = 54°$, $XZ \doteq 15.3$ m, $YZ \doteq 12.4$

14. 72.7 m   **15.** 5.3 m   **16.** 33 m

17. 56 m, 63°   **18.** About 5 cm   **19.** 74°

20. About 9°

21. Statement 2 is true. Statement 1 suggests that $\tan^{-1} 2$ is either 30° or 60°, but this is not so. Statement 3 is not specific and is not true.

22. About 1.4 m   **23.** About 59 cm

Linking Ideas: Mathematics and Technology

Using Regular Polygons to Estimate π, page 265

1. 3.141 592 65 cm   **a)** Smaller   **b)** Smaller (3.105 828 541 cm)

2. b) The formula in cell B2 calculates the central angle at BON, since the polygon has B1 sides. The formula matches the step with the pentagon, $\frac{360°}{2 \times 5}$, which is the same as $\frac{180°}{5}$. The formula in cell B4 multiplies 2 by the length of the hypotenuse OB by the sine of $\angle$BON. Multiplying the length of OB by the sine of $\angle$BON gives the length of BN. Doubling the product gives the length of AB.
The formula in cell B5 multiplies the length of AB by the total number of sides. This yields the perimeter because the polygon is a regular polygon.

3. b) i) 3.128 689 300 804   **ii)** 3.141 075 907 812
  iii) 3.141 587 485 879   **iv)** 3.141 592 653 073
  c) The perimeter of any polygon contained in the circle must be smaller than the circumference of the circle.
  d) Less

4. More than 83 sides

Review, page 266

1. a) KM, PM   **b)** KL, LP   **c)** KL, LP
  d) KM, PM   **e)** LM, LM

2. a) 0.1763   **b)** 0.4663   **c)** 0.6494
  d) 2.3559   **e)** 5.1446   **f)** 9.5144

3. a) 23°   **b)** 57°   **c)** 59°
  d) 35°   **e)** 73°   **f)** 82°

4. a) 0.2250, 0.9744   **b)** 0.6947, 0.7193   **c)** 0.3907, 0.9205
  d) 0.9613, 0.2756   **e)** 0.5, 0.8660   **f)** 0.8290, 0.5592

5. a) 52°   **b)** 47°   **c)** 53°
  d) 39°   **e)** 26°   **f)** 7°

6. a) 3.3 cm   **b)** 7.3 cm   **c)** 6.1 cm   **d)** 2.4 cm

7. a) 27°   **b)** 52°   **c)** 21°   **d)** 34°

8. a) $\angle W \doteq 48°$, $\angle X \doteq 42°$ **b)** $\angle W \doteq 63°$, $\angle X \doteq 27°$
  c) $\angle W \doteq 54°$, $\angle X \doteq 36°$ **d)** $\angle W \doteq 74°$, $\angle X \doteq 16°$

9. a) 56.4°   **b)** 41.4°

10. a) 33.6°   **b)** 48.6°

11. a) 3.0 m   **b)** 26.0 cm   **c)** 54.5°   **d)** 33.5°

12. a) $\angle A \doteq 70°$, $\angle C \doteq 20°$, $AC \doteq 35.1$ cm
  b) $\angle P \doteq 29°$, $\angle Q \doteq 61°$, $QR \doteq 15.0$ m
  c) $\angle L \doteq 37°$, $JK \doteq 18.1$ m, $JL \doteq 24.0$ m
  d) $\angle M \doteq 56°$, $\angle P \doteq 34°$, $NP \doteq 31$ m
  e) $\angle E \doteq 29°$, $DF \doteq 30.1$ m, $DE \doteq 62.1$ m
  f) $\angle X \doteq 69°$, $XZ \doteq 22.3$ cm, $XY \doteq 62.1$ cm

13. About 141 m

14. a) About 13.7 cm   **b)** About 25.9 cm

15. About 16 m   **16.** About 142 m

17. About 4.8 m, 17°

18. a) 76°   **b)** About 5.8 m   **c)** About 71°, 5.7 m

19. a) 72°, 72°, 36°   **b)** 37°, 37°, 106°

Cumulative Review, page 270

1. Calculated results are given. Key sequences may vary.
  a) 371.15   **b)** 307.44   **c)** −0.326   **d)** 1.25

2. Answers may vary.   **3.** $\frac{1}{8}$ **4.** About 3 days

5. a) $4x$; 16   **b)** 0; 0   **c)** $3x + 2y$; 6
  d) $5x − y$; 23   **e)** $2x − 3y$; 17   **f)** $3x$; 12

6. a) 15   **b)** −5   **c)** $\frac{5}{2}$, or 2.5
  d) −3   **e)** −2   **f)** 0

7. 15 and 16

8. a) $b < 2$ **b)** $g > -4$
  c) $k > -\frac{5}{3}$, or $k > -1.\overline{6}$ **d)** $t > -3$

9. a) $\triangle$ABC is congruent to $\triangle$EDF. We know two sides and the angle between them are equal to two corresponding sides and the angle between them. AB = ED, BC = DF, CA = FE
  b) $\triangle$ABC is congruent to $\triangle$HIG. We know two sides and the angle between them are equal to two corresponding sides and the angle between them. AB = HI, BC = IG, AC = GH

10. a) $\triangle$ABC is similar to $\triangle$DEF. Three pairs of angles are indicated as equal.
  b) $\triangle$GJL is similar to $\triangle$HJK. We are given two pairs of equal angles. The third angle is common to both triangles.
  c) $\triangle$RLM is similar to $\triangle$RPQ. We can show $\angle$RLM = $\angle$P and $\angle$RML = $\angle$Q, since LM||PQ. The common angle at R gives the third pair of equal angles.
  d) $\triangle$VWZ is similar to $\triangle$XWY. Since VZ||XY, we can show $\angle$V = $\angle$X and $\angle$Z = $\angle$Y. Since opposite angles are equal, $\angle$VWZ = $\angle$XWY

11. a) 34.9 m   **b)** 32.2

12. 61.2 m

13. a) 0.4695   **b)** 0.9613   **c)** 1.4281
  d) 0.6293   **e)** 0.5736   **f)** 3.4874

14. a) $41°$ b) $19°$ c) $37°$
    d) $51°$ e) $49°$ f) $60°$
15. a) 4.8 cm b) 7.8 cm c) 7.5 cm d) 5.6 cm
16. a) 0.871, 60.6° b) 0.6, 36.9°
17. a) 38.1 cm b) 22° c) 26.3 m d) 28°
18. a) 5.8 cm, 8.2 cm, 45° b) 15.6 cm, 19.8 cm, 52°
    c) 29.5 cm, 12.5 cm, 23° d) 2.2 m, 3.2 m, 48°
19. a) 16.8 cm b) 29.3 cm
20. 114 m 21. 38°

CHAPTER 5 POWERS AND ROOTS

Start With What You Know, page 275

1. a) $256 \times 256 \times 256$; 256; 3
   b) 16 777 216   c) Yes
2. a) $2 \times 2 \times 2$ b) 3×3
   c) Explanations may vary. The cube has volume $2 \times 2 \times 2$ cubic units. The square has an area of 3×3 square units.
3. a) 1000 b) 27 c) 625 d) -625
   e) 625 f) -625 g) 729 h) 9
4. a) $2 \times 2 \times 2 \times 2 \times 2 \times 2 \times 2 \times 2$
   b) $(2 \times 2 \times 2 \times 2 \times 2 \times 2 \times 2 \times 2) \times (2 \times 2 \times 2 \times 2 \times 2 \times 2 \times 2 \times 2) \times (2 \times 2 \times 2 \times 2 \times 2 \times 2 \times 2 \times 2)$
   c) Explanations may vary. The product is equivalent to $256 \times 256 \times 256$ or 256^3.
5. a) 8.7 cm b) 7.2 cm 6. 35 cm
7. a) 10^6 b) 10^9 c) 10^{12}
8. a) 2.8×10^6 b) 2.8×10^7 c) 2.8×10^8
   d) 6.0×10^9 e) 6.0×10^{10} f) 6.0×10^{11}
9. a) About 16.8 million b) About 1.68×10^7

5.1 Multiplying and Dividing Powers
Developing the Ideas, page 276

Multiplying Powers

1. a) $10 \times 10 \times 10 \times 10 \times 10 \times 10 \times 10$; 10^7
   b) $10 \times 10 \times 10 \times 10 \times 10 \times 10 \times 10 \times 10$; 10^8
   c) $5 \times 5 \times 5 \times 5 \times 5 \times 5 \times 5 \times 5 \times 5$; 5^9
   d) $5 \times 5 \times 5 \times 5$; 5^4
   e) $2 \times 2 \times 2 \times 2 \times 2 \times 2 \times 2 \times 2 \times 2 \times 2 \times 2$; 2^{11}
2. Answers may vary.
3. To multiply two powers with the same base, take the base raised to the sum of the exponents.
4. No; 2^3 and 3^5 have different bases.

Dividing Powers

1. a) $\dfrac{10 \times 10 \times 10 \times 10 \times 10 \times 10 \times 10 \times 10}{10 \times 10 \times 10 \times 10 \times 10}$; 10^3
   b) $\dfrac{10 \times 10 \times 10 \times 10 \times 10 \times 10 \times 10}{10 \times 10 \times 10}$; 10^4
   c) $\dfrac{5 \times 5 \times 5 \times 5 \times 5 \times 5 \times 5 \times 5 \times 5 \times 5}{5 \times 5 \times 5 \times 5}$; 5^6
   d) $\dfrac{5 \times 5 \times 5 \times 5 \times 5}{5 \times 5 \times 5 \times 5}$; 5^1
   e) $\dfrac{9 \times 9 \times 9 \times 9 \times 9 \times 9 \times 9 \times 9}{9 \times 9 \times 9}$; 9^5
2. Answers may vary.
3. To determine the quotient of two powers with the same base, take the base raised to the difference of the powers.
4. No; 5^7 and 10^4 have different bases.

Working with Mathematics, page 278

1. a) $3 \times 3, 2 \times 2 \times 2$ b) $3 \times 3 \times 3 \times 3, 4 \times 4 \times 4$
2. a) 7^8 b) 23^{19} c) 16^5 d) 8^{12}
3. a) 202 000 m, 10^8 m^2 b) 10^5 m
4. a) 10^2 times b) 10^5 times
5. a) 10^3 b) 10^4 c) 10^8 d) 10^6
   e) 10^5 f) 10^{12}
6. a) 3^{10} b) 7^{11} c) $(-5)^{25}$ d) 2.1^{16}
   e) $(-8)^6$ f) $(-1.7)^7$ g) $(\frac{2}{5})^{22}$ h) $(\frac{3}{11})^{36}$
7. a) 3^5 b) 2^9 c) 8^{15} d) 1.5^{12}
   e) 6^6 f) $(-2)^4$
8. a) 2^2 b) 3^4 c) $(-5)^{10}$ d) 7^7
9. a) 10^5 b) 10^{13} c) 10^{16} d) 10^4
   e) 10^5 f) 10^{12} g) $(-4)^{17}$ h) 3^{11}
   i) 7.2^{12} j) $(-5)^2$ k) 1.2^3 l) 9^8
10. a) 2, 4, 8, 16, 32, 64, 128, 256
    b) i) 256 ii) 128 iii) 32 iv) 4
11. a) -2 b) 4 c) -8 d) 16
    e) -32 f) 64 g) -128 h) 256
12. a) n is even. b) n is odd.
13. a) 10^9 b) 10^9 c) 10^{10} d) 10^{14} e) 10^8
    f) 10^9 g) 10^8 h) 10^{15} i) 10^{11} j) 10^{15}
14. a) 10^7 b) 10^5 c) 10^7 d) 10^4 e) 10^2 f) 10^3
15. a) 3^5 b) 9^2 c) $(-8)^3$ d) $(-2)^7$
    e) 5^3 f) 2^6 g) 4^{-2} h) 7^2
    i) 11^7 j) 5.2^7 k) $(-3)^5$ l) 8.3^7
16. a) 10^4 b) 2^6 c) 3^5 d) $(-5)^6$ e) 6^8 f) $(-1)^4$
17. About 10^{22}
18. a) 3 b) 2 c) 0.5 d) 5
    e) 3 f) 4 g) -0.5 h) 6
19. a) 15
    b) Answers may vary. Keep the numbers in the same places but make each entry a power with the same base. For example:

The magic product is 2^{15}.

Quest: Good News Travels Fast, page 280

It will take 20 days for at least 1 000 000 people to have tried the shampoo. In this time, 1 048 575 people will have tried the shampoo. In 25 days, 33 554 431 people will have tried the shampoo. If you start with one million and keep dividing in half, you would have to perform 20 divisions to get a number that is less than 1.

5.2 Zero and Negative Exponents
Working with Mathematics, page 284

1. Explanations and descriptions may vary.

a) $4 \times 4 \times 4$, $\dfrac{1}{4 \times 4 \times 4}$ b) $4 \times 4 \times 4$, $-\dfrac{1}{4 \times 4 \times 4}$

c) $(-4) \times (-4) \times (-4)$, $-\dfrac{1}{4 \times 4 \times 4}$

2. a) 1   **b)** 1   **c)** -1 **d)** -1
e) -1 **f)** -1 **g)** 1   **h)** 1

3. a) $\dfrac{1}{3}$ **b)** $\dfrac{1}{4}$ **c)** $\dfrac{1}{7}$ **d)** $\dfrac{1}{25}$
e) $\dfrac{1}{27}$ **f)** $\dfrac{1}{36}$

4. a) $-\dfrac{1}{3}$ **b)** $-\dfrac{1}{4}$ **c)** $-\dfrac{1}{7}$ **d)** $-\dfrac{1}{25}$
e) $-\dfrac{1}{27}$ **f)** $-\dfrac{1}{36}$

5. a) 8   **b)** $\dfrac{1}{8}$ **c)** -8 **d)** $-\dfrac{1}{8}$
e) -8 **f)** $-\dfrac{1}{8}$ **g)** 8   **h)** $\dfrac{1}{8}$

6. a) 2   **b)** 9   **c)** 25   **d)** 8
e) -16 **f)** $-10\ 000$

7. a) -2 **b)** -9 **c)** -25 **d)** -8
e) 16   **f)** $10\ 000$

8. a) 5   **b)** 16   **c)** 8   **d)** 1
e) $0.\overline{6}$ **f)** 2.25

9. a) 10^{-3} **b)** 3^{-7} **c)** 5^{-8} **d)** $(-2)^7$
e) 4^{11} **f)** $(-7)^{-13}$

10. a) Each exponent of 3 is one less than the exponent in the previous power.
b) $27, 9, 3, 1, 0.\overline{3}, 0.\overline{1}, \dots$
c) $3^{-3} = 0.037\ 037$, $3^{-4} = 0.012\ 345\ 679$

11. a) $\dfrac{1}{16}$ **b)** $\dfrac{1}{16}$ **c)** $\dfrac{1}{100}$ **d)** 1
e) 1   **f)** $-\dfrac{1}{3}$ **g)** $\dfrac{1}{25}$ **h)** $\dfrac{1}{343}$

12. a) $-\dfrac{1}{8}$ **b)** $-\dfrac{1}{16}$ **c)** $-\dfrac{1}{100}$ **d)** 1
e) -1 **f)** $\dfrac{1}{3}$ **g)** $-\dfrac{1}{25}$ **h)** $-\dfrac{1}{343}$

13. a) 10   **b)** $\dfrac{1}{16}$ **c)** -343 **d)** $\dfrac{1}{125}$
e) 3   **f)** 81   **g)** $\dfrac{1}{16}$ **h)** $\dfrac{1}{9}$
i) $\dfrac{1}{10\ 000}$ **j)** $\dfrac{1}{9}$ **k)** 2   **l)** 4

14. a) $3, -3$ **b)** $5, -5$ **c)** 2   **d)** -3
e) -2 **f)** -3

15. a) Each exponent of 2 is one less than the exponent in the previous power.
b) $8, 4, 2, 1, 0.5, 0.25, \dots$
c) $2^{-3} = 0.125$, $2^{-4} = 0.0625$

16. a) -27 **b)** 9   **c)** -3 **d)** 1
e) $-\dfrac{1}{3}$ **f)** $\dfrac{1}{9}$ **g)** $-\dfrac{1}{27}$ **h)** $\dfrac{1}{81}$

17. a) -64 **b)** -16 **c)** -4 **d)** -1
e) $-\dfrac{1}{4}$ **f)** $-\dfrac{1}{16}$ **g)** $\dfrac{1}{64}$ **h)** $\dfrac{1}{256}$

18. a) 1000   **b)** 100   **c)** 10   **d)** 1
e) 0.1   **f)** 0.01   **g)** 0.001   **h)** 0.0001

19. a) $\dfrac{1}{64}$ **b)** $\dfrac{1}{64}$ **c)** $\dfrac{1}{64}$ **d)** 1
e) $\dfrac{1}{125}$ **f)** $\dfrac{1}{36}$ **g)** $\dfrac{1}{16}$ **h)** $-\dfrac{1}{243}$

20. Explanations may vary.
a) $2^{-3} > 3^{-2}$ **b)** $2^{-4} = 4^{-2}$ **c)** $2^{-5} < 5^{-2}$

21. Explanations may vary.
a) $0.000\ 976\ 6$ **b)** 0.0016   **c)** $0.002\ 915$
d) $0.000\ 064$ **e)** $-0.004\ 63$ **f)** 0.1615

22. Descriptions may vary.
a) 64   **b)** 32   **c)** 16   **d)** 8
e) 4   **f)** 2   **g)** 1   **h)** $\dfrac{1}{2}$

23. a) 1   **b)** 2   **c)** 4   **d)** 8
e) 16   **f)** 32   **g)** 64   **h)** 128

24. a) 3   **b)** 5   **c)** $\dfrac{1}{100\ 000}$ **d)** 64
e) $\dfrac{1}{8}$ **f)** 1   **g)** $\dfrac{1}{2401}$ **h)** 6
i) -3 **j)** $\dfrac{1}{3}$ **k)** $\dfrac{1}{25}$ **l)** 16

25. a) $\dfrac{1}{64}$ **b)** $14\ 641$ **c)** 6561   **d)** $\dfrac{1}{36}$
e) 27   **f)** 125

26. a) $\dfrac{1}{512}$ **b)** $\dfrac{1}{729}$ **c)** -2 **d)** 4
e) 512   **f)** 9

27. a) 5   **b)** 2   **c)** 3   **d)** -2
e) -6 **f)** -4

28. -2

29. Ruda is correct. The minus sign applies to the entire expression following: -2^{-4} means $-(2^{-4})$.

30. 2, 4

5.3 Powers of Products, Quotients, and Powers
Working with Mathematics, page 288

1. a) $3 \times 2 \times 3 \times 2 \times 3 \times 2 \times 3 \times 2$
b) $\dfrac{3}{2} \times \dfrac{3}{2} \times \dfrac{3}{2} \times \dfrac{3}{2}$
c) $3^2 \times 3^2 \times 3^2 \times 3^2$
d) $7 \times 5 \times 7 \times 5 \times 7 \times 5 \times 7 \times 5 \times 7 \times 5 \times 7 \times 5 \times$
$7 \times 5 \times 7 \times 5 \times 7 \times 5 \times 7 \times 5$
e) $\dfrac{1}{8} \times \dfrac{1}{8} \times \dfrac{1}{8} \times \dfrac{1}{8} \times \dfrac{1}{8}$
f) $(-2)^6 \times (-2)^6$

2. a) $5^3 \times 2^3$ **b)** $5^2 \times 2^2$ **c)** $5^1 \times 2^1$
d) $5^0 \times 2^0$ **e)** $5^{-1} \times 2^{-1}$ **f)** $5^{-2} \times 2^{-2}$

3. a) $2^{-2} \times 5^{-2}$ **b)** $9^{-4} \times 3^{-4}$ **c)** $5^{-3} \times 7^{-3}$
d) $\dfrac{2^{-2}}{3^{-2}}$ **e)** $\dfrac{1^{-4}}{2^{-4}}$ **f)** $\dfrac{4^{-3}}{3^{-3}}$

4. a) 2^{-6} **b)** 3^{-8} **c)** 4^{-6}
d) 5^{-8} **e)** 8^0 **f)** 7^2

5. a) $7^2 \times 3^2$ **b)** $6^4 \times 5^4$ **c)** $10^5 \times 3^5$
d) $\dfrac{4^2}{5^2}$ **e)** $\dfrac{2^4}{7^4}$ **f)** $\dfrac{1^3}{2^3}$

6. a) 4^6 **b)** 7^8 **c)** 3^{12}
d) 10^{12} **e)** 3^{12} **f)** $(-10)^6$

7. a) 1296   **b)** 5.0625   **c)** 6561
d) About 2.8×10^{15} **e)** $0.000\ 305$ **f)** 4096

8. a) 2 or -2 **b)** 3 or -3 **c)** 2 or -2

9. a) $6^3 \times 2^3$ **b)** $3^5 \times 7^5$ **c)** $9^4 \times 5^4$
d) $\dfrac{3^5}{5^5}$ **e)** $\dfrac{1^3}{3^3}$ **f)** $\dfrac{3^{10}}{2^{10}}$

10. a) 4^6 **b)** 2^{25} **c)** 3^{18}
d) 3^{20} **e)** $(-2)^{12}$ **f)** $(-3.5)^8$

11. a) $\dfrac{3^3}{4^3}$ **b)** $\dfrac{3^2}{4^2}$ **c)** $\dfrac{3^1}{4^1}$
d) $\dfrac{3^0}{4^0}$ **e)** $\dfrac{3^{-1}}{4^{-1}}$ **f)** $\dfrac{3^{-2}}{4^{-2}}$

12. a) 3^9 **b)** 3^6 **c)** 3^3
d) 3^0 **e)** 3^{-3} **f)** 3^{-6}

13. a) $2^{-3} \times 3^{-3}$ **b)** $5^{-2} \times 4^{-2}$ **c)** $6^{-4} \times 2^{-4}$
d) $\dfrac{3^{-3}}{7^{-3}}$ **e)** $\dfrac{1^{-2}}{3^{-2}}$ **f)** $\dfrac{5^{-4}}{8^{-4}}$

14. a) 2^{-6} **b)** 5^{-2} **c)** 3^{10}
d) 4^0 **e)** $(-2)^{-6}$ **f)** $(-4)^{-6}$

15. a) 7^{16} **b)** 3^{16} **c)** 8^{56} **d)** 2^{-12} **e)** 4^{25}

f) 11^6 g) 5^{20} h) 9^{30} i) 25^{-6} j) 2.8^{30}

16. a) 3^8 b) 7^{-10} c) 4^{12} d) 12^{20} e) 5^{18}
f) 2^9 g) 6^{30} h) 16^{-15} i) 10^{-12} j) 3.5^1

17. a) 3^{14} b) 6^4 c) 7^{22}
d) 15^0 e) 8^{-32} f) 4^{-6}
g) 51^{39} h) 29^{-32} i) 101^{-3}

18. a) 3 or -3 b) 2 or -2 c) 5 or -5

19. 5^{2222}, 2^{5555}, 4^{3333}, 3^{4444}

20. a) No; $(2^3)^2 = 64$, $2^{(3^2)} = 512$
b) i) 81 ii) 256 iii) About 2.418×10^{24}
c) 4, 16, 65 536; entering the fourth expression, which is equivalent to $2^{65\ 536}$, yields an error message.
d) No

Mathematics File: Powers of 2, page 290

1. a) 1 048 576 b) 2 097 152 c) 32
d) 1 048 576 e) 262 144 f) 1 048 576

2. a) Answers may vary. For positive exponents, the last digit follows a repeating pattern of 2, 6, 8, 4.
For negative exponents, the last two digits are always 25 and the last three digits alternate between 125 and 625. The non-zero digits are the digits of the corresponding power of 5. For example, $2^{-5} = 0.031\ 25$ and $5^5 = 3125$
b) Explanations may vary.

3. a) 0.007 812 5 b) 1024 c) 1 d) 0.25
e) 524 288 f) 0.000 000 953 674 316 406 25
g) 0.000 976 562 5 h) 0.000 244 140 625

5. a) $2^{10} \doteq 10^3$
b) i) 10^9 ii) 10^{12} iii) 10^{15}

Linking Ideas: Mathematics and Technology
Half-life on a Spreadsheet, page 291

1. a) The formula in cell A5 divides the amount of iodine-131 by 2. The formula in cell B5 increases the number of days by 8.
b) 50, 8

2. 56 days 3. 80 days

4. The computer displays powers of 2 with negative exponents in column C in descending order, beginning with 2^{-1} in row 5.

5.4 Power Expressions Involving Variables
Working with Mathematics, page 294

1. a) $\frac{n \times n \times n \times n \times n \times n}{n \times n}$
b) $(n \times n \times n \times n \times n) \times (n \times n)$
c) $\frac{1}{n^5 \times n^5}$

2. Simplifying the variable expressions helps us to interpret the numerical expressions quickly, since they all have the same structure as the corresponding variable expression.
a) n^3; 2^3 or 8, 7^3 or 343, 12^3 or 1728, $(-3)^3$ or -27
b) x^5; 3^5 or 243, 5^5 or 3125, 10^5 or 100 000, $(-2)^5$ or -32
c) y^{-6}; 5^{-6} or $\frac{1}{15\ 625}$, 2^{-6} or $\frac{1}{64}$, 9^{-6} or $\frac{1}{531\ 441}$, $(-4)^{-6}$ or $\frac{1}{4096}$

3. a) m^5 b) a^{10} c) s^{12}
d) e^{11} e) y^2 f) j^3
g) b^{20} h) r^{10} i) p^{-5}

4. a) $(-a)^9$ b) $(-b)^{-4}$ c) $(-m)^{16}$ d) $(-f)^{-3}$
e) $(-t)^{17}$ f) $(-z)^5$ g) $(-g)^{-6}$ h) $(-v)^7$

i) $(-d)^{-6}$ j) $(-x)^7$

5. a) w^5 b) $(-h)^{-2}$ c) $(-s)^{12}$ d) a^{-10}
e) $(-f)^{-3}$ f) $(-c)^{-15}$ g) $(-y)^{-5}$ h) n^{-16}
i) $(-b)^6$ j) y^4

6. a) n^5 b) n^4 c) n^3
d) n^2 e) n^1 f) n^0

7. a) x^{-6} b) x^{-3} c) x^0
d) x^3 e) x^6 f) x^9

8. a) x^1 b) m^{-4} c) x^1
d) x^{-6} e) y^5 f) c^3
g) x^{-6} h) y^2 i) a^{-4}
j) b^3 k) x^{-6} l) $x^1 y^{-2}$

9. a) xy b) m^2 c) $a^2 b^{-3}$ d) $c^{-3} d^{-3}$
e) $p^6 q^{-2}$ f) $j^{-12} k^8$ g) rs^{-3} h) $u^{10} v^{10}$
i) $e^2 f^{14} g^{-10}$ j) $m^{-4} n^8$

10. a) $3a^2 b^{-5}$ b) $3b^{-4}$ c) $3a^{-2} b^{-3}$
d) $3a^{-4} b^{-2}$ e) $3a^{-6} b^{-1}$ f) $3a^{-8}$

11. a) $18x^5 y^6$ b) $16m^{-1} n^{-3}$ c) $45a^3 b^{-3}$
d) $5c^2 d^3$ e) $3x^4 y^{-5}$ f) $\frac{1}{2} p^{-3} q^4$
g) n^{-4} h) $a^2 b^{-6}$ i) $x^{-9} y^3$
j) $28mn^{-2}$ k) $\frac{3}{4} x^{-4} y^2$ l) ab^{-3}

12. a) $\frac{1}{4}$ b) $\frac{1}{16}$ c) 16
d) $\frac{1}{8}$ e) $\frac{1}{2}$ f) 4

13. a) $a^2 b^3$; 108 b) $a^{-2} b^2$; $\frac{9}{4}$ c) $a^{-3} b^{-2}$; $-\frac{1}{72}$
d) ab^2; -18 e) $2a^2 b^{-2}$; $\frac{8}{9}$ f) $3a^{-1} b^{-1}$; $-\frac{1}{2}$
g) $-2ab$; 12 h) $4a^{-1}$; -2 i) $3a^{-1} b^2$; $-\frac{27}{2}$
j) $-\frac{2}{3} a^{-2} b^{-5}$; $-\frac{1}{1458}$

14. a) x^1 b) x^2 c) x^3
d) x^4 e) x^5 f) x^6

15. a) c^3 b) c^3 c) c^3
d) c^3 e) c^3 f) c^3

16. a) a^4 b) 1 c) d^{-1}
d) m^{10} e) 1 f) b^{-5}
g) m^{-6} h) c^{-9} i) $x^4 y^{-6}$
j) p^{12} k) t^{11} l) $a^4 b^{-4}$

17. a) c^5 b) m^{-5} c) x^{-3}
d) n^5 e) a^{-1} f) z^0
g) k^9 h) r^{-4} i) x^6
j) $a^4 b^6$ k) $\frac{x^{12}}{y^6}$ l) $\frac{m^4}{n^{-2}}$

18. a) $35a^3 b^5$ b) $63c^2 d^{-2}$ c) $48x^{-5} y^{-2}$
d) $4x^3 y^{-3}$ e) $3c^{-2} d^7$ f) $\frac{7}{3} a^{-8} b$
g) $\frac{1}{4} p^{-6}$ h) $x^{-6} y^{-3}$ i) $a^{-4} b^2$
j) $60m^5 n^{-6}$ k) $3r^{-5} s^8$ l) $p^6 q^{-4}$

19. a) x^5; -32 b) x; -2 c) x^6; 64
d) x^{-3}; $-\frac{1}{8}$ e) x; -2 f) x^2; 4

20. a) $27x^{-15}$ b) $6a^{-8}$ c) $2x^2$
d) q^2 e) $\frac{27}{8} x^{-5} y^3$ f) $a^{-11} b^{-1} c^{12}$

5.5 Operating with Numbers in Scientific Notation
Working with Mathematics, page 298

1. Answers may vary.

2. a) i) 2.5×10^{12} **ii)** 6.25×10^{-10}
   b) i) 3.125×10^{-16} **ii)** 4.0×10^{24}
   c) i) 4.333333×10^{22} **ii)** 5.0×10^{-40}

3. Divide the diameter of the circle by 109.

4. Explanations may vary.
   a) 2.0×10^{3} **b)** 2.0×10^{9} **c)** 4.828×10^{14}

5. a) 1.2×10^{16} **b)** 5.18×10^{24} **c)** 1.274×10^{16}
   d) 2.124×10^{10} **e)** 5.64×10^{22} **f)** 1.312×10^{36}

6. a) 2.531×10^{2} **b)** 7   **c)** 2.28×10^{2}
   d) 2.82×10^{5} **e)** 1.057×10^{-3} **f)** 8.5×10^{5}

7. Answers may vary.
   a) About 128 pages; 1 page has a thickness of about 7.8×10^{-3} cm.
   b) About 2.7 mm

8. a) 2.0×10^{4}, 8.0×10^{9} **b)** 4.0×10^{5} cm^2
   c) 40 m^2; the result is not reasonable. The television program may have given incorrect figures.

9. About 1.2×10^{7} km

10. a) 1.43×10^{18} km^3 **b)** 2.245×10^{10} km^3

11. a) 1.98×10^{30} kg   **b)** 7.4075×10^{22} kg

12. a) 20   **b)** 20 cm

13. a) 4.05×10^{13} km   **b)** 4.0×10^{32} kg   **c)** 7.02×10^{8} km

14. About 1.5×10^{14} km

15. 1800 kg; explanations may vary.

16. 3.0569×10^{79}

5.6 Estimating Square Roots

Developing the Ideas, page 300

1. 25 cm^2

2. a) 50 cm^2 **b)** No, its area would then be 100 cm^2.

3. Estimates may vary, about 7.1 cm.

4. Estimates may vary, about 8.7 cm and 10.0 cm.

Working with Mathematics, page 302

1. a) 3.6   **b)** 4.5   **c)** 9.2

2. No; 5^2 is 25, not 50. The square of a number increases more quickly than the number itself. You can estimate $\sqrt{50}$ by considering the closest perfect square that is greater than 50 and the closest perfect square that is less than 50 and choosing a number between their square roots.

3. The square roots of 67, 78, and 80 are between 8 and 9. We know this is so, since each number falls between 64 and 81.

4. About 21.2 cm   **5.** 26.0 cm

6. a) $\sqrt{11}$, $\sqrt{14}$ **b)** $\sqrt{52}$, $\sqrt{61}$ **c)** $\sqrt{140}$, $\sqrt{130}$
   d) $\sqrt{118}$, $\sqrt{110}$ **e)** $\sqrt{190}$, $\sqrt{171}$ **f)** $\sqrt{330}$, $\sqrt{360}$

7. a) 2, −2   **b)** 3, −3   **c)** 7, −7
   d) 9, −9   **e)** 11, −11   **f)** 8, −8

8. a) $\frac{1}{4}$, $-\frac{1}{4}$ **b)** $\frac{1}{5}$, $-\frac{1}{5}$ **c)** $\frac{4}{5}$, $-\frac{4}{5}$
   d) $\frac{2}{3}$, $-\frac{2}{3}$ **e)** $\frac{5}{7}$, $-\frac{5}{7}$ **f)** $\frac{8}{9}$, $-\frac{8}{9}$

9. Estimates may vary.
   a) 8.7   **b)** 9.3   **c)** 10.8   **d)** 11.8   **e)** 6.7   **f)** 10.2

10. a) 12   **b)** 120   **c)** 1200   **d)** 1.2   **e)** 0.12   **f)** 0.012

11. a) 1100   **b)** 110   **c)** 11   **d)** 1.1   **e)** 0.11   **f)** 0.011

12. a) 6, −6   **b)** 8.66, −8.66   **c)** 2.21, −2.21

13. Estimates for parts e, g, h, and i may vary.
   a) 12   **b)** 32   **c)** 54
   d) 35   **e)** 8.6   **f)** 35
   g) 5.7   **h)** 7.3   **i)** 3.5

14. a) 20 cm   **b)** 0.5 m   **c)** 9.5 cm
   d) 12.2 cm   **e)** 17.3 cm   **f)** 158.1 m

15. Explanations may vary. When dealing with length, it does not make sense to talk about negative values.

16. a) 1517 cm   **b)** 60.68 m

17. 3.87 m by 3.87 m

18. a) 6, −6   **b)** 10, −10   **c)** 20, −20
   d) 1, −1   **e)** $\frac{1}{2}$, $-\frac{1}{2}$ **f)** $\frac{1}{3}$, $-\frac{1}{3}$

19. Estimates may vary.
   a) 6.3   **b)** 9.8   **c)** 5.5   **d)** 8.1

20. Estimates for parts e and f may vary.
   a) 14   **b)** 44   **c)** 70   **d)** 48   **e)** 8.4   **f)** 3.7

21. a) i) 1.732 050 8   **ii)** 17.320 508   **iii)** 173.205 08
   iv) 1732.0508   **v)** 0.173 205   **vi)** 0.017 320 5
   b) As each number is multiplied (or divided) by 100, its square root is multiplied (or divided) by 10, since $\sqrt{100} = 10$.

22. a) i) 9, −9   **ii)** 0.5, −0.5   **iii)** 9.8, −9.8
   iv) $\frac{2}{7}$, $-\frac{2}{7}$ **v)** 6.16, −6.16   **vi)** 2.24, −2.24
   b) Since the product of two negative numbers is positive, we can square either 3 or −3 to obtain 9. This applies for any number.

23. 3.87 m   **24.** 8.49 cm

25. a) 90, −90   **b)** 80, −80   **c)** 30, −30
   d) 110, −110   **e)** 0.5, −0.5   **f)** 0.1, −0.1

26. There are four possible solutions in each case.
   a) (0, 7), (7, 0), (7, 7); (0, −7), (−7, −7)), (−7, 0);
      (0, 7), (−7, 0), (−7, 7); (0, −7), (7, −7), (7, 0)
   b) (0, 8), (8, 0), (8, 8); (0, −8), (−8, −8), (−8, 0);
      (0, 8), (−8, 0), (−8, 8); (0, −8), (8, 0), (8, −8)
   c) (2, 7), (6, 3), (6, 7); (2, −1), (−2, −1), (−2, 3);
      (2, 7), (−2, 3), (−2, 7); (2, −1), (6, −1), (6, 3)

27. Estimates may vary.
   a) 2.2   **b)** 3.5   **c)** 5.7   **d)** 8.3

28. Estimates may vary.
   a) 6.7 cm   **b)** 7.3 cm   **c)** 8.5 cm   **d)** 9.3 cm

29. Estimates for parts c and f may vary.
   a) 5   **b)** 7   **c)** 2.6   **d)** 1   **e)** 12   **f)** 2.6

30. a) Determine four times the square root of the area.
   b) $P = 4\sqrt{A}$
   c) i) 20.4 cm   **ii)** 32 cm   **iii)** 35.3 m   **iv)** 7.8 m

31. a) 10, −10   **b)** 2.85, −2.85   **c)** 12, −12
   d) 10.95, −10.95   **e)** 9.7, −9.7   **f)** 0.1, −0.1
   g) 2.5, −2.5   **h)** 2.74, −2.74   **i)** 5, −5
   j) 10, −10

32. a) i) 1.414 213 6   **ii)** 4.472 136   **iii)** 14.142 136
   iv) 44.721 36   **v)** 141.421 36   **vi)** 447.2136
   b) In each case, the number whose square root you are finding is 10 times as great as the previous number. Thus, each answer you get is $\sqrt{10}$ times as great as the previous answer.

33. The calculator displays an error message because the square of any real number is always positive. There is no real number that can be multiplied by itself to produce a negative number.

34. There are 12 solutions. Two possibilities are provided.
(5, 0), (0, 5), (5, 5); (3, 4), (7, 1), 4, −3)

35. a) Divide the diameter by 2 and apply the formula $A = \pi r^2$.

b) $A = \pi \left(\frac{1}{2}d\right)^2$

c) Divide the area by π, then take the square root of the result to determine the radius. Multiply by 2 to determine the diameter.

d) $d = 2\sqrt{\dfrac{A}{\pi}}$

e) i) 5.3 cm   **ii)** 6.5 cm   **iii)** 7.1 cm   **iv)** 2.5 m

Quest: Can You Make One Large Square from Two Small Ones?, page 305

Fold and cut each square along one of its diagonals. Then arrange the pieces with the four right angles together to form a large square.

If the side length of each small square is 1 cm, then its area is 1 cm²; the area of the large square is 2 cm², and each side of the large square is $\sqrt{2}$ cm long.

5.7 Rational and Irrational Numbers

Developing the Ideas, page 306

1. a) 0.375   **b)** 0.583 333...   **c)** −1.4375
d) −0.875   **e)** 3.363 636...   **f)** 0.535 353...
g) 0.076 576 576 5...   **h)** 3.142 857 1...

2. a) ii, iv, and vi are rational numbers.
b) The others are not rational because they neither terminate nor repeat. Yes, they are numbers.

3. a) i) 4.999 999...   **ii)** 17.020 202 02...   **iii)** −8.512 732 73...
b) 88 175.$\overline{475}$, −0.079 218 836 758 492 000 $\overline{783}$ 9

Working with Mathematics, page 308

1. a) Rational   **b)** Irrational
c) No; 1.732 050 8 is a rational approximation of $\sqrt{3}$.

2. No, because C and d are not integers.

3. The phrase "appear to be" is used because a number that appears to repeat may eventually break from the pattern and, conversely, a number that does not repeat may eventually begin to repeat.
a) Rational   **b)** Irrational   **c)** Rational   **d)** Irrational

4. a) Rational   **b)** Integer, rational
c) Rational   **d)** Rational
e) Integer, natural, rational   **f)** Rational

5. b, d, and e

6. Answers may vary. For example:
a) 3.1, 3.$\overline{3}$ **b)** −6.4, −6.328
c) 1.21, 1.22   **d)** 2.6281, 2.628$\overline{2}$
e) −4.171, −4.172   **f)** 7.451, 7.454

7. a, b, d, e, and f   **8.** a, c, and e

9. a) Rational   **b)** Rational   **c)** Integer, rational
d) Natural, integer, rational   **e)** Natural, integer, rational
f) Rational   **g)** Natural, integer, rational   **h)** Rational
i) Rational   **j)** Irrational   **k)** Rational   **l)** Rational

10. a, b, c, d, f, g, and i are all irrational.

11. a, b, and e are rational.

12. Answers may vary.

14. No; for example, the sum of $2 - \sqrt{3}$ and $\sqrt{3}$ is 2.

Linking Ideas: Number Concepts and Geometry
Revisiting the Pythagorean Theorem, page 311

1. a) 5 cm   **b)** 17.9 cm   **c)** 5.7 cm

2. a) 9.4 cm   **b)** 7.1 cm   **c)** 1.4 m

3. a) 9 cm², 18 cm², 36 cm²
b) 3 cm, $\sqrt{18}$ cm, 6 cm
c) Moving from smallest to largest squares, the area is double that of the previous square; sides increase by a factor of $\sqrt{2}$ in each case.

4. 5 cm

5. 40 m

6. Answers may vary. The body diagonal is the line segment joining a top corner of the box to a bottom corner on the opposite side.

Review, page 312

1. a) 3^7 **b)** $(-2)^7$ **c)** -2^8
d) 15^5 **e)** 18^{21} **f)** $(-24)^{16}$

2. a) 4^2 **b)** 3^2 **c)** 7^1
d) 12^0 **e)** 16^1 **f)** 25^3

3. a) No; the bases are not the same.
b) Yes, provided you write 9 as 3^2 and 27 as 3^3.

4. a) 125   **b)** 243   **c)** $\dfrac{1}{125}$ **d)** $\dfrac{1}{243}$ **e)** −125
f) −243   **g)** $-\dfrac{1}{125}$ **h)** $-\dfrac{1}{243}$ **i)** 1

5. a) 5^4 **b)** 8^{-3} **c)** 4^4 **d)** 6^{-3} **e)** 9^2 **f)** 2^{-6}

6. 5^5, or 3125

7. a) $4^3 \times 5^3$ **b)** $3^{-2} \times 4^{-2}$ **c)** $\dfrac{12^5}{3^5}$
d) $\dfrac{27^{-3}}{9^{-3}}$ **e)** $12^2 \times 7^2$ **f)** $\dfrac{(-5)^4}{2^4}$
g) $\dfrac{24^{-5}}{28^{-5}}$ **h)** $\dfrac{(-56)^3}{84^3}$

8. a) 5^4 **b)** 8^{12} **c)** 12^{10}
d) 9^{-3} **e)** $(-5)^6$ **f)** $(-3)^{-8}$

9. a) 50 625   **b)** 0.064   **c)** 16 777 216
d) 512   **e)** 64   **f)** 33 554 432

10. a) 10^{13} **b)** 7.3^8 **c)** $(-12)^{14}$ **d)** 8^5
e) 9.4^7 **f)** $(-3)^{13}$ **g)** 3^4 **h)** 6.25^5
i) 8^7 **j)** 2^{-6} **k)** 4^4 **l)** $(-7)^4$

11. a) m^{14} **b)** $24s^2$ **c)** $-3a^{-14}$
d) $(-j)^{-3}$ **e)** $-72r^{-16}$ **f)** $(-p)^{23}$
g) $a^6 b^6$ **h)** $9q^4$ **i)** $4x^6 y^{10}$
j) $5v^{-2} y^3$

12. a) $3c^2 d^2$ **b)** $-\dfrac{2}{3}f^{-10} g^{10}$ **c)** $3s^5 t^4$
d) $(-m)^{-2} n^6$ **e)** $-9p^{-4} q^4$ **f)** $(-a)^9 (-b)^5$

13. a) About 30   **b)** About 36 cm

14. a) 120 000   **b)** 1.4 km

15. 1×10^{-5} g

16. a) $15 630   **b)** 1.3×10^{12} **c)** $237.38

17. 2×10^8

18. a) 9.467×10^{15} m   **b)** 9.467×10^{12} km

19. a) 2.18×10^{19} km   **b)** 2.18×10^{22}

20. a) 6, −6   **b)** 20, −20   **c)** 21, −21
d) 16, −16   **e)** 0.7, −0.7   **f)** 0.1, −0.1

21. Estimates may vary.
   a) 4.2   **b)** 5.9   **c)** 9.3   **d)** 10.3   **e)** 12.2   **f)** 14.5

22. Estimates may vary.
   a) 11   **b)** 9.2   **c)** 7   **d)** 8.8
   e) 18   **f)** 18   **g)** 9.1   **h)** 2.6

23. a) 28 cm   **b)** 49 cm

24. Rational: a, d, f; irrational: b, c, e

25. a) Rational   **b)** Rational
   c) Integer, rational   **d)** Natural, integer, rational
   e) Rational   **f)** Rational
   g) Natural, integer, rational   **h)** Irrational

26. Answers may vary.

CHAPTER 6 POLYNOMIALS

Start With What You Know, page 318

1. a) 301.7 cm^2, 401.3 cm^3; 337.8 cm^2, 475.2 cm^3; 490.0 cm^2, 786.7 cm^3
   b) 10.0 cm, 528 cm^3
   c) Doubling the height does not double the surface area. Doubling the height does double the volume. Explanations may vary.

2. a) 282.7 cm^2, 339.3 cm^3; 329.0 cm^2, 435.8 cm^3; 534.0 cm^2, 942.5 cm^3
   b) Doubling the radius does not double the surface area. Doubling the radius multiplies the volume by a factor of 4.

3. a) i) 6
    ii) $1 \times 1 \times 24$; $1 \times 2 \times 12$; $1 \times 3 \times 8$; $1 \times 4 \times 6$; $2 \times 2 \times 6$; $2 \times 3 \times 4$
   b) i) 9
    ii) $1 \times 1 \times 48$; $1 \times 2 \times 24$; $1 \times 3 \times 16$; $1 \times 4 \times 12$; $1 \times 6 \times 8$; $2 \times 2 \times 12$; $2 \times 3 \times 8$; $2 \times 4 \times 6$; $3 \times 4 \times 4$

6.1 The Concept of a Polynomial
Working with Mathematics, page 323

1. $37 Can, $37 U.S.

2. Explanations may vary. The bills may have different values, but the currency is the same, so we can add the money.

3. Reasons may vary. a, b, c, and e

4. Reasons may vary.
   a) Binomial   **b)** Monomial   **c)** Binomial   **d)** Monomial
   e) Trinomial   **f)** Monomial   **g)** Trinomial   **h)** Binomial

5. a) $3x^2 + 4x + 3$ **b)** $4x^2 + 6x - 3$ **c)** $x^2 - 5x + 4$
   d) $-2x^2 - 5x - 6$ **e)** $-3x^2 + 2x - 11$

6. a, b, d, e, f, h

7. a) Binomial   **b)** Monomial   **c)** Trinomial
   d) Monomial   **e)** Monomial   **f)** Binomial

8. a) 14   **b)** 7   **c)** 1
   d) −1   **e)** π **f)** $\sqrt{3}$

9. a) 6   **b)** −5   **c)** 7
   d) $-\frac{2}{5}$ **e)** 0   **f)** 0

10. a) Coefficients: 6, 2; constant term: 3
   b) Coefficients: 1, −2, 9
   c) Coefficient: 1.8; constant term: 32
   d) Coefficient: 2π
   e) Coefficients: 7, −3; constant term: −9
   f) Coefficients: 4.9, −1.2, −0.5; constant term: 2

11. a) $5a$ and $-a$ **b)** $3y^2$ and y^2
   c) $9g$ and $\frac{1}{9}g$; $9g^2$ and g^2 **d)** 16 and −8; d and $0.5d$

12. a) 7   **b)** 13   **c)** 16   **d)** 1

13. a) −5   **b)** −2   **c)** −8   **d)** 16

15. a) $2x + 4$ **b)** $8x$ **c)** $2x + 8$

16. a) $2x$ **b)** $4x^2$ **c)** $4x$

18. a) $6x + 2$, $3x$ **b)** $6x$, $2x^2$ **c)** $2x + 12$, $6x$

19. Answers may vary. For example:
   a) $\frac{1}{x}$, or $3\sqrt{x}$ **b)** $y^2 + 3$

20. a) $4x + 6$ **b)** $4x + 14$ **c)** $4x + 6$ **d)** $6x + 10$ **e)** $8x + 10$

21. a) 22 cm **b)** 30 cm **c)** 22 cm **d)** 34 cm **e)** 42 cm

22. a) 12 m **b)** 20 m **c)** 12 m **d)** 19 m **e)** 22 m

23. a) $4s^2$
   b) i) $4s^2$ **ii)** s^2 **iii)** $3s^2$
   c) i) 25 cm^2 **ii)** 6.25 cm^2 **iii)** 18.75 cm^2

24. a) 181°C   **b)** 220°C

25. a) 47.5 m   **b)** 170 m

26. a) $2\pi x$ **b)** $2\pi x$ **c)** $\frac{\pi x^2}{4}$, πx^2 **d)** $\frac{\pi x^2}{4}$
   e) Answers may vary.

Linking Ideas: Mathematics and Technology
The Search for a Polynomial to Generate Prime Numbers, page 326

1. Yes

3. b) 1681   **c)** No

5. Answers may vary.

6. a) $1681 = 41^2$
   b) Answers may vary. N = 81 generates $1763 = 41 \times 43$

7. Answers may vary. For example:
   a) 7   **b)** 17   **c)** 42

6.2 Adding and Subtracting Polynomials
Developing the Ideas, page 327

1. a) $3x^2 + 5x + 2$ **b)** $4x^2 - 3x + 1$ **c)** $-4x^2 - 8x - 5$ **d)** 0

2. Answers may vary.
   a) If we ignore the signs, the terms are the same.
   b) The like terms have opposite signs.

3. a) $-3x^2 + 2x + 1$ **b)** $2x^2 + 2$

Working with Mathematics, page 329

1. a) $-3x^2 - 7$ **b)** $-2x^2 + 5x - 3$ **c)** $4n^2 - 3n + 5$

2. 0

3. The polynomial 0 is equal to its opposite.

4. a) $-3x^2 + 2x + 1$ **b)** $3x^2 - 2x - 1$
   c) The opposite of the opposite of a polynomial is the original polynomial.
   d) Yes; explanations may vary. Each term has its sign reversed twice, so it returns to its original value.

5. a) Flip the tiles.   **b)** Change the sign of every term.

6. a) $(3x^2 + 5) + (-2x^2 - 1)$ **b)** $(x^2 + 2x) + (x + 1)$
   c) $(x^2 + 3x - 2) + (x^2 + x - 1)$

7. Explanations may vary. The tiles that produce 0-pairs are opposites and add to zero.

8. a) $9x + 6$ **b)** $7a + 4$
   c) $5 - 6m$ **d)** $6x + 2$

e) $6n^2 - 8n - 4$
f) $-2x^2 + 5x - 4$
g) $7 - 7c - 3c^2$
h) $5 - 3n + 3n^2$
i) $3ab - b - 11$
j) $mn - 6n - 2m + 5$

9. a) $-5x - 2$ b) $-2 + 3a$
c) $-7x^2 + 5x - 4$ d) $-5 + 2m + 4m^2$
e) $-6n^2 + 3n - 1$ f) $\frac{1}{2}x + 5$

10. a) $-5x + 1$ b) $2 + n$
c) $14a^2 - 2a - 10$ d) $-10x^2 + 7x - 4$
e) $-4 + 4m - 2n^2$ f) $-5 + 9x^2$
g) $2 - 5t^2$ h) 0

11. a) $2x - 1$ b) $8a + 2$
c) $4x^2 - 5x$ d) $8t - 5$
e) $3 - 6x + 2x^2$ f) $-4n + 6$

12. Explanations may vary. $x^2 + 2x + 1$

13. a) $(-2x^2 + 5x - 3) + (x^2 + x + 7)$
b) Explanations may vary. $-x^2 + 6x + 4$

14. Explanations may vary.
a) The first terms have the same sign.
b) The first terms have different exponents.
c) The last terms have the same sign.
d) The last terms are not like terms.

15. b) Explanations may vary. $2x^2 + x + 6$

16. a) $4x^2 - 2x + 7$ b) $2x^2 - 2x + 1$
c) $-m^2 + 5m - 6$ d) $-3m^2 + 5m + 6$

17. a) $-5x^2 + x - 6$ i) -10 ii) -28
b) $x^2 - 3x + 10$ i) 8 ii) 20

18. a) $x^2, 2x; x^2 + 2x$
b) $x^2, x^2, 3x; 2x^2 + 3x$
c) $2x, x^2, 3x, 6; x^2 + 5x + 6$
d) $x^2, x^2, 4x, 4x, 4x, 16; 2x^2 + 12x + 16$
e) $x^2, x^2, x^2, x^2; 3x, 3x; 4x^2 + 6x$

19. a) $-4x^2 - 2x + 10$ b) $x^2 - 4x + 15$
c) $x^3 - 10x^2 + 2x + 8$ d) $8x - 7$

20. a) $2x^2 + 3x + 7$ b) $4m^2 - 6m + 11$
c) $3a^2 - a^3 + 6$ d) $-9x^2 + 5x - 12$

21. a) $5x^2 - 15x + 3$ i) 53 ii) 3
b) $2x^3 + x^2 - 7x - 5$ i) -3 ii) 37

22. a) i) $1 - 9m + 4m^2$ ii) $2m^2 - 2m - 1$
b) i) 1 ii) -1
c) i) 35 ii) 11

23. a) i) $y^2 - 5$ ii) $10y$
b) i) 11 ii) 40
c) i) -4 ii) 10

24. a) i) $x - 7$ ii) $x + 7$ iii) $3x - 3, 3x, 3x + 3$ iv) $9x$
b) Divide the sum by 9.

25. a) $25 - 10x - 7x^2$ b) 28.25

Quest: A Magic Birthday Card, page 332

Explanations may vary.

6.3 Multiplying and Dividing Monomials
Working with Mathematics, page 336

1. a) $3 \cdot x \cdot x$ b) $2 \cdot 2 \cdot x \cdot x \cdot x$
c) $-1 \cdot x \cdot x$ d) $2 \cdot x \cdot x \cdot x \cdot x \cdot x \cdot x$
e) $-\frac{1}{2} \cdot a \cdot a \cdot a \cdot a$ f) $3 \cdot 3 \cdot x \cdot x \cdot y$
g) $-2 \cdot 3 \cdot a \cdot a \cdot b \cdot b$ h) $5 \cdot m \cdot m \cdot n \cdot n \cdot n$

2. a) $12x^5$ b) $-2x^8$ c) $\frac{1}{4}a^6$ d) $-30a^3$

3. a) $\frac{5}{2}m^2$ b) $-\frac{5}{2}x^3$ c) $-5x^4$

4. Answers may vary. There are many possible answers. For example:
a) $x, 3x^5$ b) $(-5b), b^2$ c) $(-3), 2x$
d) $4x^3, 2x$ e) $3x^4, 2x$ f) $x, 4x$

5. a) $12b$ b) $-14k$ c) $20t$ d) $-16p$
e) $5ab$ f) $-3pq$ g) $4mn$ h) $-2xy$

6. a) $6a^2$ b) $-10c^2$ c) $10a^2$ d) $21x^2$
e) $10x^2$ f) $-56y^2$ g) $5x^2$ h) $-6a^2$
i) $6a^2$

7. a) $144x^2$ b) $-27x^3y^3$ c) $-25a^2b^2$ d) $4a^2$
e) $81m^{10}n^2$ f) $9x^2$ g) $-125a^3b^6$ h) $9m^2n^8$

8. a) $4x^3$ b) $2y^4$ c) $9y^3$ d) $-3m^2$
e) $9y^2$ f) $\frac{3}{5}n^2$ g) -5 h) $\frac{3}{2}c^3$

9. a) $-x^5$ b) $6p^5$ c) $-12y^4$
d) $6a^3b^3$ e) $36x^4y^2$ f) $-4x^2y^6$

10. a) πr^3 b) x^3 c) $3x^3$ d) $8y^3$

11. a) $5x^2$ b) $-3y$ c) $-5a$
d) $3bn$ e) $5m^3a^2$ f) $3y^3$

12. a) $3r$ b) $1.5x$ c) $3m$ d) $2.5a$

13. a) $21m^9$ b) $8x^5$ c) $56a^{14}$ d) $-10b^7$
e) $-18x^8$ f) $48p^6$ g) $\frac{2}{5}y^{11}$ h) $\frac{3}{16}s^8$

14. a) $-7a^5$ b) $-4s^2$ c) $4c^6$ d) $5x^6$ e) $6y^2$
f) $7m^8$ g) $4k$ h) $7z^3$ i) $7ab^2$ j) $4y^2$

15. a) 32 b) -6 c) 7 d) -24 e) 48
f) -20 g) -30 h) -30 i) 3 j) -14

16. a) $10m^5$ b) $-3x^5$ c) $\frac{2}{3}x^2$
d) $-\frac{3}{4}m^3$ e) $3x^5$ f) $6a^3b^7$
g) $-3x^2y$ h) $-72x^{11}$ i) $\frac{25}{3}a$
j) $\frac{4}{3}a^3b^7$

17. a) $10d^7$ b) $5mn^2$ c) $-5x^3$
d) $6x^2$ e) $-\frac{5}{3}a^5$ f) $\frac{2}{3}a^4b^2$

18. a) -4 b) 4 c) -96
d) -640 e) -32 f) -72

19. a) 324 b) -405 c) -18 d) -567

20. a) $36x^6$ b) $-400m^4$ c) $\frac{3}{2}y^3$
d) $3a^2b^3c$ e) $\frac{36}{5}x^2$ f) $-m^7$

21. a) $(3x)(3x)(3x)$ b) $27x^3$ c) $42x^9$

6.4 Multiplying a Polynomial by a Monomial
Working with Mathematics, page 340

1. a) $x(x + 2)$ b) $2x(x + 2)$ c) $x(2x + 1)$
d) $x(2x)$ e) $x(3x + 1)$ f) $3x(2x)$

2. Answers may vary.

3. a) $5x - 15$ b) $7a + 7$ c) $-6 - 3n$
d) $4x + 8$ e) $-2x + 5$ f) $18x - 12$
g) $5x^2 - 30x + 15$ h) $6 - 10n + 6n^2$

4. a) B   b) F   c) E   d) C   e) A   f) D

5. a) $3x^2 + 2x$ b) $5a^2 - a$ c) $3n - 7n^2$
d) $-x^2 + 2x$ e) $5y - y^2$ f) $4x^2 - x$
g) $-7x + 2x^2 - x^3$ h) $5n^3 - n^2 + 4n$

6. a) $x^2 + 3x$ b) $-5a + 15$ c) $2b^3 - 3b^2 + b$
d) $4p - 3p^2 - p^3$ e) $-42a^2 - 49$ f) $36t^2 - 24t$
g) $-k^3 + 5k^2 - k$ h) $-21 + 6m - 9m^2$

7. a) $x^2 + x$ **b)** $3x^2 + 2x$
c) $2x^2 + 2x + 6$ **d)** $2x^2 + 4x$

8. a) $5x^3 - 6x$ **b)** $2x + 6x^2$ **c)** $-3b^4 + 3b^3$
d) $6a^2 + 2a$ **e)** $-4m^3 + 4m^2$ **f)** $x^2 - x^5$

9. a) $10x^2 + 15x$ **b)** $6a^2 - 8a$
c) $15c - 6c^2$ **d)** $-8n^2 + 4n$
e) $-14y^3 + 35y^2 - 14y$ **f)** $18k - 6k^2 + 12k^3$
g) $15s^3 - 10s^2 - 35s$ **h)** $-6p^2 + 9p^3 + 3p^4$

10. a) 1652 **b)** $14x^2 + 21x + 42, 1652$
c) Answers may vary.

12. b) $6xy$

13. a) $x(2y + 2) = 2xy + 2x$ **b)** $2x(2y + 4) = 4xy + 8x$
c) $y(2x + y) = 2xy + y^2$ **d)** $2y(x + y) = 2xy + 2y^2$
e) $y(2x + 1) = 2xy + y$ **f)** $2x(3y + 2) = 6xy + 4x$

14. a) $6xy + 3x$ **b)** $10x + 5y + 10$
c) $2y^2 + 6xy + 2y$ **d)** $6x^2 + 3xy + 12x$

15. a) $10x^2 + 15x$ **b)** $15c - 6c^2$ **c)** $-8n^2 + 4n$
d) $-14y^3 + 35y^2$ **e)** $12a^3 - 8a^2$ **f)** $6x^2 + 10x^4$
g) $15s^3 - 10s^2 - 35s$ **h)** $6p - 9p^2 - 3p^3$

16. a) $6x^2 - 3x$ **b)** $6x^2 + 3x$ **c)** $-6x^2 - 8x$ **d)** $12x^3 + 8x^2$

17. a) $6xy + 15x$ **b)** $10y - 35xy$
c) $-2x^2 - 6xy + 2x$ **d)** $14y - 8xy - 12y^2$
e) $10a^2 - 15ab + 20a$ **f)** $-12m + 30m^2 - 6mn$
g) $-12s + 6st + 3s^2$ **h)** $63pq - 21p^2 + 7p$

18. a) $6x^3 - 4x^2y^2 - 10x^2$ **b)** $3a^3b - 3a^2b^2$
c) $-2m^4n^2 + 2m^5n$ **d)** $-3p^2q^2 + 15p^2q$
e) $2x^3y^2 - 6x^4y$ **f)** $-6p^2q^2r + 12pq^2r^2$
g) $14a^3b^2 - 21a^2b^3$ **h)** $-4x^3y + 4xy^3$

19. a) $3x^3y + 3x^2y^2 + 3x^2y$ **b)** $-2ab^2x + 2bx - 2a^2bx$
c) $-3m^2n + 3m^3n + 3m^2$ **d)** $-12w^2z + 4w^3z - 4w^2z^2$
e) $2xy^3 - 4x^3y^3 + 6x^2y^3$
f) $18x^2yz^3 - 12x^2y^3z + 6xy^2z^3 - 12x^2y^2z^2$

20. a) $\frac{3}{4}x$ **b)** $\frac{3}{4}(x + 4)$ **c)** $\frac{3}{4}(x + 4)^2$
d) $\frac{3}{4}(x + 4)^2 - \frac{3}{4}x^2$ **e)** 243 square units, 363 square units

21. a) i) $15x^3 - 3x^2$ **ii)** $46x^2 - 8x$
b) i) 4998 cm^3 **ii)** 2198 cm^2

6.5 Factoring Polynomials

Working with Mathematics, page 346

1. a) x **b)** $3b$ **c)** $5y$ **d)** $3x$ **e)** $2x$ **f)** $2y$

2. a) 3 **b)** 6 **c)** 25 **d)** 4 **e)** 12
f) 18 **g)** 70 **h)** 165 **i)** 90 **j)** 100

3. a) xy **b)** $3xy$ **c)** ab **d)** 4 **e)** $-5xy^2$
f) $6pq$ **g)** 2 **h)** $3xy^2$ **i)** $6ab$

4. a) $5(y - 2)$ **b)** $6(2a + 3)$ **c)** $3x(x + 2)$
d) $2a(a - 5)$ **e)** $w(4 + 3w)$ **f)** $4y^2(2y - 1)$
g) $2s(3 + s)$ **h)** $7k^3(1 + 5k)$ **i)** $6m^2(1 - 6m)$
j) $2y^3(4y - 1)$

5. a) $7x(2x + 5)$ **b)** $5a(5 + 6a)$ **c)** $20(n^2 + 4)$
d) $5x(-1 + 2x)$ **e)** $3c(3c^2 + 5)$ **f)** $-x(x^2 + 1)$
g) $-3y^2(2 + y)$ **h)** $4x(1 + 3x^2)$ **i)** $4m^2(4 - m)$
j) $-8d(1 + d^2)$

6. a) $2(x + 1)$ **b)** $3(x + 3)$ **c)** $2(2x + 5)$ **d)** $3(x + 5)$
e) $3(k + 4)$ **f)** $4(m + 2)$ **g)** $2(2n + 3)$ **h)** $5(w + 3)$

7. a) $x(x + 2)$ **b)** $2x(x + 2)$ **c)** $3(x^2 + 3)$ **d)** $4x(x + 2)$
e) $2(2m^2 + 3)$ **f)** $3k(k + 6)$ **g)** $k(k + 1)$ **h)** $2z(z + 2)$
i) $2x(2x + 1)$ **j)** $2(y^2 + 4)$

8. a) $xy(1 + x)$ **b)** $3xy(-xy + 2)$ **c)** $ab(1 - ab)$
d) $-4(xy + 4)$ **e)** $5xy^2(1 + 2x)$ **f)** $6pq(p - 2q)$
g) $2mn(m - 2)$ **h)** $3x^2y^2(1 + 3y)$ **i)** $-xy(5x^5 + y^5)$
j) $3a^2bc(4ac - 5)$

9. a) $4(x^2 + 2x + 3)$ **b)** $7(x^2 - 3x + 1)$
c) $8(2a^2 - 3a - 2)$ **d)** $2t(3t + 2)$
e) $4(m - 1)$ **f)** $-2k(3k^2 + 3k + 5)$
g) $5(2x^2 - x + 1)$ **h)** $7(x^2 + x + 2)$

10. a) $8(2x + 5)$ **b)** $3(5n - 8)$ **c)** $-2a(a + 3)$
d) $6n(3n - 2)$ **e)** $a(a^2 + 9a + 3)$ **f)** $3x(x + 3)$

11. a) $5(2x + 3)$ **b)** $3(2x - 3)$ **c)** $5(3x + 5)$
d) $2x(x - 2)$ **e)** $4x(x - 4)$ **f)** $3y^2(y + 3)$
g) $2(x^2 + 2x + 4)$ **h)** $3x(4x^2 - 3x + 2)$

12. a) $a(a^2 - 9a + 3)$ **b)** $-3(9x^2 + 3x - 1)$
c) $x(5x^2 + 3x - 1)$ **d)** $a(9a^2 + 7a + 18)$
e) $-8d(1 + 3d + d^2)$ **f)** $17k(1 - 5k - 3k^2)$

13. $A = 2\pi r(h + r)$

14. a) $3xy(y + 2x - 3)$ **b)** $-2ab(a - 3b + 2)$
c) $5m^2n(n - 2mn + 5)$ **d)** $-7x^2y^2(4 - 2xy + y)$

15. a) $(a + 6)(a + 7)$ **b)** $(x - 9)(x - 2)$
c) $2(1 + y)(4 + y)$ **d)** $(2 - x)(5 + x)$
e) $2(x + 3)(x + 2)$ **f)** $-3(2a - 1)(a - 2)$

16. a) $2(x - 3)$ **b)** $2(x - 2)(x - 1)$ **c)** $2(x^2 + 3)$ **d)** $2(x^2 - 3)$

17. $A = Ch + \frac{C^2}{2\pi}$

18. a) $(a + 2)(a + b)$ **b)** $(3 - y)(x + y)$ **c)** $(a + b)(3 + b)$
d) $(x - 1)(4 + a)$ **e)** $(p - q)(2 - p)$ **f)** $(x + y)(y - 4)$
g) $-(m - n)(3 + n)$ **h)** $-(c + d)(5 + d)$

6.6 Dividing a Polynomial by a Monomial

Working with Mathematics, page 349

1. a) $\frac{5}{2}$ **b)** $\frac{3mn}{2}$ **c)** $-2y^2$

2. a) $3m^2 - 2$ **b)** $\frac{5}{2}x^2 - 5$ **c)** $3 - y^2$ **d)** $-3a + 1$

3. a) $3(x^2 - 4x + 2)$ **b)** $-x^2 + 4x - 2$

4. a) Divide each term by -3, or factor the numerator then divide
it by the denominator.
b) Answers may vary.

5. a) $2a + 1$ **b)** $4y - 1$ **c)** $3x^2 - 1$ **d)** $2a + 5$
e) $6x - 1$ **f)** $5 - 2m$ **g)** $-3 + n$ **h)** $3x^2 - x + 5$
i) $-a^2 - 3a + 4$ **j)** $-2a^2 - 5a + 3$
k) $-5 - 7m + 3m^2$ **l)** $2x + 3x^2 - 6$

6. a) $x - 2$ **b)** $x - 2$ **c)** $6 - 7a$
d) $-4n - 1$ **e)** $-4y^2 + y$ **f)** $-8b^2 - 2b$

7. a) $3 - x$ **b)** $1 + 3c - 2c^2$ **c)** $x^2 - 3x + 2$
d) $4 + a - a^2$ **e)** $3x^2 - 6x + 1$ **f)** $-3a^2 - a + 2$

8. $2x(x + 2l)$

6.7 Multiplying Two Binomials

Developing the Ideas, page 350

1. a) $x^2 + 3x + 2$ **b)** $2x^2 + 7x + 3$

Working with Mathematics, page 352

1. a) $(x + 3)(x + 4)$ **b)** $x^2 + 7x + 12$

2. a) $(x + 2)(x + 5)$ **b)** $x^2 + 2x + 5x + 10$

3. a) 1 **b)** 12 **c)** -10 **d)** -6

4. a) i) $(x + 6)(x + 2)$ **ii)** $(x + 1)(x + 2)$
iii) $2x(x + 3)$ **iv)** $3x(x + 1)$

b) i) $x^2 + 8x + 6$ **ii)** $x^2 + 3x + 2$
iii) $2x^2 + 6x$ **iv)** $3x^2 + 3x$

5. a) i) $(x + 7)(x + 3)$ **ii)** $(x + 2)(x + 8)$
iii) $(x + 2)(2x)$ **iv)** $(x + 3)(3x)$
b) i) $x^2 + 10x + 21$ **ii)** $x^2 + 10x + 16$
iii) $2x^2 + 4x$ **iv)** $3x^2 + 9x$

6. a) $x^2 + 4x + 3$ **b)** $n^2 + 7n + 10$
c) $a^2 + 5a + 6$ **d)** $y^2 + 6y + 5$

7. a) $a^2 - a - 2$ **b)** $b^2 - 2b - 15$ **c)** $n^2 - 5n + 6$
d) $y^2 + y - 20$ **e)** $b^2 - 3b - 18$ **f)** $a^2 - 16a + 60$
g) $z^2 - 11z + 30$ **h)** $b^2 + 15b + 50$ **i)** $x^2 - 10x + 9$
j) $a^2 + 3a - 88$

8. a) i) $(x + 2)(x + 2)$ **ii)** $x^2 + 4x + 4$
b) i) $(x + 2)(x + 3)$ **ii)** $x^2 + 5x + 6$
c) i) $(2x + 3)(x + 1)$ **ii)** $2x^2 + 5x + 3$
d) i) $(x + 1)(x + 5)$ **ii)** $x^2 + 6x + 5$
e) i) $(3x + 1)(x + 2)$ **ii)** $3x^2 + 7x + 2$
f) i) $(3x + 2)(2x + 1)$ **ii)** $6x^2 + 7x + 2$
g) i) $(2x + 3)(2x + 5)$ **ii)** $4x^2 + 16x + 15$

9. a) i) $(x + 3)(x + 5)$ **ii)** $x^2 + 3x + 5x + 15$
b) i) $(a + 2)(a + 4)$ **ii)** $a^2 + 2a + 4a + 8$
c) i) $(n + 1)(n + 7)$ **ii)** $n^2 + n + 7n + 7$
d) i) $(2k + 1)(k + 3)$ **ii)** $k^2 + k^2 + 3k + 3k + k + 3$
e) i) $(2m + 5)(m + 8)$ **ii)** $m^2 + m^2 + 8m + 8m + 5m + 40$

10. a) $x^2 + 7x + 12$ **b)** $n^2 + 8n + 12$
c) $a^2 + 8a + 15$ **d)** $n^2 + 10n + 9$

11. a) $t^2 - 5t + 4$ **b)** $x^2 + 3x - 10$ **c)** $n^2 - n - 12$
d) $a^2 - 2a - 48$ **e)** $x^2 + 2x - 63$ **f)** $x^2 + 7x - 60$

12. a) $2a^2 - 3a - 2$ **b)** $3b^2 + 16b + 5$ **c)** $2x^2 - 7x + 6$
d) $4x^2 + 9x + 5$ **e)** $6a^2 - 5a - 6$ **f)** $15x^2 + 14x - 8$
g) $6z^2 - 25z + 14$ **h)** $10b^2 + 17b + 3$ **i)** $14x^2 + 3x - 2$
j) $10a^2 + 3a - 27$

13. a) $x^2 + 10x + 21$ **b)** $x^2 - 10x + 21$
c) $x^2 + 4x - 21$ **d)** $x^2 - 4x - 21$

14. Answers may vary. In a and b, all terms are the same except the middle terms, which have opposite signs. The same is true for c and d.

15. a) $6a^2 + 7a + 2$ **b)** $6a^2 - 7a + 2$
c) $6a^2 + a - 2$ **d)** $6a^2 - a - 2$

16. Answers may vary. In a and b, all terms are the same except the middle terms, which have opposite signs. The same is true for c and d. This is the same observation as in exercise 14.

17. a) $4a^2 + 4a + 1$ **b)** $9n^2 + 6n + 1$ **c)** $x^2 - 12x + 36$
d) $a^2 - 6a + 9$ **e)** $4y^2 - 20y + 25$ **f)** $9b^2 + 30b + 25$

18. Answers may vary. The middle term is twice the product of the square roots of the first and third terms.

19. a) $x^2 - 9$ **b)** $4a^2 - 1$ **c)** $64n^2 - 9$
d) $16a^2 - 9$ **e)** $9x^2 - 4$ **f)** $25x^2 - 1$

20. Answers may vary. The middle terms add to zero.

21. a) i) $x - 8$, $x - 6$, $x + 6$, $x + 8$
ii) $x^2 - 16x + 64$, $x^2 - 12x + 36$, $x^2 + 12x + 36$, $x^2 + 16x + 64$
iii) $4x^2 + 200$
b) Subtract 200, then divide by 4. Take the square root of the quotient.

22. a) $a^2 + 9a + 18$ **b)** $b^2 - 5b - 14$ **c)** $n^2 - n - 30$
d) $y^2 + 13y + 12$ **e)** $b^2 - 11b + 18$ **f)** $a^2 - 7a - 30$
g) $z^2 - 2z - 80$ **h)** $b^2 + 17b + 66$ **i)** $x^2 - x - 42$
j) $a^2 - 18a + 45$

23. a) $12x^2 - 36x + 15$ **b)** $9b^2 - 4$ **c)** $20a^2 - 31a - 7$
d) $8a^2 + 65a + 8$ **e)** $4a^2 - 12a + 9$ **f)** $6a^2 - a - 12$

24. a) $3x^2 - x - 2$ **b)** $2a^2 - 11a + 15$ **c)** $4n^2 + 13n - 35$
d) $6x^2 + 13x - 15$ **e)** $36x^2 - 9x - 1$ **f)** $10n^2 - 12n + 2$

25. a) $14c^2 - 3c - 5$ **b)** $18x^2 - 2$ **c)** $3x^2 + 5x - 2$
d) $6a^2 - 13a - 5$ **e)** $40y^2 - 23y + 3$ **f)** $8x^2 + 2x - 21$

26. a) $6 - 5x + x^2$ **b)** $15 + 8a + a^2$ **c)** $12 + m - m^2$
d) $18 - 3t - t^2$ **e)** $49 - 14x + x^2$ **f)** $49 - x^2$
g) $12 + a - a^2$ **h)** $60 - 7b - b^2$

27. a) $x^2 + 7xy + 10y^2$ **b)** $a^2 - ab - 6b^2$ **c)** $6m^2 - 5mn + n^2$
d) $20x^2 + 7xy - 3y^2$ **e)** $6r^2 - 17rs - 3s^2$ **f)** $56a^2 + 113ab + 56b^2$
g) $2p^2 - pq - 15q^2$ **h)** $6x^2 - xy - 40y^2$ **i)** $42a^2 + ab - 56b^2$
j) $4x^2 + 4xy - 15y^2$

28. a) $2x^2 + 14x + 20$ **b)** $3m^2 + 9m - 12$ **c)** $5x^2 + 20x - 60$
d) $7x^2 - 70x + 175$ **e)** $-3x^2 - 6x + 24$ **f)** $-2x^2 + 8x + 120$
g) $-t^2 + 4$ **h)** $24 - 20x + 4x^2$

29. a) $x^2 - x - 2$ **b)** $2x^2 - 5x - 3$ **c)** $4x^2 - 14x + 12$
d) $-2x^2 - 7x - 3$ **e)** $9x^2 - 1$ **f)** $x^2 + 8x + 16$

30. a) $(n + 5)$ **b)** $(x - 4)$ **c)** $(x - 2)$ **d)** $(a + 2)$
e) $(x + 3)$ **f)** $(t + 5)$ **g)** $(x + 4)(x + 5)$ **h)** $(a - 7)(a - 2)$

31. a) $x^3 + 7x^2 + 11x + 5$ **b)** $a^3 - a^2 - 10a + 6$
c) $t^3 - t^2 - 17t + 20$ **d)** $a^3 - 8$
e) $x^3 + 6x^2 + 11x + 6$ **f)** $n^3 - 4n^2 - 7n + 10$
g) $4x^3 - 8x^2 - x + 2$ **h)** $9m^3 + 39m^2 - 29m + 5$

Quest: A Student's Letter, page 356

Explanations may vary.

6.8 Factoring Trinomials
Developing the Ideas, page 358

1. $x^2 + 7x + 10$

2. b) $x + 5$ **c)** $x + 2$ **d)** $(x + 5)(x + 2)$

3. Answers may vary.   **4.** $x + 2$, $x + 5$

5. a) $(x + 4)(x + 1)$ **b)** $(x + 4)(x + 2)$ **c)** $(x + 2)(x + 2)$

Working with Mathematics, page 361

1. a) -1, -14; 1, 14; -2, -7; 2, 7
b) -2, -7 **c)** $(x - 2)(x - 7)$

2. No; explanations may vary. For example, $(x - 4)(x + 4)$ is a binomial, $x^2 - 16$.

3. a) $x^2 + 8x + 15$ **b)** $x^2 - 8x + 15$
c) $x^2 + 2x - 15$ **d)** $x^2 - 2x - 15$
  i) Because the sign in each binomial is the same
  ii) Because the sign in one binomial is positive while the sign in the other binomial is negative
  iii) Add the numerical terms in each binomial.

4. a) 2 and 6   **b)** -2 and -6 **c)** -2 and 6   **d)** 2 and -6

5. a) $(x + 3)(x + 4)$ **b)** $(x - 3)(x - 4)$
c) $(x + 5)(x + 5)$ **d)** $(x - 5)(x - 5)$

6. Because the final term is positive

7. a) $(x - 4)(x + 5)$ **b)** $(x + 4)(x - 5)$
c) $(x - 4)(x + 6)$ **d)** $(x + 4)(x - 6)$

8. Because the final term is negative

9. a) $(x + 2)(x + 5)$ **b)** $(x + 1)(x + 10)$ **c)** $(x + 2)(x + 3)$
d) $(x + 1)(x + 6)$ **e)** $(n + 2)(n + 4)$ **f)** $(t + 1)(t + 8)$
g) $(x + 3)(x + 10)$ **h)** $(y + 5)(y + 6)$ **i)** $(t + 1)(t + 30)$
j) $(x + 2)(x + 15)$

10. a) $(x - 2)(x - 2)$ **b)** $(x - 1)(x - 4)$ **c)** $(x - 3)(x - 6)$
d) $(x - 2)(x - 9)$ **e)** $(x - 1)(x - 18)$ **f)** $(x - 5)(x - 9)$
g) $(x - 3)(x - 15)$ **h)** $(x - 1)(x - 45)$ **i)** $(x - 1)(x - 5)$
j) $(x - 1)(x - 3)$

11. a) $(x - 1)(x + 20)$ **b)** $(x + 1)(x - 20)$ **c)** $(y - 2)(y + 10)$
d) $(q + 2)(q - 10)$ **e)** $(x - 1)(x + 24)$ **f)** $(n + 1)(n - 24)$
g) $(a - 2)(a + 12)$ **h)** $(v + 2)(v - 12)$ **i)** $(x - 3)(x + 8)$
j) $(b + 3)(b - 8)$

12. a) i) $x^2 + 6x + 5$ **iii)** $(x + 5)(x + 1)$
b) i) $x^2 + 6x + 8$ **iii)** $(x + 2)(x + 4)$
c) i) $x^2 + 8x + 7$ **iii)** $(x + 7)(x + 1)$
d) i) $x^2 + 8x + 12$ **iii)** $(x + 2)(x + 6)$

13. a) $(x + 1)(x + 1)$ **b)** $(x + 2)(x + 1)$
c) $(x + 3)(x + 1)$ **d)** $(x + 4)(x + 1)$

14. a) The coefficient of the middle term is 1 more than the constant term.
b) One side of each rectangle has exactly 1 x-tile.
c) Answers may vary. For example:
$x^2 + 6x + 5$, $x^2 + 7x + 6$, $x^2 + 8x + 7$

15. a) $(x + 5)(x + 1)$ **b)** $(a + 6)(a + 2)$ **c)** $(m + 3)(m + 3)$
d) $(x - 2)(x + 1)$ **e)** $(x - 3)(x - 2)$ **f)** $(p + 4)(p - 2)$

16. a) $(x - 4)(x - 2)$ **b)** $(x + 3)(x + 6)$ **c)** $(a - 9)(a - 2)$
d) $(m + 7)(m + 4)$ **e)** $(n - 5)(n - 5)$ **f)** $(n - 10)(n - 3)$
g) $(p + 8)(p + 8)$ **h)** $(y - 7)(y - 6)$ **i)** $(x + 7)(x + 8)$
j) $(x - 14)(x + 4)$

17. a) $2(x + 1)(x + 5)$ **b)** $5(a + 2)(a - 4)$ **c)** $10(n - 1)(n + 2)$
d) $4(a + 1)(a - 5)$ **e)** $3(x - 1)(x + 6)$ **f)** $7(a - 2)(a - 3)$
g) $x(x + 1)(x - 3)$ **h)** $a(a + 6)(a - 8)$ **i)** $2y(y + 3)(y + 4)$
j) $3x(x - 2)(x + 4)$

18. a) $(x + 3)(x - 5)$ **b)** $(m - 1)(m + 3)$ **c)** $(z - 2)(z + 6)$
d) $(a + 3)(a - 7)$ **e)** $(x - 2)(x - 2)$ **f)** $(y - 3)(y - 3)$
g) $(x + 2)(x - 10)$ **h)** $(y - 8)(y - 9)$ **i)** $(x - 3)(x + 4)$
j) $(a + 2)(a - 4)$

19. a) $(x + 1)(x + 11)$ **b)** $(a + 1)(a + 12)$
c) $(x + 3)(x + 5)$ **d)** $(n + 2)(n + 7)$

20. a) $(r - 2)(r - 7)$ **b)** $(a - 10)(a + 2)$ **c)** $(n - 4)(n - 4)$
d) $(m - 4)(m - 5)$ **e)** $(k - 3)(k - 5)$ **f)** $(x + 6)(x + 4)$
g) $(a - 5)(a + 3)$ **h)** $(m + 4)(m + 5)$ **i)** $(n - 7)(n + 2)$
j) $(a + 14)(a - 1)$

21. a) $(r + 4)(r - 9)$ **b)** $(a + 5)(a - 9)$ **c)** $(n + 6)(n - 9)$
d) $(m + 6)(m - 8)$ **e)** $(k + 7)(k - 9)$ **f)** $(x + 3)(x - 10)$
g) $(9 - a)(9 - a)$ **h)** $(11 + m)(11 + m)$

22. a) $(x - 1)(x + 8)$ **b)** $(a - 2)(a + 7)$ **c)** $(t + 1)(t - 3)$
d) $(n + 6)(n + 7)$ **e)** $(x - 2)(x - 15)$ **f)** $(c - 5)(c - 6)$
g) $(m - 5)(m + 11)$ **h)** $(a + 1)(a + 9)$

23. a) $2(x + 2)(x + 5)$ **b)** $3(a + 2)(a + 3)$ **c)** $5(m + 4)(m - 6)$
d) $3(x - 1)(x - 5)$ **e)** $p(p - 1)(p - 1)$ **f)** $2c(c - 5)(c + 7)$
g) $3t^2(t - 5)(t - 5)$ **h)** $4y(x - 4)(x - 4)$

24. a) 240 **b)** $(x + 3)(x - 5)$ **c)** 240
d) Results are the same.

25. a) 2750 **b)** $(x - 4)(x - 9)$ **c)** 2750
d) Results are the same.

26. a) $(x + 7)(x + 9)$ **b), c)** Cannot be factored.
d) $(t + 3)(t + 8)$ **e)** $(n - 5)(n - 7)$
f) Cannot be factored.

27. Answers may vary.
a) 7, –7, 8, –8, 13, –13
b) –21, –12, –9, 9, 12, 21
c) 3, 7, 17, –3, –7, –17
d) 4, –6 **e)** 3, 4 **f)** 1, –48

28. a) $(x - 1)(x - 1)$ **b)** $(x - 4)(x + 1)$ **c)** $(x + 3)(x - 2)$
d) $(x - 3)(x - 3)$ **e)** $(x - 7)(x + 1)$ **f)** $(x - 2)(x - 8)$

29. a) $2x^2 + 3x + 1$; $(2x + 1)(x + 1)$
b) $6x^2 + 7x + 2$; $(2x + 1)(3x + 2)$
c) $4x^2 + 8x + 3$; $(2x + 3)(2x + 1)$
d) $3x^2 + 9x + 6$; $3(x + 1)(x + 2)$
e) $2x^2 + 11x + 12$; $(2x + 3)(x + 4)$
f) $4x^2 + 7x + 3$; $(4x + 3)(x + 1)$
g) $4x^2 + 4x + 1$; $(2x + 1)(2x + 1)$

30. a) $(2x + 5)(x + 1)$ **b)** $(4x + 1)(x + 3)$ **c)** $(3x + 1)(x + 5)$
d) $(3x + 4)(x + 2)$ **e)** $(5x + 2)(x + 4)$ **f)** $(2x + 1)(3x + 2)$

Review, page 364

2. a) $4x + 8$, $x^2 + 4x$ **b)** $6x + 8$, $2x^2 + 5x + 3$
c) $6x + 12$, $2x^2 + 11x + 5$

3. a, b, and d

4. a) Binomial **b)** Monomial **d)** Trinomial

5. a) 5 **b)** –2 **c)** 1 **d)** $\frac{1}{3}$

6. a) 4 **b)** 3 **c)** –1 **d)** 0

7. a) $6x^2 + y^2$ **b)** $12x - 1$ **c)** $14a^2 - 2a - 10$
d) $6x - 4$ **e)** $6x^2 - 6x$ **f)** $x^2 + 9x - 2$

8. a) $6x$ **i)** 12 **ii)** –18
b) $3x^2 - 2x + 12$ **i)** 20 **ii)** 45

9. a) $-200n^4$ **b)** $140c^5$ **c)** $85x^5$ **d)** $-140n^4$

10. a) $9y^2$ **b)** $\frac{3}{5}n^2$ **c)** –5 **d)** $\frac{3}{2}c^3$ **e)** $6x^3$ **f)** $-4y$

11. a) $2x(2y + 5) = 4xy + 10x$ **b)** $3(2x + y) = 6x + 3y$
c) $3y(x + y) = 3xy + 3y^2$

12. a) $4y - 8$ **b)** $8a - 24$
c) $-4x - 8$ **d)** $15x - 3x^2$
e) $2y^2 - 12y$ **f)** $-15x + 5x^2$
g) $35y - 10y^2 + 15y^3$ **h)** $-18x^3 - 30x^2 + 72x$

13. a) $15c - 6c^2$ **b)** $-8n^2 + 4n$
c) $-14y^3 + 35y$ **d)** $18k - 6k^2 + 6k^3$
e) $15s^3 - 10s^2 - 35s$ **f)** $6p^2 - 9p^3 - 3p^4$

14. a) $5(y - 2)$ **b)** $6(2a + 3)$ **c)** $-3(x^2 - 2x + 4)$
d) $2(a^2 - 5a + 1)$ **e)** $w(4 + 3w - 7w^2)$ **f)** $2y(4y^2 - 2y + 1)$

15. a) $6y(1 + 3y)$ **b)** $-3a(1 - 4a^3)$
c) $5a^2(1 - 5a)$ **d)** $a(3a^2 + 4a + 7)$
e) $3m(1 - 3m + 5m^2)$ **f)** $6k^2(2 - 8k^2 - 3k^4)$
g) $3xy(2x - 1 + 3y)$ **h)** $2ab(4 - 2ab + 3b)$

16. a) $x - 2$ **b)** $x - 2$ **c)** $6 - 7a$
d) $-4n - 1$ **e)** $-4 + y$ **f)** $-8b^2 - 2b$

17. a) $3x + 1$ **b)** $5 - 3a$ **c)** $\frac{1}{2}x - 2$
d) $a^2 - \frac{1}{2}a$ **e)** $-3 + c - 2c^2$ **f)** $\frac{3}{2}x^2 + 2x - \frac{1}{2}$
g) $m - \frac{4}{3}m^2 + \frac{5}{3}$ **h)** $y - \frac{1}{2} + \frac{3}{2}y^3$

18. a) $x^2 - 7x + 12$ **b)** $y^2 + 10y + 21$ **c)** $a^2 + 3a - 10$
d) $n^2 + n - 42$ **e)** $n^2 - 3n - 28$ **f)** $x^2 + 4x - 5$
g) $2x^2 - 5x - 12$ **h)** $6a^2 + 17a + 5$

19. a) $5x^2 - 13x - 6$ **b)** $4a^2 + 8a + 3$ **c)** $16n^2 - 14n + 3$
d) $16a^2 + 24a + 9$ **e)** $12x^2 - 17x + 6$ **f)** $30x^2 - 14x - 4$

20. a) $x^2 - 11x + 30$ **b)** $y^2 + 6y + 5$ **c)** $a^2 + 7a - 18$
d) $n^2 - 2n - 15$ **e)** $a^2 + a - 2$ **f)** $x^2 - 6x + 8$

21. a) $(x + 2)(x + 8)$ **b)** $(a + 6)(a - 2)$ **c)** $(x - 5)(x - 5)$
d) $(c - 7)(c + 5)$ **e)** $(x - 4)(x + 3)$ **f)** $(a + 6)(a - 5)$

22. a) $(x - 2)(x - 5)$ **b)** $(y + 3)(y + 3)$ **c)** $(x + 1)(x + 5)$
d) $-(x + 3)(x - 5)$ **e)** $-(x + 1)(x - 8)$ **f)** $(n - 5)(n + 8)$

23. a) $2(x^2 - 6x - 36)$ **b)** $5(m - 2)(m + 4)$ **c)** $y(y - 1)(y + 3)$
d) $a(a + 2)(a - 5)$ **e)** $4m(m - 5)(m - 5)$ **f)** $-2b(b + 3)(b + 4)$

24. a) $(x - 1)(x + 9)$ **b)** $(x - 2)(x - 5)$ **c)** $(y + 5)(y + 7)$
d) $(a - 2)(a + 7)$ **e)** $2(m - 1)(m + 4)$ **f)** $3(x + 2)(x - 2)$

25. a) $(x - 5)(x + 12)$ **b), c), d)** Not possible
e) $-(t + 7)(t - 8)$ **f)** $(3 + x)(2 - x)$

26. a) $6x^2 + 11x + 3$; $(3x + 1)(2x + 3)$
b) $4x^2 + 16x + 15$; $(2x + 3)(2x + 5)$

Cumulative Review, page 368

1. Key sequences may vary. Final calculator results are given.
a) -753.42 **b)** -220
c) $-0.857\ 142\ 857$ **d)** 0.4

2. 44%

3. b) Estimates may vary. One possible set of answers is 78 cm; 102 cm.

4. Answers may vary. Although fewer people under 25 are killed, there are many more people over 25 than under 25. We would need to calculate each number of deaths as a percent of its age group to find out which group is the lower risk.

5. For a single trial, P(success) $= \frac{1}{62}$

6. a) 2   **b)** -5 **c)** 3   **d)** -3 **e)** -4 **f)** 11

7. a) 5   **b)** 1   **c)** 2   **d)** -3 **e)** $\frac{11}{5}$ **f)** -1

8. 8 and 9

9. 42 quarters and 22 loonies

10. Length is 25 cm and width is 15 cm.

11. a) $2 < x$ **b)** $2 > k$ **c)** $-5 > b$ **d)** $-2 \le j$

12. a) Estimates may vary.   **b)** 7.7 m

13. a) $54°$ **b)** $27°$ **c)** $39°$ **d)** $83°$

14. About 9.9 m above the ground

15. The posts are leaning at angles of about $53°$ and $40°$.

16. a) $\frac{1}{125}$ **b)** 2   **c)** $\frac{1}{8}$
d) $\frac{1}{4}$ **e)** 1   **f)** $\frac{3}{2}$, or $1\frac{1}{2}$
g) 4   **h)** 1   **i)** $\frac{1}{64}$

17. a) 2^7 **b)** 4^2 **c)** 3^8 **d)** -2 **e)** $(-2)^{15}$
f) 5^{-3} **g)** $(-15)^3$ **h)** 7^{-3} **i)** 6^{-5} **j)** 3^5

18. a) x^9 **b)** k^{24} **c)** m^6 **d)** b^{-8} **e)** a^6
f) p^5 **g)** w **h)** $(-v)^8$ **i)** $125t^3$ **j)** $-32c^{10}$

19. a) $4.9 \times 10^7 \times 7.3 \times 10^5 = 3.577 \times 10^{13}$
b) $2.65 \times 10^7 \times 7.9 \times 10^3 \times 4.6 \times 10^{-3} = 9.6301 \times 10^8$
c) $\dfrac{3.2 \times 10^5 \times 6.4 \times 10^7}{1.28 \times 10^7} = 1.6 \times 10^6$

20. About 8.33×10^{-4} g

21. a) 5   **b)** 5   **c)** 7   **d)** 4   **e)** 3   **f)** -3

22. a) 8 mm   **b)** 0.9 m   **c)** 7 m
d) 1.5 cm   **e)** 0.5 m   **f)** 1.2 m
g) About 7.1 cm   **h)** About 1.4 m   **i)** About 3.9 mm

23. Answers may vary. For example:
a) 25.1, 25.2   **b)** 18.11, 18.2
c) $\frac{3}{4}$, 1.4   **d)** 3.89, 3.9

24. a) $10x^3$ **b)** $-3a^5$ **c)** $4x^3$
d) $15b^5$ **e)** $72x^8$ **f)** -2

25. a) $x^2 + 5x + 6$ **b)** $a^2 - 5a - 14$
c) $n^2 + 4n - 5$ **d)** $y^2 - 3y + 2$
e) $k^2 - 5k - 6$ **f)** $15 + 2a - a^2$

g) $t^2 - 6t - 16$ **h)** $m^2 - 9m + 20$

26. a) $5m(1 + 3m)$ **b)** $4q(-1 + 5q^3)$
c) $7q^2(1 - 5q)$ **d)** $2q(4q^2 + 2q + 1)$
e) $3m(2 - 6m + 5m^2)$ **f)** $-2k^2(1 + 4k^2 + 8k^4)$
g) $7bm(b - 3 + 2m)$ **h)** $8ab(8 - 2ab + b)$

27. a) $(x + 1)(x + 4)$ **b)** $(m - 3)(m + 5)$
c) $(a + 3)(a - 5)$ **d)** $(3 + y)(4 + y)$
e) $(3 + k)(8 + k)$ **f)** $(c + 6)(c - 7)$
g) $(n - 1)(n - 5)$ **h)** $(q - 8)(q - 8)$
i) $(7 + s)(7 + s)$ **j)** $(w + 2)(w + 7)$

28. a) $(a - 2)(a + 3)$ **b)** $5(k^2 + k + 1)$
c) $(m - 2)(m - 4)$ **d)** $-(n^2 - 2n - 4)$

29. a) $5(n + 3)(n - 1)$ **b)** $4(x + 7)(x - 3)$
c) $-2(m - 6)(m + 3)$ **d)** $12(b + 4)(b + 1)$
e) $5n(2n - 5)$ **f)** $3(w - 5)(w + 3)$

CHAPTER 7 TRANSFORMATIONS

Start With What You Know, page 372

1. A figure has line symmetry if there is at least one mirror line that divides the figure into two congruent figures.

2. a) Japan, Laos, Thailand, Bahamas, Jamaica, Israel, Switzerland, Sweden
b) Ghana, India, Indonesia, Japan, Laos, Thailand, Jamaica, Israel, Switzerland, Albania, Canada, Barbados

3. Japan, Laos, Thailand, Jamaica, Israel, Switzerland

4. A figure with rotational symmetry can be turned less than $360°$ so that it covers its original position.

5. Japan, Laos, Thailand, Jamaica, Trinidad and Tobago, Israel, Switzerland

6. Switzerland; since the flag is square it can be reflected across diagonals as well as horizontal or vertical lines. It can also be rotated through $90°$, $180°$, or $270°$.

7. Some answers may vary. Going through the list of flags from left to right, row by row:
horizontal reflection, rotation of $90°$ clockwise, vertical reflection, rotation of $270°$ clockwise
vertical reflection, $90°$ clockwise rotation, vertical reflection, $90°$ clockwise rotation
vertical reflection, horizontal or vertical reflection, $270°$ clockwise rotation, $270°$ clockwise rotation
$90°$ clockwise rotation, horizontal or vertical reflection, $180°$ rotation, horizontal reflection
vertical reflection, vertical reflection, $270°$ clockwise rotation, horizontal reflection

Mathematics File: Wax Paper Designs, page 374

1. The oval in the centre of the first design will be smaller.

2. All the lines will intersect at the centre of the circle. When the marked point is outside the circle, the design will look like the one on the right in the top photograph.

3. Answers may vary.

7.1 Translations

Developing the Ideas, page 375

Through Discussion

1. Answers may vary. Examples include boats moving up or down in locks, skiers gliding down a hill, people riding on an elevator.

2. Answers may vary.

3. No

Through an Activity

1., 2. Measurements may vary. Corresponding sides and angles should be equal.

3. $A'B'C'D'$ is congruent to ABCD; corresponding line segments are parallel.

4. $A'B'C'D'$ is in a different position from ABCD.

Working with Mathematics, page 378

1. a) i) The image figure is congruent to the original figure; corresponding sides are parallel.
   ii) The x-coordinates of the image figure are different from those of the original figure. The image is in a different position.
   b) i) Same as part a, i
   ii) The y-coordinates of the image figure are different from those of the original figure.
   c) Same as part b   d) Same as part a

2. a) 3 units right, 3 units up
   b) 2 units left, 4 units up
   c) 1 unit right, 5 units down
   d) 1 unit right, 6 units up

3. a) $A'(7, 0)$ b) $B'(2, 1)$ c) $C'(8, -5)$ d) $D'(4, -10)$
   e) $E'(11, 5)$ f) $F'(1, 0)$ g) $G'(4, 6)$ h) $H'(1, -7)$

4. a) $A'(-7, -2)$ b) $B'(-4, 5)$ c) $C'(4, -3)$ d) $D'(-6, -4)$
   e) $O'(-6, 0)$ f) $F'(-10, 9)$ g) $G'(-11, -3)$ h) $H'(0, 0)$

5. a) $A'(4, -1)$ b) $B'(-3, -11)$ c) $C'(-7, -4)$ d) $D'(2, -8)$
   e) $E'(-7, -5)$ f) $F'(5, -6)$ g) $G'(-3, 6)$ h) $H'(0, -3)$

6. a) $A'(0, 6)$ b) $B'(3, 0)$ c) $C'(0, 13)$ d) $D'(5, 15)$
   e) $E'(-3, -2)$ f) $F'(-7, 5)$ g) $G'(-5, 7)$ h) $O'(0, 7)$

7. a) $A'(-6, -4)$ b) $B'(6, 1)$ c) $C'(-1, -7)$ d) $O'(3, -2)$
   e) $E'(3, 7)$ f) $F'(8, -1)$ g) $G'(0, 5)$ h) $H'(11, -12)$

8. a) $A'(-4, -2)$ b) $B'(2, 2)$ c) $O'(-4, 5)$ d) $D'(5, 5)$
   e) $E'(-10, 7)$ f) $F'(3, 12)$ g) $G'(-6, 0)$ h) $H'(-1, 6)$

9. a) $PP' = QQ' = RR'$
   b) PP', QQ', and RR' are parallel.

10. a) Parallelogram   b) Parallelogram
    c) ABCD and $A'B'C'D'$ are congruent. The position of the figure has changed.

11. a) $P(0, 6)$, $Q(-6, 3)$, $R(-2, 0)$
    b) $P(1, 5)$, $Q(8, 2)$, $R(3, 7)$
    c) $P(-2, -2)$, $Q(-4, -5)$, $R(0, -4)$
    d) $P(8, -2)$, $Q(6, 1)$, $R(2, -5)$

12. Answers may vary.

13. a) 3 units right, 2 units down
    b) Answers may vary. Measure the sides of $\triangle ABC$ and $\triangle A'B'C'$, and check that $AB = A'B'$, $BC = B'C'$, and $CA = C'A'$

14. d) PS is parallel and congruent to $P'S'$. The positions are different.

15. b, d, and f

16. a) $O'(-2, 5)$, $A'(1, 6)$, $B'(0, -1)$
    b) $P(2, -2)$, $Q(3, 2)$, $R(-1, -4)$
    c) Corresponding line segments in each part are congruent and parallel to each other.

17. a) $A'(4, 3)$, $B'(8, 1)$, $C'(11, 2)$, $D'(7, 4)$
    b) $A'(-9, 0)$, $B'(-5, -2)$, $C'(-2, -1)$, $D'(-6, 1)$
    c) $A'(1, -3)$, $B'(5, -5)$, $C'(8, -4)$, $D'(4, -2)$
    d) $A'(-5, 3)$, $B'(-1, 1)$, $C'(2, 2)$, $D'(-2, 4)$

18. a) $AA' = BB' = CC' = DD'$
    b) Angles formed by corresponding line segments are equal. The line segments are parallel.
    c) They are equal in length and parallel to each other.

19. d) MR and $M'R'$ are congruent and lie on the same line. The segments are in different positions.
    e) $P'S'$ is parallel to PS.
    $M'R'$ is on the same line as MR.

20. a) $A'(-9, 1)$, $B'(-3, 1)$, $C'(-9, 4)$
    b) $A'(-7, 6)$, $B'(-1, 6)$, $C'(-7, 9)$
    c) $A'(2, 5)$, $B'(8, 5)$, $C'(2, 8)$
    d) $A'(-2, 1)$, $B'(4, 1)$, $C'(-2, 4)$

21. Answers may vary.

22. b) $A(1, 3)$, $B(5, 4)$, $C(8, 0)$, $D(2, -3)$, $E(3, 0)$
    c) Draw lines joining AA', BB', CC', DD', and EE'. They should be parallel and equal.

23. $A'(4, 2)$, $B'(7, 3)$, $C'(6, 6)$, $D'(3, 5)$

24. There are 4 possible translations: 1 unit right, 2 units up; 2 units left, 1 unit up; 1 unit left, 2 units down; 2 units right, 1 unit down.

25. a) $P'(1, 2)$, $Q'(7, 4)$, $R'(1, 5)$
    b) $P'(-6, -1)$, $Q'(0, 1)$, $R'(-6, 2)$
    c) $P'(-1, -3)$, $Q'(5, -1)$, $R'(-1, 0)$
    d) $P'(-8, 4)$, $Q'(-2, 6)$, $R'(-8, 7)$

26. a) 4 units left, 2 units up; $(x, y) \rightarrow (x - 4, y + 2)$
    b) 3 units right, 2 units down; $(x, y) \rightarrow (x + 3, y - 2)$
    c) 2 units left, 3 units down; $(x, y) \rightarrow (x - 2, y - 3)$
    d) 5 units right, 3 units up; $(x, y) \rightarrow (x + 5, y + 3)$

7.2 Reflections

Developing the Ideas, page 382

Through Discussion

1., 2. Answers may vary.

3. Yes, unless the mirror distorts the image.

Through Activities

Activity 1, page 382

1., 2. Measurements may vary. Corresponding sides and angles should be equal.

3., 4. Answers may vary. The answer to exercise 4 should be the opposite of the answer to exercise 3.

5. $\triangle P'Q'R'$ is congruent to $\triangle PQR$.

6. They are in different positions; their orientations are different.

Activity 2, page 383

1. to 4. Each reflection should give the same results as for steps 1 to 7 in *Activity 1*.

1. i) a) The corresponding sides and angles are equal.
     The figures are congruent.
   b) The image is entirely in the fourth quadrant, and its orientation is reversed.
   ii) a) The figures are congruent.
   b) The image is in the fourth quadrant with its orientation reversed.
   iii) a) The figures are congruent.
   b) The orientation of the image is reversed.
   iv) a) The figures are congruent.
   b) The image figure is entirely in the second quadrant with its orientation reversed.
   v) a) The figures are congruent.
   b) The image is in the second quadrant with its orientation reversed.
   vi) a) The figures are congruent.
   b) The orientation is reversed and the image is in the second quadrant.

2. a) Reflection in the x-axis
   b) Reflection in the y-axis
   c) Reflection in the vertical line 1 unit left of the y-axis
   d) Reflection in the horizontal line 2 units above the x-axis

3. a) $A'(-3, 4)$ b) $B'(1, 7)$ c) $C'(0, 5)$
   d) $D'(2, -8)$ e) $O'(0, 0)$ f) $F'(10, 0)$

4. a) $G'(8, -2)$ b) $H'(1, -11)$ c) $I'(11, 1)$
   d) $J'(1, 0)$ e) $K'(-1, 6)$ f) $L'(11, -1)$

5. a) $A'(0, -3)$ b) $B'(-6, 1)$ c) $C'(-8, 0)$
   d) $D'(5, 2)$ e) $E'(2, 0)$ f) $F'(7, -2)$

6. a) $O'(0, -6)$ b) $H'(1, -11)$ c) $I'(-2, -12)$
   d) $J'(0, -2)$ e) $K'(-2, -15)$ f) $L'(-2, -4)$

7. a) $FF' = 2$ units, $DD' = 10$ units, $EE' = 18$ units; DD', FF', and EE' are all different lengths.
   b) D and D', F and F', E and E' are each equal distances from the x-axis.
   c) DD', EE', and FF' each makes an angle of 90° with the x-axis.

8. a) Trapezoid
   b) Trapezoid
   c) They have the same side lengths and angles. GHJK and G'H'J'K' are congruent. GHJK is in the first quadrant and G'H'J'K' is in the second quadrant. Their orientations are different.

9. a) $B(0, -4)$, $C(4, -2)$, $D(2, 1)$
   b) $B(2, -1)$, $C(-3, 1)$, $D(-4, 4)$
   c) $B(3, 4)$, $C(4, -1)$, $D(-1, 2)$
   d) $B(-3, -4)$, $C(-6, -4)$, $D(0, 1)$

10. Answers may vary.

11. a) $A'(1, 1)$, $B'(4, 6)$, $C'(-1, 1)$
    b) $P(2, 7)$, $Q(-1, 2)$, $R(3, 4)$

12. e) PS and P'S' lie on the same straight line PP' with opposite orientations. They have the same lengths and are both perpendicular to AB.

13. a) $A'(2, 6)$, $B'(2, -4)$, $C'(6, -4)$
    b) $A'(0, -2)$, $B'(0, 8)$, $C'(-4, 8)$

14. c) Answers may vary. Check that BB', CC', and DD' are perpendicular to the x-axis. Also, B and B' are equidistant from the x-axis. Similarly, D and D', and C and C', are equidistant from the x-axis.

15. a) $SS' = UU' \neq TT'$
    b) S and S' are equidistant from the y-axis. T, T' and U, U' are also equidistant from the y-axis.
    c) SS', TT', and UU' each makes a 90° angle with the y-axis.
    d) The lines joining the corresponding points on a figure and its reflection image are perpendicular to the line of reflection, and bisected by it.

16. a) $S(-4, 0)$, $T(0, -3)$, $U(-4, -5)$, $V(-5, -3)$
    b) $S(2, 0)$, $T(6, 3)$, $U(3, 4)$, $V(0, 2)$
    c) $S(-4, 0)$, $T(0, 0)$, $U(-2, 4)$, $V(-5, 2)$
    d) $S(-3, 4)$, $T(2, 3)$, $U(3, -2)$, $V(-2, 1)$

17. a) $S'(7, 1)$, $T'(1, 1)$, $U'(4, 6)$
    b) $\triangle$STU and $\triangle$S'T'U' coincide, with S becoming T' and T becoming S'.

18. Answers may vary.

19. a) Kite
    b) $C'(1, 0)$, $D'(-2, 2)$, $E'(1, 9)$, $F'(4, 2)$
    c) $C''(1, 4)$, $D''(4, 2)$, $E''(1, -5)$, $F''(-2, 2)$
    d) C'D'E'F' and C''F''E''D'' are congruent with the same orientation.

20. $A'(0, -2)$, $B'(-5, 0)$, $C'(-3, 5)$, $D'(2, 3)$

21. b) $M'(-1, 5)$, $N'(-4, 4)$, $P'(-7, 3)$, $R'(-10, 2)$
    d) MR and M'R' are congruent. They are not parallel.
    e) Answers may vary. PS and P'S' are on the same line.

22. a) $C'(2, 4)$, $D'(-4, 2)$, $E'(1, -2)$
    b) $C''(-2, 4)$, $D''(4, 2)$, $E''(-1, -2)$
    c) No.

23. a) $(x, y) \rightarrow (x, -y)$ b) $(x, y) \rightarrow (-x, y)$
    c) $(x, y) \rightarrow (y, x)$ d) $(x, y) \rightarrow (8 - x, y)$
    e) $(x, y) \rightarrow (x, -6 - y)$

24. Multiple answers are possible. Descriptions may vary.

7.3 Rotations

Developing the Ideas, page 389

Through Discussion

Answers may vary.

Through Activities

Activity 1, page 389

1., 2. Measurements may vary. Corresponding sides and angles should be equal.

3. Orientations are the same.

4. It is congruent.

5. Its position is different. Angles formed with horizontal grid lines have changed.

Activity 2, page 390

1., 2. $V'(-3, 4)$, $W'(-1, 9)$, $X'(-11, 13)$

3. $V'(-10, 1)$, $W'(-12, -4)$, $X'(-2, -8)$

4. $V'(-6, -3)$, $W'(-4, 2)$, $X'(-14, 6)$

5. Corresponding sides are equal.

6. Corresponding angles are equal.

7. Same

8. Answers may vary.

Working with Mathematics, page 392

1. a) $270°$
   c) $180°$
   b) $90°$
   d) The rotations are equivalent.

2. a) $O'(1, -5)$ b) $B'(-3, 0)$ c) $C'(-1, -12)$ d) $D'(1, -10)$
   e) $E'(3, -5)$ f) $F'(-2, -5)$ g) $G'(3, -6)$ h) $H'(3, -2)$

3. a) $J'(0, -5)$ b) $K'(3, 1)$ c) $L'(-5, 1)$ d) $M'(0, 3)$
   e) $N'(-3, -5)$ f) $O'(0, 0)$ g) $Q'(3, -5)$ h) $R'(3, 0)$

4. a) $S'(2, 3)$ b) $T'(-5, -5)$ c) $U'(1, 2)$ d) $V'(-12, 1)$
   e) $O'(-6, 2)$ f) $X'(-12, 6)$ g) $Y'(-6, 4)$ h) $Z'(-11, 2)$

5. a) $A'(6, 0)$ b) $B'(0, 8)$ c) $C'(-5, -3)$ d) $D'(-4, 0)$
   e) $E'(-7, 3)$ f) $F'(4, 6)$ g) $O'(0, 0)$ h) $H'(3, -8)$

6. a) $J'(2, 7)$ b) $K'(-2, 5)$ c) $O'(7, 5)$ d) $M'(17, 5)$
   e) $N'(-1, 2)$ f) $P'(12, 2)$ g) $Q'(9, 13)$ h) $S'(7, 4)$

7. a) $180°$
   c) $90°$ clockwise
   b) $90°$ counterclockwise
   d) $90°$ clockwise

8. The rotation centre remains unchanged.

9. a) $90°$
   c) $90°$
   b) $90°$
   d) The angles are equal.

10. a) Rectangle
    b) Rectangle
    c) The two rectangles are congruent. They have the same orientation. The positions of the two rectangles are different.

11. a) $J(3, 2)$, $K(-2, 1)$, $L(1, -3)$
    b) $J(-2, -5)$, $K(2, -6)$, $L(0, 3)$
    c) $J(3, 2)$, $K(1, 5)$, $L(-1, -2)$
    d) $J(0, 4)$, $K(-2, 1)$, $L(-6, 2)$

12. Answers may vary.

13. b) $P'(-2, -2)$, $Q'(-3, 0)$, $R'(-4, 2)$, $S'(-5, 4)$
    d) PS and $P'S'$ have the same length. They are in different positions.

14. $C'(3, 1)$, $D'(3, -2)$, $E'(5, -1)$

15. a) $360°$ b) $360°$ c) 2

16. a) $90°$ b) $90°$ c) $90°$
    d) All angle measures are equal to the angle of rotation.
    e) Given an original figure (PQR), its image ($P'Q'R'$) can be obtained by using the properties:
    $OP = OP'$ and $\angle POP' = 90°$
    $OQ = OQ'$ and $\angle QOQ' = 90°$
    $OR = OR'$ and $\angle ROR' = 90°$
    for $90°$ rotations about the origin. Otherwise O should be replaced by the rotation centre.
    f) $A'(1, 1)$, $B'(-2, 3)$, $C'(3, 5)$

17. a) Trapezoid b) Trapezoid
    c) ABCD and $A'B'C'D'$ are congruent. They have the same orientation but different positions.

18. a) $180°$ b) $90°$ clockwise
    c) $90°$ counterclockwise d) $180°$
    e) $180°$

19. $\triangle MNP$ and $\triangle M'N'P'$ are congruent. The two triangles have a common vertex M (or M'). They have the same orientation. The positions of $\triangle MNP$ and $\triangle M'N'P'$ are different.

20. b) $M'(11, -3)$, $N'(14, -4)$, $P'(17, -5)$, $R'(20, -6)$
    d) MR and $M'R'$ have the same length. They lie on the same line RR' passing through B.
    e) Answers may vary.

21. a) $360°$ b) $360°$
    c) 4: $90°$, $180°$, $270°$, $360°$

22. Answers may vary.

23. a) $C'(8, -5)$, $D'(4, -6)$, $E'(5, 1)$ b) $P(9, 1)$

24. a) $(x, y) \rightarrow (-y, x)$ b) $(x, y) \rightarrow (-x, -y)$
    c) $(x, y) \rightarrow (y, -x)$

25. Multiple answers are possible. Descriptions may vary.

Linking Ideas: Mathematics and Technology
Transformations and Grids, page 396

1. Answers may vary. Yellow: rotation; dark blue: rotation; purple: rotation; maroon: translation; orange: reflection and translation; green: reflection; light blue: dilatation

7.4 Combining Transformations
Developing the Ideas

Activity 1, page 397

1., 2., 3. Answers may vary.

4. Corresponding angles are equal.

5. Corresponding sides are equal.

6. $\triangle P''Q''R''$ is congruent to $\triangle PQR$.

7. $\triangle P''Q''R''$ and $\triangle PQR$ are in different positions. They have different orientations.

Activity 2, page 398

1. to 4. Answers may vary.

5. The orientations of $\triangle DEF$ and $\triangle D''E''F''$ are the same and that of $\triangle D'E'F'$ is opposite.

6. They are congruent and have the same orientation.

7. The positions of the two triangles are different.

8. Translation 12 units right

Working with Mathematics, page 401

1. The translation 12 units right is equivalent to the two successive reflections.

2. When the second translation is opposite to the first translation, the final image will coincide with the original figure.

3. a) i) $A(5, 3) \rightarrow A'(0, 8) \rightarrow A''(3, 4)$
   ii) $B(4, -4) \rightarrow B'(-1, 1) \rightarrow B''(2, -3)$
   iii) $C(-5, 0) \rightarrow C'(-10, 5) \rightarrow C''(-7, 1)$
   iv) $D(2, -1) \rightarrow D'(-3, 4) \rightarrow D''(0, 0)$
   v) $E(-3, -5) \rightarrow E'(-8, 0) \rightarrow E''(-5, -4)$
   vi) $F(0, 2) \rightarrow F'(-5, 7) \rightarrow F''(-2, 3)$
   b) i) $A(5, 3) \rightarrow A'(8, -1) \rightarrow A''(3, 4)$
   ii) $B(4, -4) \rightarrow B'(7, -8) \rightarrow B''(2, -3)$
   iii) $C(-5, 0) \rightarrow C'(-2, -4) \rightarrow C''(-7, 1)$
   iv) $D(2, -1) \rightarrow D'(5, -5) \rightarrow D''(0, 0)$
   v) $E(-3, -5) \rightarrow E'(0, -9) \rightarrow E''(-5, -4)$
   vi) $F(0, 2) \rightarrow F'(3, -2) \rightarrow F''(-2, 3)$
   c) No; explanations may vary.

4. a) i) $E(-3, 2) \rightarrow E'(-3, -2) \rightarrow E''(3, -2)$
   ii) $F(-5, -2) \rightarrow F'(-5, 2) \rightarrow F''(5, 2)$
   iii) $G(-6, -6) \rightarrow G'(-6, 6) \rightarrow G''(6, 6)$
   iv) $H(-3, 0) \rightarrow H'(-3, 0) \rightarrow H''(3, 0)$
   v) $J(0, 8) \rightarrow J'(0, -8) \rightarrow J''(0, -8)$
   vi) $K(5, 7) \rightarrow K'(5, -7) \rightarrow K''(-5, -7)$
   b) i) $E(-3, 2) \rightarrow E'(3, 2) \rightarrow E''(3, -2)$
   ii) $F(-5, -2) \rightarrow F'(5, -2) \rightarrow F''(5, 2)$
   iii) $G(-6, -6) \rightarrow G'(6, -6) \rightarrow G''(6, 6)$
   iv) $H(-3, 0) \rightarrow H'(3, 0) \rightarrow H''(3, 0)$
   v) $J(0, 8) \rightarrow J'(0, 8) \rightarrow J''(0, -8)$

  vi) K(5, 7) → K′(−5, 7) → K″(−5, −7)
 c) No; explanations may vary.

5. a) i) J(5, 6) → J′(5, −6) → J″(8, −10)
  ii) K(4, −2) → K′(4, 2) → K″(7, −2)
  iii) L(−7, 2) → L′(−7, −2) → L″(−4, −6)
  iv) M(−3, 0) → M′(−3, 0) → M″(0, −4)
  v) P(3, 0) → P′(3, 0) → P″(6, −4)
  vi) Q(−7, −8) → Q′(−7, 8) → Q″(−4, 4)
 b) i) J(5, 6) → J′(8, 2) → J″(8, −2)
  ii) K(4, −2) → K′(7, −6) → K″(7, 6)
  iii) L(−7, 2) → L′(−4, −2) → L″(−4, 2)
  iv) M(−3, 0) → M′(0, −4) → M″(0, 4)
  v) P(3, 0) → P′(6, −4) → P″(6, 4)
  vi) Q(−7, −8) → Q′(−4, −12) → Q″(−4, 12)
 c) Yes; explanations may vary.

6. a) P(4, 7) **b)** P(−1, −2) **c)** P(8, 12) **d)** P(−4, −10)

7. Answers are based on the assumption that the reflection line is an axis.
 a) Translation 3 units left, 4 units down; reflection in the x-axis
 b) Translation 1 unit right, 2 units up; reflection in the y-axis

8. a) Corresponding sides are equal.
 b) Corresponding angles are equal.
 c) △ABC is congruent to △A″B″C″; this follows from the fact that △ABC is congruent to △A′B′C′, and △A′B′C′ is congruent to △A″B″C″.
 c) Yes; explanations may vary.

9. a) Answers may vary. For example, the two translations could be: 1 unit right, 1 unit down; and 5 units left, 6 units up.

10. a) A(−2, −1), B(5, −3), C(3, −2)
 b) D(−10, 12), E(−1, 11), F(−5, 3)
 c) G(2, 3), H(−2, −1), J(3, −5)
 d) K(−2, 4), L(−7, −1), M(−9, −5)

11. c) a) M″(0, −4), N″(−9, 1), P″(−11, −8), Q″(−4, −12)
  b) M″(−6, −4), N″(−15, 1), P″(−17, −8), Q″(−10, −12)

12. W(−2, 0), X(1, −10), Y(−7, −4), Z(−7, 0)

13. Answers may vary.
 c) Translation 12 units left.

14. b) J′(3, 6), K′(5, 9), L′(2, 11)
 c) J″(−3, 6), K″(−5, 9), L″(−2, 11)
 d) Rotation 90° counterclockwise about the origin
 e) J′(−6, 3), K′(−9, 5), L′(−11, 2), J″(3, −6), K″(5, −9), L″(2, −11); rotation 90° clockwise about the origin
 f) The final images are congruent and have the same orientation. Their positions are different.

15. a) Square   **b)** Square
 c) All sides are equal to about 3.2 units.
 d) All angles are equal to 90°.
 e) Yes, the orientation of B″C″D″E″ is different from BCDE.
 f) The image of a figure after a translation and a reflection (or a reflection and a translation) is congruent to the original figure; but its orientation is reversed.

16. Answers are based on the assumption that the reflection line is an axis.
 a) Reflection in the x-axis; translation 2 units right, 2 units down
 b) Reflection in the y-axis; translation 1 unit left, 3 units up
 c) Reflection in the x-axis; translation 4 units left, 2 units up
 d) Reflection in the y-axis; translation 3 units right, 1 unit down

17. a) , b) D″(1, 7), E″(−7, 2), F″(−4, −5)
 c) The final images are the same.
 d) Rotation of 180°

18. c) Part a: E″(−1, 16), F″(−5, 12), G″(−2, 9)
  Part b: E″(−1, 10), F″(−5, 6), G″(−2, 3)
 d) The order in which a combined translation and reflection is applied will affect the final position of the image.

19. a) G′(2, 3), H′(−3, 5), J′(4, 7)
 b) G″(2, −13), H″(−3, −15), J″(4, −17)
 c) A translation 16 units down
 d) G′(2, −13), H′(−3, −11), J′(4, −9); G″(2, 19), H″(−3, 17), J″(4, 15)
 e) They are congruent and have the same orientation. The first image of △GHJ results from a translation 16 units down, and the second image results from a translation 16 units up.

20. b) M′(−6, −3), N′(−8, −5), P′(−10, −1), Q′(−6, 0)
 c) M″(3, 6), N″(5, 8), P″(1, 10), Q″(0, 6)
 d) A 90° clockwise rotation about the origin
 e) M′(−3, 6), N′(−5, 8), P′(−1, 10), Q′(0, 6); M″(−3, −6), N″(−5, −8), P″(−1, −10), Q″(0, −6); 90° counterclockwise rotation about the origin
 f) Both the images are congruent to MNPQ. The two images are related by a 180° rotation. The two images lie in different quadrants.

21. M(−3, 7), N(−8, 1), P(1, −3) **22.** Answers may vary.

23. Answers may vary.
 c) The final images are the same.
 d) When the reflection lines are perpendicular, the final image is the same as that obtained by the two reflections in reverse order.

24. a) S′(4, −3), T′(8, 0), U′(2, 4)
 b) S″(0, −3), T″(4, 0), U″(−2, 4)
 c) A reflection in the vertical line 4 units to the right of the y-axis
 d) A reflection in the vertical line 8 units to the right of the y-axis
 e) Yes; explanations may vary.

25. a) A′(0, 2), B′(6, 3), C′(4, −2), D′(−2, −3)
 b) A″(0, 6), B″(6, 5), C″(4, 10), D″(−2, 11)
 c) No; ABCD cannot be translated to A″B″C″D″ because the two figures have reverse orientation. For the same reason, ABCD cannot be rotated to A″B″C″D″. There is no single reflection that will map ABCD onto A″B″C″D″.
 d) A′(−5, 6), B′(1, 5), C′(−1, 10), D′(−7, 11); A″(0, 6), B″(6, 5), C″(4, 10), D″(−2, 11)
 e) No

26. (x, y) → (−x, −y)

7.5 Dilatations and Similarity
Developing the Ideas, page 406

Through Discussion

1. , 2. Answers may vary.

3. Size changes but shape remains the same.

Through an Activity

1. Measurements may vary. Sides of △B′C′D′ should be double the length of corresponding sides of △BCD.

2. Measurements may vary. Corresponding angles should be equal.

3. The triangles are similar.

4. They are different sizes.

Working with Mathematics, page 409

1. Corresponding angles are equal.

2. $\angle A = \angle A'$, $\angle B = \angle B'$, $\angle C = \angle C'$

$\dfrac{A'B'}{AB} = \dfrac{B'C'}{BC} = \dfrac{C'A'}{CA} = 3$

or $A'B' = 3AB$, $B'C' = 3BC$, and $C'A' = 3CA$

3. a) Determine the ratio of:
distance from the dilatation centre to an image vertex :
distance from the dilatation centre to the corresponding
original vertex

  b) Draw lines joining the original vertices to the corresponding
image vertices. Extend the lines until they intersect at
a point.

4. a) $A'(-10, 14)$ **b)** $B'(0, 6)$ **c)** $C'(16, 6)$ **d)** $D'(-4, -10)$
  e) $E'(-8, 0)$ **f)** $F'(20, -6)$ **g)** $G'(14, 0)$ **h)** $O'(0, 0)$

5. a) $J'(0, 1)$ **b)** $K'(-2, -3)$ **c)** $L'(-2, 0)$ **d)** $O'(0, 0)$
  e) $N'(5, 1.5)$ **f)** $P'(-3.5, 3)$ **g)** $Q'(5.5, 0)$ **h)** $R'(2.5, -4)$

6. a) $S'(9, 21)$ **b)** $O'(0, 0)$ **c)** $U'(-15, 24)$ **d)** $V'(3, -6)$
  e) $W'(0, 36)$ **f)** $X'(15, 3)$ **g)** $Y'(-6, -12)$ **h)** $Z'(-6, 0)$

7. They remain unchanged.

8. a) Centre $O(0, 0)$, scale factor $\frac{1}{2}$
  b) Centre $O(0, 0)$, scale factor 2
  c) Centre $O(0, 0)$, scale factor 2
  d) Centre $O(0, 0)$, scale factor $\frac{1}{3}$
  e) Centre $C(3, -1)$, scale factor 2

9. $P'(-2, -3)$, $Q'(-8, -12)$, $R'(-11, -6)$; by measuring, determine
corresponding angles are equal.

10. $D'(-6, -1)$, $E'(0, -1)$, $F'(0, -7)$, $G'(-6, -7)$
  a) DEFG and $D'E'F'G'$ are similar and have a common vertex.
  b) The squares are different sizes.

11. $R'(-2, 1)$, $S'(-2, -1)$, $T'(2, 0)$, $U'(0, 2)$
  a) Corresponding angles are equal.
  b) $RS = 2R'S'$, $ST = 2S'T'$, $TU = 2T'U'$, and $UR = 2U'R'$
  c) The dilatation is a reduction because the image is smaller
than the original.

12. $A'(2, -5)$, $B'(-6, -5)$, $C'(-2, 3)$
  a) Isosceles **b)** Isosceles
  c) They are similar: $\angle A = \angle A'$, $\angle B = \angle B'$, and $\angle C = \angle C'$
The two triangles have different sizes.
  d) The dilatation is an enlargement because the image is larger
than the original triangle.
  e) Answers may vary. A dilatation does not change the
orientation of the figure.

13. $P'(4, 4)$, $Q'(12, 4)$, $R'(10, 12)$
  a) 8 square units **b)** 32 square units
  c) Area $\triangle P'Q'R' = 4 \times$ Area $\triangle PQR$

14. $P''(6, 6)$, $Q''(18, 6)$, $R''(15, 18)$
  a) 72 square units **b)** It is 9 times as great.
  c) Square the scale factor.

15. a) $(x, y) \rightarrow (2x, 2y)$ **b)** $(x, y) \rightarrow \left(\frac{x}{2}, \frac{y}{2}\right)$
  c) $(x, y) \rightarrow (4x, 4y)$; $A'(12, 4)$, $B'(4, 12)$, $C'(12, 8)$
  d) $(x, y) \rightarrow (kx, ky)$

Linking Ideas: Mathematics and Design
Scott Kim's Inversions, page 411

1. Answers may vary. A rotation of 180° in "Symmetry" and
"Upside Down," a rotation of 120° and 240° in "Infinity," a
reflection in "Mirror," a dilatation in "Level"

2. Answers may vary. 6

3. a) "Symmetry," "Upside Down," "Infinity" **b)** "Mirror"

4. a) "Mirror" **b)** "Upside Down," "Symmetry"

5. Answers may vary.

Quest: How Far Is It across the Street?, page 412

Answers may vary.

7.6 Identifying Transformations
Working with Mathematics, page 415

1., **2.**, **3.** Answers may vary.

4. a) Reflection **b)** Rotation

5. a) Translation **b)** Reflection **c)** Rotation

6. The transformation is a dilatation, centre $O(0, 0)$, scale
factor 2.5.

7. a) Reflection **b)** Rotation **c)** Reflection
  d) Reflection **e)** Rotation **f)** Reflection
  g) Rotation **h)** Reflection **i)** Rotation
  j) Reflection

8. a) i) Reflection **ii)** Rotation **iii)** Rotation
  b) i) Reflection **ii)** Translation **iii)** Rotation

9. a) Reflection in the x-axis
  b) Rotation 90° counterclockwise about the origin
  c) Translation 3 units right, 2 units up
  d) Reflection in the y-axis

10. Translation 3 units right, 4 units down

11. a) 90° counterclockwise rotation about the origin
  b) Answers may vary. Measure the sides and angles.

12. a) Reflection
  b) Reflection and a translation
  c) Rotation

13. Answers may vary.
  a) Reflection
  b) Rotation
  c) Rotation
  d) Reflection and translation
  e) Translation

16. a) Answers may vary.
  A → A′ is a rotation.
  B → B′ is a rotation.
  C → C′ is a translation.
  D → D′ is a translation or rotation.
  E → E′ is a reflection, translation, or rotation.
  b) Yes

17. a) Reflection in the y-axis
  b) Check that $AB = A'B'$, $AC = A'C'$, and $BC = B'C'$.

18. Translation 3 units left, 5 units down

19. Answers may vary.

20. Answers may vary.

Mathematics File: Distortions, page 419

1. Drawings may vary.

2. a) There appear to be two distorted copies of the original figure in the image.
   b) A transformation is one-to-one if each point on the original corresponds to exactly one point on the image.

Review, page 420

1. Answers may vary.
   A → B: 90° clockwise rotation
   A → C: 180° rotation
   A → D: translation, then reflection in a horizontal line
   A → E: rotation followed by a reflection
   A → F: reflection in a vertical line, then translation
   A → G: 90° counterclockwise rotation
   A → H: reflection in a diagonal line
   A → J: translation followed by a reflection

2. a) $M'(1, 6)$ b) $N'(2, -5)$ c) $O'(-5, -3)$ d) $P'(-20, 3)$
   e) $Q'(-12, -11)$ f) $R'(-5, -14)$ g) $S'(-8, -1)$ h) $T'(8, -7)$

3. a) $M'(9, 13)$ b) $N'(10, 2)$ c) $O'(3, 4)$ d) $P'(-12, 10)$
   e) $Q'(-4, -4)$ f) $R'(3, -7)$ g) $S'(0, 6)$ h) $T'(16, 0)$

4. No, it is not possible to translate a triangle to obtain a rectangle because the translated image is always congruent to the original image.

5. 6 units right, 2 units up; 2 units right, 4 units up; 6 units right, 5 units up; 1 unit right, 2 units up

6. a) $A'(3, -2)$ b) $B'(-4, -5)$ c) $C'(0, 7)$ d) $D'(-3, 9)$
   e) $E'(11, 1)$ f) $F'(6, 0)$ g) $G'(0, -5)$ h) $H'(-4, 8)$

7. a) $A'(-7, 2)$ b) $B'(0, 5)$ c) $C'(-4, -7)$ d) $D'(-1, -9)$
   e) $E'(-15, -1)$ f) $F'(-10, 0)$ g) $G'(-4, 5)$ h) $H'(0, -8)$

8. a) $W'(0, 5)$, $X'(4, 5)$, $Y'(2, -1)$, $Z'(-2, -1)$
   c) $W''(0, -5)$, $X''(4, -5)$, $Y''(2, 1)$, $Z''(-2, 1)$
   d) It appears to be a reflection in the y-axis, but the vertices do not map onto corresponding vertices.

9. $A(-2, 3)$, $B(4, 1)$, $C(-2, 0)$

10. a) $G'(-5, -4)$ b) $H'(7, -2)$ c) $I'(-3, 8)$ d) $J'(-9, 0)$
    e) $K'(6, 7)$ f) $L'(0, -5)$ g) $M'(8, 0)$ h) $N'(-9, 12)$

11. a) $G'(-4, 5)$, $H'(-2, -7)$, $I'(8, 3)$, $J'(0, 9)$, $K'(7, -6)$, $L'(-5, 0)$, $M'(0, -8)$, $N'(12, 9)$
    b) $G'(5, 4)$, $H'(-7, 2)$, $I'(3, -8)$, $J'(9, 0)$, $K'(-6, -7)$, $L'(0, 5)$, $M'(-8, 0)$, $N'(9, -12)$
    c) $G'(10, 5)$, $H'(-2, 3)$, $I'(8, -7)$, $J'(14, 1)$, $K'(-1, -6)$, $L'(5, 6)$, $M'(-3, 1)$, $N'(14, -11)$

12. Answers may vary.
    a) I and II, II and III, I and IV, IV and V, III and IV, V and VI
    b) I and III, II and IV, VI and VIII, V and VII
    c) IV and VI, III and V

13. a) $G'(2, 0)$, $H'(6, 1)$, $I'(7, -6)$
    b) $G'(4, -2)$, $H'(0, -3)$, $I'(-1, 4)$
    c) $G'(-5, -9)$, $H'(-6, -5)$, $I'(1, -4)$
    d) $G'(-1, 7)$, $H'(0, 3)$, $I'(-7, 2)$
    e) $G'(-4, 2)$, $H'(4, 4)$, $I'(6, -10)$
    f) $G'(2, 4)$, $H'(3, 0)$, $I'(-4, -1)$
    g) $G'(-4, 2)$, $H'(-8, 1)$, $I'(-9, 8)$
    h) $G'(-8, 5)$, $H'(-4, 6)$, $I'(-3, -1)$

14. a) Larger   b) Larger   c) Smaller
    d) Larger   e) Smaller   f) Smaller

15. a) $Z'(-12, 4)$ b) $Y'(8, -20)$ c) $X'(0, 24)$ d) $W'(-16, -4)$
    e) $V'(40, -20)$ f) $U'(32, 0)$ g) $T'(0, -12)$ h) $S'(-8, -24)$

17. Dilatation centre in each case is $(0, 0)$.
    a) $\frac{1}{3}$ b) 2   c) 1.5

18. a) 3: △LOD, △KOE, △JOF
    b) 2, 3, and 4, respectively
    c) 3: △AOC, △KOE, △JOF
    d) 0.5, 1.5, 2

19. a) $J'(-3, 4)$, $K'(-1, -1)$, $L'(-4, -2)$
    b) $J''(9, 4)$, $K''(7, -1)$, $L''(10, -2)$
    c) A translation 10 units right
    d) A translation 10 units left

20. b) $R'(-5, 3)$, $S'(-6, -1)$, $T'(-4, 1)$
    c) $R''(-5, -3)$, $S''(-6, 1)$, $T''(-4, -1)$
    d) A 90° counterclockwise rotation about the origin
    e) A 90° clockwise rotation about the origin

21. Answers may vary.
    a) I and II, I and IV
    b) I and II, III and IV, II and IV
    c) III and IV, I and III, II and III, I and II
    d) Parts I, II, III, and IV can be related to the large figure that contains all 4 triangles.

22. Answers may vary.
    I Translation 5 units left, 3 units up
    II Dilatation with centre the origin, scale factor 3
    III Reflection in the y-axis
    IV Reflection in the y-axis followed by a translation 3 units left, 1 unit up
    V Rotation of 180° about the origin followed by a translation 2 units left, 2 units down
    VI 90° clockwise rotation about the origin
    VII Translation 2 units right, 5 units down

23. Answers may vary.
    a) Reflection in the y-axis
    b) Translation 5 units left, 3 units up
    c) 90° clockwise rotation about the origin
    d) Reflection in the x-axis followed by a reflection in the y-axis; or 180° rotation about the origin
    e) Reflection in the x-axis
    f) Dilatation with centre the origin, scale factor $\frac{1}{3}$

CHAPTER 8 GEOMETRY

Start With What You Know, page 428

1. 21 m²   2. 3 m²   3. 420 L or 470 L   4. 17.5 m

5. Answers may vary.
   a) The distance between two points
   b) A measure of the surface covered by a figure
   c) A measure of the space filled by a solid

6. a) Area of a rectangle, area of a square, volume of a rectangular prism, circumference of a circle, volume of a cylinder, perimeter of a square, area of a circle, volume of a cube, circumference of a circle, area of a triangle, surface area of a cylinder, perimeter of a rectangle
   b) Summaries may vary.

Linking Ideas: Mathematics and Art
Representing 3-Dimensional Objects in 2 Dimensions, page 430

1. *The Annunciation* has perspective.
2. Answers may vary.
3. Answers may vary.
4. Answers may vary.

8.1 Sketching Polyhedra
Developing the Ideas, page 432

1. c) Answers may vary.
2. Answers may vary. Some of the views will have the same shape.

Working with Mathematics, page 434

1. Yes 2. Length, width, and height
3. a) A: tape dispenser, B: mail box, C: dictionary, D: kettle
   b) Diagrams may vary.
4. a) Cube b) Square pyramid
5. a) Cube b) Rectangular prism
   c) Rectangular pyramid d) Triangular pyramid
   e) Octahedron f) Triangular prism
8. a) Cube, rectangular prism, square pyramid, triangular prism
   b) Square pyramid, octahedron
9. a) Triangular prism, any pyramid
   b) Triangular prism
   c) Any prism, rectangular pyramid
15. The other side.
18. Square pyramid
19. a) No
    b) The views are a square, a circle, and a triangle
    c) A rolled-up tube of toothpaste without a cap

8.2 Sketching Paths and Regions
Developing the Ideas, page 438

Activity 1

1. a) A circle b) A circle
3. Answers may vary. The region is a long rectangle with semicircular ends.

Activity 2

1. No; explanations may vary.
2. A square 1 m by 1 m, or 1 m^2
3. Answers may vary. 53 m plus the distance walked at each turn
4. Answers may vary. 53 m plus the distance walked at each turn
5. Answers may vary. 53 m plus the distance walked at each turn
6. Answers may vary. There is an assumption that we can disregard the need for overlapping strips of lawn.
7. Answers may vary. The method that involves the fewest turns may require fewer steps, even though the distance covered is the same.

Activity 3

1. a), b) A circle with radius 2 m
2. a) 1 m^2
3. a) 16 m^2 b) 4π m^2 c) 3.434 m^2 d) 30.906 m^2
   e) $\frac{30.906}{144}$; 21.46% f) No
5. Answers may vary.

Working with Mathematics, page 441

1. It would increase the distances.
2. Answers may vary. Oscillating sprinklers can cover a rectangular region.
3. A circular region with radius 1.8 m
4. Answers may vary. The tip of the board traces an arc of a circle.
5. Circular region of approximate area 2800 km^2
6. The region is shaped like a rectangle 103 cm by 64 cm, with rounded corners on the side away from the wall.
7. The region is roughly a circle with the rectangular shape of the dog house cut out of it.
8. a) The region is a circle with radius 6 m.
   b) 12 m by 12 m
   c) $\frac{1}{4}$ of the region; 6 m by 6 m
10. b) Answers may vary. Both paths are curves.
14. a) The paths form a similar pattern.
    b) The pattern formed by point Q is larger than the pattern formed by point P.
15. The region is roughly rectangular, 6 m by 3 m.
19. Answers may vary.

8.3 Surface Areas of Pyramids
Developing the Ideas, page 444

Predictions may vary. It is a rectangular pyramid.

Through an Activity, page 445

2. Rectangular pyramid
3. Explanations may vary.
   a) 5 b) Yes, two pairs of triangular faces
   c) Base: 24 cm^2; side faces: 7.5 cm^2 and 6.5 cm^2
   d) 52 cm^2
4. Answers may vary. Calculate the area of the base. Calculate the area of one face and multiply by 4. Add these two areas.
5. Answers may vary. Calculate the area of each face. Add the four areas.

Working with Mathematics, page 446

1. Answers may vary. Usually only exposed faces need to be considered.
2. Answers may vary.
3. a) Answers may vary. Three faces are congruent when the base is an equilateral triangle. There may be no congruent faces if the base is a scalene triangle.
   b) Answers may vary. Six faces could be congruent if the base is a regular hexagon. There may be no congruent faces if the base is not regular.
4. Part a; the side faces of a pyramid are triangles with a common vertex.

5. a) 40.0 cm^2 **b)** 85.0 cm^2 **c)** 260.0 cm^2 **d)** 366.3 cm^2

6. a) 15.6 cm^2 **b)** 35.1 cm^2

7. a) 122.7 cm^2 **b)** 373 cm^2 **c)** 29.1 cm^2

8. Spreadsheets may vary.

9. a) 756 cm^2 **b)** 1887 cm^2
   c) 18.7 m^2 **d)** 10 491 mm^2

10. About 1975 m^2

11. a) 47.1 m^2; 19.3 m^2 **b)** The square pyramid
   c) Rounding up to the nearest 0.5 m^2: $724.38, $297.38

12. a) 156 cm^2 **b)** 624 cm^2 **c)** 1404 cm^2
   d) When side length and height of a square pyramid are
   doubled, surface area becomes 4 times the surface area of
   the original. When they are tripled, surface area becomes
   9 times the surface area of the original.

13. a) KL = 1.2 cm; LM = 1.6 cm; KM = 2.0 cm
   b) 6.0 cm^2, 0.96 cm^2

14. 380.8 cm^2

Quest: Which Cylinder Has the Greater Volume?, page 448

The cylinder with the short side as the height has the greater
volume.

8.4 Solving Design Problems in Two Dimensions
Developing the Ideas, page 450

1. a) 10   **b)** 9 m by 30 m   **c)** 270 m^2

2. See table below.

3. b)

Number along width	Number along length	Width of enclosure (m)	Length of enclosure (m)	Area enclosed (m^2)
3	10	9	30	270
4	9	12	27	324
5	8	15	24	360
6	7	18	21	378

   c) 6 stands for width, 7 stands for length; 18 m by 21 m

Working with Mathematics, page 451

1. 21 m by 21 m; 441 m^2

2. a) 7 stands by 8 stands, which is 21 m by 24 m, or 504 m^2
   b) No; explanations may vary. An area of 50 m^2 requires
   fractions of stands, which is not possible.

3. a) 1 tile by 36 tiles, or 0.6 m by 21.6 m
   b) 6 tiles by 6 tiles, or 3.6 m by 3.6 m.

4. a) , b)

Number along width	Number along length	Width of garden (m)	Length of garden (m)	Area enclosed (m^2)
1	4	1.8	7.2	12.96
2	3	3.6	5.4	19.44

5. Explanations may vary. 5 m by 5 m

6. a) Explanations may vary. Yes

b) , c) , d)

Length of side parallel to beach (m)	Length of side perpendicular to beach (m)	Total length of rope (m)	Area enclosed (m^2)
300	50	400	15 000
250	75	400	18 750
200	100	400	20 000
150	125	400	18 750
100	150	400	15 000

   e) 200 m by 100 m; length is twice the width

7. a) 1.5 m by 1.5 m   **b)** 1.5 m by 3 m   **c)** 3 m by 3 m

8. a) Either 42 m by 18 m or 36 m by 21 m, for an area of
   756 m^2
   b) 39 m by 39 m, for an area of 1521 m^2

9. a) 216 m^2
   b)

Number along each of 3 sides	Number along each of other 2 sides	Overall width (m)	Overall length (m)	Combined area (m^2)
2	10	6	30	180
4	7	12	21	252
6	4	18	12	216

   c) 4 stands along 3 sides, and 7 stands along the other 3 sides,
   for a total area of 252 m^2

10. a) For a rectangle, it is a square with side length $\frac{1}{4}$ of the
   circumference of the loop. However, the largest region is
   a circle.
   b) Answers may vary.
   c) For a rectangle, it is a square with sides approximately
   10.6 cm long. The largest region is a circle with a diameter
   of approximately 13.5 cm.

11. 30

8.5 Solving Design Problems in Three Dimensions
Developing the Ideas, page 453

1. a) 100 cm^2 **b)** 10 cm   **c)** 700 cm^2

2. , 3. a)

Length (cm)	Width (cm)	Height (cm)	Volume (cm^3)	Surface area (cm^2)
20	5	10	1000	700
25	4	10	1000	780
25	8	5	1000	730
10	10	10	1000	600

   b) 20 cm by 5 cm by 10 cm
   c) Answers may vary. 10 cm by 10 cm by 10 cm, giving a
   surface area of 600 cm^2
   d) A cube

Working with Mathematics, page 454

1. No; answers may vary. The box would have to have a volume
   of 8000 cm^3 for the side length to be 20 cm. The side length
   for a volume of 2000 cm^3 is $\sqrt[3]{2000}$ cm, or about 12.6 cm.

2. a)

Length (cm)	Width (cm)	Height (cm)	Volume (cm³)	Surface area (cm²)
1	1	24	24	98
2	1	12	24	76
2	2	6	24	56
2	3	4	24	52
3	1	8	24	70
4	1	6	24	68

b) 2 cm by 3 cm by 4 cm, with a surface area of 52 cm²

3. a)

Length (cm)	Width (cm)	Height (cm)	Volume (cm³)	Surface area (cm²)
1	1	32	32	130
2	1	16	32	100
2	2	8	32	72
4	1	8	32	88
4	2	4	32	64

b) 4 cm by 2 cm by 4 cm, with a surface area of 64 cm²

4. a)

Length (cm)	Width (cm)	Height (cm)	Volume (cm³)	Surface area (cm²)
1	1	100	100	402
1	10	10	100	240
2	1	50	100	304
2	2	25	100	208
2	5	10	100	160
4	1	25	100	258
5	1	20	100	250
5	5	4	100	130

b) 5 cm by 5 cm by 4 cm, with a surface area of 130 cm²

5. a) , b) , c)

Length (cm)	Width (cm)	Height (cm)	Volume (cm³)	Surface area (cm²)
10	10	40.00	4000	1700
12	12	27.78	4000	1477
14	14	20.41	4000	1339
16	16	15.63	4000	1256
18	18	12.35	4000	1213
20	20	10.00	4000	1200
22	22	8.26	4000	1211
24	24	6.94	4000	1242
26	26	5.92	4000	1292
28	28	5.10	4000	1355
30	30	4.44	4000	1433

d) 20 cm by 20 cm by 10 cm, for a surface area of 1200 cm² Answers may vary. The base is a square and the height is half the side length of the base. This would probably not be a good idea for movie theatres because the box is too shallow. The popcorn would get cold faster, and it would spill easily.

6. a) 384 cm²; 768 cm²; 1536 cm²
b) 3072 cm²

c) Multiply the area by 2.
d) 196 608 cm²

7. a) 216 square units
b) Answers may vary; 2 cubes by 8 cubes by 9 cubes, or 212 square units; 2 cubes by 3 cubes by 24 cubes, or 252 square units; 3 cubes by 3 cubes by 16 cubes, or 210 square units
c) 4 cubes by 6 cubes by 6 cubes, to use 168 square units
d) Explanations may vary.

8. a) Answers may vary. 40   **b)** 320

9. a) Standard juice box size is approximately 4.1 cm by 6.3 cm by 10.5 cm. Surface area is approximately 270 cm². The box contains 250 mL of juice.
b) Answers will vary. To one decimal place, the best dimensions are 6.4 cm by 6.4 cm by 6.4 cm, with an area of 246 cm².
c) Answers may vary. It would probably not be a good idea to change because people are used to the current shape of the box. Also, a cubical box might be harder to hold without spilling the juice.

10. a) , b) , c)

Length of cut out square (cm)	Length of box (cm)	Width of box (cm)	Height of box (cm)	Volume (cm³)
1.0	26.0	19.6	1.0	509.6
2.0	24.0	17.6	2.0	844.8
3.0	22.0	15.6	3.0	1029.6
4.0	20.0	13.6	4.0	1088.0
5.0	18.0	11.6	5.0	1044.0
6.0	16.0	9.6	6.0	921.6
7.0	14.0	7.6	7.0	744.8
8.0	12.0	5.6	8.0	537.6
9.0	10.0	3.6	9.0	324.0

d) i) About 1088 cm³, when the height is 4.0 cm
ii) About 6.1 cm; about 2.2 cm

11. b) , d)

Length (m)	Width (m)	Height (m)	V (m³)	Outside SA (m²)	Ratio of SA to V
30	30	3	2700	1260	0.467
30	15	6	2700	990	0.367
25	18	6	2700	966	0.358
30	10	9	2700	1020	0.378
25	9	12	2700	1041	0.386

e) A low ratio of surface area to volume would be better. Answers may vary. When a lower surface area is exposed to the cold, less heat is lost through the walls and windows. Therefore, heating costs would be lower.

12. a) 486 cm²   **b)** 378 cm²

13. a) 16   **b)** 150

Linking Ideas: Measurement and Graphing
Total Surface Areas and Volumes of Cylinders with the Same Radius, page 457

Answers may vary.

Linking Ideas: Mathematics and Technology
Designing Package Sizes, page 458

1. Divides the base diameter by 2; divides the volume by π and by the square of the radius; multiplies π by the square of the radius; multiplies π by 2, by the radius, and by the height; adds twice the area of the base to the area of the label
2. Answers may vary.
3. a) Answers may vary.   b) Height equals diameter.
4. Yes

8.6 Volume of a Cone
Developing the Ideas, page 460

2. a) 3
3. a) The volume of the cone is one-third the volume of the cylinder.
   b) $V = \pi r^2 h$ c) $V = \frac{1}{3}\pi r^2 h$

Working with Mathematics, page 462

1. a) About 785 cm^3; 262 cm^3 b) About 78.5%; 26.2%
2. Use the Pythagorean Theorem: $h = 12$
3. 32 cm^3 4. 162 cm^3
5. a) 235.5 m^3 b) About 187.7 cm^3
   c) About 197.1 cm^3 d) About 412.2 cm^3
6. a) 9.38 cm^3 b) 0.23 m^3
   c) 1808.64 cm^3 d) 105 240.24 cm^3
7. 146.2 cm^3 8. About 1466.1 m^3 9. 21.2 m
10. Cone A: 654 498 cm^3; Cone B: 26 179 939 cm^3; Cone B has the greater volume.
11. 6.0 cm, 5.3 cm, 199.8 cm^3; 4.0 cm, 6.9 cm, 115.6 cm^3; 2.0 cm, 7.7 cm, 32.3 cm^3
12. 20.6 m^3 13. About 2834.9 m^3
14. 3.0 cm   15. 10.0 m
16. a) 83 cm^3 b) 84 cm^3 c) 83 cm^3 d) 83 cm^3
    The volumes are approximately equal.
17. a) 52.4 cm^3 b) 20.9 cm^3

8.7 Volume of a Rectangular Pyramid
Developing the Ideas, page 464

1. The volume of the pyramid is one-third the volume of the prism.

Working with Mathematics, page 466

1. The formulas are the same: one-third base area times height.
2. a) 4, 4, 6   b) 5, 5, 8   c) 6, 6, 10   d) 7, 7, 12
3. The numbers of faces and vertices equal 1 + the number of sides in the base. The number of edges is twice the number of sides in the base.
4. All volumes are the same.
5. a) 24 cm^3 b) 126 m^3 c) 367 m^3 d) 391.7 cm^3
6. a) 192 m^3 b) 384 m^3 c) 384 m^3 d) 768 m^3
   e) 1152 m^3 f) 768 m^3 g) 1024 m^3
7. 4500 cm^3
8. a) Doubled; tripled
   b) Doubled; tripled
   c) Quadrupled; multiplied by 9

---

d) Multiplied by 8; multiplied by 27
9. About 9023 m^3
10. a) 2 569 609 m^3
    b) About 1.117 m^3
    c) About 6.348×10^9 kg
    d) Answers may vary. The pyramid has weathered and its height has decreased.
11. a) About 2.2 times   b) Answers may vary.
12. Answers may vary. 8.0 cm^3

Review, page 468

2. a) Triangular prism   b) Rectangular prism
3. Square pyramid
7. The volumes of the rectangular prism and the cylinder are three times the volumes of the rectangular pyramid and the cone.
8. a) 182 cm^2 b) 203.3 cm^2
9. a) 14.9 cm^2 b) No; answers may vary.
10. About 1350 m^2
11. a) 1 cm by 64 cm, 2 cm by 32 cm, 4 cm by 16 cm, 8 cm by 8 cm
    b) 1 cm by 64 cm, with a perimeter of 130 cm
    c) 8 cm by 8 cm, with a perimeter of 32 cm
12. 4 lengths by 4 lengths, or an area of 16 square units
13. a) 1 cm by 1 cm by 64 cm, 2 cm by 1 cm by 32 cm, 2 cm by 2 cm by 16 cm, 4 cm by 1 cm by 16 cm, 4 cm by 2 cm by 8 cm, 4 cm by 4 cm by 4 cm
    b) 1 cm by 1 cm by 64 cm, with a surface area of 258 cm^2
    c) 4 cm by 4 cm by 4 cm, with a surface area of 96 cm^2
14. 5 cm by 5 cm by 5 cm, with a surface area of 150 cm^2
15. a) 2788 cm^3 b) 2219 cm^3 c) 46 502 cm^3
16. 7.5 m^3
17. a) 5 m^3 b) 3800 cm^3 c) 53 cm^3 d) 22 341 cm^3
18. 5772 cm^3

Cumulative Review, page 472

1. Key strokes and explanations may vary.
   a) About 3.90   b) −23.406
   c) About −3.57   d) About −0.786
2. $43 470
3. $40 580
4. b) Answers may vary. One possible answer is 9 cm.
   c) Answers may vary. After 8.0 h, the line of best fit may not lead to a reliable prediction. The snow may fall at a constant rate over 4 h but likely would not fall at a constant rate over 8 h. Also, as snow piles higher over time, its weight packs down the snow already in the container. This means the line of best fit would have to change as more snow falls.
5. a) $\frac{1}{9}$
   b) Answers may vary. The assumptions for the answer provided are that the brand of car is not important, and that the first test drive does not result in a sale. (The 6 cars are still on the lot when the second customer arrives.)
6. a) It is possible, since the groups of widows and widowers do not include *all* men and *all* women.

b) No, because she has focused her data on women only, not men.

c) She needs data on both women and men, whether single, married, widowed, or divorced.

7. a) 6   **b)** 0   **c)** −4
d) −7.5   **e)** 7   **f)** $-\frac{1}{21}$

8. 20 and 21

9. Length is 11 cm and width is 6 cm.

10. 18 $2 bills and 7 $5 bills

11. About 182 km

12. Explanations may vary.
  a) 1   **b)** 1
  c) 1   **d)** An infinite number
  e) 3   **f)** 1

13. a) $\triangle$ABC, $\triangle$EDC; $x = 2$, $y = 2.25$
  b) $\triangle$FHJ, $\triangle$FGL; $x \doteq 9.3$, $y \doteq 10.5$
  c) $\triangle$LPN, $\triangle$MON; $x = 7.5$, $y = 8.5$

14. a) $\angle$W = 43°, $\angle$X = 47°   **b)** $\angle$W = 78°, $\angle$X = 12°
  c) $\angle$W = 57°, $\angle$X = 33°   **d)** $\angle$W = 72°, $\angle$X = 18°

15. a) $\angle$A $\doteq$ 33.7°, $\angle$C $\doteq$ 56.3°, AC $\doteq$ 8.7 cm
  b) $\angle$D $\doteq$ 45.7°, $\angle$F $\doteq$ 44.3°, DF $\doteq$ 11.3 m

16. About 25.3°

17. About 134.6 m

18. a) $\frac{1}{9}$ **b)** $\frac{27}{8}$ **c)** $\frac{1}{32}$
  d) $\frac{1}{100}$ **e)** 1   **f)** 5
  g) 81   **h)** $\frac{1}{125}$ **i)** 1

19. a) y^5 **b)** k^{10} **c)** 1
  d) m^{-15} **e)** n^4 **f)** n^{-3}
  g) s^{-2} **h)** $-v^3$ **i)** $81t^4$
  j) $25c^4$ **k)** $\frac{1}{64y^2}$ **l)** $\frac{1}{64y^2}$

20. About 1.384×10^{21} kg

21. a) About 1.2×10^5 s, or 33 h 20 min   **b)** About 3150 L

22. a) 6.7 cm   **b)** 1.7 m   **c)** 8.5 mm

23. Many answers are possible.
  a) 99.81, 99.9   **b)** 3.51, 3.53   **c)** 2.3, 2.4   **d)** 7.01, 7.02

24. a) 162   **b)** 8   **c)** 21   **d)** −8   **e)** 128   **f)** 18

25. a) $6m^2(3 + m)$ **b)** $8w(-1 + 2w^2)$
  c) $5q(1 - 5q^2)$ **d)** $7c^2(c^2 + 2c + 6)$
  e) $6(1 - 3m^2 + 4m^3)$ **f)** $3k^2(-1 - 8k - 4k^2)$
  g) $3ab(9 - 7a + 3b)$ **h)** $ab(1 - 4ab + 8b)$

26. a) $(x + 1)(x + 1)$ **b)** $(x + 3)(x - 5)$
  c) $(x + 1)(x - 7)$ **d)** $(x + 7)(x - 8)$
  e) $(x + 6)(x + 7)$ **f)** $(x - 7)(x - 6)$
  g) $(x + 5)(x - 10)$ **h)** $(x + 3)(x + 12)$
  i) $(x - 4)(x - 6)$ **j)** $(x - 2)(x - 8)$

27. a) $7(3 + y)(-4 + y)$ **b)** $3(m + 3)(m + 3)$
  c) $3(c + 2)(c + 4)$ **d)** $8(d - 2)(d - 4)$
  e) $-4(m - 1)(m + 9)$ **f)** $5(-w^2 - 3w + 24)$
  g) $4a(b - 5)(b + 3)$ **h)** $2k(m - 2)(m - 7)$
  i) $-3x(y - 4)(y + 1)$ **j)** $2pq(r - 6)(r + 1)$

28. a) A$'$(3, −4), B$'$(5, 5), C$'$(7, 1)
  b) P$'$(4, −2), Q$'$(8, −1), R$'$(4, 2)
  c) W$'$(6, 0), X$'$(3, −3), Y$'$(2, −7), Z$'$(5, −6)

29. Each figure is the same size and shape as its image but is in a different position on the grid.

30. a) O$'$(0, 0), B$'$(−2, 9), C$'$(−4, 5)
  b) P$'$(−1, 2), Q$'$(−5, 3), R$'$(−1, 6)
  c) W$'$(−3, 4), X$'$(0, 1), Y$'$(1, −3), Z$'$(−2, −2)

31. a) a) O$'$(0, 0), B$'$(2, −9), C$'$(4, −5)
  b) P$'$(1, −2), Q$'$(5, −3), R$'$(1, −6)
  c) W$'$(3, −4), X$'$(0, −1), Y$'$(−1, 3), Z$'$(2, 2)
  b) a) O$'$(6, 0), B$'$(4, 9), C$'$(2, 5)
  b) P$'$(5, 2), Q$'$(1, 3), R$'$(5, 6)
  c) W$'$(3, 4), X$'$(6, 1), Y$'$(7, −3), Z$'$(4, −2)
  c) a) O$'$(0, −8), B$'$(2, −17), C$'$(4, −13)
  b) P$'$(1, −10), Q$'$(5, −11), R$'$(1, −14)
  c) W$'$(3, −12), X$'$(0, −9), Y$'$(−1, −5), Z$'$(2, −6)

32. a) O$'$(0, 0), B$'$(−2, −9), C$'$(−4, −5)
  b) P$'$(−1, −2), Q$'$(−5, −3), R$'$(−1, −6)
  c) W$'$(−3, −4), X$'$(0, −1), Y$'$(1, 3), Z$'$(−2, 2)

33. a) a) O$'$(0, 0), B$'$(−9, 2), C$'$(−5, 4)
  b) P$'$(−2, 1), Q$'$(−3, 5), R$'$(−6, 1)
  c) W$'$(−4, 3), X$'$(−1, 0), Y$'$(3, −1), Z$'$(2, 2)
  b) a) O$'$(0, 0), B$'$(9, −2), C$'$(5, −4)
  b) P$'$(2, −1), Q$'$(3, −5), R$'$(6, −1)
  c) W$'$(4, −3), X$'$(1, 0), Y$'$(−3, 1), Z$'$(−2, −2)
  c) a) O$'$(10, 0), B$'$(1, 2), C$'$(5, 4)
  b) P$'$(8, 1), Q$'$(7, 5), R$'$(4, 1)
  c) W$'$(6, 3), X$'$(9, 0), Y$'$(13, −1), Z$'$(12, 2)

35. All the figures are similar.
  a) The sides are 3 times as great. The area is 9 times as great.
  b) The sides are 0.5 times as great. The area is 0.25 times as great.
  c) The sides are 2 times as great. The area is 4 times as great.
  d) The sides are 0.5 times as great. The area is 0.25 times as great.

36. a) Translation 2 right, 3 up
  b) Reflection in the y-axis
  c) Dilatation, centre (0, 0), scale factor 2

38. Square pyramid, octahedron

40. a) 134.7 m^2 **b)** 404.0 m^2

41. a) 780.3 m^2 **b)** 8667 shingles
  c) $5465.25

42. a) 1 cm by 200 cm, 2 cm by 100 cm, 4 cm by 50 cm, 5 cm by 40 cm, 8 cm by 25 cm, 10 cm by 20 cm
  b) 1 cm by 200 cm, with a perimeter of 402 cm
  c) 10 cm by 20 cm, with a perimeter of 60 cm

43. Answers may vary. For example:
7 cm by 8 cm by 10 cm, or 8.25 cm by 8.25 cm by 8.25
Explanations may vary.

44. 10 cm by 10 cm by 10 cm

45. a) 720 cm^3 **b)** 7.9 m^3

46. a) About 1893.5 cm^3 **b)** About 372.5 cm^3

GLOSSARY

acute angle: an angle measuring less than 90°

acute triangle: a triangle with three acute angles

additive inverses: a number and its opposite; the sum of additive inverses is 0; for example, +3 + (−3) = 0

algebraic expression: a mathematical expression containing a variable: for example, $6x − 4$ is an algebraic expression

alternate angles: angles that are between two lines and are on opposite sides of a transversal that cuts the two lines
Angles 1 and 3 are alternate angles.
Angles 2 and 4 are alternate angles.

altitude: the perpendicular distance from the base of a figure to the opposite side or vertex

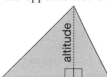

angle: the figure formed by two rays from the same endpoint

angle bisector: the line that divides an angle into two equal angles

approximation: a number close to the exact value of an expression; the symbol $\doteq$ means "is approximately equal to"

area: the number of square units needed to cover a region

array: an arrangement in rows and columns

average: a single number that represents a set of numbers; see *mean, median*, and *mode*

balance: the result when money is added to or subtracted from an original amount

bar graph: a graph that displays data by using horizontal or vertical bars whose lengths are proportional to the numbers they represent; see page 87

bar notation: the use of a horizontal bar over a decimal digit to indicate that it repeats; for example, $1.\overline{3}$ means 1.333 333 …

base: the side of a polygon or the face of a solid from which the height is measured; the factor repeated in a power

bias: an emphasis on characteristics that are not typical of the entire population

binomial: a polynomial with two terms; for example, $3x − 8$

bisector: a line that divides a line segment into two equal parts
The broken line is a bisector of AB.

box-and-whisker plot: a diagram in which data are plotted horizontally and values between the upper and lower quartiles are enclosed in a box

broken-line graph: a graph that displays data by using points joined by line segments; see page 59

capacity: the amount a container can hold

centroid: the point where the three medians of a triangle intersect; see page 226

circle: the set of points in a plane that are a given distance from a fixed point (the centre)

circle graph: a diagram that uses parts of a circle to display data; see page 56

circumcentre: the point where the perpendicular bisectors of the sides of a triangle intersect; see page 227

circumcircle: a circle drawn through each of the vertices of a triangle, and with its centre at the circumcentre of the triangle

circumference: the distance around a circle, and sometimes the circle itself

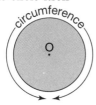

coefficient: the numerical factor of a term; for example, in the terms $3x$ and $3x^2$, the coefficient is 3

commission: a fee or payment given to a sales-person, usually a specified percent of the person's sales

common denominator: a number that is a multiple of each of the given denominators; for example, 12 is a common denominator for the fractions $\frac{1}{3}$, $\frac{5}{4}$, $\frac{7}{12}$

common factor: a number that is a factor of each of the given numbers; for example, 3 is a common factor of 15, 9, and 21

commutative property: the property stating that two numbers can be added or multiplied in any order; for example, $6 + 8 = 8 + 6$ and $4 \times 7 = 7 \times 4$

complementary angles: two angles whose sum is 90°

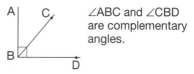

composite number: a number with three or more factors; for example, 8 is a composite number because its factors are 1, 2, 4, and 8

compound event: a combination of two or more events

compound interest: see *interest*; if the interest due is added to the principal and thereafter earns interest, the interest earned is compound interest

cone: a solid formed by a region and all line segments joining points on the boundary of the region to a point not in the region

congruent: figures that have the same size and shape, but not necessarily the same orientation

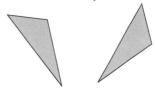

consecutive numbers: integers that come one after the other without any integers missing; for example, 34, 35, 36 are consecutive numbers, so are −2, −1, 0, and 1

constant term: a number

Consumer Price Index (CPI): the change in the costs of goods and services, based on their costs on a set date

coordinate axes: the x- and y-axes on a grid that represents a plane

coordinate plane: a two-dimensional surface on which a coordinate system has been set up

coordinates: the numbers in an ordered pair that locate a point in the plane

corresponding angles: angles that are on the same side of a transversal that cuts two lines and on the same side of each line

Angles 1 and 3 are corresponding angles.
Angles 2 and 4 are corresponding angles.
Angles 5 and 7 are corresponding angles.
Angles 6 and 8 are corresponding angles.

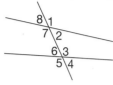

cosine: for an acute ∠A in a right triangle, the ratio of the length of the side adjacent to ∠A, to the length of the hypotenuse; see page 247

cube: a solid with six congruent, square faces

cubic units: units that measure volume

cylinder: a solid with two parallel, congruent, circular bases

data: facts or information

database: an organized collection of facts or information, often stored on a computer

denominator: the term below the line in a fraction

density: the mass of a unit volume of a substance

diagonal: a line segment that joins two vertices of a figure, but is not a side

diameter: the distance across a circle, measured through the centre; a line segment through the centre of the circle with its endpoints on the circle

digit: any of the symbols used to write numerals; for example, in the base-ten system the digits are 0, 1, 2, 3, 4, 5, 6, 7, 8, and 9

dilatation: a transformation in which the image is the same shape as the object, but is enlarged or reduced in size

Distributive Law: the property stating that a product can be written as a sum or difference of two products; for example, for all real numbers a, b, and c:
$$a(b + c) = ab + ac \text{ and } a(b - c) = ab - ac$$

double-bar graph: a bar graph that shows two sets of data

equation: a mathematical statement that two expressions are equal

equidistant: the same distance apart

equilateral triangle: a triangle with three equal sides

evaluate: to substitute a value for each variable in an expression

even number: an integer that has 2 as a factor; for example, 2, 4, −6

event: any set of outcomes of an experiment

exponent: a number, shown in a smaller size and raised, that tells how many times the number before it is used as a factor; for example, 2 is the exponent in 6^2

expression: a mathematical phrase made up of numbers and/or variables connected by operations

extremes: the highest and lowest values in a set of numbers

factor: to factor means to write as a product
to factor a given integer means to write it as a product of integers, the integers in the product are the factors of the given integer to factor a polynomial with integer coefficients means to write it as a product of polynomials with integer coefficients

formula: a rule that is expressed as an equation

fraction: an indicated quotient of two quantities

frequency: the number of times a particular number occurs in a set of data

grouping property of addition (and multiplication): when three or more terms are added (or multiplied), the operations can be performed in any order

hectare: a unit of area that is equal to 10 000 m^2

hexagon: a six-sided polygon

histogram: a graph that uses bars, where each bar represents a range of values, and the data are continuous; see page 56

hypotenuse: the side that is opposite the right angle in a right triangle

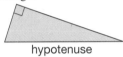

hypotenuse

identity for addition: a number that can be added to any number without changing the number; 0 is the identity for addition of real numbers

identity for multiplication: a number that can be multiplied by any number without changing the number; 1 is the identity for multiplication of real numbers

image: the figure that results from a transformation

incentre: the point at which the three angle bisectors of a triangle intersect; see page 227

incircle: a circle drawn inside a triangle, with its centre at the incentre and with the radius the shortest distance from the incentre to one of the sides of the triangle

independent events: two or more events for which the occurrence or nonoccurrence of one does not change the probability of the other

inequality: a statement that one quantity is greater than (or less than) another quantity

integers: the set of numbers… −3, −2, −1, 0, +1, +2, +3,…

interest: money that is paid for the use of money, usually according to a predetermined percent

interpolate: to estimate a value between two known values

intersecting lines: lines that meet or cross; lines that have one point in common

interval: a regular distance or space between values

inverse: see *additive inverses* and *multiplicative inverses*

irrational number: a number that cannot be written in the form $\frac{m}{n}$ where m and n are integers ($n \neq 0$)

isometric view: a representation of an object as it would appear in three dimensions

isometry: a transformation that preserves length; for example, a translation

isosceles acute triangle: a triangle with two equal sides and all angles less than 90°

isosceles obtuse triangle: a triangle with two equal sides and one angle greater than 90°

isosceles right triangle: a triangle with two equal sides and a 90° angle

isosceles triangle: a triangle with two equal sides

kilojoule: a measure of energy

kite: a quadrilateral with two pairs of equal adjacent sides

lattice point: on a coordinate grid, a point at the intersection of two grid lines

legs: the sides of a right triangle that form the right angle

light-year: a unit for measuring astronomical distances; one light-year is the distance light travels in one year

like terms: terms that have the same variables; for example, $4x$ and $-3x$ are like terms

line of best fit: a line that passes as close as possible to a set of plotted points

line segment: the part of a line between two points on the line

line symmetry: a figure that maps onto itself when it is reflected in a line is said to have line symmetry; for example, line *l* is the line of symmetry for figure ABCD

magic square: an array of numbers in which the sum of the numbers in any row, column, or diagonal is always the same; see page 279

magic sum: the sum of the numbers in a row, column, or diagonal of a magic square

mapping: a correspondence of points or figures under a transformation or rule

mass: the amount of matter in an object

mean: the sum of a set of numbers divided by the number of numbers in the set

median: the middle number when data are arranged in numerical order

median of a triangle: a line from one vertex to the midpoint of the opposite side

midpoint: the point that divides a line segment into two equal parts

mode: the number that occurs most often in a set of numbers

monomial: a polynomial with one term; for example, 14 and $5x^2$ are each a monomial

Monte Carlo method: the procedure of performing an experiment whose outcomes have the same probability as the outcomes in another experiment that is more difficult to perform

multiple: the product of a given number and a natural number; for example, some multiples of 8 are 8, 16, 24,...

multiplicative inverses: a number and its reciprocal; the product of multiplicative inverses is 1; for example, $3 \times \frac{1}{3} = 1$

natural numbers: the set of numbers 1, 2, 3, 4, 5,...

negative number: a number less than 0

numeracy: the ability to read, understand, and use numbers

numerator: the term above the line in a fraction

obtuse angle: an angle greater than 90° and less than 180°

obtuse triangle: a triangle with one angle greater than 90°

octagon: an eight-sided polygon

odd number: an integer that does not have 2 as a factor; for example, 1, 3, −7

operation: a mathematical process or action such as addition, subtraction, multiplication, or division

opposite angles: the equal angles that are formed by two intersecting lines

opposite number: a number whose sum with a given number is 0; for example, 3 and −3 are opposites

opposites: two numbers whose sum is zero; each number is the opposite of the other

Opposites Principle: when two equal expressions are multiplied by −1, the results will be equal

order of operations: the rules that are followed when simplifying or evaluating an expression

order property of addition (and multiplication): two terms that are added (or multiplied) can be added (or multiplied) in any order

orthocentre: the point at which the altitudes of a triangle intersect

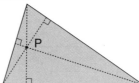

outcome: a possible result of an experiment or a possible answer to a survey question

parallel lines: lines in the same plane that do not intersect

parallelogram: a quadrilateral with both pairs of opposite sides parallel

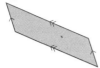

pentagon: a five-sided polygon

per capita: for each person

percent: the number of parts per 100; the numerator of a fraction with denominator 100

perfect square: a number that is the square of a whole number; a polynomial that is the square of another polynomial

perimeter: the distance around a closed figure

perpendicular: intersecting at right angles

perpendicular bisector: the line that is perpendicular to a line segment and divides it in two equal parts
The broken line is the perpendicular bisector of AB.

pi (π): the ratio of the circumference of a circle to its diameter; π ≐ 3.1416

pictograph: a graph in which a symbol represents a certain amount, and repetitions of the symbol illustrate the data

plane geometry: the study of two-dimensional figures; that is, figures drawn or visualized on a plane

point of intersection: a point that lies on two or more figures

polygon: a closed figure that consists of line segments; for example, triangles and quadrilaterals are polygons

polynomial: a mathematical expression with one or more terms, in which the exponents are whole numbers and the coefficients are real numbers

population: the set of all things or people being considered

population density: the average number of people for each square unit of land

positive number: a number greater than 0

power: an expression of the form a^n, where a is called the base and n is called the exponent; it represents a product of equal factors; for example, $4 \times 4 \times 4$ can be expressed as 4^3

prime number: a whole number with exactly two factors, itself and 1; for example, 3, 5, 7, 11, 29, 31, and 43

prism: a solid that has two congruent and parallel faces (the *bases*), and other faces that are parallelograms

probability: if the outcomes of an experiment are equally likely, then the probability of an event is the ratio of the number of outcomes favourable to the event to the total number of outcomes

proportion: a statement that two ratios are equal

pyramid: a solid that has one face that is a polygon (the *base*), and other faces that are triangles with a common vertex

Pythagorean Theorem: for any right triangle, the area of the square on the hypotenuse is equal to the sum of the areas of the squares on the other two sides

quadrant: one of the four regions into which coordinate axes divide a plane

quadrilateral: a four-sided polygon

radius (plural, radii): the distance from the centre of a circle to any point on the circumference, or a line segment joining the centre of a circle to any point on the circumference

random numbers: a list of numbers in a given range such that each number has an equal chance of occurring

random sample: a sampling in which all members of the population have an equal chance of being selected

range: the difference between the highest and lowest values (the *extremes*) in a set of data

rate: a certain quantity or amount of one thing considered in relation to a unit of another thing

ratio: a comparison of two or more quantities with the same unit

rational number: a number that can be written in the form $\frac{m}{n}$ where m and n are integers ($n \neq 0$)

real numbers: the set of rational numbers and the set of irrational numbers; that is, all numbers that can be expressed as decimals

reciprocals: two numbers whose product is 1; for example, $\frac{3}{4}$ and $\frac{4}{3}$ are reciprocals, 2 and $\frac{1}{2}$ are reciprocals

rectangle: a quadrilateral that has four right angles

rectangular prism: a prism that has rectangular faces

rectangular pyramid: a pyramid with a rectangular base

reflection: a transformation that maps every point P onto an image point P' such that P and P' are equidistant from line l, and line PP' is perpendicular to line l

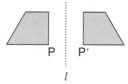

reflex angle: an angle between 180° and 360°

regular hexagon: a polygon that has six equal sides and six equal angles

regular octagon: a polygon that has eight equal sides and eight equal angles

regular polygon: a polygon that has all sides equal and all angles equal

relative frequency: the ratio of the number of times a particular outcome occurred to the number of times the experiment was conducted

rhombus: a parallelogram with four equal sides

right angle: a 90° angle

right circular cone: a cone in which a line segment from the centre of the circular base to the vertex is perpendicular to the base

right triangle: a triangle that has one right angle

rotation: a transformation in which the points of a figure are turned about a fixed point

rotational symmetry: a figure that maps onto itself in less than one full turn is said to have rotational symmetry; for example, a square has rotational symmetry about its centre O

sample/sampling: a representative portion of a population

scale: the ratio of the distance between two points on a map, model, or diagram to the distance between the actual locations; the numbers on the axes of a graph

scale factor: the ratio of corresponding lengths on two similar figures

scalene triangle: a triangle with no two sides equal

scatterplot: a graph of data that is a series of points; see page 66

scientific notation: a number expressed as the product of a number greater than −10 and less than −1 or greater than 1 and less than 10, and a power of 10; for example, 4700 is written as 4.7×10^3

semicircle: half a circle

Sharing Principle: when two equal expressions are divided by the same number, the results will be equal

similar figures: figures with the same shape, but not necessarily the same size

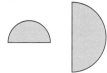

sine: for an acute ∠A in a right triangle, the ratio of the length of the side opposite ∠A, to the length of the hypotenuse; see page 247

spreadsheet: a computer-generated arrangement of data in rows and columns, where a change in one value results in appropriate calculated changes in the other values

square: a rectangle with four equal sides

square of a number: the product of a number multiplied by itself; for example, 25 is the square of 5

square root: a number which, when multiplied by itself, results in a given number; for example, 5 and −5 are the square roots of 25

statistics: the branch of mathematics that deals with the collection, organization, and interpretation of data

stem-and-leaf diagram: an arrangement of a set of data showing the concentration of the values; for two-digit values, the tens digits are shown as the "stems" and the ones digits as the "leaves"

straight angle: an angle measuring 180°

straightedge: a strip of wood, metal, or plastic with a straight edge, but no markings

supplementary angles: two angles whose sum is 180°

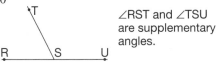

∠RST and ∠TSU are supplementary angles.

symmetrical: possessing symmetry; see *line symmetry* and *rotational symmetry*

tangent: for an acute ∠A in a right triangle, the ratio of the length of the side opposite ∠A, to the length of the side adjacent to ∠A; see page 233

term: of a fraction is the numerator or the denominator of the fraction; when an expression is written as the sum of several quantities, each quantity is called a term of the expression

tessellation: a tiling pattern

tetrahedron: a solid with four triangular faces

three-dimensional: having length, width, and depth or height

transformation: a mapping of the points of a figure that results in a change in position, shape, size, or appearance of the figure; for example, translations, rotations, reflections, and dilatations are transformations

translation: a transformation that moves a point or a figure in a straight line to another position in the same plane

transversal: a line crossing two or more lines

trapezoid: a quadrilateral that has only one pair of parallel sides

tree diagram: a branching diagram used to show all possible outcomes of an experiment; see page 98

triangle: a three-sided polygon

triangular number: a natural number that can be represented by arranging objects in a triangle; for example, 1, 3, 6, 10, 15,...

10

trinomial: a polynomial with three terms; for example, $3x^2 + 6x + 9$

two-dimensional: having length and width, but no thickness, height, or depth

unit fraction: a fraction that has a numerator of 1

unit price: the price of one item, or the price for a particular mass or volume of an item

unit rate: the quantity associated with a single unit of another quantity; for example, 6 m in 1 s is a unit rate

unlike terms: terms that have different variables, or the same variable but different exponents; for example, $3x$, $-4y$ and $3x^2$, $-3x$

variable: a letter or symbol representing a quantity that can vary

vertex (plural, **vertices**): the corner of a figure or a solid

volume: the amount of space occupied by an object

whole numbers: the set of numbers 0, 1, 2, 3,...

x-axis: the horizontal number line on a coordinate grid

y-axis: the vertical number line on a coordinate grid

Zero Principle: the sum of opposites is zero

PHOTO CREDITS AND ACKNOWLEDGMENTS

The publisher wishes to thank the following sources for photographs, illustrations, articles, and other materials used in this book. Care has been taken to determine and locate ownership of copyright material used in this text. We will gladly receive information enabling us to rectify any errors or omissions in credits.

p. 26 Canapress/p. 27 Dave Starrett/p. 38 Jack Zehrt/Masterfile (photo manipulation by Jun Park)/p. 39 Pronk&Associates /p. 40 (top) James Balog/Tony Stone Images/p. 40 (centre) Canapress/p. 40 (bottom) Glenn Christianson/Tony Stone Images/p. 42 "Estimated Percents of Households Using Selected Products" – The Globe and Mail /p. 43 "Canadian Content in NHL" reprinted with permission –The Toronto Star Syndicate/p. 43 David Michael Allen/p. 44 (left) Pronk&Associates/p. 44 (right) Canapress/p. 44 (girl) Pronk&Associates/p. 46 "Papers Shrink Pages" John Partridge/The Globe & Mail /p. 47 (left) Pronk&Associates/p. 47 (right) David Michael Allen/p. 48 "Milking the Rules to the Smallest Drop" Alan Freeman/The Globe & Mail /p. 52 (top) Courtesy Trevor Poczynek/p. 52 (bottom) David Michael Allen (photo manipulation by Jun Park)/p. 53 "Pennies from Hell: Businesses Starting to Keep the Change" © 1993 By The New York Times Company. Reprinted by permission./p. 53 David Michael Allen/p. 56 John Foster/Masterfile/p. 56 (inset) E.R. Degginger/Earth Scenes/p. 57 (top) Norman Piluke/Tony Stone Images/p. 57 (bottom) David Michael Allen/p. 58 (top) Dave Starrett/p. 58 (bottom) Ian Crysler/p.61 David Michael Allen/p. 64 (left) © 1988 Allsport USA/Gray Mortimore/p. 64 (right) © 1993 Allsport USA/Gray Mortimore/p. 65 © 1990 Allsport USA/Gray Mortimore/p. 71 (top) Mike Powell/Allsport/p. 71 (middle) UPI/Corbis-Bettmann/p. 71 (bottom) UPI/Corbis-Bettmann/p. 82 "Hi & Lois" reprinted with special permission of King Features Syndicate./p. 83 Used by permission of Ann Landers and Creators Syndicate./p. 84 "Winter Resort Industry Takes Off" reprinted from 200% of Nothing by A.K. Dewdney. Copyright © 1993 A.K. Dewdney. Reprinted by permission of John Wiley & Sons, Inc./p. 85 Corbis-Bettmann/p. 86 David Michael Allen/p. 90 David Michael Allen/p. 92 "Shoe" cartoon reprinted by permission: Tribune Media Services/p. 96 David Michael Allen/p. 98 Dave Starrett/p. 102 David Michael Allen/p. 111 (left) © Fred Sharp/SHARP IMAGES/p. 111 (right) Pronk&Associates/p. 112 Pronk&Associates/p. 118 David Michael Allen/p. 120 David Michael Allen/p. 131 Pronk & Associates/p. 133 David Michael Allen/p. 140 Photos courtesy of Tourism Regina/p. 142-143 Peter Turner/The Image Bank Canada (photo manipulation by Jun Park)/p. 148 (top left) Pronk&Associates/p. 148 (centre, bottom left, bottom right) David Michael Allen/p. 149 Pronk&Associates/p. 150-151 Pronk & Associates/p. 151 David Michael Allen/p. 152 Telegraph Colour Library/Masterfile/p. 153 Don Landwehrle/The Image Bank Canada/p. 154 Pronk & Associates/p. 156 (top) Bill Ivy/p. 156 (bottom) The Hamilton Spectator/p. 162 (top) Lynn M. Stone/The Image Bank/p. 162 (bottom) Pronk&Associates/p. 163 (top) A. de Cruz/Masterfile/p. 163 (bottom) David Michael Allen/p. 170 Ian Crysler/p. 171 David Michael Allen/p. 176 Vic Thomasson/Tony Stone Images/p. 177 (top left) Peter Miller/Photo Researchers/p. 177 (top right) Paolo Koch/Photo Researchers/p. 177 (bottom) Hilarie Kavanagh/Tony Stone Images/p. 178 (top) Corbis-Bettmann/p. 178 (bottom) Ian Crysler/p. 179 Ian Crysler/p. 182 The Geometer's Sketchpad, Key Curriculum Press, P.O. Box 2304, Berkeley, CA 94702, 1–800-995-MATH/p. 183 David Michael Allen/p. 184 Ian Crysler/p. 185 Ian Crysler/p. 189 Guy Motil/First Light/p. 190 Ian Crysler/p. 192 Ian Crysler/p. 198 Richard Chester/Masterfile/

p. 199 (top) Ian Crysler/p. 199 (bottom) Jerry Kobalenko/First Light/p. 216 (top) Courtesy of Kustom Signals, Inc./p. 216 (bottom) Courtesy of Tribar Industries Inc./p. 218 Joe Lepiano/p. 219 Dave Starrett/p. 220 Gary Newkirk/Allsport/p. 226 David Michael Allen/p. 231 Dave Starrett/p. 232 Ian Crysler/p. 258 (left) Bill Brooks/Masterfile/p. 258 (centre) Malcolm Carmichael/Lake Louise Limited/p. 258 (right) Jasper Tourism & Commerce/p. 259 David Michael Allen/p. 261 Mike Dobel/Masterfile/p. 264 Corbis-Bettmann/p. 268 Ian Crysler/p. 269 Ian Crysler/p. 274 Pronk & Associates/p. 275 Pronk&Associates/p. 278 Ken Biggs/Tony Stone Images/p. 279 Courtesy of NASA/Finley Holiday/p. 280 Nancy Brown/The Image Bank/p. 291 Reuters/Corbis-Bettmann/p. 296-7 Pronk&Associates/p. 297 M. Kage/Peter Arnold/p. 300 Sherman Hines/Masterfile/p. 305 David Michael Allen/p. 309 David Michael Allen/p. 310 (top) David Michael Allen/p. 310 (middle) Yale Babylonian Collection/p. 314 NASA/p. 315 (top) K. Iwasaki/Masterfile/p. 315 (middle and bottom) Courtesy of NASA/Finley Holiday/p. 318 David Michael Allen/p. 319 David Michael Allen/p. 320 David Michael Allen/p. 331 David E. Myers/Tony Stone Images/p. 332 Card courtesy of Recycled Paper Greetings/Pronk&Associates/p. 342 Dave Starrett/p. 344 Albert Klein/p. 349 Michael Salas/The Image Bank Canada/p. 354 Johan Elzenger/Tony Stone Images/p. 355 Pronk&Associates/p. 356 Pronk&Associates/p. 357 David Michael Allen/p. 366 (top and bottom) Courtesy of Marsha Falco/p. 366 (middle) David Michael Allen/p. 367 David Michael Allen/p. 374 Ian Crysler/p. 375 (top) Corbis-Bettmann/p. 375 (bottom) Ian Crysler/p. 381 Air Canada/p. 382 Ian Crysler/p. 389 (top) Sunnyside Incorporated/p. 389 (bottom) Ian Crysler/p. 390 Ian Crysler/p. 397 Dave Starrett/p. 398 Photo courtesy of Moniika Vega/p. 406 Dave Starrett/p. 407 Ian Crysler/p. 411 From Inversions by Scott Kim. Copyright © 1989 by Scott Kim. Reprinted with permission of W.H. Freeman and Company/p. 412 Ian Crysler/p. 422 David Michael Allen/p. 430 (top) Reproduced courtesy of the Trustees, The National Gallery, London/p. 430 (bottom) From the collection of Städelsches Kunstinstitut, Frankfurt am Main/Artothek/p. 431 (top) Copyright British Museum/p. 433 Ian Crysler/p. 434 (top) David Michael Allen/p. 434 (middle left) Joe Lepiano/p. 434 (middle right) David Michael Allen/p. 434 (bottom) David Michael Allen/p. 435 Murray and Associates/Tony Stone Images/p. 437 Ian Crysler/p. 438 Ian Crysler/p. 443 Dave Starrett/p. 444 (left) David Sutherland/Tony Stone Images/p. 444 (right) Jean Marc Truchet/Tony Stone Images/p. 445 Stephen Studd/Tony Stone Images/p. 447 Jean Marc Truchet/Tony Stone Images/p. 448-449 Pronk&Associates (photo manipulation by Jun Park)/p. 452 Dave Starrett/p. 455 Dave Starrett/p. 457 David Michael Allen/p. 460 Pronk&Associates/p. 463 David Michael Allen/p. 464 Ian Crysler/p. 465 Cosmo Condina/Tony Stone Images/p.467 John Sutton/Photo Search/p. 470 David Michael Allen/p. 471 David Michael Allen

Digital photo retouching and manipulation by Jun Park.

ILLUSTRATIONS

Steve Attoe 31, 49, 69, 76-77, 208, 209, 276, 289, 290, 301, 325
Don Gauthier 46
Bob Hambly 24-25
Michael Herman 99, 113, 120, 233, 260, 331, 428, 429, 439, 440, 450, 453
Steve MacEachern 166, 214, 221, 222, 223, 224, 225, 238, 239, 251, 252, 257, 258, 262, 263, 267, 271, 368, 418, 419, 441, 442, 468
Ted Nasmith 63, 129

Martha Newbigging **26**, **32**, **37**, **81**, **110**, **132**, **133**, **207**, **319**
Jun Park **106**, **107**, **230**, **261**, **297**, **433**, **458–459**
Ian Phillips **219**, **236**, **249**
Margo Davies Leclair/Visual Sense Illustration **475**
Technical art by Pronk and Associates unless otherwise stated.
Technical art (Answers section) by Margo Davies Leclair/Visual Sense Illustration.